WADERS

THEIR BREEDING, HAUNTS AND WATCHERS

BOOKS BY DESMOND NETHERSOLE-THOMPSON

The Greenshank (Collins 1951)

The Snow Bunting Oliver & Boyd 1966)

Highland Birds (Highlands and Islands Development Board and Collins 1971. 3rd ed. 1978)

The Dotterel (Collins 1973)

The Cairngorms (with Adam Watson) (Collins 1974. 2nd and enlarged ed. Melven Press 1981)

Pine Crossbills (Poyser 1975)

Greenshanks (with Maimie Nethersole-Thompson) (Poyser 1979)

WADERS

Their Breeding, Haunts and Watchers

by DESMOND and MAIMIE
NETHERSOLE-THOMPSON

Illustrated by
DONALD WATSON

T & A D POYSER

Calton

© Desmond and Maimie Nethersole-Thompson 1986

ISBN 0 85661 042 9

First published in 1986 by T & A D Poyser Ltd
Town Head House, Calton, Waterhouses, Staffordshire, England

British Library Cataloguing in Publication Data
Nethersole-Thompson, Desmond
    Waders: their breeding, haunts and watchers.
    1. Charadriiformes   2. Ciconiiformes
    I. Title   II. Nethersole-Thompson, Maimie
    598'.33   QL696.C4

    ISBN 0-85661-042-9

Text set in 9/10½ pt Linotron Ehrhardt, printed and
bound at The Bath Press, Avon

For

RICHARD

1961–1982

Contents

List of Plates

List of Figures

List of Tables

Preface

D. B. A. Thompson, Ph.D.
Zoology Department, Liverpool University

P. S. Thompson, B.Sc.
Biology Department, Liverpool Polytechnic

It is early spring – a glorious time. Our noisy and active waders are back; and one's heart is thumping in keen anticipation. Lapwing, curlew, oystercatcher, redshank and snipe display over pasture, heath and bog. Common sandpipers teeter by still and running waters, uttering their beautiful 'willy-wicket' songs. In the hills, among bog and pools and on moorland slopes, golden plover peep mournfully, dunlin trill, and greenshank song dance high in the sky. You may be luckier still! By the coast we have seen whimbrel give their 'steady rise – rapid fall' bubbling displays, red-necked phalarope spin on small reedy ponds, and Temminck's stint make moth-like flights above damp pasture-land. And on the desolate high plateaux we have been with dotterel – beautiful and bright little gems tinkling and bobbing on the skyline. Of course there are others. Fierce looking stone curlew occupy open heathland on chalk downland, woodcock make roding flights over their chosen woods, and on fenland and saltmarsh small concentrations of ruff lek on bare patches of earth.

Away from Britain, Scandinavian forest marshes and upland bogs hold spotted redshank, green, purple and wood sandpipers, and bar-tailed godwit. In the vast tundra of North America and Greenland, pectoral and Baird's sandpipers, knot and sanderling breed in short seasons of almost complete daylight. The list is long. One feels wonderfully excited and eager in the first days of spring for there is so much to learn about waders.

This book is an intimate and detailed account of the biology and behaviour of waders in their breeding haunts. It presents a wealth of information in a lucid and splendidly informative style. The authors are world authorities. Before turning to them let us look at the birds.

The waders (shorebirds in the New World) comprise two sub-orders – Charadrii and Scolopaci (according to some, all twelve families are in the one sub-order Charadrii). Among birds they provide some of the best opportunities for tackling questions about evolution, behaviour and ecology. Representatives are everywhere with most sharing an affinity for water. Generally conspicuous and observable at close range, they exhibit great behavioural and ecological diversity.

Perhaps two aspects have brought waders to the forefront of research. The first is their near ubiquity for much of the year along our coastline. At least sixty per cent of wader species spend most of the non-breeding season in coastal habitats. Much interest has focused on the importance of winter feeding behaviour for survival and population dynamics. There is great concern about the increasing encroachment by man and conurbia upon coastal areas. Estuarine tidal flats, harbouring tens of thousands of waders, are especially vulnerable. In winter their birds are an aesthetic delight and, more importantly, are essential consumers in the estuarine ecosystem. Estuaries, after all, degrade much of our effluent.

The variety and plasticity of wader social systems also justify attention. Of all taxonomic groups they exhibit the fullest range of mating systems. Polyandry (one female mates with more than one male), for instance, occurs in more wader species than in all other bird species put together. Nest spacing varies widely: some species are markedly colonial, others are solitary and territorial. Variation in social system may be explained by latitude and altitude, as well as by food supply, predation risk and climate.

Not surprisingly, therefore, waders are highly regarded by field biologists. Studies of foraging, spacing and competition have taught us much about the mechanisms involved in winter survival; and in spring and summer, work on breeding systems and territoriality has contributed substantially to our general understanding of behavioural and population ecology. A copious supply of facts is available on migration, moults, evolution and geographical variation in distribution. At present our knowledge of waders is being revolutionised by detailed studies of marked individuals both within and between years. Age, sex and consistent individual differences in diet selection, feeding efficiency, competitive ability, territorial behaviour and mortality in the non-breeding grounds facilitate a more precise evaluation of the importance of threatened habitats for population size and regulation. Improved access to Arctic breeding grounds, sophisticated telemetric equipment, recording and analytical apparatus, as well as extensive ringing programmes, are providing new insights into breeding biology, population dynamics and movements and migration. Some of these exciting developments are embodied in contributions to *Shorebirds: breeding, behaviour and populations* and *Shorebirds: migration and foraging behaviour* forming volumes 5 and 6 of the multivolume series *Behaviour of Marine Animals* edited by Burger and Olla (1984). Nevertheless, much basic information is missing. This is especially noticeable for breeding waders. Close examination of the literature reveals a very patchy treatment indeed of such important issues as courtship, nest site selection, egg laying, incubation, brooding and, surprisingly, voice. This book fills many of these lacunae. In doing so it provides a fund of fresh questions.

Now to provide a potted reflection of developments in our knowledge of wader biology without mentioning Nethersole-Thompson is, to say the least, remiss.

Of Irish stock, Desmond was educated at St Paul's School and then the London School of Economics. A large powerful man and a fine athlete he captained the British Universities Badminton team in his youth. His early career – teaching history and classics – served mainly one purpose: to fund his weekend egg collecting forays in the spring and early summer! In the 1930s he published papers on his southern studies of peregrine, hobby, stone-curlew and Dartford warbler. Fortunately, though, he settled in Speyside in 1934, beginning a fifty year spell of free-lance research in the Scottish Highlands.

His early training in field craft was done largely under 'Jock' Walpole-Bond, Edgar Chance, C. V. Stoney and contemporaries. It was Francis Jourdain who first told him that to study breeding habits was more important than egg collecting. The taking of eggs ceased. The skills of the oologist were then put to better use – nests were found to facilitate work on life histories of individual birds. By the late 1930s and early 1940s he was well known to H. F. Witherby (contributing much original material to the *Handbook of British Birds*, volume 4). In 1939 he was awarded a generous grant by the Institute (now Association) for the Study of Animal Behaviour, and between 1940 and 1942 he held a highly prestigious Leverhulme Research Fellowship. He was sponsored by Julian Huxley, who later wrote the preface for Desmond's first, now classic, monograph *The Greenshank* (1951). The Fellowship enabled him to write pioneer papers (with Carrie, his first wife) on egg-shell disposal and nest site selection.

Besides this Desmond was an Irish volunteer to the British Army, receiving a commission in 1942. A passionate advocate of socialism, he stood twice for parliament, and became vice-president of the District Councils Association of Scotland in 1957. Throughout this spell he worked on greenshanks and other waders, crossbills, crested tits and siskins in Speyside; and on dotterel and snow buntings on the Grampian tops and Cairngorms massif. Publications of several lucid and exciting essays in Bannerman's *Birds of the British Isles* (1960–63) presented some of the findings.

In 1961 Desmond and Maimie settled in Sutherland, NE Scotland, to embark on a new programme of fieldwork and writing. Remember that the early 1960s were exciting times. *Animal Dispersion in Relation to Social Behaviour* (1962) by Wynne-Edwards, advocating group selection, did much to focus people's minds on the evolution of social behaviour. Crook's seminal comparative study of weaver birds (*Ploceinae*) (1964: *Sym. Zool. Soc. London.*, 14: p 181–281) showing correlations between social organisation and ecological factors, and Hamilton's foundating papers (1963: *Amer. Nat.*, 97: p 354–356 and 1961: *J. Theor Biol.*, 7: p 1–52) on the evolution of altruism and the role of kin-selected traits in social behaviour, marked the dawn of a new era in the way people thought about social behaviour and population biology. Desmond was aware of all this by reading widely and through his close contact with Professor Wynne-Edwards and colleagues in the Department of Zoology, Aberdeen University. He also fostered close ties with Adam Watson and colleagues, and enjoyed keeping abreast of heady theories through active discussions. Desmond's fresh objective was to examine differences between individuals in a population of breeding waders.

So, in spring 1964, he and Maimie hatched a study of greenshanks in a remote valley in NW Sutherland. Their family worked from a small hut situated on the bank of a meandering river. Over the years a wealth of data on individual birds and their populations has been amassed. Here a debt of gratitude is owed by the family to Derek Ratcliffe, for he discovered the area and remarked on the high numbers of greenshanks present.

Between field seasons the output of books and papers was prolific, in no small part because of freedom granted by awards from the Natural Environment Research Council (1967–82). *The Snow Bunting* appeared in 1966, *The Dotterel* in 1973 and *Pine Crossbills* in 1975. Desmond thus became the only person to produce monographs on four bird species. It is a feat that probably will never be repeated! In 1971 the beautifully illustrated *Highland Birds* was published and has since gone into three editions. *Highland Birds Map* and *Highland Birds Cassette* (with Bill Sinclair) appeared in 1978 and 1979 respectively. *The Cairngorms* (written with Adam Watson and, appropriately, with a Preface by Wynne-Edwards) appeared in 1974 to describe their natural history and scenery. A most scholarly and inspiring treatise, it has been acclaimed all over the world.

Discoveries from the early phase of the Sutherland greenshank project were embodied in Desmond and Maimie's *Greenshanks* (1979). The book contained especially valuable and original sections on voice, food, individuals and nesting behaviour, as well as abundant comparisons with Speyside populations and other waders. The large data set, supplemented since 1978, has recently been used to examine factors involved in timing of laying and population fluctuations over nineteen years. Long term research of this kind is marvellous because it enables one to address questions concerning the evolution of, and intrinsic/extrinsic factors affecting, breeding biology. Changes in climate, habitat, food and pollution levels, and in breeding density, competition, mortality and recruitment, all play variable but essential roles. As we write this Preface, the results of a 31 year study of kittiwakes just published by Coulson and Thomas (1985: *J. Anim. Ecol.* 54: p 9–26) reinforce the importance of adopting a far-sighted approach when considering the adaptive value of changes in population size and breeding strategies.

After *Greenshanks*, other writing continued apace. In 1980 Dieter Fiucynski and Desmond published a comparative population study of hobbies in Germany and England. That year also saw the reprinting of Seton Gordon's *The Golden Eagle*, with a typically warm foreword by Desmond. Between the turn of the century and the time when Desmond moved to the Scottish Highlands, Seton Gordon was the Highlands' sole full time naturalist.

Fifty years after Desmond first saw a 'Highland' bird he was awarded the Neill Prize by the Royal Society of Edinburgh (1981). In 1983 he received his accolade, an Honorary D.Sc. from the University of Aberdeen. Amongst those who championed his case was Professor George Dunnet, the successor to Wynne-Edwards at Aberdeen.

Desmond would be the first to acknowledge that in large part his success is a measure of the debt owed to Maimie. With superb efficiency, Maimie has organised annual six-week camps to NW Sutherland, transcribed all field notes and shared the writing. Her still tireless efforts stand as a remarkable testimony to her faith in Desmond. *Waders: their breeding, haunts and watchers* is very much a joint effort.

Their book opens with an appreciation of those who have studied waders. We are given a fascinating insight into how wader research has evolved and how it may develop. Then, following on from spacing and dispersion, the book deals chapter by chapter with waders characteristic of different habitats. In each, topics covered include courtship, nest site selection, egg laying, incubation, hatching and breeding area fidelity, as well as food and voice. Here there is substantial new information. Nethersole-Thompson's data, much until now unpublished, stretch from the 1920s to 1985. There is also a distillation of a colossal correspondence from wader biologists around the globe. The final two chapters on 'new or returning' and 'pipe-dream' waders reflect this and are truly exciting; they are pleasantly speculative and full of hope for the future.

Yet throughout there are messages of concern. Waders breed in an environment threatened by many pressures. Of these, afforestation and land drainage pose the greatest threat to moorland birds. Large expanses of blanket bog, for example, are being replaced by dense uniform blocks of sitka spruce and lodgepole pine. These plantations reduce availability of nesting habitat and harbour predators, such as crows, which limit breeding success on moorland near the forest edge. On the mountain tops, disturbance, litter and erosion threaten nesting individuals. In Britain part of the upland wilderness has taken some ten thousand years to develop; in less than ten years it can be irrevocably destroyed. Uplands are terribly fragile and rely on their immense size and integrity for persistence. The welfare of breeding birds is a good indicator of the changing fortunes of an important ecosystem. Other habitats are threatened too; old grasslands are rapidly being converted to arable farmland; saltmarsh drained and reclaimed; and scrub now engulfs many south-east sites used by stone curlew. In one stroke we lose aesthetic and biological legacies. Only by understanding the lives and population ecology of breeding waders, and their use of different habitats, can we made sensible suggestions for their conservation. If this book stimulates some new avenues of thought or research then it will have achieved a great deal.

The writing is fresh and the atmosphere evocative. As raw students of wader biology we are so very grateful that this special book has reached fruition.

Liverpool, February 1985

Acknowledgements

We owe an enormous debt of gratitude to our family for their constant support. Without their loving encouragement this book would not have been completed.

Since 1964 they have all contributed to the field work in our wader research. From 1972 they carried out most of the nest finding and tape-recording and we thank them for the use of their field notes. They have all shared our many nights in the hut in north-west Sutherland and all have camped on the high Grampians while studying dotterel. In addition, each member individually worked on the wader groups close to our home and in other study areas in the Highlands.

In particular, we thank Eamonn for his patience in building up our library of tape-recordings, and Katharine for regularly collecting food samples for analysis.

We warmly thank Bruin and Patrick for the Preface and they wish to thank Prof. J. C. Smyth for reading and commenting on an early draft.

Bruin went to much trouble to prepare a piece on 'Timing of breeding and breeding performance' for the greenshank chapter and we thank him for allowing us to use Fig 3. We also thank him for his unpublished notes on the winter ecology of golden plover, for correcting our sections on 'Food' in each chapter and for writing the introduction to sonagrams.

We owe special thanks to Patrick for his original and unpublished redshank data which has greatly advanced that chapter. He wishes to thank Prof. Bill Hale for his support, Chris McArty for his help and friendship in the field, and Frances, for her support and help with his research. Pat has allowed us to use material from his Iceland diary and to cite many original notes from his dotterel notebooks.

Our daughter, Maimie, has been responsible for updating the greenshank data and has extracted material from her own and Richard's diaries for the chapters on lapwing, common sandpiper, golden plover, dunlin and curlew. We also greatly appreciate her patience in checking and correcting our Tables and Figures.

Bruin and Patrick have gone to immense trouble to obtain and photo-copy scarce wader material for us and have drawn our attention to many papers in the current literature.

This book brings our work on waders up to date and summarises the discoveries of many other wader watchers. We happily acknowledge our debt to two great handbooks: *Handbuch der Vögel Mitteleuropas*, edited by Urs Glutz von Blotzheim, K. M. Bauer and E. Bezzel (1975, 1977) and *The Birds of the Western Palearctic*, edited by S. Cramp and K. E. L. Simmons (1983). To those who live far from a scientific library, the concise summaries in these books are invaluable.

Between 1970–82 our wader project had generous support from the Natural Environment Research Council. Prof. George Dunnet, Regius Professor of Natural History, University of Aberdeen, Prof. W. G. Hale, Biology Department, Liverpool Polytechnic, and Prof. V. C. Wynne-Edwards, have been great friends and supporters of our work. We thank them for all their encouragement over these years. In 1982 the Highlands and Islands Development Board assisted us with a grant to help towards the writing of this book.

We warmly thank the Proprietors and Keepers on the Estates on which we have worked. Between 1964–81 our friend, Mrs Marjorie Fergusson, kindly allowed us the use of one of her fishing huts in her deer forest in Sutherland. Robert McLeod, keeper on the estate, became a valued personal friend and gave us unstinted practical help throughout our years of reserch.

Dr J. Morton Boyd, formerly Director (Scotland), Nature Conservancy Council, Stewart Angus, Assistant Regional Officer, NCC, Golspie, and David Duncan, NCC Warden for Sutherland, have been generous with their help at all times. We also thank David for his notes on the woodcock.

Bill Sinclair, our leading Scottish bird recordist, has spent many days with us in our camps, using his sophisticated equipment to capture some of the great moments and exciting calls of waders. Prof. Bill Thorpe kindly arranged for Mrs Joan Hall-Craggs to make sonagrams from these tapes at Madingley Field Station, Cambridge. We also warmly thank Dr Tony Hawkins, Deputy-Director Marine Laboratory, Aberdeen, for his enthusiasm and interest and for allowing us to prepare additional sonagrams at the Laboratory. We appreciate Pat Sellar's advice and thank V. C. Lewis and Philip Hollom for kindly allowing us to use two tape recordings.

Two special friends, Dr Derek Ratcliffe, Chief Scientist, NCC and Dr Adam Watson, Institute of Terrestrial Ecology, have been involved with our research and have always been willing to offer helpful advice.

Abroad, Prof. D. F. Parmelee, of the University of Minnesota, USA, and Prof. A. I. Ivanov, of Leningrad, have taken a great interest in our work, as well as giving practical help.

Our friends Ivan and Mary Hills have enthralled us with tales of their hunts for waders in the far north. We thank them for their notes. John Little and Evelyn Meek have also given us original material on waders.

We are most grateful to Lennart Raner – 'King of the Duskies' – for allowing us to use his unpublished field notes and for stimulating discussions while visiting us here.

For many years we have corresponded with our friend, Dr Hugh Blair, whose special knowledge of the *Limicolae* and meticulous notes and comments have always been appreciated by us both.

The late Normal Gilroy was one of the great nest hunters of all times. We have extracted material from his unpublished diary. Our friend, the late Prof. Bill Hobson, gave us unpublished notes on the nesting of green sandpipers and described some of his wader hunts in the Arctic.

We have had productive correspondence, as well as happy meetings, with Prof. S.-A. Bengtson and Dr John Kålås. John, along with Dr Ingvar Byrkjedal, has kept us in touch with their latest discoveries in wader research.

We appreciate our friendship with Ray Parr, remember happy days together in the field, and pay tribute to his splendid studies of golden plovers in north-east Scotland.

John Mitchell has described many of his successful hunts for the rarer waders and has given us reprints of his papers. Graham des Forges gave us unpublished notes on woodcock. Charlie Young, a most experienced nest hunter, has contributed notes on red-necked phalarope, Temminck's stint and wood sandpiper. John Mullins and David Clugston, two most skilful wader watchers and nest finders, have kindly kept us posted about their many successful quests.

Our friend, Donald Bremner, Head of Physics at Golspie High School, has been a welcome visitor to our wader camps and a grand companion in the field. Donald showed us our first whimbrel's nest.

Over the years we have had a vast correspondence with colleagues at home and abroad. We are indebted to the following for permission to use unpublished material, for practical help, or for their company in the field.

FINLAND: Dr Olavi Hildén, Prof. E. Pulliainen and Dr L. Saari.

SWEDEN: Ulf Houmann and Viking Olsson.

NORWAY: Dr Y. Hagen

NETHERLANDS: J. F. Sollie.

AUSTRIA: Hans Franke and E. Hable.

GERMANY: Hans Rittinghaus.

SPAIN: Alfredo Noval.

USA: Drs Walter Graul, Helen Hays, Lew Oring and Dick Phillips.

CANADA: Prof. Dave Boag, Dr E. O. Höhn and T. E. Randall.

BRITAIN: John and Trina Barrett, David Bates, Dr K. W. Brewster, Miss S. Bull, Niall Campbell, Andrew Currie, M. S. Davies, Colin Galbraith, Dr J. A. Gibson, Malcolm Harvey, C. Headlam, Mark Hope, Dr Mike Harris, Bill Henderson, G. M. Ireson, John Kirby, Dr Art Lance, Barry Larking, Sheriff D. Macdonald, Dr Calum Mackenzie, Duncan Matheson, Dr Robert Moss, Dr Ian Newton, Dr Ian Pennie, B. Nethersole-Thompson, the late C. Nethersole-Thompson, Roger Powell, A. J. Prater, Tony Rendall, Derick Scott, K. V. Tayles, Valerie Thom, Adam Watson, Sr., R. B. Weeden, Douglas Weir, David Whitaker and L. Wray.

Institutions

Doctors David Snow, Colin Harrison, Philip Burton and Derek Goodwin, along with our friend Michael Walters, all went to great trouble to help when we were working in the British Museum Bird Room at Tring. At the Royal Scottish Museum, Edinburgh, Ian Lyster went out of his way to show us the egg collections, diaries and data in his charge. We thank the Director of Museums and Art Galleries, Brighton, and the Staff of the Booth Museum, for their helpful cooperation.

When Director, Dr Jim Flegg and his staff at the BTO Tring, particularly Robert Morgan, kindly allowed us to study data on breeding waders. We greatly miss the friendship and presence of the late Ken Williamson. Dr Chris Perrins, of the Edward Grey Institute, Oxford, kindly arranged for us to have photocopies of the late Arthur Whitaker's diaries on waders.

Many Librarians have helped us. We especially thank Mrs Mary Stevenson, formerly Librarian at Brathens Field Station, Banchory, and Richard Ardeen, Research Librarian, HIDB, Inverness. The University Librarian at Aberdeen and the Librarian and staff at Inverness have always been willing to locate scarce material for us.

Illustrations

We thank our old friend, Donald Watson, for designing and painting the magnificent jacket. As always, his delightful black-and-white sketches add atmosphere and feeling to the text. Donald wishes to thank Keith Brockie for useful discussions on one or two of the Scandinavian nesting birds and sites.

At the suggestion of Trevor Poyser, we cast our net widely for black-and-white photographs. The response was so magnificent that we had the choice of around 500 wader photographs. We have had to disappoint some photographers, but we are most grateful for their help and enthusiasm.

We particularly thank Dr I. Neufeldt, Academy of Sciences, Leningrad, Dr Olavi Hildén, University of Helsinki, Dr Yngvar Byrkjedal, Bergen University, and Lennart Raner, Sweden, for valuable contacts. The great Arctic wader authority, Professor D. F. Parmelee, went to much trouble to look out prints of knot and sanderling which he had photographed at the nest.

Eric and Dorothy Hosking, friends of many years, worked with me in Spey Valley in 1940 and 1947; and in 1976 they visited our Sutherland wader camp where Eric took a grand series of greenshank photographs.

Our daughters, Maimie and Katharine, have been generous with their help and have lightened the burden of proof reading and Index preparation.

Finally, we thank Trevor Poyser for his enthusiasm, skill and good advice throughout the preparation of this book. Ornithologists owe him a great debt for his publications.

1:   Wader birds

All naturalists have favourite groups of birds. Ours are the waders; but despite early adventures our love for them took long to grow. My first impressions are of a marsh in Sussex on a warm moist evening in April 1925. A snipe was bleating almost overhead, lapwings were tumbling over a rough green patch and, in the distance, a single redshank was displaying and yodelling. Even now the wonderful atmosphere of the dykelands comes back to me.

But, for any boy, the attraction of birdsnesting and tree climbing was then all powerful. I often looked wistfully at rooks with their bulky nests far out on thin branches of tall elms, but I could never find any that I could reach. It was not until I was 12 years old that I came upon a small rookery in a windbreak of pines in Somerset to which I was able to climb. For many years I prized those spotted green eggs which I carried down in my mouth and blew with jagged pinholes at each end. A few years later, while living in London, I became fascinated by the herons in Richmond Park. In the pale light of dawn those large sky blue eggs, lying on black twigs on great rafts of sticks high up in Spanish chestnuts, were marvellous trophies.

Then, the great field naturalist, John Walpole-Bond, showed me the peregrines on the chalk cliffs of Sussex. I now learnt to be a cragsman and to sway and slither down the slimy white walls with their large dark and embedded flints. The blood red eggs were always a magnet. I also loved the aerobatics of courting peregrines and to listen to their harsh screams as they flew over the grey waters of the English Channel.

Hunting for hobbies' nests on English heaths and downlands was a different but equally exciting challenge. In May I lay out on the commons and marked down the clumps of pines where I could hear their wryneck-like courting cries. For 2s. 4d. old money, for a day-return ticket, I could visit the haunts of two pairs; and a 4s. 6d. early morning 'workman's ticket' took me to the nesting grounds of a further four pairs.

All this time great birdmen like Bond and Cecil Stoney, a famous Irish squire, were telling me about the Scottish Highlands, where they had hunted greenshanks in Sutherland and dotterels on the whalebacks of the Grampians. As I listened eager-eyed to their adventures, I sometimes doubted that greenshanks and dotterels could really compare with peregrines and hobbies. How wrong I was! Before long the waders had started to cast their spell.

In 1925 I found 20 snipes' nests on the Amberley Wild Brooks and did learn a little about their behaviour. But my work was never sufficiently continuous to achieve a real insight. While searching for nests of shoveller, garganey and shelduck, on the Cooling marshes in the Thames estuary, I also watched redshanks flipping up from their tented nests in the wetlands.

My first real challenge was with the stone curlew on the downs of Sussex and Salisbury Plain and on the breckland of East Anglia. I puzzled over its system of dispersion and the relationship of breeding pairs to those flocks which still persisted during incubation. I can never forget the wonderful experience of lying out on the breck one bright moonlight night and watching the stone curlews feeding, calling and displaying. In 1931 I found one of the last Kentish plover's nests in Britain on the stony waste of pebbles near Dungeness. It was great to watch the bird run back and to find the three small spotted and blotched khaki-coloured eggs.

In the late 1920s, while hunting for hobbies, I watched my first curlews, found their nests, and listened to their lovely bubbling songs on the heaths and commonlands of Surrey. It would be a poor creature who cannot delight in the guttural sounds of a pair of courting curlews, with the cock standing behind the hen, flapping his wings for minutes on end before he jumps or floats onto her back. And what a thrill to listen to those amazing bugle-like calls given by a sitting curlew to chicks struggling out of the eggshells.

I first went to Sutherland to search for greenshanks in 1932, but I did not cover myself with glory. A year later I was more successful in hunting them in the clearings of the old Caledonian pine forests of Spey Valley and in watching dotterel on the Cairngorms tops. Later, while living in cottages in Abernethy and Rothiemurchus, my wader watching expanded. Around us there were golden plovers on the moor, oyster-catchers, ringed plovers and sandpipers close to loch and river, and lapwings on the farm fields and moorland edges.

In those early years we learnt a little about the courtship and breeding behaviour of common sandpipers. What a wonderful range of exciting sounds and airplays they had in the early days of courting. Then there was silence or only intermittent singing and calling. Later, in our greenshank valley in Sutherland, we were to learn much more about the sandpipers' displays and breeding biology; it is now one of our favourite waders. Dunlins also nest in our greenshank valley. We have watched and described their sex lives and their egg laying and incubation behaviour. Their breeding system is full of puzzles. Why, for example, are the pairs spaced so far apart on the river flows and at a much higher density in the gneiss hillocks?

Beside Loch Morlich, and on the Dorback Burn in Spey Valley, there were a few pairs of ringed plovers whose courtship I always enjoyed. It was exciting to see the cock 'marking time' behind the hen before mounting her; and later to watch the pairs frequently changing guard at the nest.

Over the years the breeding behaviour of lapwings has always delighted us. Small groups have nested almost beside our different homes in the Highlands; it has been a joy to watch and listen to them. Some have nested semi-socially but most hold quite large territories which they zealously defend against others. Their sexual behaviour seems to differ from group to group. There was much more adultery in the Abernethy groups than in those studied in Ross and Sutherland. But lapwings are highly sexed birds, often coupling during incubation and while rearing their chicks.

Oystercatchers, too, have often baffled us. What determines their very different patterns of spacing – isolated pairs holding well separated territories on farm fields, well burnt moors or sea cliffs, and the clusters on river shingle with nests occasionally placed almost side by side?

Golden plovers have given us many happy days. From the time that the first trips arrive on the fields until they flock in late summer these lovely waders never fail to fascinate. They seem to depend greatly on the grasslands for food, sometimes flying over 5 km from the nest to visit them. Grassy patches on farm, croft and old ley are also important in their ecology. No sound more piquantly symbolises the wild places than a solitary unseen golden plover piping mournfully in the dusk.

The woodcock, our only true forest and woodland wader, has always intrigued me. I could sometimes identify a particular roding cock by peculiarities of its calls. When I watched woodcocks in Spey Valley they seemed to have regular roding routes from which they drove away trespassers. I once saw a cock alight beside a nest on which the hen had just started to incubate. Another time I watched a roding cock dip low over the edge of a small pinewood and saw a second woodcock fly out, apparently from a nest with fresh eggs. But, at other nests, the sitting hens ignored the roding cocks however closely they passed over them; and they left for their evening feeds quite independently of the cocks' flights.

To us, the greenshank is the most marvellous bird that flies, with nest finding a field sport which is the first step to greater knowledge. We have written two monographs about greenshanks and hope that at least one member of our family will continue and greatly expand the story in years to come. We now have many of the greenshanks' calls recorded on tape. On dreary winter nights it is grand to listen to the excited little cries of the hen greenshank apparently encouraging a chick as it 'explodes' the eggshell. And how evocative it is to listen to a recording of the passionate song dance of the cock greenshank; suddenly, you are no longer sitting by the fireside but shivering on the grey stony flows of our well-loved Sutherland valley!

On the high Cairngorms and Grampians we have spent over 300 days and nights in small tents on the whalebacks, while discovering something about the dotterel and its most unusual reversed courtship. The hens here are occasionally polyandrous; they put a second cock down on eggs after the first mate is sitting; and then they sometimes share incubation with the second mate. At first the cocks usually drive away hens which attempt to approach their own broods. Yet, on the Hardanger Vidda in Norway, John Kålås found that hen dotterels regularly laid second clutches for cocks which had lost their first nests and then helped to hatch them.

Dotterels have prospered in the last 30 years. A pair nested in North Wales in 1969, in Ireland in 1975, and now they again breed quite regularly in the English Lakeland. On the Continent they have colonised reclaimed polders in the Netherlands where they have actually nested below sea-level. Thriving groups now breed in Austria and isolated pairs have nested in Switzerland and Spain. In Scotland, since *The Dotterel* (1973), we have had many reports of dotterels nesting in new or long-deserted haunts in Argyll, Perth, Ross, Inverness, and the southern Uplands.

We have been fortunate in our generation. In the last 50 years we have gained or regained avocet, little ringed plover, Temminck's stint, purple sandpiper, ruff, black-tailed godwit and wood sandpiper, all of which now breed regularly in different parts of Britain. Black-winged stilt, green and spotted sandpipers, and recently turnstones, have all nested at least once.

In 1956 I flushed a Temminck's stint from its nest in the Spey Valley. Today these dainty little waders are established in several different haunts in the north of Scotland. The green sandpiper, one of the most thrilling of all waders, is my greatest disappointment. How often I have pictured myself finding one sitting in an old thrush's or crow's nest on the edge of a big bog! The wood sandpiper story is a happier one. In 1968 we recorded the calls of parents and chicks beside a loch in Sutherland. In 1969 Bruin and I watched a pair exchange, and then flushed the cock from three eggs in a rather dry part of a vast flow.

There are 'pipe-dream' waders, mouth-watering birds of which we have read much and talked about with those who have hunted and tried to understand them. In the forest marshes we particularly think of dusky redshank, bar-tailed godwit, jack and great snipe and broad-billed sandpiper. In the Canadian muskegs the greater and lesser yellowlegs and solitary sandpipers are intriguing. We should love to have comparative studies of these with greenshank, redshank, dusky redshank and green sandpiper. The barrens of the high arctic, so challenging to work but now more accessible, have superb waders. The knot will always be a blue riband bird to the searcher. Sanderling, black-bellied plover and buff-breasted sandpiper are now also slowly yielding their secrets.

With their intriguing displays and their haunting voices the waders have always attracted dedicated enthusiasts. Over the years they have drawn the watcher to many of the wild places of the world as well as to softer haunts close to towns and cities.

2: The wader watchers

The 19th century was a period of hunting, exploring and discovery, with hardy naturalists more eager to acquire and possess than to isolate and solve problems. In 1838, Thomas C. Heysham of Carlisle, with his 'able assistant' James Cooper, published his observations on the dotterel; and in 1868 Edward Booth, the Harrovian trophy hunter, further advanced the dotterel story by discovering that the cocks reared the chicks and the hens gathered in small 'trips'. In mid century two German foresters, Weise and Hintz, discovered that green sandpipers laid their eggs in the old nests of tree-nesting birds and in the dreys of red squirrels.

A few contemporary wader watchers worked on different lines. Rich, tireless, adventurous and hardy men, they explored exciting wader grounds in northern Europe. In 1853 the old Etonian, John Wolley, assisted by groups of local collectors, was in the forest marshes. His diaries describe the behaviour of some of the attractive waders – dusky redshank, jack snipe and broad-billed sandpiper. Wolley then gave the classic description of the song dance of the minute jack snipe which, to his ear, sounded like the 'cantering of a horse in the distance over a hard hollow road: it came in fours with a similar cadence and a clear yet hollow sound'. At Muonio, Fenno-Scandia, Wolley's assistants also found many broad-billed sandpipers' nests, 'just where the thickest clouds of gnats rose from the water'.

A little later other wealthy Victorians explored the vast marshes of the Rivers Pechora and Yenesei. In 1875 Henry Seebohm, the Sheffield Ironmaster, and John Harvie-Brown, laird of Dunipace in Stirling, worked in the Pechora Valley in NW Russia, where they and their helpers collected 11 clutches of eggs and some downy chicks of the little known grey plover. They were also the first British ornithologists to find eggs and chicks of little stints. In 1877 Seebohm returned to Siberia but failed to find nests of Asiatic golden plovers on the Golchika tundra, although his 'scouts' brought him a clutch of eggs. Hugh Leyborne Popham, a peppery critic of younger collectors, worked in the Yenesei delta in N. Siberia. On 3 July 1877 he tracked down a nest and eggs of curlew sandpiper. He also found Asiatic golden plovers' nests and was able to distinguish between their calls and those of the European golden plover.

By the early 1900s a remarkable group of egg collectors had largely replaced the trophy hunters. A most unusual Highland laird, William Stirling, of Fairburn in Easter Ross, was a link between the bird-killing trophy hunters and the later egg collectors. Stirling chose his gamekeepers for their skill in nest hunting and ability to climb to siskins' and crossbills' nests in the tall pines and larches around his mansion. His stalkers with their telescopes had a duty to mark down greenshanks' nests on his deer forests. When the stalker reported a find, Stirling set out in his dog cart. Between 1897 and 1902 he had collected 23 clutches of greenshank's eggs; and before his death in 1914 the tally exceeded 70, enough to cover his billiard table! A most generous host, Stirling invited many famous egg collectors to Fairburn, almost as he would guests for fishing and stalking. F. C. Selous, lion and elephant hunter, John Walpole-Bond, Norman Gilroy, the Chances, J. Baldwin Young, and the artist George Lodge, all stayed at Fairburn. His great collection of greenshanks' and other eggs, along with his Catalogue, is now in the Inverness Museum.

Some amazing men and women raised the sport of nest finding from an art almost to a science. At the same time a few gifted and purely observational ornithologists began to pioneer a new approach to the study of the living bird. Among the hunters was a woman of high intellect, Maud Haviland, who tracked down a curlew sandpiper's nest in the Yenesei marshes. To find the nest she scattered white feathers on the tundra to mark the approximate place from where the bird had flown up far ahead of her.

In the Arctic the finding of a knot's nest was a great challenge. In 1876 H. W. Feilden and his companions of the Nares Expedition found downy chicks in Grinnell Land in the Canadian arctic, but failed to find a nest. In 1909, however, Robert Peary, on his return from the North Pole, found two knots' nests and eggs on Floeberg Beach north of 82° in Grinnell Land. Meanwhile, in 1901, the Russian ornithologist A. Birula had found two nests in Taimyr and in 1902 a third on New Siberia Island. Two Danish ornithologists, W. E. Ekblaw and A. L. V. Manniche, did excellent work in north-east Greenland. Ekblaw's companions found two knots' nests behind North Scar Bay and Manniche made notable observations on the sanderling.

At home the egg collectors soon split into two different groups. The first restricted themselves to Britain and Ireland where they hunted the scarcer and more attractive waders; particularly greenshank, dotterel, red-necked phalarope, Kentish plover and stone curlew. The others, often wealthy men, travelled abroad to hunt for knot and sanderling in the high Arctic, and dusky redshank, bar-tailed godwit, jack and great snipe in the forest marshes of northern Europe. What formidable hunters these eggers were! John Walpole-Bond of Sussex, the brothers Edgar and Macomb Chance, Arthur Whitaker and J. Baldwin Young of Sheffield, and Cecil Stoney from Co. Donegal in Ireland were among the most skilful and successful.

A tall powerful man with a great red viking moustache, Jock Bond was a nest hunter extraordinary. Greenshanks in Sutherland, stone curlews on the Sussex Downs and Kentish plovers around Lydd and Dungeness in Kent were his favourite waders. He had a sufficient income to 'bird' in Sussex and more affluent friends sometimes took him on longer trips to Wales, Ireland and the Scottish Highlands. His famous three volumes *History of the Birds of Sussex* are still a joy and inspiration to many.

The brothers Macomb and Edgar Chance, Directors of Chance and Hunt, Birmingham chemical manufacturers, were also outstanding wader men. Small, sturdy and aggressive, gifted with a wonderful eye and keen hearing, Macomb, the older brother, pitted his skill against the most challenging birds, particularly the greenshank in Sutherland and on the foothills of the Cairngorms. Macomb seldom published his discoveries, but a correspondent kindly gave us a copy of his MS notes on the greenshank. He

found their nests by watching and waiting rather than by searching. On the Dornoch Firth a greenshank spotted him on his stance. 'The cock was very restless and kept on coming to look for me … his mate subsequently appeared and they pitched on dry ground almost 200 yards from the nest. After finding me, one bird then settled down for some minutes on an old disused gull's nest by a stump while the cock bird stood nearby. This performance was, I am convinced, merely a blind for my edification and may explain some of my previous failures with other greenshanks'. Macomb also succeeded with other scarce waders. In 1893 he used a special sheepskin coat for his dotterel hunts in the Grampians! On 15 June, assisted by two gamekeepers, he found three nests. 'I donned my special sheepskin coat and took up a position about 50 yards from where she was running. I was in full sight but she did not seem to notice me. No doubt this was due to my coat'.

His younger brother, Edgar, achieved classic research on the cuckoo about which he wrote two books *The Cuckoo's Secret* (1922) and *The Truth about the Cuckoo* (1940)). A determined and obsessional egg collector, Edgar Chance was another field ornithologist and nest finder of great skill and powers of concentration. He made exceptionally good use of his Zeiss Deltrintem field glass. A great wader enthusiast, greenshank, dotterel, stone curlew and dunlin were his favourites. An excellent organiser, he alternately wheedled and hectored his companions, seldom sparing their feelings when they fell short of his own high standards. He had a great 'nose' for a nest, but would often dance over the ground, bellowing, admonishing and loudly instructing those around him. I can still see the small figure in a large cloth cap and with loud foxy plusfours, galloping over the braes around Loch Morlich, flogging the heather with a long stick as he tried to flush a sitting greenshank. Yet E.P.C. could sit and wait when the occasion demanded. On 5 May 1932, while helping to study a trio of greenshanks in Rothiemurchus Forest, he wrote: 'I lay up on a commanding hill among the trees from 11 a.m. until 6 p.m. On a bitterly cold day. Intermittent heavy snowstorms added to the deep snow already extending low down beside the Cairngorms. But never a greenshank came into view or near its nest all day'.

In 1907, as a young man, Edgar Chance spent a spring in Orkney where, assisted by the great Orcadian field naturalist, John Douglas, he found 107 dunlins' nests. All these clutches and their data cards are now in the British Museum Collection in Tring. The scientific interest of this long series is largely confined to the precision of the laying dates. Chance periodically visited the Grampians for dotterel which he hunted with considerable success but without adding much to our knowledge of its breeding biology. In southern England, stone curlews on Salisbury Plain and on the brecks of Norfolk and Suffolk were among his other favourites.

A professional timber buyer and inspector, Norman Gilroy is particularly remembered for his vividly written brochure *Field Notes and Observations of the Greenshank* (1923). In 20 exciting pages he described how he and his friends found 18 nests in Sutherland and six more in west Inverness. In 1922 Gilroy also spent a week in the Grampians on which he found seven dotterels' nests. This led to a stimulating paper describing his experiences.

Gilroy's nesting exploits were not restricted to the British Isles. Lacking a private income, he sometimes accepted invitations from more wealthy colleagues who sought to use his skill to enrich their own collections. In 1928 he accompanied Dr Edward Steward, of Windermere, to the Pasvik marshes in Finnmark. The two men shared lodgings at a Customs House on the Norwegian border from which they daily went their separate ways. Then, as so often, Gilroy was quite amoral, concealing many of the clutches he had taken and telling his 'patron' that he had been 'quite out of luck'. There are two columns in his diary: one listing the nests known to Steward and the other accounting for eggs he had blown and hidden away. The second column includes three clutches each of bar-tailed godwit, greenshank and dusky redshank, two clutches of wood sandpiper and one clutch of broad-billed sandpiper. He also describes the finding and taking of two clutches of waxwing and a clutch of great grey shrikes' eggs. This exciting diary also gives beautiful descriptions of the previously unrecorded song dances of dusky redshanks and bar-tailed godwits and many fascinating details of their behaviour.

A Sheffield architect, Arthur Whitaker, was interested in all waders, with greenshank,

dotterel and stone curlew as favourites. In his diaries he recorded the contents of every nest that he had seen. A tough, hardy man, Whitaker usually hunted bare-headed, wearing plusfours and shoes with turned-up toes. Whitaker watched greenshanks in Inverness, dotterel in the Cairnogrms and Grampians, stone curlews in Norfolk, Suffolk and Wiltshire, and Kentish plovers in the Channel Isles. His small egg collection, and the much more important diaries, are now in the Edward Grey Institute at Oxford. Another Yorkshireman, J. Baldwin Young of Eckington, solicitor and colliery director, went further afield, seeking waders in the wilds of Finland. Great snipe and dusky redshank particularly captivated him.

Cecil Stoney, the Donegal squire, was a great character with a marvellous sense of fun. Over 50 years on I can still hear the silky purr of his brogue as he told me about his wader hunts in the rough places of Ireland and Scotland. He was one of the first to watch a pair of dotterels changing over at a nest and to describe the homing flights and nest relief of greenshanks. In one season he found 20 red-necked phalaropes' nests in the estuarine marshes of Co. Mayo. He also told me about large concentrations of curlews on the Shannon Bogs in Roscommon where he sometimes watched 4–5 curlews running back to nests which were less than 50 m apart. Rich in knowledge and experience, with an immaculate sense of timing and positioning, Stoney, like so many of his generation, unfortunately committed little to paper.

An Anglican parson, Francis Jourdain, an excellent linguist, had read more of the literature of Palearctic birds than any other of his generation. Married to an heiress, Jourdain travelled widely all over Europe and North Africa. On the Oxford University Expedition to Spitsbergen in 1921, of which he was the leader, Jourdain and A. H. Paget-Wilkes found 19 turnstones' nests and wrote a good account of their breeding behaviour. With his neat beard and piercing green eyes, Jourdain stood out in any company. Known to his contemporaries as Pastor Pugnax, for his many disputes and quarrels, he was a Father Figure and a true friend to young ornithologists. But he did not suffer fools gladly! When I first went to live in the Highlands, in 1934, Jourdain wrote almost weekly, always asking questions and sending me stimulating papers. Every summer I stayed at his home in Bournemouth where I added my latest notes to his concise digests of breeding biology. He was remarkably good at condensing and disciplining unwieldy data. Among many fine essays in A. C. Bent's *Life Histories of North American Shore Birds*, Jourdain contributed a masterly précis of Edmund Selous's discursive but most exciting observations on ruff and reeve in the Netherlands. 'J' will always be remembered for his part-authorship of *The Handbook of British Birds*.

Between the wars, H. M. S. Blair and John McNeile studied waders in northern Europe. Blair's original observations, supplemented by much reading and a wide circle of Norwegian correspondents, led to many polished essays on waders in Bannerman and Lodge's *Birds of the British Isles*.

A Guards Officer, captured at Antwerp in 1915, John McNeile was probably the greatest British exploring egg collector of his generation. Although he published little he kept marvellous leather-bound diaries which are now in the Royal Scottish Museum at Edinburgh. In 1930 McNeile and his friends found knot 'downies' on the Reindeer Peninsula, Spitsbergen. On 12 July 1931 he did better: 'The snow had almost gone and I was making my way back to the shore after a long and unsuccessful day in driving rain and sleet, when I suddenly heard a commotion at my feet and saw a knot fluttering almost on the ground, just as a purple sandpiper does when put off eggs'. In these exciting years McNeile and his companions also found eight sanderlings' nests. In one of his diaries we read; 'sanderlings calling; female running with back feathers ruffled, uttering a soft but excited call which sounded to me like 'chuzzle' or 'churzle' repeated four or five times'. I was at a British Oologists Association Dinner in 1931 when McNeile exhibited four clutches of sanderlings' eggs and that famous clutch of knot. I recall that a small group of excited and perhaps rather envious colleagues gathered round the table with its glass-covered boxes!

McNeile also had many successes in northern Europe. In the Muonio Valley, on the borders of Sweden and Finland, he found eight greenshanks' nests. The mysterious leks of great snipe fascinated him; in the 1930s he saw 30 nests in Finland. Equally exciting were his hunts for green sandpipers' nests in the forest marshes of Tartu in Estonia where, between 1935–38, he also saw 30 nests. No British ornithologist has equalled his record.

Sons of a Norfolk parson, the brothers Charles and Edward Bird had a fine record in north-west Greenland. After landing on 11 August 1936, Edward over-wintered for one year and Charles for a second. In 1937 they worked together in MacKenzie Bay and in 1938 Charles sledged and tramped over the stony Hochstetter Foreland. In 1937 the Birds tracked down five knots' nests near Myggbukta and in 1938 Charles found a further three on the Hochstetter Foreland. They also located nine sanderlings' nests, one containing two blue eggs with mauve blotches. Apart from their nest finding they learnt many new facts about the breeding strategy of the knot. 'Sometimes two or three birds were seen chasing each other at great altitudes …. We obtained both males and females on the nest. Our observations led us to believe that the female sits in the early stages of incubation and the male in the later …. After the bird is flushed it is extremely shy about returning; it will sit on a tussock and watch the observer until he goes away'.

I met the brothers at a dinner in London in 1939 when Charles read a paper on the periodic non-breeding of Arctic birds and then spoke extempore about the knot. Afterwards Charles Bird, my friend Jack Vine and I, continued to discuss waders as we moved from one night spot to another. This was the last time that I saw Charles Bird who was killed in 1941 when the *Exeter* was sunk in the Indian Ocean. No British ornithologists of their own or previous generations equalled the Birds' outstanding contributions to Arctic ornithology.

In the 1920s and 1930s some grand ornithologists were studying North American waders. William Rowan, Professor of Zoology at the University of Alberta, wrote intriguing accounts of the breeding behaviour of greater and lesser yellowlegs and solitary sandpipers. The greater yellowlegs, like the greenshank in Europe, posed a tremendous challenge. In 1929 wrapped in blankets on a night of severe frost, Rowan and his companions sat from 2 o'clock until 6.30 in the morning while trying to discover whether greater yellowlegs changed over at the nest. 'Several greater yellowlegs sang and switch-backed overhead as they flew towards distant haunts'; but the baffled watchers found no answer to their questions. In another year, after they had searched and searched without success, they later watched greater yellowlegs leading their broods far into the muskegs. 'The whole locality seemed to be swarming with them'. Rowan was also an exceptionally skilful taxidermist. His former student, Dave Boag, now in Rowan's Chair at Edmonton, learned his own craft as a taxidermist from his old Professor.

In the early 1930s two settlers from Britain, T. E. Randall and A. D. Henderson, discovered much that was new about the breeding behaviour of the Canadian waders. Randall, a smallholder, was another who contributed fine essays to Bannerman and Lodge's *Birds of the British Isles*, writing on the behaviour of greater yellowlegs, lesser yellowlegs and other waders. He told me that he had found 61 nests of the greater yellowlegs. Henderson, also an expert on the solitary sandpiper, worked near Belvedere, Alberta. We knew a retired Indian Judge who used to visit Henderson who helped him to take a clutch of greater yellowlegs' eggs for his collection. I saw the four fine eggs lying on sawdust in his cabinet!

From the early 1900s onwards, when the pioneer egg collectors were working in the Arctic and northern Europe, a few ornithologists were starting to work on different lines. In 1901 Edmund Selous described the 'piping parties' of oystercatchers; and in 1906 aspects of the social behaviour of stone curlews. He also wrote an orginal paper on the sexual selections of ruffs on leks in the Netherlands. A brother of Frederick Courteney Selous, Edmund disapproved so strongly of his brother and of the whole egg collecting fraternity, that he refused to share the farmhouse in Iceland in which Jourdain was lodging! An inspired thinker and interpreter of bird behaviour, Selous had a discursive style which made his accounts difficult to read. But he was the prophet of a new generation.

Julian Huxley was a man of outstanding talents. As a student at Oxford, he took first-class Honours in Zoology, the Newdigate Prize for Poetry, and won a half-blue for the high jump. I well remember my first meeting with him when he was Secretary of the Zoological Society of London. Tall, spare, ascetic-looking, with a scholar's stoop, he spoke at high speed, but was extraordinarily understanding of a young ornithologist's hopes, plans and problems! Julian Huxley gave a new slant to ornithology by helping to make the field notebook an acceptable tool in academic studies. In 1912, while on a holiday in Wales, he wrote a beautiful description of the courtship of redshanks. Later, in 1925, he went to the Netherlands with F. A. Montague to study the sex-lives of oystercatchers, black-tailed godwits and avocets. This led to a series of papers, all easy and pleasant to read, which still further advanced the ornithological revolution.

Between the wars, wader watchers carried out several good studies of breeding behaviour. In 1926 the Cumbrian R. H. Brown published his observations of lapwings, and in Germany G. Stein a pioneer paper on common sandpipers. While studying snow buntings in East Greenland in 1933, Niko Tinbergen also described the reversed courtship, nest-site selection, and egg ceremonies of red-necked phalaropes. In Holland, in 1936, G. F. Makkink wrote a detailed study of the behaviour of avocets; and J. E. Sluiters's fine observations on the little ringed plover were published in 1938.

In the early 1940s, Continental ornithologists published several good papers. In Germany H. Laven increased our knowledge of ringed plovers in 1940 and Brunhilde Laven that of the lapwing in 1941. In Holland there were excellent studies of the lapwing by G. L. Rinkel in 1940 and on oystercatchers by G. F. Makkink in 1942.

Ornithology has developed on much tighter lines, with egg collectors ceasing to be the main contributors to our knowledge of wader biology. The summaries in the Wader volumes of *The Handbook of British Birds, Handbuch der Vögel Mitteleuropas*, and *The Birds of the Western Palearctic* indicate great advances.

From 1950 onwards an outstanding German ornithologist, Hans Rittinghaus, described and filmed many aspects of the breeding-cycle of ringed plover, Kentish plover, oystercatcher and dotterel. Gerhard Grosskopf started to publish the results of his splendid research on the breeding behaviour of redshanks on the coastal marshes of the North Sea in 1958. European wader watchers also greatly expanded Huxley's study of the black-tailed godwits. In the Netherlands, J. H. van Balen (1959), H. Lind (1961), F. Haverschmidt (1961) and H. Kirchner (1969) have all taken an exciting story further forward. In a well-researched project in Schleswig-Holstein, in 1963, H. Kirchner summarised his family's experience of nesting wood sandpipers; and in 1972 he described the breeding biology of green sandpipers. A. J. Hogan-Warburg, in her doctoral thesis in 1966, made many discoveries about the lekking of ruffs and reeves in the Netherlands. In 1966, M. S. Soikkeli in Finland and R. W. Heldt in Germany published fine studies on the behaviour and population dynamics of the dunlin. In Alaska, in 1967, R. T. Holmes also wrote two detailed papers on the dunlin.

Aeroplanes and permanent military bases have enabled continuous work to be carried out on the waders in the high Arctic. Between 1967–69 D. G. Hassell and G. W. Page studied the black-bellied plovers and published an excellent account in 1976.

David F. Parmelee, now Professor and Field Biology Program Director at the University of Minnesota, and S. D. Macdonald, of the Canadian Wildlife Service, investigated the birds of West-Central Ellesmere Island, N.W.T. in 1955. Here they found eight knots' nests with eggs and two broods of chicks, one sanderling's nest and twenty turnstones'. In 1960 they published *The Birds of Western Central Ellesmere Islands and Adjacent Areas* which contains a mass of new data about all these waders, particularly the knot. 1960–62 found Parmlelee, with H. Stephens and R. H. Schmidt, on Victoria and Jenny Lind Islands in the Canadian arctic, studying the arrival, displays and nesting of the American golden and black-bellied plovers. They also learnt much about the little known stilt sandpiper and white-rumped and buff-breasted sandpipers, as well as carrying out massive research on other species. In 1968 and 1969, while working on Bathurst Island N.W.T., Parmelee suspected that sanderlings had an unusual breeding pattern whereby some hens laid two clutches in the same season. In 1970, with R. B. Payne, he examined the ovaries of two incubating sanderlings and then discovered that both had laid two clutches in quick succession.

In every sense a big man, David Parmelee, who served as a sergeant in the US Marines during the war, is the outstanding Arctic research ornithologist in the western world. He is also a fine bird artist. After we had corresponded from 1960 onwards, Dave briefly visited our greenshank camp in Sutherland in 1976; and in 1979 he and his wife, Jean, were with us in our home. We shall always remember a meal during which Dave imitated the knot's courtship calls and used his hands to show us the wing movements of its song dance!

A big, genial Yorkshireman, Professor Bill Hobson, at one time chief 'trouble-shooter' for the World Health Organisation, was another great wader enthusiast. An egg collector, with an irrepressible drive to hunt down the nests of the really challenging birds, he treated egg collecting as a field sport. In Britain, greenshanks in Sutherland and dotterel on the Grampians; green sandpipers in Denmark and purple sandpipers in Iceland were all challenges to his skill. The mysterious knot was a powerful magnet. He found three nests at Thule in Greenland in 1967 and in 1968 two nests on Fosheim Peninsula of Ellesmere Island. In 1976 Hobson published a brochure on the knot, based on personal experiences and those of others. Professor V. E. Flint of Moscow described his observations on the knot on Wrangel Island in 1964–65 and gave a summary of A. Birula's work in Taimyr in 1901 and on New Siberian Island in 1902. In 1974 the story of the blue riband knot was greatly advanced by David Nettleship's paper. For the very first time an ornithologist was able to publish a continuous account of the breeding cycle which he studied from 3 June–15 August 1974 at Hazen Camp, Ellesmere Island.

In the 1970s there have been so many excellent wader studies in Europe and America than we can only give a personal and subjective selection. From his seventh birthday the northcountryman, Bill Hale, was fascinated by the eggs of the redshank. In 1956 his first paper suggested that the redshank had not developed a territorial system. Nearly thirty years on, and now Professor of Biology at Liverpool Polytechnic, Bill Hale is still a redshank enthusiast. His post-graduate students work on the Ribble estuary where they continue to make stimulating discoveries about the redshank, a précis of which appears in the Wader Volume of *The Birds of the Western Palearctic.*

Several ornithologists have amplified Makkink's massive studies of avocets by intensive work in the breeding colonies on Havergate Island in Suffolk. Graham des Forges described unusual incubation patterns of woodcocks in Sussex; and G. Hirons has used telemetry to probe some of the secrets of their roding flights. Monica Shorten's brochure summarises contemporary knowledge of a most difficult and mysterious wader.

Our very good friend Derek Ratcliffe, now Chief Scientist with the Nature Conservancy Council, is a professional botanist as well as a dedicated ornithologist. Derek is equally attracted to waders and raptors. His research on the peregrine falcon and the development of the eggshell test has made him famous throughout the world. His monograph *The Peregrine Falcon* (1980) is a classic. As a wader watcher, the lovely dotterel has drawn him to the English Lakeland and to the hills of Drumochter and Ross, where he has learnt much about a most unusual bird's breeding ecology. He has been a most welcome visitor to our greenshank camp in Sutherland. In 1976, *Bird Study* published his beautifully written paper on his long-term study of golden plovers in the Pennines and southern Uplands.

Ray Parr, of the Institute of Terrestrial Ecology, has been for many years Adam Watson's field assistant in the programme of research on red grouse. I well remember the session at Blackhall Field Station – alas, no longer with us – when Ray decided to study the local golden plovers, in addition to his professional red grouse research. That was indeed a most happy decision. A man of parts, Ray also runs a successful dance band in the evenings, after hard days out in field. By colour ringing a group of goldies in Kincardine, he discovered that, after the earlier pairs had hatched their chicks and led them away, new pairs immediately moved in and nested in the vacated territories. Many pairs in these habitats appeared to stay together in winter and then held their own breeding territories in successive years. Ray published papers summarising his discoveries in *British Birds* (1979) and *Ornis Scandinavica* (1980).

Ornithologists in Finland continue to make discoveries about waders. In 1970 and 1971 Professor Erkki Pulliainen, Director of the Värriö Sub-arctic Research Station, published observations on the breeding biology and polyandrous system of the dotterel. Another valued correspondent, Olavi Hildén, of the University of Helsinki, also described his most original observations on the dotterel; and in 1972, with S. Vuolanto, wrote a detailed account of the breeding ecology and population dynamics of red-necked phalaropes. Then, in 1975, he summarised his remarkable discoveries on the unexpected breeding patterns of Temminck's stints. Hildén is now making comparable studies on little stints which appear to have similar systems, though they are not so markedly territorial as Temminck's stints.

An inspired teacher and wader researcher, Professor S.-A. Bengtson, formerly of Bergen University, Norway, and now of Lund University, Sweden, wrote detailed papers on grey phalaropes (1968) and purple sandpipers (1970), based on his original work in west Spitsbergen. Bengtson collected a group of gifted post-graduate students around him, several of whom are doing splendid work on waders on the Hardanger Vidda in Norway. Common and purple sandpiper, whimbrel, Temminck's stint, oystercatcher, turnstone and dotterel were all on the programme. We first met Bengtson and his students over breakfast in Banchory in 1978. At the BOU Conference in Glasgow in 1981 we had more time together. It was marvellous to listen to all these young people talking enthusiastically and at high speed about their special waders, and all in perfect English! John Kålås, who carried out his dotterel research from a small hill hut in the middle of the Hardanger Vidda, showed us some of his dotterel habitat slides. Sometimes he can watch a sitting dotterel from the window of the hut! How I would have loved, as a young man, to have spent a season or two in that vast country. A colleague of Kålås, Ingvar Byrkjedal, has done fine research on golden plovers, particularly by studying groups of lighter and darker birds which have posed many interesting problems. In 1983 Byrkjedal and Kålås published 'Plover's Page turns into Plover's Parasite: a look at the Dunlin/Golden Plover association', about which we shall write some more in the relevant chapters.

Our friend, Lennart Raner, a retired Swedish businessman, first came to visit us in March 1983. Lennart has an immense knowledge of northern waders, and it was a joy to sit and listen to him talking quietly and modestly about his work. He has seen 66 dusky redshanks' nests, of which he found 51; over 50 green sandpipers' and 13 jack snipes' nests in the boreal forest marshes; and he saw five knots' nests in Greenland. He discovered that a hen dusky redshank produced clutches for two different cocks at intervals of about 12 days. He also found out, by colour-ringing, that some red-necked phalaropes were polyandrous.

In 1966 and 1967 Lew Oring, later a Professor at the University of Minnesota, spent many weeks studying the song, calls and territories of green sandpipers in Västergottland, Sweden. With the skilled assistance of Raner, Oring collected enough tape recordings to produce a splendid series of sonagrams which he later compared with those of the closely-related solitary sandpiper in Alberta. While in Sweden, Oring also met with a golden plover which was laying eggs at much shorter intervals than those that we have recorded in Scotland.

A few British ornithologists still go north to hunt those challenging waders in the forest marshes of Fenno-Scandia. Between 1978–83 our friends Ivan and Mary Hills have annually driven their well-stocked dormobile to Norway, Sweden and northern Finland. They stay in the far north for over two months at a time and have often suffered from severe weather and occasionally have been driven out of their van to look for shelter in a house or hut. The finding of six bar-tailed godwits' nests and nests of dusky redshank and little stint, have led to many new facts and some grand colour slides. A beautiful print of a dusky redshank is on our sitting room wall and one of a bar-tailed godwit with chicks hangs in our study. While in Finland, Ivan and Mary visited Olavi Hildén and his wife, Ruth, at their home near Helsinki and they also stayed with Erkki Pulliainen at his field station in a Finnish forest. During the winter months Ivan keeps up a ceaseless correspondence with his Scandinavian friends and it was he who invited Lennart Raner to come to Britain and brought him to see us here.

Ivan, who was brought up in Essex and went to school at Stowe, chose to live and work in the Scottish Highlands until the outbreak of war. I first met him in 1937 when he came to Spey Valley to watch greenshanks, crested tits, siskins and crossbills. He had already had a fabulous trip to Argyll and the Drumochter Hills while searching for golden eagles' eyries, at one of which he was almost killed. Ivan has also enjoyed much success in finding the nests of dotterel, golden plover, red-necked phalarope and other Scottish waders. Ivan and Mary's visits to us are always a pleasure. He puts on a slide show especially for us and we all enjoy seeing the birds, people and places about which he talks so vividly. We hope that one day Ivan and Mary will write up their exciting experiences of 'Living with the Lapps'.

John Little, a professional golfer from Hindhead, Surrey, has also enjoyed much success in the northern marshes. He has found the nests of 20 broad-billed sandpipers, 7 dusky redshanks, 5 great snipe, 3 bar-tailed godwits and 2 jack snipe; a remarkable record by any standard. His unpublished observations make fascinating reading. Mrs Evelyn Meek, a great greenshank hunter, always writes to tell us of her annual successes in wader hunts in the Highlands. In 1983, for the first time, she visited the fells and forest marshes of Fenno-Scandia. Here she tracked down 2 dusky redshanks' nests with eggs and 3 broods of small chicks; and she also found 4 broad-billed sandpipers' nests with eggs. She kindly sent us a colour photograph of 3 pure blue dotterels' eggs from one of the fells. Some start in the north!

In North America, W. G. Sheldon, in his *Book of the American Woodcock* (1971), successfully tackled many problems in the life-history of an extremely difficult bird.

The Canadian Wild Life Service published *The Snipes* (1972), a grand monograph by Leslie Tuck, based largely on his own work on Wilson's snipe in Newfoundland. In 1965 Tuck received an Honorary Doctorate from Memorial University for his ornithological research.

The rolling hills of Colorado in the 1970s were the laboratory for Walter Graul's doctoral research on the little known mountain plover. A tremendous enthusiast and a splendid field man, Walter discovered much that was new about the mountain plovers. After pairing, the hen lays one clutch of eggs which the cock alone incubates and then she lays a second clutch which she broods. Some hens stay with their original mates, but others switch mates before laying their second clutches; some cocks copulate with more than one hen. In 1974 Graul also published a detailed account, with sonagrams, on the voice of this remarkable wader.

The voices of the waders are always evocative. We think of dotterel tinkling on the misty high tops, the wing music of lapwings, the evening chorus of golden plovers, and sandpipers 'wickering' low over loch and river. What memories they recall! Since the war, sound recording has become a vital tool. The irrepressible Ludwig Koch, the great pioneer of natural history recording, came to Spey Valley in 1946 to record the sounds of a greenshank hatch; and in the next year he captured the cock's song dance on disc, with the cacophony of a busy sawmill in the background. In those years recording apparatus was extremely clumsy and heavy and most difficult to move. Lightweight portable tape recorders have revolutionised the art. John Kirby, a steel man from Middlesbrough, is a most successful recorder of wader sounds. He recently recorded a green sandpiper song dancing somewhere in Spey Valley. Pat Sellar of Surrey has recorded the calls and cries of waders all over Europe, the Arctic and Iceland for the archives of the British Library of Wildlife Sounds.

In the Highlands, our friend Bill Sinclair is an enthusiastic and successful amateur bird recordist. Throughout the 1970s he visted our greenshank camp in north-west Sutherland where he sat over one of our nests and taped many of the greenshank's calls, including a wonderful series at a hatch. While travelling all over the Highlands, Bill, who always has his portable machine beside him, has made many superb recordings, including those of the copulation cries of greenshank and redshank. One marvellous sound picture unfolds as you hear the lovely sounds of cock lapwings thrumming in the moonlight.

The sonagram, a more exact and definite method of showing bird calls, is supplanting purely subjective verbal descriptions. Comparison of the Voice sections in the German *Handbuch* and in *The Birds of the Western Palearctic*, with the verbal descriptions given in the *Handbook of British Birds* shows how rapidly we are advancing. However, some calls are so quiet and difficult to reproduce as sonagrams that written descriptions will still always have to suffice. I shall never forget my visit to Cambridge in 1978 when Joan Hall-Craggs prepared the 59 sonagrams shown in *Greenshanks*. It was, to me, a thrilling experience to watch the machine print out the sounds which I knew and loved so well.

Waders have always attracted the photographers. In 1939 I first met Eric Hosking – then we were both quite young men! In 1940 and 1947 Eric worked with me in Spey Valley and in 1976 he and Dorothy came to our greenshank camp in Sutherland. The marvellous series of greenshank photographs, some showing the greenshanks removing their eggshells, are among his greatest works of art. Eric has photographed waders all over the world. Northern and southern Europe, USA, the Canadian Arctic and Greenland are among his many laboratories. We particularly delight in those wonderful portraits of stone curlews in Suffolk, the courtship and nest relief of black-winged stilts, and an intimate study of a pair of avocets at the nest, all of which appear in his fine *Waders* (1983) for which Professor W. G. Hale wrote a splendid text.

John Markham, another outstanding nature photographer, was a most sensitive naturalist who had a great love of all living things. He joined me in the field in 1940, 1946 and 1948. His beautiful shots of dotterel chicks hatching out on a wild Cairngorm whaleback and his studies of *Old Glory*, the famous hen greenshank, will always remind me of great days on the hill and in the forest. Our friend John Fisher photographed dotterels in the central Grampians and took beautiful pictures of lapwings at the nest on his farm near Newark. Every Christmas John sent us a print of some favourite bird, often a wader; all these are now framed and hanging on our walls. And, as I write this, I look up at a grand print of a dotterel with chicks, given to us by Sandy Tewnion, formerly Head of Biology at Dollar Academy, and a great montane naturalist.

Wader watchers only need a pen, a notebook and a pair of good field glasses; many still maintain the spirit of the old timers. Even in those years of austerity men and women of many kinds of professions tell us of their adventures with waders, at home and abroad. Quite out of the blue came a letter from Eric Hable, who is making a study of dotterel in the mountains of Austria. He later sent us a Christmas card showing him sitting beside a dotterel on its nest. A great and most successful nest hunter, John Mullins, periodically writes to tell us about his discoveries in Scotland and Europe. He is one of the few British ornithologists who has found a nest of the elusive green sandpiper.

Tony Rendall, a Chartered Accountant from Surrey, has an unusual method of hunting greenshanks. He parks his car on the main road close to a feeding loch and then sits in comfort until the greenshank starts to fly into the hills! Another keen wader watcher, Mark Hope, has made most interesting observations on dunlin in the Outer Hebrides. One of our correspondents, a Durham miner, has almost become a legend in his own lifetime. He spends all his holidays in trips to the Highlands where he hunts and finds the nests of dotterels as well as those of osprey, golden eagle, peregrine and other rarities. When we last saw him he was making his seventh trip of the year to the Highlands! As always, he was sleeping in his car and making the most of his money. Any spare cash he spends on the purchase of books by the old masters which he reads and absorbs from A to Z. One of our friends, a worker on an off-shore oil rig, has taken excellent photographs of red-necked phalaropes at nests on the Scottish mainland. He has also found and photographed the nest and eggs of Temminck's stints. In the summer of 1983 a Devon blacksmith arrived here with two friends; and on his return south wrote a fascinating account of their finds. As well as watching dunlin and golden plovers at the nest they had watched a pair of bramblings in a suitable birch wood near a shooting lodge in Sutherland.

A very keen bird watcher from Yorkshire, and a small group of friends from Yorks and Lancashire, discovered the valley in which we watch greenshanks. Frank Oates then wrote to ask if he could visit us there, which they did in 1981. Each year they work in the haunts of some rare bird new to them and write up their experiences in a beautifully illustrated diary.

Since *The Dotterel* (1973) and the three editions of *Highland Birds* we regularly have letters from mountaineers and hill walkers who have found nests and eggs or seen broods of dotterel, often in hills where previously they had seldom been recorded. A little time ago we heard from Miss S. P. Bull of Petersfield, who had located two broods of dotterel in the classic stamping grounds of old Edward Booth in Glen Lyon. We would not wish anyone to believe that all our correspondence is pleasant. Following a letter to *The Scotsman*, aimed at conserving the wonderful haunts of hill birds in the Drumochter Hills, there was a long letter in the post from an angry gentleman – a mountaineer too! – who was set on commercialising the hills for winter sports and downhill skiing!

My own observations on waders, summaried in *The Handbook of British Birds* (1940) led to the New Naturalist monograph *The Greenshank* (1951). I later wrote essays on lapwing, golden plover, oystercatcher, dotterel and stone curlew for Bannerman and Lodge's *Birds of the British Isles* (1961). *The Dotterel* was published in 1973. Later, when Maimie and I lived in Sutherland, we started on an entirely new study of green-shanks, first working in different deer forests each year and finally choosing a new and wonderful valley for our laboratory. Here, as a family team, we have worked from 1964–82. We have told the story in *Greenshanks* (1979). In the valley are golden plover, dunlin and sandpiper; and over the years our work was expanded to include these waders.

As children, our family had little choice but to join us in our wader hunts – after all they could not be left at home! But it has given us great joy that four of them became wader watchers in their own right.

Our small team has now dispersed but its members are still dedicated to the group. Sadly, our dear Richard, who was the best field naturalist of them all and who became a fish farmer, was killed in a motor accident just after his 21st birthday in 1982. Richard was a great nest finder and kept beautiful field notebooks to which we have constantly referred throughout this book. He always went to endless trouble to help us, giving up all his holidays and weekends to join us in the valley which he loved. We miss his quiet humour, his thoughtfulness, and his presence, but as a family we are grateful for our memories.

Bruin and Patrick are now professional zoologists. For his doctoral thesis Bruin studied the foraging economics of lapwings, golden plovers and gulls at Nottingham University. Patrick has already hunted for waders in Iceland; and, for his doctoral thesis, he is studying the population dynamics of a redshank group in Lancashire.

Our older daughter, Maimie, as yet unborn when we first went to the greenshank valley, has always been a dedicated wader watcher. From an early age she was tagging along behind her brothers, always asking innumerable questions. Before long she was pointing the way and the others asking questions! She has become an equally successful nest hunter of all waders. Now at Paisley College, working for a degree in Biology, any excess energy is put to good use in the hockey field.

One bitterly cold night, when he was a small boy, I kept Eamonn out until 1 a.m. while tracking down a most elusive greenshank. Inevitably we had just been ready to pack it up when the exchange started. Not surprisingly, this sickened him of green-shank hunts for a long time. But, as he never likes being left out of anything, he eventually took up his place as a valued member of the team, concentrating on tape recording. His own career has taken him into Hotel Management, where he much prefers communicating with the human animal.

Katharine, now a law student at Aberdeen University, was our rebel. She hated the cold and wet of the flowlands and could see no point at all in the study of birds. She was once talked into going on a dotterel trip, camping in the high Grampians in atrocious weather, but perhaps the less said about that the better! However, she would never allow me to go out alone in the valley; she was always there, willing to pull me out of bogs. When I sat down she invariably produced a novel from her bag and happily read while I waited for the homing greenshank. Over the years she absorbed a lot of knowledge about waders and their environment, and can be a formidable debater on the subject.

How many different drives have motived the wader watchers! But all have patiently jotted down what they have seen and heard and so helped to advance a most fascinating story.

3: Spacing and dispersion

The different systems by which nesting waders space themselves in their chosen habitats has always fascinated us. Cock **lapwings** establish arenas which they defend against rivals and into which they entice hens. Their lovely corkscrew song-flights show off the contrasts of black and white and indicate possession of a territory which they defend by wing fighting in the air and by special displays on the ground. Simultaneously, elaborate nest dances help to break down the hen's inhibitions and ultimately achieve pair bonds, as well as synchronising the sex rhythms of both birds. Yet in many lapwing haunts there are isolated pairs, possibly some of low status in the hierarchy, which are forced to accept less favourable environments. In other habitats, however, we have met with groups in which the pairs were nesting close together, almost in clusters, with nests sometimes placed only 2 m apart. Sometimes, when disturbed, the sitting birds flew up simultaneously, almost like a resting flock.

Less aggressive than lapwings, **golden plovers** have evolved an orthodox pattern of territorialism, with nests usually quite evenly distributed. The richness of their feeding grounds, however, probably determines the spacing. In the limestone grasslands of Mallerstang, in the Pennines, for example, Derek Ratcliffe (1976) recorded an average distance of 210 m between nests, as opposed to a mean of 423–443 m on blanket bogs on Alston moor in the Pennines and in the Moorfoot Hills in south Scotland. In parts of the Scottish Highlands, however, spacing has been less regular, with nests closer together on the moorland edges beside farms, crofts and old grasslands; and a few pairs spaced further apart in less favourable habitats, such as forest bogs and clearings. Some pairs appear to stay together in the winter flocks, returning in consecutive springs to their old nesting territories. New pairs form in the flocks, with the cocks establishing display centres in territories to which they later introduce their hens. Territorial boundaries are settled by the cocks fighting one another and by giving the wailing advertisement flight, often high in air or at a lower level, while beating their territorial bounds.

In Ray Parr's study area in Kincardineshire some territories were occupied by two pairs in the same season, a new pair taking over a territory in which the earlier pair had already hatched out a brood of chicks.

Ringed, little ringed, and **Kentish plovers** have different dispersion mechanisms. Little ringed plovers are the most aggressive in defending their territories, cocks patrolling and advertising living space by means of a pretty butterfly-flight and by singing over the boundaries. These persistent flights are not entirely restricted to the pre-incubation period. K. E. L. Simmons (1956) noted that little ringed plovers attacked low-flying intruders and evicted others by various forms of agonistic behaviour on the ground. This behaviour, which helps to space out the pairs, decreases after the young have started to fly. In the Netherlands little ringed, ringed, and Kentish plovers attempt to keep one another out of their respective nesting territories (J. E. Sluiters 1954). In Sweden, S. Durango (1943) watched two pairs of ringed plovers take over nests of little ringed plovers, in each of which two eggs had already been laid; and they then laid their own clutches in the stolen scoops. Ringed plover and little ringed plover usually feed on neutral ground where they seldom fight or compete.

The spacing mechanisms of **oystercatchers** are most remarkable. This bird, which sometimes lives for over 30 years, and usually only starts to breed between its third and fifth year, regulates its dispersion in different ways in its various habitats. On seashores, estuaries, river spate banks, lochsides, sea cliffs, farmlands and moors, many pairs form in the flocks in which there is some promiscuity and often 'trial marriages'. But once formed the pairs seldom divorce.

Breeding hierarchy is probably decided in the flock, with territorial aggression sometimes determining spacing between successful pairs. In Spey Valley, for example, nests ranged from 45–225 m apart on the spate banks of the Dorback burn. Outwith these habitats, a few pairs were dispersed at irregular distances on burnt heath and farmland; pairs defended the environs of their nests but usually fed on neutral farm fields. On sea cliffs in north Cornwall, the oystercatchers nested on broad grassy ledges at distances often of over 400 m apart. The oystercatchers' territorial patterns are thus extremely flexible. On Skokholm Island, Pembroke, some pairs fed their chicks on limpets taken from defended but well-separated feeding territories, while others found the food for the chicks within the limits of the nesting territory. What is the balance between these two different systems? The young oystercatchers are clearly more likely to be predated when their parents are collecting limpets from a distant territory.

The functions of the beautiful butterfly flight, in which the bird wails while slowly beating its wings, is probably primarily an aggressive or territorial signal. Sometimes a cock follows a party, wailing and 'butterflying' at a height of 50 m, or more; or he may make a series of these flights, each time returning to his territory. In the roosting groups the successful animals probably know their fellow members.

JDW

A few pairs of **avocets** place their nests well apart, but most are colonial with separate clumps or clusters of nests within the larger colonies. In some colonies each pair defends a small core-territory. In addition to the small defended nest territory, each pair ejects intruders from one or more feeding plots close to the nest (H. E. Axell 1977).

Black-winged stilts usually nest in groups or colonies varying from 10 to above 100 pairs. In the larger and denser groupings they defend the colony collectively. Both cocks and hens of isolated pairs or small colonies defend their small nesting territories against other stilts. Colonies are often situated close to nesting avocets, lapwings, red-shanks and nesting groups of gulls and terns.

Stone curlews appear to use their loud and far-carrying cries to achieve dispersion. Their presence in places where they are scarce or little known has sometimes been revealed when they have replied unexpectedly to recordings of their calls. The group evidently plays an important, but not clearly known, part in the spacing between nests. Social behaviour continues during incubation, with the non-sitting partners, unmated birds, and those that have lost their eggs, periodically meeting on afternoons, evenings, and at night; thus possibly enabling members of the community to know what is happening and, if necessary, to supply mates to birds that have lost their partners. These noisy meetings often take place well away from the nesting grounds and thus do not assist predators to find nests. On their nesting habitats, agonistic and territorial behaviour, as well as cries and calls, help to space out nests equitably. Again calls and cries probably aid dispersion. What a lot of new discoveries are in the making for those who use telemetry to wrest some secrets from these exciting stone curlews!

A few waders are occasionally polyandrous and have evolved a reversed courtship. In some haunts **red-necked phalaropes** appear to be orthodox territorialists. In east Greenland, for example, N. Tinbergen (1935) found that, after laying a clutch and putting her mate down on the eggs, the hen continued her ceremonial flights to attract another mate while she herself repelled rival hens from her territory. This form of orthodox territorialism is, however, less definite in other habitats where the cock, rather than the territory, is the defended object. The nature of the habitat, and the number of birds, probably decides whether territorialism is rigid, lapsed, or absent.

Grey phalaropes form stable pair bonds in Spitsbergen; but hens seek mates by means of 'circle flights' rather than by defending particular plots of land and pools of water. They later gather into flocks and move together all over the area. Afterwards, cocks direct 'driving flights' at hens that attempt to pursue their own mates 'back to the nest during incubation . ...'. The mere proximity of a bird of either sex was sufficient to elicit the driving flight' (M. W. Ridley 1980). **Wilson's phalaropes** appear to lack a rigid territorial system, but aerial pursuits of cocks by hens tend to disperse the pairs. In some years a few cocks are polyandrous. Behaviour and calls, rather than an active defence of territory, is probably the spacing mechanism.

In northern Scotland the cock **dotterel**, another bird with a reversed courtship pattern, uses an unusual territorial system to space out nests. Most pairs form from the trips, with the hen attempting to isolate and woo a cock. Afterwards newly-formed pairs are extremely mobile during their nest dancing, which sometimes takes place on different flats and hill flanks 1 km or more from where the hen ultimately lays her first egg. Before the nest site is finally fixed, two pairs may fly in together and fight; often hen against hen and cock against cock, until one pair dominates the other and establishes its nesting territory. There the two birds 'nest dance' together, and hollow out and partly line a few scoops, in one of which the hen lays her first egg, sometimes indicating in advance the chosen scoop to her mate.

During incubation the cock dotterel sometimes leaves the nest to drive away intruding cocks, hens or even trips. Meanwhile, the hens form parties of 'grass widows' which wander around. But we have occasionally seen a hen – possibly the mate of a sitting cock – leave the trip to drive away her companions which have temporarily approached her nest and sitting mate. Later, when the cock is herding his brood, he sometimes drives her away as well as strange dotterels – singles, pairs, or parties – when they have approached his chicks. In turn, a cock sitting on eggs may attack him if he and his brood intrude on the sitting bird's living space.

On Hardanger Vidda, where dotterel nest at a high density on the fells, John Kålås found that they were not strictly territorial and had not evolved a strong dispersion mechanism. As in Scotland, hens seeking new mates made 'winnow-glide flights', accompanied by rhythmic sequences of *peep peep* cries, performed at a height of 30 m or more. If a cock rises while the hen is displaying she chases him until he alights or fails to respond. The spacing systems of dotterel are flexible and apparently easily re-geared to meet high numbers or to the availability of food.

Hen **spotted sandpipers** are sometimes polyandrous, laying two, and exceptionally up to four, clutches for particular cocks. On Gull Island, New York, Helen Hays found that hens patrolled and defended a large area while maintaining the isolation of their different mates. Territorial fighting, and agonistic behaviour, helped to create the condition favouring polyandry, possibly in areas with exceptionally rich feeding habitats. Like some dotterels, the hens shared in the incubation of the final clutch.

Olavi Hildén studied groups of **Temminck's stints** which have an extraordinary pattern of pair bonds. Each cock attracts and mates with two different hens in his territory. After the first hen has completed her clutch she abandons it and offers herself to another cock on a different territory. Meanwhile, the cock of the first territory, even while sitting, entices and copulates with a second hen which then lays and incubates her own clutch, while the cock sits on the clutch laid by the first hen. Thus, each territory holds two clutches of eggs, each by a different hen: and each cock and each hen is responsible for the incubation and hatching of a clutch of eggs and for the rearing of a brood of chicks. Spacing and dispersion are achieved by the cock's song dances and agonistic behaviour.

Little stints appear to have evolved a different system from that of Temminck's stints. They are less strongly territorial and do not defend any particular living space after incubation has started. Each hen lays two clutches in different areas, with the first clutch incubated by the cock and the second by herself. Spacing appears to be opportunistic with no fidelity to a particular location from year to year.

Dunlins carve out and defend nesting territories by means of characteristic song flights and by fighting and chasing on the ground and in the air. R. T. Holmes (1970) found that territories were larger in north Alaska, where food is probably scarcer than further south. By a removal experiment he also discovered that there was a surplus population containing birds capable of breeding but prevented from doing so by the territory holders. In north-west Sutherland we found that if a singing cock failed to attract a mate he left his territory and gave songs and advertisement flights up to 4.5 km from his main display centres. In these habitats spacing between nests averages about 400 m in the gneiss hillocks west of the river; and roughly 900 m in the river blanket bogs to the east, where there are fewer feeding pools. But on the machair of South Uist, where dunlins nest in high numbers, there is a tendency to 'clumping' with nests sometimes only 7–20 m apart (B. Etheridge 1982).

What then are the advantages or disadvantages of those very different systems in Alaska? Is richness of food on the machairlands the answer to the system in the Uists?

In west Spitsbergen, S.-A. Bengtson discovered that pairs of **purple sandpipers** were well spread out and seldom had fights over boundaries. He watched the cocks climbing to 35 m, or higher, then singing and flying in circles before gliding down with their wings held above their backs. C. H. Hartley and J. Fisher (1936) estimated a breeding density of 6 pairs/5 km of coast in one of the haunts in west Spitsbergen. C. Cane (1980) recorded 2–3 pairs/km² on the fells of the Hardanger Vidda.

In the marshes of northern Europe cock **broad-billed sandpipers** fiercely defend territories in loose colonies of 2–10 pairs, concentrated in rich patches of marsh of about 20 ha. In Yakutia, USSR, V. E. Flint (1973) also reported groups with 2–4 nesting territories which cocks apparently did not defend; nests were usually 40–100 m apart, and exceptionally much closer. In wetlands in different parts of Fenno-Scandia, John Little tells us that he always found more than one pair in a marsh or none at all. Up to seven pairs nested in the richest bogs, with nests as close as 40 m apart. Spacing and dispersion appears to be achieved by the cocks' display flights and the availability of special nesting habitats.

Another high Arctic wader, **turnstone**, has a remarkably complex but adaptable range of dispersion mechanisms, some of which are not unlike those of oystercatchers. In open country, breeding pairs are more widely dispersed than are those in coastal habitats. Isolated inland pairs sometimes site their nests 1,000 m or more apart; but on favourable coasts and islands in Norway, Sweden and USSR, breeding densities are much higher, with clusters of nests occasionally only a few metres apart. On Ellesmere Island, David Nettleship (1973) found nests fairly regularly spaced; 13 breeding pairs on a census area of 240 ha, with a maximum of 4 breeding pairs/km².

Before laying, the cocks establish and defend their territories by calls and advertising displays. During incubation, territorial fighting is less intense as neighbouring pairs tend to respect one another's living space. However, off-duty territory-holders attacked intruders flying over territories on their way to neutral feeding grounds. This spacing pattern appears to avoid clumping of nests which would assist predators and possibly restrict food available for the chicks. In arctic Canada, Parmelee and Macdonald (1960) discovered that territories were maintained from the formation of the pair until hatching; thereafter family groups tended to join up. On Finnish coastal habitats, however, D. M. Brearey found that territorialism actually became more intense after the young had hatched. On coasts and islands, where the food supply is concentrated, turnstones often nest in colonies of gulls and terns. Various forms of agonistic behaviour, on the ground and in the air, help to determine these different patterns in diverse habitats.

Common sandpipers are usually orthodox territorialists. Particularly during courtship and immediately before copulation, cocks hold and defend stretches of river containing spate and shingle banks and small islands. The cocks then make many song flights at a height of about 3–30 m above the territory. Just before the hens start to lay, the cocks sing almost continuously by day and in the small hours of the morning, on the ground and in the air. During incubation the cocks sing and display much less but they continue to hold their territories, chasing intruders and sometimes sparring with or dipping down at greenshanks which feed on the same stretches of shore shallows and shingle. Later the sandpipers largely rear their chicks in these nesting territories.

Patterns are a little different on territories beside large lochs, with the birds sometimes nesting anything up to 200 m inland and leading the chicks to feeding places close to water. Territories around smaller lochs carrying 1–3 pairs are more complex, with considerable chasing, trespassing and overlap. However, common sandpipers success-fully use advertisement flights and aerial and ground chases to establish and maintain multi-purpose territories, which equitably space out the pairs, with the availability of gravel ribs, banks and islets as the governing factors. This enables incubation and the fledging of the chicks to proceed without valuable energy lost by fighting. Dispersion of the broods also makes it more difficult for predators to locate them. Soon after the young are flying, parents and broods move away from the nesting territories.

Tringa species have evolved different systems than those used by common sandpipers. On the wide open moors of northern Scotland a few scattered pairs of **redshanks** sometimes nest at well-spaced intervals, with the cocks periodically chasing away intruders. In many other parts of Britain, however, redshanks are semi-social birds, often breeding in small irregular groups, sometimes with nests less than 10 m apart. On the Ribble Estuary in Lancashire, W. G. Hale and Bob Ashcroft (1982) found that redshanks paired up by means of the cock's switch-back song-dance to the accom-paniment of the single sweet *tü-tü-tü* notes, uttered at 40 m or more above ground. The object of this display is to cause a hen to rise and join the song-dancing bird. Cocks also carry out a modified form of these flights to greet hens returning from their feeding grounds. Redshanks have a special greeting ceremony, on the ground, in which they hold up their wings; this display apparently helps to maintain the pair bond.

In fields heavily grazed by cattle the dispersion of nests is partly determined by the vegetation, particularly large tussocks of grass. Rivulet edges with high grass are also important. Hale found that lack of suitable high grass sometimes holds up nesting.

Redshanks periodically nest close to other *Limicolae*; we have found nests of redshanks and golden plover less than 10 m apart. They also frequently nest close to pairs or groups of lapwings, using these more vigorous and aggressive birds to give warning of, and battle to, ground or flying predators. Redshanks themselves collectively mob predators after the young have hatched.

L. Oring (1968) discovered that **green sandpipers** in Sweden used their dramatic and acutely-angled song flights to advertise living space and presumably to find mates. The precise difference between the pairing and isolating quality of these wonderful song dances are not yet fully understood. However, rival males are chased and hens pursued in erratic swerving flights high in the air. The pair then meet and later test suitable nests in the trees of their territory. In some parts of their range green sandpipers also mark out and use feeding territories in the marsh which are 400 m or more from their nesting woods. In the Swedish forests there was a minimum spacing of 400 m between nests.

Wood sandpipers have song dances in which hens as well as cocks take part. These are usually given at a lower height than those of green sandpipers and greenshank; but an unmated cock wood sandpiper, attempting to call in a hen, sometimes 'dances' many metres above ground. In a Spey Valley haunt, wood sandpipers arrived paired, but a possibly unmated cock song-danced over several different centres up to 2 km apart (J. Duthie and R. Leavett 1982). The song-dances probably help to disperse the loose breeding groups.

The mysterious **dusky redshank** has an unusual spacing pattern. Both cocks and hens 'song dance' but the cock establishes the territory and makes the scoops, one of which the hen chooses and prepares as the nest. In most Fenno-Scandia habitats nests are well dispersed, but in the Taimyr Peninsula territories are sometimes com-pressed, with about 250 m between the nests. In Swedish Lapland, Raner also found that a hen, which had put a cock down on a clutch of four eggs, mated with another cock for which she completed a second clutch 13 days later in a nest 2 km away. T. Marshall also records two nests only 7.5 m apart, with eggs apparently laid by the same hen. In this unusual system only the cock appears to incubate the eggs and rear the young, while the hens often leave the nesting grounds before the chicks are hatched. The various cocks and hens are probably aware of their neighbours' movements and, like greenshanks, space themselves out to allow special feeding places in the marsh for the sitting cock. Sometimes, however, Lennart Raner found that two cocks synchronised their movements and meals and flew back together to their respective nests. The chicks also possibly need a wide range of feeding niches.

At one stage in its evolution was the dusky redshank living in such a harsh environment that the hen was compelled to concentrate on producing eggs in a short period for one, and possibly two, males in years of their surplus; and then compelled to leave the breeding grounds before the cock had reared the brood? And have the apparently less exacting habitats of *Tringa totanus* enabled it to breed semi-socially on saltmarshes, grass heaths, meadows and farmlands?

Greenshanks have flexible and adaptable territorial and spacing mechanisms. Unmated cocks carry out their spectacular song dances over river, loch or firth, in some haunts close to their nesting grounds, but in others up to 4 km or more away.

Here they have feeding and mating niches which they usually defend against rivals and to which they attract new or former partners by advertising themselves with these high and spectacular flights. They also periodically advertise over entirely unsuitable nesting habitats, such as forests, farmlands, and large expanses of water. However, they sometimes sing or *chip* loudly from trees or rocks in the future nesting territory in a forest clearing or on a large stony flow. The song dance high in air is also given before nest site selection or in anticipation of the laying of earlier eggs. This display presumably informs neighbouring pairs of what is happening, or is about to happen. Bursts of song also sometimes coincide with the hatching of the chicks, thus communicating likely moves to near neighbours. We believe that each pair of greenshanks is acquainted with the song and calls of its neighbours and of their movements, thus assisting to space out the population with a minimum of energy lost in fighting.

In the old Caledonian forests, suitable nesting habitats are fewer and more restricted than those in the huge flows of Sutherland. Characteristic nesting habitats, however, have a recognisable profile, usually containing a few grey stumps or tall dead trees with a scattering of decaying logs, stocks, twigs and branches; and at least one tarn and a few boggy pools scattered in short or burnt heath. The moist and squelchy patches and the tarns, often with overgrown edges, are of special value as nurseries and shelter for the chicks in their first few hours and days before their parents herd them to the edges of large lochs, sometimes up to 2 km or more away. These tarns are also often used as staging posts before and after nest relief in early morning and late evening. In Sutherland, on the other hand, every nesting territory contains numerous distinctive nesting and feeding niches, each with special features, large look-out rocks, feeding pools, dubhlochans and usually countless embedded stones and blocks. Here some pairs annually shepherd their broods to a particular part of a flow, while others sometimes invade and take over the nesting territories of pairs which had earlier hatched their broods and led them to different wetland complexes. But in the evening pairs often clash when they are leading their young to roosting pools. In these wildernesses of stone and water it is often easy for the experienced eye to recognise apparently perfect nesting sites, but these are often far too many to search!

In our Sutherland study area, between 1964–82, there has always been a small surplus of non-breeding birds, some singles of both sexes, and others in pairs, at least some of which were capable of breeding and providing partners for the survivors of pairs. Yet, in 1964, when surplus birds mated with survivors in two different territories, a cock, passionately song-dancing in a territory which was occupied for 16 out of the next 19 years, stayed unmated.

Common snipe achieve dispersion through the cock's bleating and by dramatic agonistic displays and calls. Intruding cocks are attacked and visiting hens courted, but rigid territorial defence lapses towards the end of incubation, and breaks down completely after the chicks have hatched, thus allowing younger or more lately arrived cocks to settle within the original boundaries of the territory. The hen appears to choose the nest site and, with the cock in attendance, forms the nest within his territorial bounds (L. Tuck 1972).

Curlews space themselves by means of aerial displays and ground fighting. The cock advertises his territory by rising acutely on fluttering wings, then briefly hanging or hovering in mid-air before parachuting down with wings held in V position above his back, often repeating these flights several times before alighting with wings briefly

held almost vertically. Rival males fight quite fiercely, in the air and on the ground, where they sometimes raise their wings and leapfrog over one another. Hale (1980) found that an unmated cock used the parachute display to flush and then chase a hen. Although there is much intrusion on one another's air space these displays help to disperse the pairs, which often site their nests 400–1,000 m apart.

In the 1930s territories of curlews on the Surrey Commons were well dispersed, each pair usually dominating a large block of heath. On the Shannon bogs in Roscommon, however, some wet meadowlands in south central Wales, and in parts of Orkney, territories are small and boundaries overlap, with nests sometimes 100 m or less apart. We do not know the decisive factors leading to the contraction of territories, but later-arrived cocks first probe and then sometimes insert themselves into spaces between the earlier pairs. Feeding habitats and cover for the adults, and particularly for the chicks, are probably important. In Rothiemurchus Forest the same territories were occupied annually.

Whimbrels have similar spacing mechanisms, using aerial displays, singing, and agonistic behaviour on the ground. There is usually a spacing of up to 1,000 m between nests, but occasionally only 200–300 m (E. Kumari 1977). The profile of the habitat partly determines the dispersion of a whimbrel population.

In a study of **little curlew** in east Siberia, Y. V. Labutin and colleagues (1982) located groups of 3–30 pairs, with nests sited within a radius of 200–300 m. Spacing was probably adjusted by means of song dances in which the birds alternate wing shivering with slow sailing flights describing irregular circles of 100–200 m, which they synchronise with brief sweet trills preceded by a downward plunge, which gives a peculiar whistling sound; a fast upward zoom follows. Sometimes two cocks simultaneously take part in these flights, which often end with one of the song dancers plunging down to the top of a dead larch tree before dropping to the ground. In their haunts these very scarce and local waders tend to group their nests around occupied golden eagles' eyries which are sited about 5–7 km apart. By attacking foxes and other predators, the eagles probably assist the little curlews.

On the damp heaths of western Europe, unmated cock **black-tailed godwits** establish and defend mating territories over which they make ceremonial flights to attract hens. Once paired, they desert these display grounds and then search widely for a nesting territory in which they make scoops, later defending quite small areas around the nest. Black-tailed godwits often nest semi-socially and close to lapwings whose aggressive behaviour helps to repel predators.

Nests of **bar-tailed godwits** in the great forest marshes of northern Europe are well spaced out, possibly partly through the cock's dramatic song dances high above the marshes. These ceremonial flights also probably have sexual and mate-attracting functions.

The spacing mechanisms of **woodcocks** are still imprecisely known, but Graham Hirons (1979–81) has considerably advanced our knowledge. The 'roding flights' of cocks, frequently repeated over particular woods and the surrounding fields or moors, are defended against other roding cocks. Where we watched these flights in Spey Valley, particular cocks, identified by peculiarities of their calls, patrolled roughly the same area, noisily chivvying intruding rivals and apparently using different cries when pursuing any hen which had risen from the ground below. As cocks are not known to incubate the eggs or to assist in rearing of the young, the main function of the 'roding' is probably to enable the cock to locate a sexually receptive hen which may either attract or call him down to her or fly up from the ground. When cock and hen have met and mated they stay together for a brief courtship, lasting up to 11 days, before the hen starts to lay and the cock resumes 'roding'. In parts of Derbyshire, where there are many woodcocks, Hirons discovered, by telemetry, that 'marked cocks' did not maintain exclusive roding territories and that their flight-paths considerably overlapped. The hens, however, did not appear to hold territories. Four hens laid within a circle of 170 m and there were two nests only 75 m apart. These hens, however, were possibly aware of one another's movements. This spacing system is thus probably based on an unusual form of promiscuity or successive polygamy.

Lek waders have several different systems of nest spacing and dispersion. F. S. Andersen (1944) sometimes found **reeves'** nests sited 20–200 m from the lek; but the usual distance was between 100–300 m. John Little also tells us that reeves nested quite close to the leks on Hardanger Vidda. Each reeve probably knows the movements of its neighbours and chooses a nest site close to satisfactory feeding niches for the chicks. The reeves may even sometimes have special associates. Simson (1966) watched one laying her first egg. After she had disappeared into a tuft of vegetation a second, lighter-coloured reeve, ran over and peered into the tussock in which the bird was sitting. Ten minutes later both reeves ran off together. This may help to explain why two nests of a lek species are sometimes found almost side by side.

In the vast sub-arctic forest marshes **great snipe** often place their nests a long way from the lek, but cocks are sometimes found in their vicinity. Before the hens have started to lay, Little put up 'pairs' well away from the lek. F. Godman and P. Godman (1961) found nests about 200 m apart in Norway; and A. Dyrcz and colleagues (1972) found clusters of three and eight nests, with an average spacing of 40 m in Poland.

The **buff-breasted sandpiper** in Victoria and Jenny Lind Islands in arctic North America has evolved an unorthodox semi-lek system, entirely different from those of ruff and great snipe. D. F. Parmelee *et al* (1967) found that a dozen or more cocks sometimes simultaneously gave displays in which they stood upright, raising and spreading one or both wings, giving the illusion of wing-flashing. Sometimes a dozen cocks 'flash' at short distances from one another and defend small territories against competitors. Surprisingly, however, they may abandon these leks after defending them for several days and then establish new leks elsewhere. Courtship takes place on swampy ground, but the hens lay their eggs on higher and drier ridges.

The waders have thus evolved many different systems of dispersion, but these are sometimes modified by pressures, like numbers and topography, predators and food.

4: Downs, brecks and farmlands

The Sussex Downs in the late 1920s and early 1930s were soft, rolling, sweet-scented, but rather birdless. A few pairs of stone curlews nested on flinty fallows and on bare fields in some of their folds or along rabbit-nibbled swards on hog backs, with scattered thorns, gorse, and juniper bushes. In the evening, and sometimes by day, you heard the wailing and creaking clamour of small groups in the distance. Here the thickknees had few exciting bird neighbours; wheatears nested in rabbit holes, magpies sometimes chattered in bushes, and the occasional carrion crow skulked over distant slopes. You might see a kesterel hovering, or hear rooks cawing on the flanks. In the early 1930s hobbies sometimes nested in Cissbury and Chanctonbury Rings and one year a hen hobby laid in a rook's nest on the flank of Rackham Down. In the summer you always hoped to watch a hobby hunting and to track it down to the nest.

John Walpole-Bond lovingly described the downland haunts of stone curlews in Sussex as, 'wild wastes sown broadcast with jagged flints, interspersed with low rank weeds and maybe a few starveling elders, thorns and brambles. Next ... come more or less hog-backed ridges, now sparingly, now strongly, studded with thorn, elder, gorse, bramble and perhaps particularly juniper, with ... mole hillocks, stones, a sprinkling and fragments of dead wood marring the smoothness of the virgin sward. Third on the list are real fallows, and fourthly, but rarely, fields of sprouting grain, both haunts bearing on hill country as well as on ground just beneath'. In those years between the wars, Bond estimated that about 60 pairs of stone curlews annually nested in Sussex, but now the tally is much less and many old flint-shot fields have been ploughed up and reclaimed.

The great chalklands of Salisbury Plain, much more exciting places, held several grand haunts of stone curlews. Here there were many rows and belts of weathered pines, a few larger pinewoods, and scattered clumps of oaks and beeches. These haunts were the headquarters of the hobby in Britain. Sometimes, sitting hidden along their edges, we also waited for the thickknees. In those years Porton Down, Easton and Great Ridge were particularly favoured. This was well-keepered country, but many carrion crows survived and provided nests for the hobbies. Here, as in Sussex, stone curlews often slipped off their eggs and ran into the junipers whenever intruders approached. On chalkland farms quails occasionally called and Montagu's harriers were known to nest in corn fields. In the largest wood, where two or more pairs of hobbies sometimes nested in the same year, honey buzzards were reported although no nest was found. In the early 1950s, when myxomatosis almost exterminated the rabbits and the downland grass grew much higher, stone curlews became scarcer, but a few pairs still nest on arable farms. There are some splendied haunts, particularly Porton Down, where both stone curlews and hobbies breed.

The East Anglian brecks are the real home of the stone curlew in England. These flint-strewn warrens, heaths and grasslands, with their light and sandy soils, were often surrounded by long deep belts of mature planted pines. Derek Ratcliffe (1979) has described the old breckland country as 'a low-lying dissected plateau, forming a flat to gently undulating landscape, crossed by four main rivers, Lark, Wissey, Thet, Little Ouse and their tributaries, flowing westward to the fenland basin'. This is unique country, its roots deep in ancient history, with relicts of Mesolithic, Neolithic, Bronze Age, Roman and Anglo-Saxon Man. Neolithic Man cleared the forests and slowly created the grassland which is not unlike the steppe country in south-east Europe. Later, for many years, innumerable rabbits grazed, scratched and burrowed; and sheep also helped to break the surface and maintain the smoothness of the sward.

In the 19th century some East Anglian landowners grew pines as windbreaks to check erosion and to give cover for pheasants. In 1919 the Forestry Commission started to plant conifers on some of the brecks, but at first this caused only a slight danger to the stone curlews. Indeed the trees then possibly helped the thickkness, which slipped into cover at the first sight or sound of danger. On the grassy edges woodlarks nested; it was always exciting to track down the cock and watch him make a long flight with his hen as he escorted her back to the nest. In those years nesting common crossbills were almost restricted to roadside pines and those around houses; in the breck there was no water for them. On some of the great warrens up to ten or more pairs of stone curlews sometimes bred. You might watch one or more sitting on their nests as you crouched in a shelter-belt; at other times you climbed a tree and watched them run back to their eggs. In the evening, and sometimes in the afternoon, the clamour and wailing of distant groups was evocative and quite unforgettable. On this well-preserved country there were few kestrels, and nesting hobbies were seldom reported.

Thetford and Barnham Heaths, Icklingham and Lakenheath in Suffolk, Eriswell in Norfolk, and a few brecks near Newmarket, were all famous for stone curlews. What attractive haunts these remarkable heaths were. A few ringed plovers nested along with stone curlews on open breck and kestrels and carrion crows sometimes escaped the keepers in the pine rows. On flinty edges wheatears and stock doves used rabbit burrows; and on fens beyond, graceful Montagu's harriers occasionally courted and nested. There were fair numbers of gadwall and occasionally pairs of garganey. In the evening the *churring* of nightjars was a familiar sound. Good numbers of red-backed shrikes nested in bushes and in small stunted trees on the edges. It was always thrilling to watch the cock shrike fly in to feed his sitting hen; how directly he would fly to the nest. Whinchats and stonechats often nested in different niches close to the roadside. In shrubby coppices nightingales, blackcaps and garden warblers all sang as you walked out to watch the thickknees.

During and after the second world war many of the best brecks were ploughed up and planted with conifers or with farm crops; others were levelled for airfields.

At first the stone curlews adapted to the new order, often nesting in broad forest rides and sneaking into the trees long before you saw them. But myxomatosis brought a different danger; the almost total extermination of rabbits in 1952–53 led to a great increase in the growth of grass. Without the rabbit warrens, wheatears and stock doves almost disappeared; and common curlews colonised some overgrown habitats of the stone curlews.

Thickknees now nest in many new habitats, as well as on the open heaths. A. P. Robertson (1954) reported pairs sitting in fields of rye and wheat, one in a field of flowering swedes left over from the previous autumn, another in a gravel pit, and two pairs on the outskirts of an oak wood. Other stone curlews nested among clumps of elder bushes or in patches of withered broom. In 1974 David Glue and Robert Morgan recorded that stone curlews were nesting in forest rides, young conifer plantations, forest clearings, and in old nurseries. Many other pairs choose arable farmlands where they lay their eggs on bare fallows and in fields of sugar beet, wheat, barley, kale, parsnips, and in recently ploughed brecks.

Thankfully, however, there are still some wonderful open brecks and heaths where the stone curlews maintain. On the Dunwick Heaths in Suffolk, good habitats with a mixture of heather and fern, stone curlews, nightjars and red-backed shrikes still nest in good numbers. The open heathland of Icklingham Plains and Triangle, which are sand dunes dominated by *Carex arenaria*, acidic grasslands, and mixed ferns, carry stone curlews, ringed plovers and wheatears; redshanks, snipe and ducks nest on the grazed fenland. Deadman's Grave, to the north-east, is largely dry chalk grassland; here winter grazing by sheep make these heaths as attractive to stone curlews as they were formerly to woodlarks. Nightjars, kestrels, green woodpeckers and redstarts nest in old mixed hard woods and conifers. Sheep graze the high and low warrens of Eriswell, thus attracting stone curlews and ringed plovers. On Wangford Warren, Suffolk, now the only surviving expanse of the great open sand dune system that stretched to Laken-heath, stone curlews, ringed plovers and wheatears all breed.

The chalk grasslands of Weeting Heath in Norfolk are unusual; 20 ha have been enclosed and fenced in for rabbits, thus producing a sparse cover of small mosses and lichens and much bare ground sprinkled with many flints. Stone curlews, wheatears and ringed plovers have increased; woodlarks are now scarce but common crossbills nest in the woods. Staverton Park in Suffolk, where the heath grows on drained glacial sands, is another fine bird haunt where there are still a few stone curlews.

How very different are the haunts in the Scottish Highlands where I watched oyster-catchers. Normally these are birds of the sea shore, but the pairs I studied nested on hill farms and croftlands, along moorland edges, on river spate and shingle banks, and on shores and edges of inland lochs. At first oystercatchers seem to be strange and unexpected constituents of hill and croftland bird communities. But they are always fascinating and most welcome. A few pairs always laid eggs on the fallows and on short or newly-burnt heather on Dorback Moor; others on moorland edges of the crofts. But most were in groups on the spate banks and shingle ridges of the river which flowed through the sheep walks.

On the fields, lapwings and golden plovers were neighbours during courtship but they competed little for living-space. Here, lapwings dominated and golden plovers occasionally contended for well-burnt patches of moor, with the lapwings usually prevail-ing. The carefully preserved red grouse was the dominant bird of the moor, but curlew, golden plover, redshank and snipe all had their niches in this attractive environment.

Wheatears and stock doves bred in rabbit holes in the sand dunes. Mallard and teal fed in stagnant pools and nested in patches of moorland heather. In the early morning or evening of late April it was good to sit on the sand hills and watch and listen to the often frenzied activity. Here the oystercatchers had few natural enemies. Hoodies, from the old pine woods across the hill, occasionally flapped low over moor or river on the look out for plunder. Merlins and kestrels sometimes nested in old crows' nests in trees, but they seldom escaped the gun and trap. A solitary pair, and once a triangle, of common gulls, and black-headed gulls from valley and forest gulleries, often hawked insects over river and moor. Rooks from distant colonies lower down the valley visited the moors, particularly in late summer. Considerable predators, they often hacked the eyes out of live snared rabbits; and in late June or July, while picking berries, they sometimes sucked eggs in late nests of golden plovers and other waders. Herons fished the shallows and, at least once, a trio nested in a large windbreak beside the Dorback. You seldom saw foxes, but stoats and weasels were always present when rabbits were plentiful.

We have often watched oystercatchers on coastal fields and on stony patches close to the Dornoch Firth where hooded crows and the larger gulls are always likely enemies. In some haunts peregrines from inland and coastal crags occasionally drop down and fly away with well-grown chicks. Under stress, the oystercatcher is a good aerobat, and we have watched one foil a peregrine by plunging to water and diving.

I have many happy memories of hunting for lapwings in the Amberley Wild Brooks. These wonderful marshes were then large expanses of rough grazing for cattle, with many fields all separated by an elaborate system of narrow dykes and ditches. The lapwings were scattered in pairs and groups on the drier fields. How marvellous it was to see the lovely cocks wheeling and somersaulting as they delivered their most evocative songs. Here I also searched for snipe; there were then certainly plenty of them. In 1925 I found 20 nests by continuously tramping over the ground in my rubber thigh-boots! Solitary pairs of redshanks – 'whistlers' the local marshmen called them – often laid their eggs in well-cropped fields. It was always satisfying to mark down a nest after the sitting bird had risen a long way ahead. Mallard, and a few pairs of teal, also bred on the Brooks; and water rails 'sharmed' in one big reed bed close to the River Arun.

The birds on the Brooks suffered from quite a concentration of predators. At least five pairs of carrion crows nested in small clumps of trees growing on the Brooks or on their wooded surroundings. Judging from the many broken eggs these crows were formidable egg robbers. Magpies also built domed nests in thicker spinneys on the edges and jays bred in adjacent woods. Two pairs of kestrels often worked different parts of the Brooks and laid eggs in old crows' nests far out in the marsh or in deciduous trees on the edges. I once watched a cock Montagu's harrier, in the full glory of his grey-blue plumage, tilting and swerving as he hunted; and hobbies sometimes flashed over the marshes in summer. A pair of barn owls occupied a broken and dilapidated house on the fringe; I often watched one hunting in the twilight.

A few meadow pipits nested on the fields; I found my only clutch of blue eggs here. Skylarks sang over drier fields and in one rushy field grasshopper warblers nested in summer. In May 1944, while I was in the Army and stationed at Portsmouth, I returned to my happy hunting ground of the 'twenties. How disappointed I was to find that the Wild Brooks had been drained and were already far less exciting. However, before I left, I saw a pair of yellow wagtails in one of my old haunts.

On the Dorback Moor lapwings were all around the cottage. Most pairs displayed, courted and laid their eggs on open fields, arable, fallow, and grassland. But small groups were also scattered along the moorland divides and solitary pairs occasionally held territories on river shingle. These haunts have many memories. On the moor the lapwings nested on bare patches, particularly those with short well-burnt heath. On one study area, with short grass-heath and a few larger clumps of heather, a small group of up to five pairs nested annually. Snipe and a few redshanks had niches in wet places. Here, and on other parts of the Dorback Moor, the red grouse was dominant; but lapwing, golden plover and oystercatcher gained from the well-regulated muirburn.

The moors were also alive with meadow pipits and skylarks; and pied wagtails nested in old dykes, buildings, fanks, and along the stony river bank. On river shingle grey wagtails were occasional neighbours of the lapwings and dippers bobbed and fished in the waters. Hooded crows, rooks, stoats, weasels, foxes and sheep dogs were predators. Particularly in warm, dry, late springs and early summers, black-headed gulls sometimes flew off with young lapwing chicks.

On an exceptionally warm and sunny day in June 1979 we returned to my old hunting grounds in Dorback. As we lay up above the river, excited lapwings with their chicks ran over the rough grasslands, just where, as a young man, I used to watch them. We heard snipe and curlew; and golden plovers, scarcer that year, cried mournfully in the distance. Sandpipers and ringed plovers were still along the river. A buzzard flew across the moor on its way to the pine forest beyond.

From 1945 onwards I studied lapwings in quite different habitats in Rothiemurchus Forest. Here most pairs nested on farmlands with only a few on the moorland edges. They also nested in groups on the fields of Upper Tullochgrue, and a few pairs haunted the edges of Loch Morlich. I particularly studied the different behaviour of these isolated pairs.

Between 1957–61, when we lived in south-east Sutherland, lapwing groups divided the rough pasture and moorland fringes around us. One pair nest-danced almost beside the house; we took turns sitting at the scullery window, watching these colourful displays. Rooks, jackdaws and hoodies were likely predators; the cock lapwing often drove them away. He also sometimes violently attacked curlews which had dropped down to feed on his stamping ground. We also studied a group of half-a-dozen pairs, some with nests only a few metres apart, in the grass-heath of a sheep walk. Scattered pairs of golden plovers, which nested in heather and peat mosses, were other nesting neighbours. We watched sparrowhawks, buzzards, and hoodies, all of which nested in adjacent woods; and there was a pair of hen harriers on a moor nearby. Foxes and sheep dogs were menaces.

In the early 1970s, as new croft land was broken in, a small group of up to ten pairs of lapwings started to colonise the edges of our greenshank study area in north-west Sutherland. But our happiness was short. The lapwings never successfully settled on the flowland edges; in 1979 there was only one pair and between 1980–84 there were none on the ground. The lapwings' neighbours were golden plovers on the flows, and occasional pairs of snipe and common sandpipers on the lochs and lochans below the fields. Here there is a wonderful mixture of habitats. While watching lapwings on the re-claimed croftlands you could also hear redwings, blackbirds, chaffinches and dunnocks calling and singing in small conifer plantations beside the shooting lodge; and in the background were the evocative wails of red-throated divers, advertising songs of golden plovers, and perhaps the ecstatic song dances of greenshanks.

A group of lapwings, whose numbers have greatly fluctuated, nest on the gently sloping pastures and old leys above the hamlet where we now live. In one of the habitats there are two pairs of curlews, nesting redshanks and snipe. The lapwings continuously chase and harrass egg-thieving hoodies, rooks and particularly jackdaws. Hen harriers from the moor, kestrels from a tumbledown house, short-eared owls from a forestry conifer plantation and common gulls from a moorland colony are other likely predators. These are most fulfilling haunts. Meadow pipits are in the heather, skylarks on the grasslands; and below one of the lapwing fields Patrick found a redwing's nest, with young, in 1977.

These nesting grounds of waders, on the downs, brecks and farmlands are not usually particularly wild and dramatic; but each in its different way is the home of fascinating waders along with their neighbours and predators.

STONE CURLEW

Every wader is special; each has its own charm. But the stone curlew stands alone; an unusual wader bird which some good systematists consider has affinities with bustards and cranes. It is a long brown bird with a rounded, almost bullet-like head; stout yellow legs which look paler in certain lights; the coldest and most cruel-looking straw-yellow eyes; and a short stout bill with a black tip and yellow base. Sometimes it runs fast, low to ground, and is most difficult to watch. At others it stands upright, looking almost like a bustard; and perhaps suggestive of some imaginary hawk.

Ever since I read about them I always hoped to hunt for stone curlews. In early May 1927 John Walpole-Bond kindly arranged for a birdwatching doctor to take me to haunts on the Sussex Downs. We had a great day. For several hours we watched and searched, but we saw no stone curlew until quite late in the evening when we caught sight of one flying fast, its double white wing bars most conspicuous; it was evidently off a nest. Three times we hid up and tried to watch it back, but the nest was evidently high up on a gentle flint-strewn hill flank densely covered with juniper bushes. Each time the bird was too quick for us; it must have ran through the juniper and escaped our eyes. By now my doctor friend had started to look at his watch. It was time for us to catch the late bus and for his evening meal!

On 24 April 1929 the story had a happier ending. This time Jock himself was to meet me at the little station at Bramber in West Sussex. I arrived an hour early, by motor cycle, and decided to try my luck in the neighbouring fields. I was high up in an oak tree, at a carrion crow's nest, when I saw the small train arrive and justly received a tongue lashing for my lateness! Up on the Downs we cautiously approached each haunt, always lying up overlooking any stony field where we hoped a stone curlew was sitting. At last Bond spotted one flying away, fully 100 m ahead of us. He hurried me back to a juniper bush well up on the hillside; within 20 minutes we watched the stone curlew fly in and land. Then, after a series of quick runs and pauses, when it apparently fed and moved on again, it reached a flinty ridge about 50 m from where we were crouching. How beautifully it harmonised with its surroundings, and how difficult to mark. A few minutes later Jock stood at the nest, pointing at the eggs with his stick. 'A very ordinary pair', he exclaimed. To me, they were pearls without price!

We now walked from one old nesting place to another. Then, just as we breasted a rise, first one stone curlew, then a second, rose and flew slowly from a fallow field. This time I had a better mark. One egg! 'A good type', he said. When I returned on the 26th the second egg was also there. The two eggs in the nest were quite dissimilar, as is so often the way with stone curlews' clutches.

From mid March onwards, in the early 1930s, while watching crossbills in roadside pines in Norfolk and Suffolk, we sometimes listened to the wails and whistles of newly-returned stone curlews far out on the breck. In those happy years the great flint-strewn sandy fields and warrens had not been ploughed up; the vast stands of conifers were still only in the minds of forestry planners. What fantastic haunts these brecks were with stone curlews and ringed plovers on the flats and gadwall, garganey and the occasional Montagu's harrier on the river fens. Salisbury Plain held fewer pairs of stone curlews than in Breckland, but many downs had two or more pairs. On 19 and 20 July, 1930, Arthur Whitaker casually mentioned seeing half-a-dozen pairs there. I also watched stone curlews, and found a nest, on a great stretch of shingle near Dungeness in Kent.

In the next few years I hunted stone curlews with delight and relish. In early May 1933 three of us found 12 nests in a single day near Barnham in Suffolk; and 34 nests during a long weekend. The thickknees usually nested well out in the open breck. We would approach the field by walking quietly to the nearest windbreak where we sat down and hid ourselves behind trees. Sometimes we crept into a break so cautiously that we were able to mark down one or more stone curlews sitting on their nests. How thrilling it was to see the dark brown bird brooding low to ground, with black bill and tail in line. As we waited, we also picked up non-sitting birds and occasionally watched a nest relief. The incoming bird ran fast in short or long bursts; and then you might see the second bird, from a previously unfound nest, suddenly run away. Those were great moments. It was always less easy to mark down a nest which the bird had quit after seeing some slight movement in the trees. A still more rewarding ploy was to rush out and flush the sitting birds and then walk back and lie up in the pines to wait for them to return. One marvellous day, working alone, I stalked and marked three different thickknees sitting on nests on a large breck. A suspicious bird would leave its eggs, running low for a few yards, then fly away, often only uttering a squeal of alarm when it was far from the nest.

Stone curlews vary greatly in the time taken to return to their nests; weather, state of incubation and individuality all contribute. One very rough day, four different birds each took over an hour to resume incubation. On the next day all five birds walked back within 10 minutes. They return in different ways. One skims back in quick low flight and then starts to run, sometimes almost creeping, bill and tail in line. It may then make a short flight before the final nest run. Another bird returns entirely on foot. I particularly remember one which ran fully 500 m before settling down on its eggs; it was a strain holding the field glass steady all the time. Other birds flew to within 20 m of the nest, only making the briefest run in. An anxious bird sometimes made several runs, each time flying away before it came back, running in from another direction. The non-brooding bird often accompanied its mate for part of the way; but the sitting bird usually makes the final approach while its partner stands on guard, perhaps 50 m away. Once I saw a stone curlew crouch for 15 minutes at the mouth of a rabbit burrow. Most birds run fast for a few metres, stop, peck nervously, swerve, run back, and then forward again; occasionally one stops and appears to brood. Almost always, however, you can see the bird puff out the feathers around its brood patches and it often touches or turns the eggs with its bill. It is seldom safe to move until you see this! Stone curlews, disturbed from their nests, often run for cover into shelter belts on the brecks or junipers on the downs, where they skulk until danger has passed.

When birds nest high up on rising ground, which cannot be controlled from above or below, you have plenty of trouble ahead. Your patience and determination will soon be sorely tested; your first clue is usually the squeal of a bird on the wing. I sometimes defeated particularly difficult birds by climbing high up on a pine tree. On large brecks, where there are no pines in which to hide, I have had to lie flat to earth; but the running stone curlew then often disappeared into a fold and the struggle had to start all over again.

Stone curlews return to their nesting grounds from mid March onwards, flying back in ones, twos (possible pairs) and threes, or in small trips. In his study area in the Weeting Heath National Nature Reserve in Norfolk, N. J. Westwood (1983) recorded first arrivals in the first week of April, but once as early as 16 March. The cocks appear to arrive first and the hens a few days later. As soon as they have rested you hear them calling; then, after the hens arrive, the most fascinating courtship begins.

J. K. Baker and R. Morgan's colour-ringed birds sometimes paired up when one or two years old, but none actually bred until they were 3 years of age. In other haunts, however, stone curlews have bred in their first full summer (O. von Frisch 1959). Ringed birds have also nested in the same territory in consecutive years.

DISPLAYS

In 1934 I went to live in the Highlands where there were so many fascinating birds. But I did miss the stone curlews and often thought of them as I lay up in the wader country of Speyside, so different from the brecks and warrens of East Anglia. Then, in April 1944, an unsuspecting War Office most kindly posted me to Lakenheath in Suffolk. Place and timing were perfect! I borrowed the Company bicycle and field glasses, and on many days pedalled away to the brecks to follow up my earlier work on the stone curlews.

What a lot there was to watch! Like great bustard and crane, the thickknees do not make well-defined display flights. A wonderful selection of special sounds and a clutch of equally exciting ground displays advance their courtship. One day I watched a cock run towards a hen, bending stiffly forward at an angle of about 60°. The hen walked towards him in the same posture; then she squatted, raised and rippled her neck and ruffled her neck feathers. As the cock pased her he rolled over and over as if he had been wounded. This reminded me of the display of the cock great bustard which Bernard Tucker described as 'a billowy mass of white on the ground'. Others have seen this extraordinary display used in different situations. Edmund Selous described it in their autumn dances. 'Running forward with wings extended and slightly raised, the bird would suddenly fling them high up and then, as it were, pitch above the ground, waving and tossing them, stopping short, turning and pitching forward again ... as if the birds were being blown about over the ground in a violent wind'. After a hen had been flushed from a nest and was unwilling to return, the cock ran

around her with raised and extended wings and then pitched violently about over the ground, first to one side and then the other (S. Smith 1946). This display is thus used in situations other than those of sex and courtship.

Before the two birds were firmly paired I watched a cock run up to a hen and bow forward from the almost vertical. The hen now stood upright and extended head and neck towards him, with her neck feathers ruffled. Another time the two birds faced one another, wings taut to their sides, bills pointing down and necks crooked like umbrella handles.

Arthur Whitaker and Fred Glenny saw a slightly different display by a pair on a warren near Brandon. While watching a hen from a distance of about 80 m they heard another thickknee calling loudly; and almost immediately a cock pitched close to the hen. He now ran round her with feathers tightly compressed and looking remarkably trim. Time after time he stopped, raising himself first erect, and then, his tail straight up in the air, he bent stiffly forward to touch the ground with his bill tip. Meanwhile, the hen held her head and neck straight out, pointing her beak towards him and slightly curving her neck, first down and then up. At the same time she puffed out and ruffled her neck feathers. The thickknees continued these displays for two or three minutes and then the cock flew away without mounting the hen.

A. W. P. Robertston (1954) watched another display. A pair uttered *pic-pic* notes, the cock following a few metres behind the hen. She then 'brushed past him, swerved to the right and gave the ventral display, bill touching the ground, tail raised and widely fanned, wings held loosely to the sides'. When they reached a sheltered spot the hen began to make a scrape, picking up small objects and throwing them over her shoulder. For over 10 minutes she continued to do this while the cock stood and occasionally tilted forward in display, varying *pic-pics* with deep *cu-lees*.

On 20 April 1944 I watched a pair run towards one another, bent stiffly forward, bills almost touching the ground and tails and bodies elevated. Crying softly, *bobo-link*, *bobo-link*, they bowed to one another; both then started the movements of nest-dancing, although their breasts barely touched the ground while passing through arcs of about 180° to 270°. After a few moments the hen sat down in the brooding position and raised her tail almost vertically while the cock stood beside her. Several times she stood up and with a flick of her neck threw little flints sideways or over her shoulder. For about 10 minutes she brooded; then she rose and the cock tilted forward and followed her. Again the hen crouched, tail cocked up; but the cock did not copulate with her.

On another breck, on 24 April, I watched a cock standing for 25 minutes opposite a hen which was brooding an empty scrape. Three times the hen stretched and raised her neck at an angle of about 45°. The cock bowed and touched her bill; then he swung backwards in an erect posture, holding his partly spread tail almost at right angles to the ground, presumably to display the black tail tips; twice he raised his wings, creating a flash of brilliant white. The display ended when the hen left the scrape, followed half-heartedly by her mate.

I watched several courtships throughout these wonderful days. I saw single and paired birds making scoops and others brooding empty scrapes for long spells; over an hour in one instance. I watched pairs flick splinters of flint, small stones or rabbits' droppings sideways over their shoulders in sexual excitement, quite unconnected with scrape ritual. Even more exciting were the extraordinary groups which I sometimes watched late in the evening. One cock made little tripping steps, while half-raising its wings, in front of a group of four hens which ran excitedly after him. Another cock ran away from the group with his head lowered and neck outstretched and fluffed body feathers; he then let his wings droop and fanned his tail upwards. A trio of hens ran behind him. Is this the way in which younger or unmated cocks pair up later in the season, perhaps partly accounting for some late clutches in the larger group areas? These groups, however, are not restricted to non-breeders; off-duty birds join them. Robertson, for instance, watched a pair leave nest and eggs and fly away into the dusk, 'calling loudly and being answered by others'.

I have watched trios of stone curlews, a cock with two hens, but was unable to discover what finally happened. Robertson (1954) watched two cocks courting a hen. At first all three dusted in the sand, but when one cock approached the hen, both rose and ran together with the hen in the middle. 'She ran with head held low, neck retracted and shoulders rounded, but both males ran with neck upward. A constant piping was kept up by at least two and probably all three birds'. When they stopped the hen sank to ground; and both cocks stood at an angle of about 70°, with their tails fanned and depressed and folded wings partly raised to display the white bars and stripes. Almost immediately the cocks started to pipe, rising about 3 m into the air and sparring with one another. At last one cock left but the dominant one returned. The hen now crouched with raised tail and the cock copulated, flapping his wings to balance himself. Afterwards he flew away and the hen started to call before running to the previous year's nest site where she began scrape-making.

Stone curlews, particularly cocks, often confront and attack one another; rivals then lean forward and call angrily. Before attacks, the dominant bird partly opens its bill as a threat. It may then spread its wings and direct the underbanners towards the rival. In other anger situations stone curlews half erect or lower fanned tails; they also bow forward, particularly when the drives to attack and to retreat clash sharply. Raising and lowering of the spread tail also features in aggressive behaviour; sometimes the central tail feathers of the aggressor touch the ground. I have often watched rival males chasing, sometimes leap-frogging or jumping into the air, then fencing with their bills a few metres above ground. At other times a stone curlew has chased another along the ground for many metres or continued to pursue it when it flew away.

DISPERSION AND BREEDING DENSITY

Isolated pairs of stone curlews sometimes establish themselves on small fields, or half-a-dozen or more pairs divide the larger warrens. Two and three pairs sometimes nest along the fire-breaks of forestry plantations. In the groups of the 1930s, nests were sometimes less than 300 m apart; and in the most favoured brecks two pairs occasionally laid their eggs within 100 m of one another. On 11 May 1925, for example, Whitaker and Glenny saw three nests in a conifer plantation where the trees had grown to a height of 15–30 cm; two nests were within 85 m. On another breck near Swaffham in Norfolk in 1935, seven pairs had nests within 5 km². On the Sussex Downs and on Salisbury Plain some nests were separated by up to 2 km or more; but there were favoured Downs carrying small groups, where nests were distributed at regular intervals of about 350–450 m. Parts of the Berkshire Downs also showed an equally high nesting density.

There are some observations on the spacing of stone curlews in Europe. On the stony fields of Crau in southern France, G. Cheylan (1975) found that each pair claimed a living space of 75–100 ha; and Bozec (1969) found four pairs nesting in 200 ha. In Alsace, P. and C. Vögel (1972) recorded an average density of one breeding pair/km² on small fields and patches of vineyards between the Ill and the Rhine. Between Mulhouse and Neu-Breisach nests were usually 800–1,000 m apart. In larger fields to the east of these habitats density was lower, possible 0.5 breeding pairs/km². Open country near Chalkide in northern Greece showed an even higher density, twice with two and once with three nests recorded in 30 ha. Parts of Hungary also sometimes carry high density groups, with nests only 200 m apart.

NEST, EGG AND CLUTCH

The parts played by cock and hen in establishing territory and choosing the final nest scoop is not necessarily invariable. In captivity, von Frisch (1956) found that the cock selected a nesting area, in a small exclusive part of which he made the scoops to which he attracted a hen. In the Zoo at Basel, on the contrary, C. Stemmler-Morath (1951) recorded that the hen first started the scrape ritual and that thereafter the cock behaved aggressively.

Some hens annually lay their eggs in the same patch of ground. Geoffrey Dent (*pers comm*) knew of one which laid her clutch in three successive years within a radius of 3 cm.

Before the hen lays her first egg I have also watched both birds standing close to the chosen scoop. In this phase the hen, and possibly the cock, periodically broods for periods of at least half an hour in one or more of the empty scrapes. While excavating, the birds toss sideways small flints or stones and tiny fragments of chalk and rabbits' droppings. Later some of these are placed in the scoop and form a kind of lining.

Stone curlews favour ground with a broken surface. The scoop, a rudimentary hollow about 16–23 cm across (Glutz 1977), is usually scraped out in dry ground among very low vegetation on open breck or down; but when the birds are nesting in conifer plantations the hen lays among small saplings or quite tall trees, as well as on the rides and broad fire-breaks. Stone curlews are also nesting increasingly in growing crops of cereals. Some hens in Suffolk and on Salisbury Plain lay their eggs beside juniper stumps or other sticks, much as greenshanks and dusky redshanks do in forest country. The sitting thickknees apparently use the sticks as rests for neck and tail; and are 'almost invariably placed to the northward or eastward of the nest'. These also protect the birds from drifting sand. This reminds us of the dotterels which nest beside or between stones; 'In exceptionally exposed habitats the shelter of a rock or stone is possibly a real advantage' (Nethersole-Thompson 1973).

On the great shingle wastes around Dungeness the stone curlews usually nested on the edges of patches of lichen or among the remains of 'a dead broom bush often between two or three plants of flowering foxglove' (N. Ticehurst 1909). At Jury Gap, on the borders of Sussex and Kent, they seldom laid their eggs on shingle but usually on the little plots of soil which had forced their way up through the pebbles and which formed the skirts of the scattered plants, stunted bushes of broom, wild sloe and juniper (Walpole-Bond 1938).

In Sussex, the impression of a rabbit's scratching, or a shallow natural depression, was sometimes used to start the scoop. The bird also occasionally made its scrape 'in the crumbled earth of a low mole heap'. A ready-made scrape varied much in size; 'some only 5 inches by 3 inches across, with a depth of under an inch, but others were as much as 9 inches by 7 inches diametrically, or two inches or more in depth'. Some of the scoops entirely excavated by thickknees were 'as much as a foot across with a depth of even four inches' (Walpole-Bond 1938). Although many stone curlews return annually to the same nest sites, some pairs, particularly in Sussex, had alternative sites up to 800 m apart.

On the Continent, where nests are sometimes placed on cow pats or beside wheel ruts, the primitive nest linings included gravel, hares' or rabbits' droppings, horse manure, bits of charcoal and wood.

Westwood (1983) found that the interval between the first arrival and the laying of the first egg varied from 11–48 days. At Weeting the first eggs were usually laid during the last week in April. Many hens regularly start to sit in the last few days of April and the first week in May. My own earliest record was of slightly incubated eggs on 24 April. Whitaker's records give an average clutch date of 4 May for 19 clutches; and Edgar Chance had 22 clutches ranging from 13 April–19 May, with the same mean date of 4 May. Westwood found that 'except in 1977 the first pair to lay each year nested in the same place and usually produced larger eggs'. Robertson (1954) noticed that particular Suffolk hens had remarkably consistent laying dates from year to year. On a high wind-tossed warren all three pairs laid within the space of five days in the third week of May 1952. On a more sheltered breck about 1.6 km away, on the other hand, two clutches hatched out during this period, while three out of four clutches in crops hatched between 14–18 May; and those of two pairs nesting in oakwood habitats had chicks between 28–31 May. It was roughly possible to forecast the laying dates of hens in particular haunts. Is this because different feeding grounds affect the hens when they are 'storing up' before producing their eggs?

In Sussex, Walpole-Bond records an average annual peak between 25 April–4 May, with a few pairs a little later. In his two earliest records the hens had laid up in the first week of April. R. C. Britton and G. Clarke (both *in* Walpole-Bond 1938), also recorded hens sitting on eggs laid before 10 April. Five clutches on Salisbury Plain were completed between 16 April–25 May; and five on the Berkshire Downs between 15 April–9 May. Glue and Morgan (1974) record a late clutch on 24 July; possibly this was a second brood.

Dates for other parts of Europe vary considerably. In southern Spain laying begins in early April (J. A. Valverde 1960). In France a few hens in Orleans, Crau and Normandy clutch as early as 20–25 March, but most lay between the last few days in March and early April. Laying begins about 10 April in the Netherlands; and in East Germany full clutches are recorded between 15–23 April (R. Gerber 1952; G. Creutz 1953). In all these countries the peak laying period falls between the end of April and mid May. Fresh clutches have also been regularly recorded in June, often in July, and occasionally up to the end of August. The latest record of hatching took place between 11–12 September; this was presumably a genuine second laying after the pair had previously reared a brood. David Bannerman found clutches in the Canary Islands between 15–26 May.

At three nests – one in Sussex and two in Breckland – the hens laid their eggs on alternate days at approximate intervals of 36–48 hours; one hen laid her second egg in the afternoon. E. Meade-Waldo found that a captive hen laid her first egg early and the second later in the day.

Many stone curlews' eggs are beautiful. Most are elongated, ovate in shape, but are occasionally almost eliptical. Ground colour varies from creamy white, through shades of buff or sandy or yellowish brown to rich reddish brown. They are blotched, speckled, splashed and streaked with various shades of brown, sepia and lavender, in the form of caps, zones, and particularly streaks. A network of thin lines is a special characteristic of many of them. The two eggs in the same clutch are often quite dissimilar both in shape and colouring. A few closely resemble particular types of oystercatchers' eggs. In the scoop the eggs are usually placed in opposite directions. An interesting quirk of the stone curlew is that it always seems to keep its two eggs apart in the scrape; the sitting bird possibly places its foot between them. In this the stone curlew is akin to the peregrine which also normally have their three or four eggs apart in the eyrie.

One hundred English eggs averaged 53.7×38.43 mm; max: 61.7×38.5 and 49.0×41.5 mm; min: 47.8×38.7 and 53.5×35.6 mm (Jourdain 1940). One hundred and fifty-nine eggs from north-west Saxony averaged 53.4×38.99 mm; max: 65.9×45.5 mm. A dwarf egg measured 38.5×30.2 (Gerber 1952). A Dorset clutch contained particularly broad eggs; 58.7×43.4 and 57.8×43.0 mm (Jourdain 1936).

The eggs are light in proportion to the hen's body weight. In England 29 fresh eggs varied from 36.7–48.2 gm (mean 42 gm); and 20 well-incubated eggs varied from 32.6–39.6 gm (mean 36.9 gm) (Morgan 1983). The mean weight of 24 Weeting Heath clutches, including those of one egg but not repeats, was 78.96 gm (±14.5). The earliest clutches tended to be heavier than those laid later. The mean weight of eight fresh eggs which failed to hatch was 38.5 gm (±1.02) (Westwood 1983). Seven eggs from Czechoslovakia varied from 34.7–44.6 gm (mean 38.8 gm); nine eggs from Hungary ranged from 34.0–39.0 gm (mean 36.2 gm) (Table 3). As the body weight of eight hens averaged 449 gm, a clutch of two eggs only represents approximately 19.0% of the hen's body weight (Table 2). This possibly helps to explain why stone curlews are sometimes able to produce second broods after rearing their first. M. Schönwetter (1963) found that eggshells averaged 3.35 gm.

There are normally two eggs in a clutch, one occasionally, and three rarely (Table 4). Walpole-Bond records two clutches of three in Sussex, both found in 1905; one near Seaford on 9 May, the other at Cissbury on 3 June. On 11 May 1934 J. T.

Mayo found a nest with four eggs at Wilmington Hill in East Sussex. In his opinion, two females had laid in the same scoop; but he took the eggs before the possible triangle was investigated. If they lose their eggs, stone curlew complete replacement clutches in 13–15 days.

Some pairs are double brooded. Walpole-Bond and Cecil Smeed in Sussex, W. Banzhaf in Germany, and P. and C. Vögel in Alsace have all proved this. von Frisch considered that double-brooding was regular in Crau in southern France where he recorded five double-brooded pairs. In three territories one parent was attending the young of the first brood; the other incubated the second clutch. On 27 July he watched a pair which had two flying young as well as two freshly-hatched chicks (Glutz 1975).

INCUBATION

Steady incubation starts with, or shortly before, the laying of the second egg, but some stone curlews sit for brief spells on the first egg. In most pairs that I have watched the hen has undertaken longer brooding spells than the cock, but the pattern is not inflexible. Some hens sit for periods of over four hours and cocks one hour or less.

Nest relief is always fascinating. On 24 April 1944 I watched the non-brooding bird, which was standing between 50–100 m from its sitting mate, suddenly make a series of short sprints. Just before reaching the nest it picked up a small stone and stood in front of its mate for four minutes; it then bent down and touched the sitting bird's beak. The bird on the nest then stood up, bowed, and passed small objects, probably stones, to the non-sitter and then ran from the nest. Eric Hosking has photographed this ritual. At other times I have seen a stone curlew arrive at the nest and prod its mate to induce it to leave. A relieving bird also sometimes pushes itself under the brooding bird as it stands over the eggs; or it calls its mate off the nest and feeds before starting to sit.

After change-over the relieved bird sometimes flies off to its feeding ground or it may run about 50–100 m and then stand on guard until the next exchange. When both birds are off the nest they often return together, although the non-incubating partner usually allows its mate to make the final run to the eggs. Walpole-Bond and I sometimes saw third birds accompanying a pair back to the nest after they have been disturbed. This could be a first-year bird or one which has not succeeded in mating; or it was possibly one of the pair's feeding companions.

H. Laven (1941) described how a brooding stone curlew rose very slowly off eggs, keeping its bill on the ground until its head, neck, tail and body in line formed an angle of about 60° with the ground. It then picked up several small objects, moving them back and to one side, with a little jerk as it moved the last. Finally, still picking up small objects, it walked from the nest extremely slowly, rotating the axis of its head and body into the horizontal when a few metres away and then leaving with legs flexed with the same slow movements. Meanwhile the relieving bird had slipped under its tail and on to the eggs.

In exceptionally hot weather, Robertson discovered that some pairs allow the sun to hatch chipping eggs. At two nests in Suffolk the hen visited the pipped eggs only once in three hours; at a second nest, containing one chipped and one addled egg, the parents were absent for $1\frac{1}{2}$ hours. The incubation period varies from 24–27 days. One Weeting pair hatched its eggs in 25 days and two in 26 days.

HATCHING

Some stone curlews' eggs are pipped from 14–41 hours (Glue and Morgan 1974) and up to 61 hours (E. Hosking and C. Newberry 1940). Long before the chicks have hatched, the sitting parent almost continuously talks to them. E. Simms and Bob Wade made a fine series of recordings of conversations between parents and chicks at the nest.

The eggshell disposal of the stone curlew is unusual and most interesting. Ralph Chislett (*pers comm*) watched a cock approach a hen which was brooding a chick and egg. Just before he reached her the hen rose and Chislett saw a wriggling of wet down, the hatching of the second egg. The cock then picked up the larger portion of shell and ran away with it. At another nest Hosking watched the cock wrench the top off both eggs. Holding one of these in his beak he continued to sit for nearly a quarter of an hour. Later he deliberately stamped on, crushed, and ate pieces of both large and small shell fragments. The hen also walked away with, broke and ate, other large pieces. Hosking also saw another cock carry away large bits of shell, shaking and teasing them to pieces. This bird later returned and ate all the small pieces which he appeared to have no difficulty in finding. Have the stone curlews evolved this special nest-relief ceremony, with the passing of small objects, and this extraordinary eggshell disposal pattern, to prevent the incoming birds from attacking and eating their own eggs or young? N. Tinbergen (1962) discovered that robber gulls preferred to eat wet rather than dried-off nestlings. This behaviour possibly inhibits parent stone curlews from attacking their own chicks.

Glue and Morgan (1974) show that hatching success is adequate. Of 64 English clutches containing 128 eggs, 93 hatched (73%). Farm operations accounted for the loss of 11 and man for five eggs; two eggs were addled or failed to hatch. Natural predators, including carrion crow, herring gull and fox were responsible for the loss of a further 14 eggs; and a mole caused the desertion of another nest with two eggs.

At Weeting, hatching success varied from 54.5% in 1975 to 100% in 1978. Seventy-four eggs laid during eight years produced an average hatching success of 77%. The stone curlews which laid earliest tended to rear more young than those laid later. But it is not known whether this was an effect of the date or of egg weight. Between 1973–78 the 12 eggs laid by the earliest pair produced nine young; whereas 31 eggs of subsequent layings produced only 11 young, replacement clutches excluded (Westwood 1983).

YOUNG

Stone curlew chicks usually hatch within a few hours of one another, but a little longer if incubation has started before the second egg. Their upper parts are sandy brown, and a black streak crosses the forehead and through the centre of the crown; other black streaks run from nape to tail. Their breasts are sandy brown or buff and their legs are lead-coloured. Walpole-Bond recorded that the irides are grey. Newly-hatched chicks weigh 29–34 gm, averaging 40 gm, when they are five days old (Glutz 1977) (Table 5).

They are soon active, staying in the nest only a few hours, but occasionally as long as 1–2 days. At first, particularly in rough weather, the parents brood them. The sitting bird then sometimes accidentally carries one of them under its wing. Hosking and others also record parents carrying chicks in their bills for 3–9 m. The chicks are soon on the move; some have been found 400 m from the nest when they were about 2–3 days old. The parents sometimes herd them from the bare ground where they were hatched to overgrown or marshy places. On Weeting Heath, however, where there is a wire-netting fence to maintain a high rabbit population, the chicks stayed close to the nest for at least a week.

In reaction to their parents' warning cries the chicks squeal almost as soon as they are hatched. W. Farren (1908) noted that 'after a week they fully extend and press down their necks in line with the body and by the end of the second week they stretch out in an extremely flat attitude'. They squat more firmly and persistently in open brecks or fields than on ground with good cover.

When the chicks are small the parents do not readily leave them, only quitting when danger is imminent. They warn their chicks with loud cries and exceptionally carry out 'broken wing' distraction behaviour. Walpole-Bond described the behaviour of the old thickknees while he was examining their chicks. 'At one time they lie flat, head and neck on the ground, stretched straight out in front of them, just as their progeny so often lie'. The anxious parents also sometimes tilted aggressively at partridges or lapwings.

Stone curlews are among the few waders which feed their chicks. Stemmler-Morath (1951) found that chicks in captivity fed themselves when only 2–3 days old by killing earthworms and other prey; but in the wild the parents continue for many days to import food from near and far. On two successive evenings in June 1924 Whitaker watched pairs visiting cultivated fields adjoining the breck. Every few minutes they flew back with a bunch of large earthworms hanging from each side of their beaks, like a fringe; the worms were still alive, twisting and squirming about. The birds made a bee-line for the middle of the breck where they had left their young.

The parents lead their chicks to food for about a week (A. Kraatz and W. Wegner 1969). These feeding grounds are also used by the parents, which lift and drop items in front of the young, as well as indicating them with their bills. The chicks themselves then learn to pick up food.

The hen is often more active in defending the brood against predators. In other respects, however, cock and hen combine in rearing the young.

Creutz (1953) discovered that young stone curlews start flying after a period of 36–40 days. At Weeting Heath, on the contrary, one chick could just fly after 42 days. In captivity, chicks flew strongly after six weeks and were independent after two months (O. Heinroth 1927). The number of young reared per pair ranged from 0.4 in 1971 to 1.5 in 1978 (Westwood 1983).

DISTRACTION BEHAVIOUR

Stone curlews have a limited battery of distraction displays. When I 'bumped' a thickknee off a nest with small young it flew away with a partly spread tail and dangling legs. G. K. Yeates watched one with young, half-flying and half-jumping. It finally lay on its breast with its wings stretched over the ground and then raised its head and bent it backwards. While returning to nest I have often watched them accentuating their steps, bowing deeply, 'false feeding' and occasionally 'mock brooding'. Morgan and P. D. Miéville (*in* Cramp and Simmons 1983) watched parents distracting stoats by lifting and flapping their wings; and N. J. Collar saw a thickknee foil a fox by opening its wings at the shoulder and fanning and depressing its tail. A cow or bullock approaching the nest is also diverted by the bird giving hissing and spitting cries and spreading out its wings (Baumgart 1970). Stone curlews use this behaviour against stoats, foxes and dogs; one distracted a fox by squatting down in brooding posture. G. Mountfort (1958) describes the removal of a snake from a nest.

SOCIAL BEHAVIOUR

Although they establish and defend individual nesting territories, stone curlews are social animals. Edmund Selous (1901) described their extraordinary autumn dances. 'Running forward with wings extended and slightly raised, the bird would suddenly fling them high up and then, as it were, pitch about over the ground, waving and tossing them, stopping short, turning, pitching forward again, leaping into the air and descending and continuing till, with another leap, it would make a short eccentric flight over the ground, coming down in a sharp curve .... Each violent run or plunge ending in fact with a sudden pitch forward of the body, the wings straggling about in an uncouth dislocated sort of way'. Do these social dances compare with the autumn lek displays of blackcock, probably caused by a minor sex rhythm which does not lead to copulation? These fantastic dances also take place in the nesting season; even while the stone curlews are sitting or when off-duty birds, breeding pairs, and possibly first-year or unmated birds, meet on down or breck. In the 1930s I noticed that birds which had lost their eggs joined the groups.

Stone curlews often dance in the afternoon, in evening twilight or on moonlit nights, on ridges and flats which are sometimes well away from their nesting grounds. It seems likely that one of the functions of these gatherings enables new pairs, or the survivors of pairs, to come together. I have also watched sexual behaviour in feeding groups in the dusk and in moonlight. It was beautiful to watch a cock displaying to two hens, skipping ahead of them with wings drooped and tail partly raised. Walpole-Bond also watched stone curlews dancing in spring, generally in the afternoon. 'Some or all of the pairs in any given area forgather for half an hour or more in one of several rendezvous, these – in Sussex at any rate – usually being on a ridge or slope and generally some way from the nearest laying site. Thereupon on the part of the males revels ensue. Some run about calling vehemently. Others literally leap into the air. Then one charges another, both being on the ground, half in play, half in earnest. An individual close by, though, struts pompously in front of his lady with stiffened legs, tail spread and deflected until at times its sweeps the soil, and wings drooped and maybe slightly expanded .... The general effect of the bird now is that of a cross between the little

STONE CURLEWS at the nest in typical breckland habitat; the sitting bird is asleep.
Afforestation has eliminated many former breeding haunts in East Anglia.
(Photo: Arthur Gilpin)

OYSTERCATCHER returning to eggs at a nest among rocks and stones. This fascinating and often long-lived bird has many different habitats. (Photo: S. C. Porter).

GOLDEN PLOVER at nest, about to fly away with eggshell. Sometimes the shells are dropped more than 100 metres from the nest. (Photo: Eric Hosking).

LAPWING at nest with eggs. This is a beautiful species with a fascinating sex life.
(Photo: Richard Vaughan).

bustard and some impossible breed of turkey, though on other occasions, especially when running, it looks more like an overgrown leggy partridge'.

At the end of the breeding season adults, together with young, non-breeding birds, and probably those which have lost their eggs, gather together in small trips or flocks. Moulting groups also gather, usually in parties of 20–50, before they migrate in September and October. Some of these flocks are quite large; Fred Glenny and G. F. Pearse recorded one of about 200 in Breckland.

VOICE

It is thrilling to listen to the haunting wails and gutturals of stone curlews far out on breck and down. These cries symbolise so well that wonderful country; many are quite impossible to describe adequately.

(1)   The call note *kourr-lee* or *kour-loo* and in forms, like *kira-mee*, starts quickly, rises, and becomes loud and clear. Some calls strongly resemble those of common curlew although they lack their richness.

(2)   Some cries, *ker-vic-ker-vic*, sound rather like a rusty pump handle or well winch. Towards evening, or on days of soft rain, they give these calls almost incessantly, particularly during incubation.

(3)   Von Frisch (1959) described the cock's invitation to copulation cry as *büde-büde*. I have heard a note used in nest dancing and in other sexual situations which I have rendered as *bobo-link bobo-link*. Robertson describes it, when used by a nest-scraping hen, as a loud rapid rippling *cu-mick cu-a-mick-a-mick-a-mick*. While the hen was rotating on the ground the cock stood by and gave *pic-pics*.

(4)   Nest-relief cries appear to vary. I have heard the two birds exchange rather quiet whistles; this was also Hosking's experience. O. Wadewitz (1955) describes the nest relief cry of the sitting bird as a rather soft and subdued *rait*. Robertson also heard an incubating hen calling *cu-lee* three times at intervals of 20 second, to summon her mate which approached the nest giving gruff *co-ik co-iks*. When the hen has been disturbed from the nest the cock sometimes follows the intruder and then runs back, giving an 'all clear' call, 'a low tremulant double call indicating by lower pitch the change from anxiety to security' (Robertson).

(5)   The alarm cry of a frightened bird is a loud squeal.

(6)   Parent stone curlews have a battery of subtle cries to communicate with their chicks. They warn them with loud *kwee-kwees*, reply to their distress cries with growling moans, and call them to food with subdued *quigs* (Cramp and Simmons 1983).

(7)   The cries of chicks in the nest, though fainter, resemble the contact cries of adults. Later they give their own version of the adult cry *par-dur-mit* (S. Morris 1938).

(8)   Stone curlews have many different and almost undescribable cries while in the flock or when feeding and challenging one another. One cry is a long drawn whistling *kira-mee* and another, possibly a note of challenge, a penetrating boy-like whistle *mhee*.

They also have softer flock cries *dik-dika*, or a sharper *dillit* (Glutz).

Stone curlews are at their noisiest in the evening or, sometimes, very early in the morning. I always remember lying up on a mound at the side of a great breck near Icklingham in Suffolk. At first the grey dusk of late evening made it difficult to see, but when the moon rose there was the congregation of thickknees. Some ran with quick steps, feeding greedily; others stood on one leg in most grotesque attitudes. One cock, with half-raised wings and partly spread tail, skipped in front of two hens which excitedly followed him. It was worth an age of waiting.

PREDATORS

Carrion crows and rooks sometimes rob stone curlews' eggs; after their raids I have found eggshells lying on the breck. When a jay hopped about near a nest, which Robertson was watching, the stone curlew opened its big yellow eyes and 'its hackles bristled like a dog'. Another sitting thickknee rushed savagely at a jackdaw. In other habitats marsh harriers, goshawks and herring gulls are all likely predators.

In Spain, in 1983, friends of Hugh Blair watched a booted eagle strike down a stone curlew within 20 m of their landrover. Foxes, stoats and stray dogs are occasional predators in other haunts. Egg collectors have sometimes taken many clutches, but never, we think, on a sufficiently large and systematic scale to affect the bird's status in England.

FOOD

Stone curlews feed largely at night and in the hours of twilight when they take a wide spectrum of animal food. Insects include beetles, among them the larger Carabidae, Scarabaeidae dor beetles *Geotrupes*, cockchafers *Melolontha*, earwings (Dermaptera), spiders (Araneae) and wood lice (Isopoda). Crickets and grasshoppers (Orthoptera) are favourite foods. They also catch caterpillars of moths (Lepidoptera); and Diptera (among them Muscidae and Sarcophagidae and their maggots). Many earthworms Lumbricidae are taken, particularly for the young, also small snails *Helix nemoralis*, sometimes Crustacea in winter, and from time to time adult Amphibia and tadpoles.

In the 1930s some breckland gamekeepers complained that thickknees often killed pheasant chicks, but we have no evidence of this. However, Glenny and Pearse disturbed one from a song thrush which was still warm and blood-stained. G. Brown described how a stone curlew drove away a carrion crow from a pheasant's nest which had been uncovered during hay cutting; it then carried off the egg, or part of the egg, in its beak. Lapwings' and partridges' eggs are occasionally taken. On Weeting Heath two adults and a half-grown chick fed on rabbit guts, killed a five-day-old lapwing chick, and a fourth found, broke and ate a clutch of four skylark's eggs (Westwood 1953). Stone curlews also occasionally kill and eat field mice (Muridae) and field voles (Microtidae). In captivity they sometimes devour their own chicks.

Almost like herons, they stalk their prey making their kills by means of quick dashes. Stone curlews fly over 1000 m or more from breck to arable to feed. Morgan watched them walking after the plough to catch 'exposed invertebrates'. Occasionally, too, they feed on the seeds and shoots of heather *Calluna*, sorrel *Rumex*, and other plants.

DISTRIBUTION AND NUMBERS

In 1960, K. H. Voous showed that stone curlews were rapidly decreasing in central and north-west Europe, largely through radical changes in their traditional habitats. They are now probably extinct in the Netherlands, West Germany, and possibly East Germany. But they have become adapted to cultivated farmlands in France, where between 1,000–10,000 pairs breed. In central Europe, excluding little-investigated breeding grounds in Hungary, there may now be no more than 100 breeding pairs. Stone curlews are also now scarce in Czechoslovakia, Austria, Poland and Albania; and have decreased in Italy and probably on the Canaries. In Spain, however, they are still breeding in good numbers, with possibly up to 3,000 pairs in Andalucia alone. In most parts of USSR they are scarce, but many nest between the Rivers Ural and Volga, though they are now scarcer in the Crimea. They are plentiful in Syria and some thousands breed on the plains of Israel.

A few stone curlews winter in England, but most probably travel to southwest France, Spain and Portugal. For example, a bird ringed in Hampshire, on 7 June 1980, was recovered on 29 September 1981 in the Pyrenees Atlantiques.

In England, where thickknees are breeding on the western fringes of their range, they greatly increased in the 1920s and early 1930s when the downs, brecks, and other marginal land were no longer cultivated. The breeding population then probably rose to at least 1,000–2,000 pairs (J. T. R. Sharrock 1976).

In 1905, Ticehurst recorded the nesting of 17 pairs on the great shingle wastes of Dungeness in Kent. In 1964 numbers had fallen to 6–8 pairs (R. Scott 1965); by 1974 they had ceased to breed regularly. The causes of the decline are not understood. Is it possible that this unique group was genetically different from the breck and downland stock?

All over England the stone curlew's range is now slowly constricting and breeding numbers declining. They formerly bred as far north as the Yorkshire wolds and west to the east Midlands and Gloucester. Groups have markedly decreased or disappeared from many old haunts in Herts, Bucks, Berks, Oxford and Kent; fewer pairs also now breed in Dorset, Wilts and Hants. Suffolk is still their headquarters, with habitats largely on farmlands; but the former proud groups in Norfolk and Cambridge are pitifully small. In East Anglia, where many of their traditional haunts have been afforested with conifers, they have fortunately adapted to breeding on farmlands.

In 1976 Sharrock estimated that the total English population lay between 300–500 breeding pairs. A more recent survey suggests a smaller number – 200 pairs in Cambridge, Essex, Herts., Norfolk and Suffolk and 100 pairs in Dorset, Wiltshire and Hampshire – 300 pairs in all. We believe, however, that the number is probably larger, for some curlews are difficult to locate. Soon these lovely birds, with their cold lemon-coloured eyes, may largely depend upon newly-colonised farmlands and a few carefully managed breckland reserves in East Anglia.

OYSTERCATCHER

My first memory of these exciting piebald birds was watching a pair at Blakeney Point in Norfolk in July 1926; few then nested on the Norfolk coast. Later, from 1927 onwards, I became better acquainted with these extraordinary birds when I was climbing to nests of ravens, buzzards and peregrines on the high broken cliffs of north Cornwall. Here oystercatchers seemed to be birds of the sea crags, with pairs holding territories and nesting at least 200 m apart on rocky promontories and on the gentler slopes of great headlands. I now listened to the excited trilling and occasionally saw what I later knew as piping parties. But in those years I had not read Julian Huxley and F. A. Montague's classic account of their observations on Texel in Holland. On my early trips to Scotland I often found nests and made casual notes; but I did not begin to understand oyster-catchers until 1935 when I was living in Spey Valley.

There is no mistaking an oystercatcher with its long, stout and powerful orange-red bill and pink legs. Head, breast and wings are jet black, rump and underparts snowy white, and its tail is also white with a broad black band. Oystercatchers fly fast, beating their wings quickly through a very small arc. They are also very noisy, giving loud ringing cries on the ground and from the wing.

In mild years the oystercatchers started to drift back to Dorback in the last ten days of February, usually arriving on moonlit nights when one heard their evocative calls overhead or in the distance. They returned singly, occasionally in pairs, in trips, and later in larger parties; but there was seldom a long interval between the first perhaps solitary bird and the arrival of larger groups. Oystercatchers came back a little earlier to the large flats along the Spey at Newtonmore, where Richard Perry usually recorded the earliest birds between 20–24 February; but in hard winters at some time between 6–21 March. On Skokholm Island in Pembroke, Mike Harris (1967) also found that the earlier oystercatchers arrived in late February and that most of his colour-marked birds had been identified by 22 March.

At first oystercatchers assemble in groups and flocks; on fallow fields in Dorback, on water meadows along the River Spey, at roosts on rocks and at night on a pond in the middle of the Island of Skokholm.

PIPING PARTIES

Soon you hear the famous piping or trilling and watch the behaviour which Huxley and Montague described so vividly well over 50 years ago. 'Any number of birds, from 1 to 7 or 8, or possibly more, may take part in it. Typically, what occurs is as follows. One or more birds begin the loud characteristic piping which typically again is given in a special attitude, the head and bill directed straight downwards, the bill held open and very slightly vibrated, the neck thrust forward so that the shoulders show up with rather a horsey look. Sometimes, but not always, the whole body is bobbed up and down at intervals in the way common to so many wading birds, but not very markedly. Frequently, but again not always, the performers trot rapidly round when piping, very often close side by side and usually in a serpentine course, with short quick steps. Sometimes one of the performers will suddenly turn right through 180° in the middle of the performance; one I saw turned through the complete 360° in two spasms'.

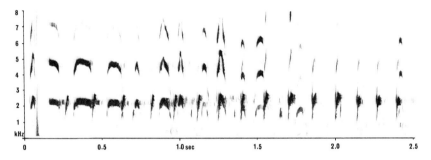

Oystercatcher piping display, Sutherland (Bill Sinclair)

G. F. Makkink (1942) suggested that only mature birds participate in these dances which help the oystercatchers to form pairs, select partners, and to 'position themselves against fellow birds to show to one another whether they are friendly or hostile'. However, H. Lind (1965) watched a 29-days-old youngster, standing close to a piping party of adults, take up the piping posture and perform a characteristic movement of 180°. These dances usually last less than three minutes, but Perry recorded a prolonged duel which continued for a quarter of an hour.

Oystercatchers often carry out the postures and give the calls of the piping dances in flight when the two birds hold their necks and beaks downwards. Two cocks chasing and switchbacking in pursuit of one another may start others piping. On 22 March 1939 a pair flew between two switchbacking cocks and started to pipe as they passed between them. Almost any emotional upheaval or excitement may spark off the ritual. The loud penetrating cries then alert every oystercaatcher within hearing range, although they do not all respond to the situation. After the group has broken up the pipers are often still excited. They now lift and drop bits and pieces of straw and grass, small stones or other objects, peck at the ground, bob and curtsey and often make feeding movements.

What is the origin of these extraordinary ritual dances? With their powerful bills, oystercatchers endanger one another when they fight. The ritual of piping has thus probably evolved to syphon off violent emotions without the need to use the bill in anger. You become aware of this after seeing a couple of oystercatchers fight in earnest when blood is sometimes drawn and feathers dislodged.

SEXUAL MATURITY

Oystercatchers take two years to acquire adult plumage. A few breed in their third or fifth, but most in their fourth years. Mature hens, on average, possibly breed earlier than younger hens; in 1964 the youngest breeding hen laid her first egg on 27 April, a week earlier than the average clutch date for the year (Harris 1967).

These are exceptionally long-lived birds (Table 1). F. Goethe (1966) knew of a cock which lived for 36 years; it was then still sexually active although it had not mated in every year. At Skokholm the average expectation of future life of an oystercatcher which had reached breeding age is 8.3 years; and the mean age of the breeding population is 11.8 years. G. Schnakenwinkel (1970) estimated that the average ages of the oyster-catcher population at Mellum was 14.3 years. Various birds in these groups lived to an age of 25–32 years, some averaging 28–30 years. These lifespans are not unique. An oystercatcher in the Netherlands was known to be 29 years old; and a Swedish bird 33 years and 7 months old. In Scotland an albino oystercatcher was traced for at least 12 years.

After they have mated and bred, many oystercatchers stay paired and together in the autumn and winter. They later return in the winter flock and re-establish their old territories. At Oldeoog the longest recorded pairing lasted for 20 years. Few established pairs divorce in the lifetime of the two partners; at Mellum the divorce rate was only 6.3% in 733 pairs. At Skokholm, 18 colour-ringed pairs stayed together from 1963–65; 22 other pairs continued for two consecutive years. In 1964, 76% of the pairs, in which both birds still lived, re-mated; and in 1965, 97% of known pairs maintained their previous pairings.

SEXUAL DISPLAYS AND BEHAVIOUR

In every year some new pairs must be formed. This is always exciting to watch. On Dorback Moor, some of the oystercatchers paired and hived off from groups in the fields. At an isolated territory near Loch Garten, however, the two birds always returned together. I knew the hen well by the shape and colour of her eggs; she always laid four; between 1940–42 they were always in the same scoop on the open moor.

In this phase there was much 'free love' and some 'trial marriages' in the Dorback groups. The bond between newly-formed pairs is easily broken. On 22 March 1941,

DW.

for example, I watched a pair feeding on a field, often digging into patches of snow. Suddenly the cock started to call *kip-kip-kip* and ran quickly towards the hen, which immediately turned at right angles and bent stiffly forward with loosened wings and taut legs. The cock then turned back and mounted her, beating his wings violently and uttering a screechy note during copulation. After he had flounced off her back both birds began to feed. Another oystercatcher then came up and the cock at once flew away, calling, but the hen did not follow; she remained with the new cock and eventually flew away with him. This had evidently been a stolen mating.

Huxley considered that the hens had no special invitation posture before copulation. However, the cock often indicates his desire and intention by a quick series of *kip-kip-kip* cries and he bends forward with hunched neck, head and tail in line, and then runs towards the hen with quick vibratory steps. She then tilts forward stiffly, sometimes to an angle of 60°. This is the commonest sexual invitation pose and one which is quite unmistakable. A hen may also indicate desire without the cock giving any recognisable sexual signal; she may even run towards him in this stiff tilted posture. I have also watched a cock advance piping towards a hen which fully stretched her legs and dipped forward during the act of sex. With his legs trailing and wings flapping a cock may copulate twice in quick succession; or he may merely balance himself with half-open wings. After sex the cock often flounces off the hen's back or walks over her. During copulation the hen may turn her head back; the two birds then sometimes touch bills and the cock may peck at the hen's crown feathers. Before mounting, a cock sometimes stands behind the hen, violently beating his wings as he positions himself; and she often tilts forward more acutely.

On 13 April 1942 I watched a hen squat and give a shrill reedy note as the cock ran piping towards her. He then beat his wings for nearly half a minute before copulating. In April 1939 a cock approached a hen which was brooding a single egg. He ran up with short quick steps, then mounted her while she sat on the nest. After copulation the hen started to brood her egg more closely. That year three other hens solicited their mates by squatting in this way.

After copulation, oystercatchers somtimes preen or 'false preen', feed rapidly, go through the motions of feeding, peck at the ground, curtsey, lift bits and pieces of straw or grass, or even start making scrapes; or the hen describes a semi-circle or one attacks the cock. Sometimes, however, there is no post-copulation excitement. The partners in newly-forming pairs, for example, sometimes fly away without further ado. Oystercatchers often copulate on fields or open moor which are 1 km or more away from and quite unconnected with their nest or nesting territory. This frequently takes place up to three to four weeks before the first egg is laid.

Makkink watched cock oystercatchers rape hens, but after the forced mating the hen sometimes attacked the cock; or she moved before he mounted and so prevented successful union. Cocks and hens each sometimes signal their desire to copulate in the absence of sex partners. Makkink also found that cocks occasionally indulged in homosexual copulation, but suggested that this was due to mistaken identity.

The pair usually cease to copulate after incubation has started. However, D. G. Andrew (1952) watched a hen lie on top of a chick, apparently trying to force it to hide. The cock then immediately mounted the hen, possibly because her posture excited him or as a displacement activity. Makkink also discovered that hens did not attack their unfaithful mates, but violently assaulted the hens with which they had copulated.

Oystercatchers are usually monogamous but a few cocks pair with two hens. We have never met with a certain example of bigamy but, on Handa Island in 1973, Bruin found two nests separated by less than 3 m. In Holland, F. Hoogerwerf (1968) recorded two hens which laid their complete clutches of six eggs in the same scoop in consecutive years. In England, J. A. G. Barnes (1950) also knew of a trio in which the hens shared a nest in five consecutive years.

Colour banding often reveals instances of unexpected behaviour. In 1963 a Skokholm cock sat on two different nests which were about 100 m apart. He was apparently the mate of the hen with the second nest and an interloper at the first, on which another male and female were trapped. It was impossible to follow up these unusual birds. 'The pair at the first nest separated and did not breed in 1964 and had different mates in 1965'. The interloper was killed in France in December 1963 (Harris 1967).

Oystercatchers have several different kinds of display flights. In the 'butterfly flight', which Huxley described, the displaying bird usually flaps its wings while singing a wailing *kweea-kweea* or *kwip-kwip-kwip-kweea keweea keweea kwip-kwip*. Cocks make these lovely flights in various emotional situations; for example, chasing a hen or rival cock, or following a flying group. They fly high in the air, then low down, sometimes to within 6 m of the ground; in wide sweeps, occasionally in semi-circles, ellipses, or in straight lines. On 21 March 1938 I watched a cock start from his display centre on a spate bank. Three times he circled the moor, each time returning to his stance. One of the possible functions of these flights, like one form of the cock golden plover's advertising flight, is to 'beat the bounds' of his living space. Either cock or hen may start to sing on the ground and then he stretches his wings vertically above his back before flying away on a 'butterfly flight' (Makkink 1942). Oystercatchers also fly modified patterns of these 'butterfly flights' when they are excitedly demonstrating over chicks or hard-set eggs.

Rival cocks chase one another, or less frequently pursue hens in switchback flights. In these, the rivals synchronise their movements and sometimes fly side by side. Members of piping parties may rise and drive away rivals with 'whirr flights', in which their wings are beaten very rapidly through shallow arcs.

Oystercatchers have evolved various ritualised forms of submissive and threat behaviour. The hunched ('thick set') attitude is a submissive posture; the lateral display ('diplomatist attitude') is defensive; and the high stepping threat walk ('crow attitude'), with head held up, tail depressed and partly fanned, is often the fore-runner of an attack (Makkink 1942). There are many examples of displacement behaviour in conflict situations. The birds throw material sideways or over their shoulders, make scoops, 'false brood', give distraction behaviour, 'false feed', bathe; or they 'false sleep' with their bills pressed into their shoulder feathers. 'False sleeping' is particularly adapted by the submissive bird in an aggressive situation.

DISPERSION, BREEDING DENSITY AND TERRITORY

The spacing of pairs and broods greatly varies from habitat to habitat. On the Dorback Moor the ridges and spate banks of the river carried the highest density; between Ballintuim and Dell 7–10+ pairs annually nested, with nests 45–225 m apart. Isolated pairs also nested on burnt patches of moorland and on farm fields where they were often separated by 450 m or more. There was a rather similar pattern in Rothiemurchus, where two or more pairs often had nests on the larger spate banks of the Spey and its tributaries and single pairs nested on the moors. In Inshriach two pairs often nested on two different stony patches of marsh, each of which carried a single pair. No pairs nested on the moor.

Around Newtonmore groups had nests on stony beaches and islands of shingle in and beside the Spey, while others favoured ridges, hillocks and moors up to 900 m from the nearest stretch of river. The highest density was on a 1,450 m length of the river at 225 m ASL, where an average of 25 pairs nested annually, with a peak density of seven pairs along 240 m of stony beach. The nests were grouped in twos and a few metres apart, or sometimes less than 2 m from one another. The same territories and nest scoops were occupied year after year (Perry, *pers comm*).

On Handa Island in Sutherland, Bruin, along with his friend Calum MacKenzie, located 25 nests in 1973. Most of these were sited within 9 m of the edge of cliffs or along the coastline; some were on ledges similar to, but rather more accessible than, those sometimes claimed by fulmars. Here the nests were spread out at 90 m or more, two hens each with clutches of three sitting within 3 m. Our friend Sheriff Donnie Macdonald tells us that oystercatchers on the east Sutherland coast, close to Dornoch, site their nests about 90–135 m apart.

In north Cornwall the pairs were well separated, often with 400 m or more between nests. B. H. Ryves (1948) noted that 'each pair holds its own stretch of cliff or beach'; nests were never less than 180 m apart. In the Scilly Isles, however, some nests in 1937 were in clumps at intervals of about 9 m.

On the Continent some oystercatcher groups breed at very high density. At Norderoog in Schleswig-Holstein there were 230 breeding pairs/10 ha; up to 40 breeding pairs/62 ha at Suderoog; about 35 breeding pairs/57 ha at Sudfall; and up to 30 breeding pairs/10 ha at Habel. On the larger of the small north Friesian Islands there were 3–15 breeding pairs/10 ha (Schnakenwinkel 1970).

Density is less on the mainland of Schleswig-Holstein and diminishes away from the coast. In north Friesian inland habitats, oystercatchers have an average spacing of 1–2 breeding pairs/10 ha.

Oystercatchers have flexible territorial patterns. In the Dorback groups I have frequently watched them drive away trespassers from around their nests. On 22 March 1939, for example, a cock advanced piping at an intruder and four times in succession chased him away from his display centre on a spate ridge. At the end of each pursuit the cock flew back to his stance where he piped furiously. Four days later I watched him behaving in the same way. On 29 March a cock, probably the same bird, had a hen with him on this territory; exactly one month later I found a nest with three eggs. I often watched this pair expelling single birds, pairs or parties which had trespassed upon their living space. These skirmishes were usually cock against cock and hen against hen. In many territories I watched similar behaviour with hens as well as cocks defenders of living-space.

In inland habitats, rivers and lochside, oystercatchers are often highly territorial; but pairs breeding on open moors, arable fields and meadows, although seldom nesting close together, usually succeed in spacing themselves without much active fighting. The rather flexible territorialism of these groups tends to disperse the pairs and by spreading out the nests possibly helps to prevent heavy predation. However, the nesting territory probably has only a limited food value to moorland pairs as they feed mainly on common or neutral ground on fields or grasslands. Dispersal may help the chicks which first feed or are fed quite close to where they hatch. In the Dorback groups the parents defended parts of the shingle ridges and spate banks but often later led their broods to fields where there were no regular food territories; but they did defend the area round the chicks.

Oystercatchers nesting on islands have different patterns. On Skokholm, Harris (1967) found that they spent much time in territorial displays, although boundaries were flexible and only very small areas were periodically defended. Many pairs annually occupied the same territories and even sometimes laid in the same nest scoops. All the pairs, which were unchanged in three seasons, retained the same territories; but in no case did they use the same nest scoops in all three seasons; sometimes the scrapes were up to 100 m apart.

In these groups, U. Safriel (1967) found that parents fed their chicks on terrestrial food taken in the territory itself, thus enabling them simultaneously to feed and defend their broods. They had a most interesting food pattern, giving their chicks the largest items and themselves subsisting on smaller items. Other groups, which fed their young on limpets, established separate feeding territories away from their nesting territories. These parents had to carry back limpets in their beaks, thus leaving the young temporarily undefended. Limpet-eating oystercatchers were apparently less successful than those holding all-purpose territories in more usual habitats.

On Skokholm, non-breeding pairs visited the higher parts of the island in late May, possibly to stake out territories for use in the following spring. Pairs were usually formed at the roost and the two birds then established territories together. In the Dorback groups, however, the cocks sometimes returned and defended their territories in advance of the hens. In heavily populated island groups, like those on Skokholm, territorial behaviour is also possibly responsible for maintaining a stable breeding population. Between 1963–68, for example, numbers of annual breeding pairs at Skokholm stood at 40–50 pairs. In each year, however, there was always a group of non-breeding adults in the roosts. These groups contained some birds which had bred in previous seasons and then, for unknown reasons, no longer belonged to the breeding hierarchy. One 10-years-old bird bred only once in 10 years. Other adults established small territories after the breeding population had clutched, but they did not lay eggs. Possibly this behaviour helped them to learn the features of the island and to develop their territorial displays, rather than marking out territories for use in future years.

Between 12–20 March 1969, Harris caught and removed six of the 1968 breeding birds; and between 26 April–9 May, 15 birds, including the cocks and hens of four pairs. Subsequently, all 13 birds left mateless paired and bred with new partners. Four cocks mated with new hens in one, two and four (2) days, thus suggesting that non-breeding groups contained surplus hens which were capable of breeding. A hen, removed on the day that she laid the last egg of her clutch, mated with another cock on an adjacent territory and laid the first egg of her second clutch within nine days. Four replacement cocks came from neighbouring pairs but most were supplied by the non-breeding groups which then bred for the first time. Most of these replacement birds would otherwise have failed to breed.

Some replacement pairs were formed on the territories, as in the Dorback groups. Three of the ten cocks whose mates were removed re-mated with hens stolen from neighbouring cocks. A hen, whose mate was taken, bred with a neighbouring but previously mateless cock which had a rather small territory. The only other hen without a mate changed territories and displaced a hen breeding for the first time which had laid and then lost a clutch of eggs. All these birds found mates without having to return to the roost. Harris concluded that on Skokholm territorial behaviour regulated breeding numbers.

The natural regulation of numbers is, however, more likely to apply to populations with high density and limited suitable habitat, particularly island groups or those surrounded by unsuitable feeding grounds. The existence of a surplus potential breeding population is known in a number of other species. Populations of waders – greenshank (Nethersole-Thompson 1951 and D. and M. Nethersole-Thompson 1979), golden plover (R. Parr 1979), and dunlin (R. T. Holmes 1966) – are among those known to carry surplus birds, some capable of breeding. Removal experiments by A. Watson and D. Jenkins (1965) on red grouse also showed that territorial birds shot in autumn were quickly replaced; and that those shot in November and December were replaced after longer intervals. Watson (1965) also showed that cock ptarmigan shot in March were replaced, but those removed at the end of April were seldom substituted.

It is possible that some of the surplus birds, which did not succeed in establishing territories on the spate banks of the Dorback, nested on the fields and moors. However, only a few moorland territories had a long history of nesting. Here lapwings competed with oystercatchers for living-space.

Oystercatchers usually nest on the ground in open country or on islands. In the British Isles they choose many different habitats, from sea-level to about 450 m. They particularly favour the pebbles, shingle, sand dunes and saltings of the sea coast, and the spate banks and shingle islands of rivers. They lay their eggs on bare and grassy ledges and on the slopes and talus of sea cliffs; in short vegetation on rocky outcrops, headlands, stacks and promontories and occasionally in new herring gulls' nests among boulders; in the turf of small islands; in short or burnt patches of *Calluna*; in glacial drift in forest bogs and in clearings and occasionally in the roots of old pines in open forest glades; sometimes in rubble beside railway tracks or on disused wooden jetties; in crops of cereals and in fallow, stubble, meadow, and newly ploughed fields on farms and croftlands; and recently on the flat roofs of houses in Aberdeen and other Scottish towns. A few pairs also periodically nest in tern and gull colonies.

On the Continent, Glutz (1975) records a still more catholic choice of nesting habitat, in worked and fallow fields of oats, barley, rye, maize, beans, brussel sprouts and potatoes. Some choose most unusual sites. A pair on Texel nested on the thatched roof of a barn; others laid on the tops of poles about 2 m high, on pollard willows, decayed wooden fences, and once on a platform about 10 m above the ground. Nests were recorded in sand pits, building sites, rubbish dumps, roadsides, and beside water gauges, concrete viaducts, dug-outs, and ashphalt covers. In northern Germany, eccentric pairs laid eggs on the scaffolding of an old rocket site, on the iron rims of a military railway and on an overturned bunker. Others nested in polders among bushes surrounded by high trees, and in small spinneys or nurseries. The parents often quickly desert chicks hatched in unusual nest-sites. H. Rittinghaus (1963) knew such a pair which never reared a single chick over a period of 13 years.

Many nests on the Continent are placed beside hummocks, walls, stones, rocks or sticks. They are also occasionally sited in marram grass in sand dunes or close to dykes. Vegetation in the nesting habitat usually grows from low to middle height, but some pairs nest on bare and others on overgrown ground.

Some coastal oystercatchers line their scoops with mussel shells which they sometimes carry in from a distance; R. Dircksen (1932) recorded a nest containing 673 shells. Other coastal nests are lined with small stones, but a few on sand are entirely bare and unlined. Many nests have a diversity of lining materials; snail shells, sheep, rabbit, hare and goose droppings, fish bones, small twigs or stalks of heather, seaweed, and bird rings, have all been recorded. John Markham watched a sitting oystercatcher lift and place cigarette ends into a nest which he was photographing. The contents of nests thus varies from unlined hollows to substantial nests of heather and seaweed.

Both cock and hen make scrapes, together or separately. Later the pair change places at the scoop. In forming the scrape an oystercatcher presses breast and wing wrists to the ground and vigorously scratches with its feet, while its wing tips are pointed almost vertically upwards and the tail is pressed down and waggled from side to side or up and down. A pair often moves from place to place, rotating in and scraping out several different scoops. Established pairs, however, sometimes tend to scamp these displays and lay in the same scrape in consecutive years.

'Nest dancing' starts in late March and continuous throughout April, but some birds in the Dorback groups did not begin until the second week of April. The hen probably selects the final nest scoop. On several days before laying her first egg she periodically broods the empty scrape much as we have seen stone curlews, greenshanks and lapwings doing. The cock is usually thereabouts when she is laying; I watched one squat almost beside his mate when she was laying her second egg. The hen now sometimes rises and flicks bits and pieces sideways. Unlike hen redshanks or greenshanks, however, an oystercatcher often lays her first egg in a well-prepared and partly-lined scoop.

The breeding season of oystercatchers varies greatly in different regions. On the moorland of Spey Valley some hens started to sit between 16–23 April; the hen which annually laid four eggs in the same scoop from 1939–42 yearly completed her clutches between 21–24 April. The Dorback groups tended to nest later. Between 1936–42 only one hen clutched as early as 29 April; the mean date for 34 clutches was 28 May, with a range of 23 May–7 June. Was this an adaptation by a river group where spates and floods in early summer so often flooded most of the nests?

Groups in other parts of Britain also have a varied and often extended breeding season. On Skokholm, where the birds return at the end of February, the first copulation took place on 16 March and the earliest clutch was laid at the end of that month. The peak laying season is, however, about 1–15 May (Harris 1967). Paul Heppleston (1969 and 1979) found that laying starts 3–4 weeks earlier in Scottish inland haunts, probably because the supply of food there deteriorates rapidly. The main laying season in Fair Isle is from late April to mid May.

On the Continent, between Ijsselmeer and the lower Weser, laying takes place from 10–15 April to mid May. However, from the east and north Friesian Islands to the Netherlands and Germany inland haunts the earliest hens lay between 20 April and early May; in some seasons there are no April clutches. In Finland the laying season accords with latitude, starting at the end of April or early May, but most clutches are laid in mid May with the latest recorded about 10 July (L. von Haartman 1963, 1966). In Kandalashka Bay the earliest hens start to sit between 16–24 May, with the last about 25 June (V. V. Bianki 1967).

The latest replacement clutches were recorded on Skokholm about 4 July; the last egg laid at Oldeeog in Germany was on 13 July (Rittinghaus *in* Glutz 1977); and at Amrum on about 17 July (H. Kumerloeve 1950).

There is no set time for egg-laying. I have been present when two hens laid their third egg between 08.00–09.00. Another hen laid her third egg between 15.00–15.30; the first two eggs in that particular clutch were unusually elongated and the third was intermediate in breadth.

I have known three different hens lay eggs at daily intervals. Most hens, however, lay on alternate days with a spread of at least two days between the second and third and between the third and fourth eggs. There are, however, regional differences. Bianki (1967) recorded that 50 hens all laid daily; there was not a single record of a 2-days gap between the eggs.

Oystercatchers' eggs vary greatly. They are usually oval-shaped but occasionally long and pointed or broad and dumpy; they lack gloss. Ground colour varies from yellow-stone to olive-brown or pale buffish brown; some eggs have a reddish tinge and others are greenish white. Others, almost unmarked eggs, have only a few stipples and streaks. Unmarked white or blue-green eggs are rare, but on record. I once found a clutch in which one of the eggs was encircled by a green band. The eggs are spotted, streaked, blotched, striped, stippled and scrawled with brownish black and sepia. They sometimes have violet, purple and ash coloured under-markings. M. Schönwetter (1962) found that the interior of the egg, if held to the light, shows more or less green; and B. Cott (1961) noted that the yolk is of a brilliant reddish colour.

One hundred British eggs averaged 56.7 × 40.9 mm (Jourdain 1940). The mean of 375 eggs (56.0 × 40.1 mm), measured by Bianki in Kandalashka Bay, USSR, is slightly smaller.

Table 3 tabulates weights of freshly-laid eggs. A clutch of three eggs, weighing approximately 140 gm, represents about 23% of the hen's body weight (616 gm) at the start of incubation (A. J. Mercer 1968) (Table 2). Schönwetter (1962) weighed 200 oystercatchers' eggshells on the Continent which varied from 2.40–3.90 gm (mean 3.38 gm).

Oystercatchers normally lay three, but occasionally two or four eggs. Clutches containing only one egg are usually incomplete and those containing five or more eggs are possibly due to two hens laying in the same nest. Large sets have occasionally been recorded when replacement eggs have been laid in a scoop still containing a flooded clutch. Bianki (1967) found that clutches of four eggs increase from north-west to south-west Europe. In some habitats c/4 occurs in up to 40% of the nests. To the north of the Gulf of Bothnia c/4 is more frequent than in the Åland Islands in south-west Finland (von Haartman MS). In island groups on the North Sea coast of Germany, 3,234 clutches averaged 2.85 eggs, with 20.7% containing c/4. On the British coast c/4 occurred in only 6.6% of 918 clutches, with a mean of 2.65 eggs. In one year at Skokholm, however, 20% of the clutches contained c/4. Table 4 gives further data on clutch size in different locations.

Clutch size is different in inland and coastal habitats. Inland the proportion of four-egg clutches is considerably larger than that of two-egg clutches. On the coast of the Netherlands the clutch averaged 3.00 eggs whereas on inland haunts, in north-west Friesland, mean size is 3.5 eggs (J. B. Hulscher 1970). These differences are not considered to be caused entirely by the predation of gulls and rats.

In Dorback and Abernethy I recorded 9/4, 55/3, 13/2 and 2/1 (mean 2.89) an incidence of 11.4% four-egg clutches. In Upper Spey, Perry found that 5–7% of the hens laid four eggs in different years. Between 1939–50 J. Keighley and E. J. Buxton (1948) recorded mean clutch size on Skokholm, varying from 2.5 to 3.0 eggs. Harris (1967) found that the peak clutch size, 3.2, occurred between 22–30 April; and the lowest average, 2.2, between 26–30 May. From 31 May onwards clutch size dropped to 1.9 eggs.

Oystercatchers often lay replacement clutches and sometimes second replacements. These clutches are usually completed in eleven to 19 days. At Mellum, on the north German coast, four hens failed to replace lost clutches. In White Sea habitats no replacement clutches were recorded.

INCUBATION

Hens often brood their first eggs for short spells lasting an hour or less; but some cover them throughout the night. Cocks and hens share incubation, but the cock broods less closely than the hen. Nest relief sometimes takes place without any special ceremony, the sitting bird flying away before its mate appears. Sometimes, however, I have watched the relieved bird walking off, pecking at the ground, and tossing bits and pieces sideways; or the incoming bird walks cautiously to the nest, with a bit of heather in its bill. After the non-brooding bird has fed, often at a distant feeding ground, it returns and keeps watch over its sitting partner. In groups and colonies a sentinel oystercatcher often alarms all the sitting birds. Oystercatchers do not sit closely, but if they are surprised by the sudden appearance of a human they often run in a curiously guilty-looking attitude before they fly away.

Oystercatchers usually start steady incubation after completing their clutches; but a few hens in Spey Valley began on the penultimate egg. On Skokholm and Skomer Islands, Keighley and Buxton (1948) made observations on 51 nests; steady incubation started on the last egg in 48 nests, two on the third egg of c/4, and one on the second of three eggs.

At Dorback I watched a nest in the last days of incubation when the two birds exchanged at intervals of 3–5 hours; but more casual observations at other nests suggest that oystercatchers normally take longer brooding stints.

Five incubation periods in the Abernethy-Dorback groups varied from approximately 25.1 to 31.3 days (mean 27.5 days). On these sheepwalks, however, the birds were often disturbed from their nests. At Skokholm and Skomer, Keighley and Buxton (1948) recorded measurements of 25.04 ± 0.48 to 28.28 ± 0.39 days (mean 26.5 days). At Norderoog, off north Germany, 22 clutches hatched after incubation lasting 26–27 days and 18 between 27–28 days, with an average of 26.9 days in observations on 49 clutches. A much disturbed pair brooded 34.5 days before hatching their eggs (Dircksen 1932).

On the White Sea, Bianki (1967) gives a spread of 24–29 days, with an average of 26.9 days for 17 clutches. O. B. Kistyakivski (1957) recorded a long period of 34.5 days for *H.o. longipes*; one pair brooded an infertile clutch for 41 days.

N. Tinbergen (1953) carried out experiments showing that oystercatchers prefer giant eggs to their own and five eggs rather than three. Large numbers and exceptionally large eggs appear to stimulate the incubation drive.

Oystercatchers readily retrieve eggs which have been placed or rolled outside their nests. On 23 April 1941 I watched a hen deal with an egg which I had placed 28 cm from the nest. When she returned she sat and then rose; and in three separate movements, extending her neck and bill and sitting down between each movement, she rolled the egg back to the nest; it took her $1\frac{1}{2}$ minutes to achieve this.

HATCHING

There is usually a long gap between the first chip or bump in an egg and the hatching of the chick; I measured approximately 53 and 67 hours at two nests. Keighley and Buxton (1948) recorded spreads of 1.59 ± 0.42 to 4.4 ± 0.5 days (mean 2.9 days). Even after they have started to break shell the chicks sometimes take up to 24 hours to liberate themselves. The sitting parent converses continuously with the chicks in the eggs by means of a succession of *chuk* calls. It later prods the chick with its bill.

I have watched oystercatchers walk off with large fragments of eggshell, with which they fly away and drop at a distance of usually less than 100 metres. Occasionally, however, they carry the shells considerably further than this. At other times they leave shells in the nest or continue to brood them. John Markham watched a hen drop an eggshell in a pool; and Seton Gordon saw one dip the shell in water and then eat the softened membrane. The brooding bird sometimes breaks up and eats small shell fragments, but I have not seen addled or infertile eggs ejected or removed. One brooding oystercatcher ate part of an egg and removed pieces of shell after a sheep had trodden on the nest.

Hatching success varies greatly in different populations. Between 1939–68 success at Skokholm varied from 82% in 1939 to 44% in 1965 when the herring gull colonies had built up.

Schnakenwinkel (1970), who studied the Mellum groups, found that, on average, 100 eggs produced 9.4 flying young, but in bad years only 0.36 young flew. In 1968 S. Kuttner (1975) recorded 0.87 flying young per pair. However, in 1925, 1928–30 and 1932, with herring gulls 2–4 times less, the average recruitment rate was 1.4 young per pair. Rittinghaus, at Oldeoog in 1950 – a year without herring gulls – found that up to 45% of the eggs produced young, from which 16.2% flew; a recruitment rate of 0.67 per pair. In 1937, 79% of the marked eggs produced young at Norderoog; there were then no herring gull colonies. Three clutches, 8.3% of the marked eggs, were robbed or deserted; 10.3% infertile and embryos died in 2.4%.

On the coast of Wattenmeer there were heavy losses on the mudflats. Of 85 clutches marked on the east coast of Schleswig-Holstein up to 64 (75%) were destroyed. The main causes of loss was trampling and egg collecting by humans and robbery by gulls. Three clutches were deserted, two taken by foxes, one by crows, one destroyed by farming operations, and one sanded or washed out. Of 61 eggs, of known fate, 37 young (62.3%) hatched. In 53 other records, in 14 different breeding haunts on the north and east coast and in inland habitats in Germany, estimates varied from 0.27–2.0 (mean 0.95) young per flying pair per year.

A group on the Åland Islands in Finland had a high breeding success. Fourteen nests, containing 40 eggs, produced 36 chicks (90%) of which 28 (70%) flew.

YOUNG

Chicks have blackish crowns tipped with black and grey, with a faint black streak extending to the nape. Their mantles are blackish-grey with greyish-white and light brown tips; and neck, throat and cheeks are blackish-brown tipped with buff. Feet and legs are coloured dull lead-grey, later turning to rusty-grey. Their calves, the back of the tarsus and under the toes are dull-yellow. The bill is dark horn-brown with a patch of reddish or brownish-yellow at the base. Irides are dusky-brown.

Both parents brood the hatching eggs and chicks; they later shuffle the chicks under their wings. Chicks are capable of leaving the nest soon fter they are dry and, if disturbed, they may leave within an hour. Other chicks stay under the wings of the parents, in the scoop or its surroundings, for at least two days.

Like common snipe, stone curlew and pratincoles, oystercatchers feed their chicks, sometimes starting to do this while they are still in the nest. One pair brought nine offerings of food within 18 minutes; but the chicks only attempted to feed five times.

Chicks can run and swim well on their third day. At first they often stay in high vegetation but 'freeze' when they hear the alarm calls of their parents. Like young stone curlews, they now squat down with heads outstretched and bodies pressed to ground. Once a young oystercatcher 'froze' for 1¾ hours. When they are older they scuttle away when they hear the alarm cries of their parents or those given by other oystercatchers.

Otto von Frisch (1959) found that captive chicks started to feed themselves in two days; but they take differing times in learning to fend for themselves. At 15 days, however, they sometimes successfully take worms.

Coastal oystercatchers sometimes take their broods on long treks, occasionally up to 7 km from the nest; possibly to lead them away from mud flats where they might be drowned.

Two young oystercatchers of the Dorback groups first started to fly some time between their 29th and 32nd days, but their full rearing period varies greatly. In inland habitats they start to break away from their parents after about 6–8 weeks. Coastal birds, feeding on crabs and cockles, take longer, due to the young birds' need to strengthen their bills. A pair feeding young on cockles may continue to do so for 12 weeks; but there are records of the parents feeding broods for 26 weeks and exceptionally as long as 44 weeks. The birds which exploit coastal crabs feed their young for 23–26 weeks and exceptionally 43 weeks (M. Norton-Griffiths 1969). Rittinghaus also knew of a ringed juvenile which remained with its parents, from which it solicited food, until

the start of the next breeding season. Parents 'pipe' angrily at young which continue to beg for food.

Norton-Griffiths discovered that when a chick ran towards its parent, before it had started to find and take its own food, the parent waited for it to approach, while holding the food between the tips of its mandibles. The old oystercatcher then moved its bill in semi-circles, just in front of the chick's own bill; at other times the parent dropped the food and pointed at it with its bill, or it left the offering on the ground and then flew away to find more, leaving the chick to pick it up.

Oystercatchers are sometimes very active in feeding their chicks. Goethe (1936) recorded a pair feeding nine-days-old chicks 31 times in eight minutes; and giving 27-days-old young 114 feeds in 33 minutes. Parents continue to feed their young during the night.

Both parents usually tend the brood, but towards the end of the fledging period, when the chicks are flying strongly, one parent only sometimes accompanies them. In the Dorback groups I found that a particular hen alone remained with a brood of three fledged young; her mate had apparently joined a flock.

DISTRACTION BEHAVIOUR

In Britain oystercatchers seldom direct elaborate distraction displays at man, but I once watched one leave its eggs and violently flap its wings while successfully distracting a stoat from a nest on river shingle. At other times, when I have surprised a bird from hard set eggs, it has run off in a kind of mammal run, crawling stealthily over the ground, periodically stopping, going through the movements of feeding, and occasionally 'false brooding' when about 50–100 m from the nest. Oystercatchers use 'false brooding' and occasionally 'false sleeping' when young are in danger. This pattern of distraction display is sometimes triggered off when the off-duty bird, or another sentry in the group, has called in alarm; the sitting bird then crawls away in this posture. Perry recorded that a few oystercatchers in the upper Spey groups, while watching their chicks swimming, sometimes reacted to a man and dog by beating their outstretched wings. A particularly bold parent occasionally flew at the head of a man, or landed

CURLEWS at the nest. A wonderful portrait of these moorland birds. (Photo: Derick Scott).

WHIMBREL about to brood her eggs. Shetland, with up to 300 breeding pairs, is the British headquarters of this grand wader. (Photo: P. O. Swanberg).

GREENSHANKS in a Highland flow. A rare portrait of nest relief. (Photo: Clifford Heyes).

SNIPE female at nest and eggs. The hen somtimes dives straight down to her nest; at other times she runs through the undergrowth. (Photo: Dennis Green).

DUNLIN hen in this charming study is sitting on eggs at her nest. (Photo: J. T. Fisher).

only a few feet away, and crawled over the ground, slowly spreading its wings.

Ken Williamson found that distraction displays in the Faroes often followed aggressive behaviour. The oystercatchers were possibly treating man as if he was a sheep or some other large but harmless mammal. These displays were sometimes quite elaborate. The birds made use of their black and white colour patterns and crept away with depressed fanned tails and half-open wings which they beat rapidly and rhythmically. Sometimes one or both wings were trailed as the bird passed over irregular ground. Every 20–30 m or so it stopped and then rose before moving forward with lowered head and bill, spread wings and expanded tail; it then also sometimes mimed brooding. Larger young respond to 'false sleeping' parents by giving threat behaviour.

Oystercatchers are often aggressive, circling around, calling angrily and even sometimes mobbing men or cattle. B. Hoffmann watched an oystercatcher rise from its eggs almost under the nostrils of a wandering bullock, striking at it with its bill, and forcing it to change course. Sheep and lambs are also sometimes attacked and pecked. When gulls, crows or birds of prey are flying over the territory the oystercatchers fly under them, striking upwards at their breasts and bellies.

FLOCKING

On coastal habitats breeding birds join non-breeders on mudbanks; at first, young of the year and moulting adults stay apart as the moulters resort to special niches. Towards high tide the oystercatchers grow very excited and often assemble in great numbers in their roosting places; and, at high-water mark, they often consort with curlew, bar-tailed godwits, knots and dunlins. Later in the season breeding birds assemble with fledged young and adults which have lost broods. Before leaving their nesting grounds parties of juveniles join up, and eventually leave, in company with the few remaining adults.

In parts of north-east Scotland Heppleston (1968) found that winter roosting flocks included males and females of all age classes. J. M. Dewar (1915) discovered that particular winter flocks on the Firth of Forth had special feeding grounds to which they returned year after year and that they avoided those favoured by other groups; some flocks had their own special refuges. P. J. Dare (1966) noticed that the largest assemblies in Britain largely consisted of adults of both sexes. Some of the winter flocks in Britain and Europe amount to thousands.

VOICE

Oystercatchers have a wide variety of cries and calls, subtle variations of which they understand. Great rewards await anyone who analyses the voice of the oystercatcher throughout a whole season. Without these sharp, ringing cries the moors, fields, rivers and sea-shores of Scotland would never be quite the same.

(1) The social contact cry is a loud *keep* or *keep-a* or *kee-eep*. Excited birds call a still quicker and more vigorous *keepa-keepa*.

(2) Flock calls on the ground are quieter, conversational *kip-kip-kips*.

(3) The exciting cries accompanying the extraordinary piping ritual of one or more birds are almost impossible to put into words. This fantastic performance starts quite slowly with a well-spaced series of *kewit-kewits*; it quickly gathers speed before sinking into quick *kik-kiks*; and then slowly runs down like an unwound gramophone record. During the same performance the trill may rise and fall twice or more. An abbreviated piping trill is sometimes given in the air as well as on the ground. A single oystercatcher, or a pair, sometimes trills when passing between a pair on the wing.

(4)   *Copulation cries*. A cock oystercatcher often gives a series of loud *kip-kip-kips* as he runs towards the hen. These cries are so distinctive that one is usually able to forecast what is about to happen. Occasionally, however, a cock trills on his run up to the hen. During copulation the cock often gives a shrill screeching cry to which the hen sometimes replies.

(5)   *Display-flight songs*. A cock beats the bounds above his living-space, slowly flapping his wings and giving his song *kwip-kwip-kweea-kweea-kwip-kwip*. Often, however, he restricts his song to the wailing *kweea-kweea*. Before flying, a cock sometimes raises his wings and sings briefly.

(6)   *Brooding calls*. Norton-Griffiths (1969) recorded a brooding parent giving a series of *chuk* calls to the hatching chicks.

(7)   *Nest cries*. An oystercatcher flushed from the nest often uses a series of quick *piks-piks*.

(8)   *Calls to chicks*. Oystercatchers use at least two different calls when they are feeding young. An adult gives a long *meep*, a cry which rises towards the end of *eep*, when flying with food to its chicks, but it seldom uses this cry on the ground while waiting for the chicks to approach it.

It gives a second call, *chuk*, when running forward to the chicks and is about 10 m from them. The young respond to the *meep* by moving towards the flying parent (Norton-Griffiths 1969).

(9)   *Chick calls*. Chicks call like adults but their cries are quieter and less perfectly formed.

(10)   *Aggression*. When fighting and leap-frogging over one another, the fighting oystercatchers use distinctive tinny *toop-toop* cries.

PREDATORS

In haunts where oystercatchers nest inland, as on Dorback Moor, they had a few natural enemies. Hooded crows, and occasionally common gulls, robbed nests and took chicks; foxes, stoats and certainly sheep dogs were other potential predators. But sudden spates in summer and late spring were far greater hazards. In 1938, for example, a great summer flood swept away almost all the nests on the upper Dorback. On 6 and 7 June a flock of 50–60 oystercatchers were feeding on a nearby field. By 9–10 June, however, they were again in pairs and some were already making scrapes on the dried out shingle banks and ridges.

In parts of the Highlands peregrines take adult oystercatchers and unflown young; we have records of this in south-east Sutherland. But this predation is not significant. In 1961–62 D. A. Ratcliffe (1963) recorded the remains of 144 waders in the eyries or plucking stations of peregrines in the Scottish Highlands. Eight oystercatchers in inland and five in coastal habitats were among the items of prey (9.0%). Douglas Weir, who studied the prey of 23 pairs of peregrines in the central Highlands, found only one adult oystercatcher (0.9%) among the remains and pluckings of 102 waders. The central Grampian peregrines, however, also took some oystercatcher chicks and unflown young.

Predation is sometimes much more severe in the coastal groups. In 1963–5, Harris found that 75% of nests away from gull colonies were successful, while those nesting among gulls produced only 50% of young. On Skokholm, lesser black-backed gulls evidently found it easy to kill young oystercatchers just before they flew, when they were conspicuous and easily caught.

FOOD

In the Dorback haunts oystercatchers particularly favoured meadows and old leys where they fed mainly on insects and earthworms. The worms were probably located through hearing their movements or feeling their vibrations. On the stony edges of the moor, and on the spate banks, they had little difficulty in finding and catching large insects, but I did not make a detailed study of their food. On the water meadows of the upper Spey and in Rothiemurchus their food and feeding behaviour was similar. Perry watched one parent lead its brood to feed on the Newtonmore golf course.

Oystercatchers nesting and rearing their broods on coastal fields have a rather similar diet. Dare and A. J. Mercer (1973) analysed the crop and stomach contents of 181 birds; 97.8% (by frequency) contained earthworms; 13.3% inland feeding birds by Morecambe Bay Diptera; 11% Lepidoptera; 1.1% Coleoptera; and 0.5% Dermaptera. Coastal birds mainly fed on animals found between the tides. They particularly favoured molluscs, especially bivalves, edible mussels *Mytilus edulis*, cockles *Cardium edule*, *Macoma balthica* and *Tellina tenuis*.

The characteristics of a particular feeding ground largely determine the choice of food. At Morecambe Bay, Lancashire, Dare and Mercer (1973) found that 97.99% of the crop and stomach contents of oystercatchers feeding on mussel beds contained the remains of mussels. On the sandbanks, 78.8% contained mussels and 19.8% cockles. Their diet on sandy flats was different; 68.6% had the remains of cockles, 41% tellins *M. balthica* and *T. tenuis*, and only 5% mussels. The main food of the oystercatcher was second-year cockles. In the hard autumn of 1962 cockles were unable to close up quickly or tightly, thus rendering them easy prey. Predation is remarkably quick; oystercatchers consume 1.2 cockles per minute – 336 in each daylight tide per bird. Each oystercatcher average six cockles in 7 minutes and five cockles in 6 minutes; a consumption of 505 cockles, amounting to a weight of roughly 327 gm of cockles per bird per day. Predation is also heavy at night. R. E. Drinnan (1957) showed that when cockle stocks were of moderate size, oystercatchers might eat 70% of the entire second winter stock; even in years of high density they might take up to 20% In some localities oystercatchers are therefore serious predators of cockles and are partly responsible for the annihilation of the cockle population in the Dee estuary in Cheshire and Morecambe Bay in Lancashire, where cockle fishing previously provided a viable industry for local fishermen.

Complaints by fishermen that oystercatchers were devestating cockle beds at Burry Inlet, South Wales, led to a cull of 10,000 birds. Conservationists reacted swiftly. Re-analysis of the original data suggests that the predation was greatly exaggerated (Hopgood and Goss-Custard 1977). It is now unlikely that such a disastrous cull will be repeated.

DISTRIBUTION AND NUMBERS

In the British Isles oystercatchers are largely birds of islands and the sea coast, where they now nest on cliffs as well as on the pebbly shore.

A few pairs nest in gravel pits in the English midlands, and in East Anglia on coastal fields, but oystercatchers are missing from many parts of southern England. This is not entirely due to recent human pressures, as in the 1920s few pairs nested in the Norfolk sea bird reserves like Blakeney Point. Irish oystercatchers are mainly coastal and particularly island-breeding birds. There is, however, a large and unexplained gap on their south coast breeding distribution between Cape Clear Island and east Waterford (J. T. R. Sharrock 1976).

From at least the 18th century, and probably much earlier, oystercatchers have continuously spread inland, particularly in Scotland; in the last 40 years this practice has increased. They are now nesting in good numbers on inland rivers, on hill farms, moorland edges, and estuaries, as well as on river islands, beside lochs, and on meadows, arable fields and moors. K. H. Voous (1960) has recorded a rather similar spread of inland nesting in Holland, Sweden and north-west Germany.

Dare (1966) estimated that there were at least 19,000 (possibly up to 30,000–40,000) pairs breeding in Britain and Ireland. About 75% of this population nests in Scotland, 10% in England and Wales, and the rest in Ireland.

The Breeding Atlas observers confirmed breeding in 1909, probable breeding in 174, and possible breeding in 219 10 km squares. Given an average of 20 pairs to each confirmed or probable 10 km square, Sharrock (1976) suggests that the entire population for Britain and Ireland probably exceeds 30,000 pairs.

Dare (1966) estimates that between 10,000–30,000 pairs breed in Iceland and 30,000 pairs in the Faroes. There are about 100 pairs in Italy while breeding strength in France is likely to be between 550–700 pairs (Yeatman 1976). In 1980, 17 pairs nested in Spain (A. Martinez). There were 160 pairs in Belgium in the early 1980s (P. Devillers) and 50,000–60,000 pairs in the Netherlands (R. M. Teixeria). In 1976–77 around 13,000 pairs nested in East and West Germany (Glutz 1977) and roughly 5,000 pairs in Denmark (Dybbro 1976). J. Kålås and I. Byrkjedal (1981) estimate the Norwegian population at 40,000 pairs and in Sweden there are about 10,000 pairs (S. Ulfstrand and G. Högstedt 1976). Only about 600 pairs breed in Finland (E. Merikallio 1958). In USSR, about 300 pairs breed in Estonia (Onno 1966) and 1,500–2,000 pairs along the shores and surroundings of the White Sea (Bianki 1967). Distribution is scattered in Turkey where there are probably under 1,000 breeding pairs (Cramp and Simmons 1983).

What a remarkable bird this is, with its long life and amazingly successful exploitation of so many diverse habitats. Over the years may they continue to puzzle and delight inquiring ornithologists at home and overseas.

LAPWING

From mid February, on moonlit nights the family used to lean out of their bedroom windows, always listening, and hoping, to hear the lapwings returning. For the peevish and haunting cries of these first 'peewits' are most thrilling and exciting.

My love for the lapwing goes back a very long way. I remember, so vividly, that soft grey evening on the Amberley Wild Brooks. First one, and then a second snipe was bleating over the marshes. Suddenly, a cock lapwing was corkscrewing, tumbling and somersaulting in its wonderful spring flight; and its wing music was marvellous to hear. I was all alone, but remembered the trick which an old marshman, Charlie Elliot, had shown me. I placed a stick where I thought a sitting bird had risen; and then I walked round it in every-widening circles, until, at last, there at my feet was the nest, with its four, beautifully speckled brown eggs.

I have come to know the lapwing in all its many moods; for fifty years I have always lived within hearing of its haunting and evocative cries. In Spey Valley there were fine colonies and communities in the fields and rough pastures of Dorback Moor. It was there that I made my most intensive study of the breeding behaviour of this lovely bird.

The lapwing is special among British waders. Its long erectile wispy crest, and the dark and white contrasts of its plumage, are outstanding. Through the glass you see that the bird has dark bottle green wings, with the cock showing a purple sheen in strong light. Their wings are rounded; with those of the cock distinctly broader than those of the hen. Cocks and hens have black crowns and gorgets, but the back of the head, the side of the face and the nape are white; across their cheeks there is a black streak. The tail is white, terminated with a broad black band, and the russet brown undertail coverts are conspicuous in the cock's display. The usual flight of the lapwing is quite unmistakable, slow, flapping and deliberate.

Lapwings are remarkably quiet on their way to the nesting haunts. A few cocks are usually the first to appear; on isolated territories they may come back fully a week before the earliest party of mixed sexes. At first they settle on the fields. Then, often in the dusk of evening, in the small hours around dawn, or frequently by moonlight, you again hear the wild spring songs in the semi-darkness. If the moon rises late the cocks also return to sing, call and somersault over their living-space, warning you that the exciting period of courtship and territorial establishment is approaching.

COURTSHIP AND SEXUAL BEHAVIOUR

Day after day I have watched the subtle changes of the lapwings' behaviour which, at this stage, is partly determined by the weather. On early mornings, in fields not yet divided into territories, the cocks are often peevish and aggressive. While still in the flock they run stiffly towards one another, or they dip forward with retracted necks and partly depressed crests. Sometimes they face one another, standing rigidly upright with wings loose at their shoulders, showing off their snowy-white breasts and black throat patches; and they tilt forward with raised crests and loosened wings.

The awakening sex impulse soon emerges. The cocks bend forward very stiffly; the first nuance of the 'rocking' display, in which they stand on taut legs. Or, dipping slightly forward, they advance, waggling their tails and giving the scratchy, sizzling *ur-ur-ur* notes of the full ground display. Sometimes they also stand rigid and unbending, beak and body horizontal and crest retracted.

On the moor, rough pasture, flats and gentle slopes, you now hear and watch the beautiful song flight. Rising from the ground, with a few slow, soft and almost owl-like flaps of his broad wings, the cock climbs steeply and, perhaps when 10–30 m or more above the ground, he flies faster and faster and then throws himself through the air, plunging, sometimes somersaulting or flying on his back, while singing his nostalgic spring song. Then, rolling and tilting from side to side, he produces that wonderful throbbing wing music, which is always at its most evocative when two or more cocks are challenging and competing against one another in the moonlight. Time after time the cock performs these aerobatics, before rising steeply and then plunging to earth where he alights in his arena after a few slow deliberate wing flaps.

These spring flights advertise, but are not entirely restricted to, territory; they are sometimes even carried out over the broad waters of a large loch. Several cocks may perform simultaneously when the birds are nesting in groups or loose colonies; they now doubtless cross and invade the air space of their neighbours. Later, already-wedded cocks seeking additional partners, and unmated cocks still advertising their territories, often give these flights before they are capable of successful coupling.

In a battle-zone consisting of several adjacent arenas the cocks often sing and fly against one another. I have watched exciting air fights, with the two contenders striking one another with their wings before instantly somersaulting apart and then giving song flights over their respective territories. At first a cock, which only displays on his territory in short spasms, periodically returns to the group in fallow or ploughlands outside his own defended area.

We watched a cock re-claim an old territory in east Sutherland. When he started, his displays were incomplete and uncoordinated. He ran an erratic twisting course over the rough pasture; sometimes waggling his tail and at others lying on his breast, partly 'rocking', but without actually scraping with his feet, and thus leaving no mark of his movements. He 'rocked' in over 20 different places, but mostly in the old scrapes in which the eggs had hatched in the two previous years. It was exciting to watch him apparently recalling this and other vital parts of his former living space. Time after time he appeared deliberately to choose old 'rocking' places; and sometimes passed them by, and then turned back to a mound or tussock which he had used in the previous year. Soon he was flying from one 'rocking' hollow to another, with the heavy wing flaps of the first part of the spring flight. He also made low corkscrew flights a few feet above the ground, but without singing the evocative song; occasionally, however, he did sing a full song while running over the ground. Before evening he seemed at better ease and his display chain was more complete.

Hens stay in the group, but within a few days the cocks attempt to entice them to their territories. Here, with head and breast down, tail slightly elevated, the cock runs rapidly through his arena, where he periodically sinks onto his breast, scratches vigorously with his feet, and shuffles his body while waggling his closed tail up and down. In full display he leans on his wing wrists while his wing tips point upwards; and his tail is first held upright and then rhythmically waggled up and down to show off the russet undertail coverts. In a short time he scrapes out a few small rounded unlined scoops, usually three or four, but sometimes ten or more. One or two of the most favoured scoops are often sited in quite different parts of the territory.

The cock, by flying rather slowly and deliberately to his territory, subtly entices a hen to leave the group; also he sometimes rises to chase a female which is flying low over his arena. At first the hen behaves rather furtively, often standing coyly on the edge of the territory. Here she may wait for many minutes before flying away without making a further move; or she may advance slowly, a few metres at a time, seemingly feeding unconcernedly, but always moving in the direction of the frantically displaying cock; or she may suddenly fly away or walk past or round him. Always, as the hen approaches, the cock steps up the tempo of his displays; or he runs stiffly towards her, neck and head forward and crest depressed. Then he slowly walks back to the scrape. In the course of these ritualised movements he gives the sizzling *ur-ur-ur* display cries. Standing on taut legs he again moves his tail up and down before crouching and displaying in the 'rocking' hollow. A cock also calls peevishly in and around the scoop and the hen may then call to him. If the hen flies away the display chain breaks abruptly; the cock then rises and makes a tilting corkscrew flight low over the arena before alighting, feeding, or going through the motions of feeding.

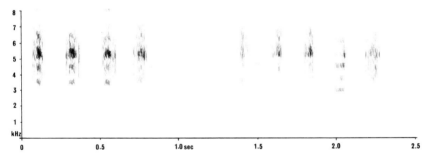

Lapwing, sizzling ground display cries, Inverness-shire (Bill Sinclair)

In his 'rocking', the cock directs his tail towards the advancing hen, thus presumably exciting her by the flashing movements of the russet-red undertail coverts or, running towards her in the stiff erect posture, he puffs out his black gorget; while the hen slightly retracts her neck, points her beak slightly downwards, and holds her body in a rigid horizontal posture. Later the hen stands beside or immediately behind the displaying cock, which jerks bits of grass or stalks of heather sideways or over his shoulders, while from time to time she bends slightly forward and jerks her head and neck up and down. A little later the hen herself 'rocks', jerks grasses, and runs a few metres past the cock when she again lifts and tosses bits and bents sideways. Or the birds change places on the scrape; and while the hen is 'rocking' the cock often 'upends' beside her, wing tips vertical and tail pulsating. Sometimes both stand together on opposite sides of the nest, jerking stalks or bents over their shoulders.

These displays may attract trespassing cocks which put down a few metres from the hen and 'rock' to her while the territory holder himself is displaying on his scoop. This always creates a flurry; the tenant almost immediately rises and drives off the intruder.

During these spasms of 'nest dancing', a cock half-heartedly attempts to mate the hen. She signals to him, dipping stiffly forward on taut legs; but he fails to respond. At other times, when he attempts to mount, the hen refuses, twisting aside or moving away. If the cock's sex drive is not strong enough, or if not in accord with hers, she leaves him to visit the arenas of other potential mates.

I have watched a hen visit several adjacent arenas, much in the manner of a greyhen selecting a mate at the lek. On a moorland edge in east Sutherland we watched one attack the two cocks which were displaying to her. This is always a period of tension and occasionally of frustration. Cocks and hens sometimes join in nest dances and even couple, apparently successfully; but they still fail to stay together as a pair.

At this stage the two lovely birds may copulate within a few metres of the scoop or, exceptionally, while the hen is standing in it. The cock has a special copulation flight in which he corkscrews over the moor a few metres above ground, tilting from side to side and often flying straight on to the hen's back; or he runs up to her in the stiff erect posture, often flying the last few metres before mounting.

After coupling, a Dorback Moor cock turned and ran back to his scoop where he directed the backward display at the hen. A few minutes later, as she slowly walked up to him, he swung round bowing low to display the black gorget, and tossed heather sprigs sideways. The hen then 'upended' beside the nest and he 'waggled' while dipping forward and standing on stiff legs.

Lapwings are vigorous and strongly-sexed birds. In some groups there is much promiscuity and many adulterers and adulteresses. The cock directs copulation flights at every hen which visits his arena, thus occasionally leading to stable bigyny.

We have known four firmly established lapwing triangles and have watched several other less regular trios. One cock copulated with both hens on consecutive days and joined them in nest dancing; the two nests were placed roughly 50 m apart. In two triangles both hens laid the fourth egg of their clutches within 48 hours of one another. A trio in Sutherland in 1981 had a different pattern. After the second hen had laid in one of the scoops, about 70 m from where his first hen was sitting, the cock entirely ignored her; I never saw him attempt to sit. This second hen's nest was within 10 m of a wire fence, an unusual nest site, in my experience. By daily moving my stance a few metres I was eventually able to sit within 20 m of the nest; the hen nervously returned to her eggs and sat on them while I was watching. Other bigynous cocks helped to incubate one of the two clutches. F. Freitag (1969) also knew one which took an equal share at sitting on both mates' nests.

In Holland, G. L. Rinkel (1940) was the first to discover that a cock lapwing could have three different mates. On 15 April 1967, J. Wilson also watched a Lancashire cock lapwing mating and showing nest scrapes to two different hens; one of them was sitting on 23 April and the other on 26 April about 25 m away. On 25 April the cock was displaying to a third hen with which he mated on the 26th; on 1 May she was sitting on eggs about 35 m from the other two nests. The cock later joined a fourth hen in nest dances; but after four days she left, without lining any of his scrapes. This virile cock was not known to sit, but he patrolled his territory and drove off all trespassing rivals. The first two hens lost their eggs, the third reared two young.

Formal polygyny is, however, only a page in a colourful chapter. We have watched a trespassing cock suddenly fly in and copulate with a hen which was sitting on her nest just after laying her second egg. The furious 'husband', standing a few metres away, frantically mobbed his 'wife's' impudent seducer. A cock sometimes flies from his territory to mount a hen which is signalling to her own mate. One hen left her eggs and flew about 200 m to offer herself to a strange cock which was standing in the stubble. Several pairs regularly copulated, almost as a ritual, before changing places at the nest. These hens seek their mates, incite and accept them, and then fly away to feed while the cocks start their brief brooding stints. Hens also sometimes leave their eggs to couple with their mates, and then run or fly back to their nests.

Unmated males, with quite isolated arenas far out in the peat moss or forest bog, sometimes have remarkable sex lives. We should like to know more about the status of these birds, some of which are in magnificent feather and give exciting song flights and vigorous 'rocking' displays. I spent many hours watching a cock with a display stance in an old peat moss in Rothiemurchus Forest. This territory was mid-way between the large groups nesting on the fields of Tullochgrue and the few pairs which then haunted the western flows of Loch Morlich. Between their brooding stints the Tulloch-grue birds often flew over the moors and across the open forest and clearings to bathe and feed beside Loch Morlich. Sometimes they momentarily slowed down when passing over the lone bird, when he was singing and somersaulting over his living-space. Just occasionally a hen dropped down to watch him, but she usually soon flew away. Two hens, however, stayed longer; these he mated, flying straight onto their backs before they continued on their way to the lochside. The sex life of this cock was remarkable but not unique. On 30 April 1942 an unmated cock, with an arena on the mud flats of one of the Inshriach dams, also enticed and coupled with a mated hen from a distant nest.

The displays of some cocks which fail to hold hens gradually lose force, vigour and persistence. In east Sutherland one which had started 'rocking' on 24 March continued to do this until 22 May; but in the last fortnight he displayed less vigorously and for spells lasting only a few minutes. During his nest dances he coupled with, but failed to hold, two different hens. To the end he stood on his territory, occasionally performed song flights, and ran over the ground in a stiff, almost dotterel-like fashion. He also half-heartedly drove off rivals and mobbed and evicted hoodies, rooks, jackdaws and occasionally visiting curlews.

DISPLACEMENT BEHAVIOUR

Various excitements and emotional upsets sometimes lead to copulation, possibly as a displacement activity. For example, a cock often mates his hen after he has chased away a crow or rook. Disturbance at the nest also sometimes triggers off sexuality. While a pair of lapwings was dealing with an unusual situation – two of their eggs were lying outside the nest and the grass lining had been removed – the cock twice copulated with his mate within six minutes; 20 minutes later, while re-building the nest, he suddenly rose and flew straight to the hen which was standing 100 m away. She dipped in the copulation posture and he flew straight onto her back; she then returned to the nest and continued reconstruction.

The ritualised jerking of material sideways or over the shoulder is not confined to nest dancing; either bird may do this when it is emotionally upset. An agitated lapwing also sometimes stamps (possibly the same action that it uses in pattering for food), or it drives its beak into the herbage, probably a re-directed attack; or it bobs excitedly, a clash between two different drives, and twitches its tail.

DW.

AGONISTIC BEHAVIOUR

Lapwings have many formal and informal patterns of agonistic behaviour.

(1)   Aggressive birds run stiffly towards others, bending slightly forward and retracting their necks.

(2)   A cock stands rigid and erect to show off his black gorget and white breast.

(3)   He often tilts forward with raised crest and loose wings.

(4)   A threat display, with erect and upstretched banners, is used against sheep, cattle or sometimes humans. A cock also sometimes uses this display when advancing upon possible predators like crows, rooks or jackdaws.

(5)   In attacking rivals, cocks spread and stretch out their wings before raising them and leapfrogging over one another. The attacked bird often counters its opponent by lifting and stretching back its wings; at other times it runs away rapidly with closed tail, or loosens his wings at the shoulders and then turns to meet the aggressor.

Angry lapwings loosen their wings before attacking their rivals; the two opponents may then scuffle and simultaneously jump into the air. The attacked bird, if on the ground, often ducks when its adversary mobs it from the air. When they are established on their territories two or more cocks often try to out-fly one another, sometimes striking rivals with their wings before somersaulting apart. Mobbing lapwings attack flying enemies as well as those on the ground. Cocks in particular show aggression towards singles or pairs of golden plovers, solitary birds or groups of oystercatchers, to lone curlews which have intruded in their living-space, and occasionally to starlings and rabbits.

After the chicks have hatched, neighbouring pairs frequently join territory-holders in making concerted attacks on flying or grounded enemies.

In northern Scotland, territorial and agonistic behaviour often revive in August or early autumn. Cocks then fight, scuffle, and perform usually incomplete 'rocking' displays; and they carry out modified display flights high in the air; but they seldom sing.

PAIRING AND SEXUAL MATURITY

Some lapwings form pairs in their first spring; but many only breed for the first time in their third calendar year. Cocks are usually most active in the pairs of one-year-old birds. H. Matter (1975) discovered that young unmated cocks were often pushed into less favourable habitats on the periphery of the group's living-space. In Switzerland, Glutz (1975) found that first-year birds arrived late – often in the second half of May – and eventually settled on very marginal ground on the edges of traditional habitats.

Without colour banding, it is difficult to determine how often individuals re-establish partnerships on the same territories. On Dorback Moor several hens, which laid remarkable and easily recognised eggs, bred in more than one year in consecutive years; partly because cocks and hens are attracted to the old territory, and thus tend to re-mate with one another. Other pairs only endure for single seasons (B. Laven 1940).

P. A. Rayfield (*pers comm*) discovered that three banded chicks nested in their first spring. A young hen, ringed as a chick in 1950, nested in its native territory in 1951; but was in another territory in 1952–53, when it was probably mated to a different cock. Two other banded chicks also nested in their first year. Another Scottish chick, ringed in 1947, was back in its birthplace in 1951, 1952 and 1954. In Lancashire, J. Boon ringed a nestling on 14 June 1944 and recovered it sitting on a nest 48 km away, on 19 May 1945. There are other records from abroad. A chick, ringed at Sjaelland in Denmark, was on its birth habitat in 1960 and 1968; and one trapped there in 1958 was back in 1959 and 1962. A Hungarian lapwing had a similar history. Ringed in 1930, it returned to its birthplace in 1932 and 1934.

TERRITORY

Lapwings are strongly territorial birds. The cock starts by visiting his future territory in early morning and late evening. Thereafter he gradually spends more time in his arena; here he drives away rivals, performs nest dances, courts, copulates, and attempts to hold a mate. In richer habitats, cock and hen feed much in their territories (G. Högstedt 1974). In moorland territories, however, both birds feed mostly on neutral ground on farmlands.

During incubation the non-sitting birds, in all our moorland study areas, spent some time feeding in and maintaining their territories, but they fed largely on neutral ground on arable, fallow or grasslands, usually 100–150 m or more from the nest. In Rothiemurchus, however, off-duty birds, particularly hens, sometimes flew up to 7 km to feed and bathe beside a large loch. Several cocks often return together after feeding. One after the other, they make wide-ranging tumbling song flights high in the air before plunging back to their own territories and sitting hens.

After the young have hatched, some isolated pairs tend and rear the broods in their arenas. The parents periodically fly away to feed on the farmlands, but return quickly whenever they hear the distress cries of the young. In close groups, however, territories tend to break down after the young have hatched; broods then wander far from their birthplace.

Is there a point when it becomes a selective advantage to exchange isolation and dispersion in favour of group nesting and collective defence? If so, what is the mechanism that leads to the partial break down of territory? A better defence against predators must be balanced against opportunities for the latter of discovering and destroying several nests rather than one. There are many examples of this ambivalence: *e.g.* redshank, avocet, kestrel, little tern, and snow bunting. When nesting in clusters, however, each pair of lapwings usually maintains a small core territory although its air space is almost continuously violated.

Territory performs several different functions for lapwings.

(1)   An orderly dispersion of pairs; possible regulation of breeding numbers and attainment of a breeding hierarchy.

(2)   It provides a meeting place for the pair in which courtship and copulation usually proceed without great disturbance.

(3)   In richer habitats the territory is frequently a food reserve while the hen is building up her resources for egg laying.

(4)   It is of varying value as a rearing place for the young.

DISPERSION AND BREEDING DENSITY

Sometimes lapwings breed in quite close groups or in loose colonies with well-separated pairs. Isolated pairs have arenas on moorland, river shingle, peat bog or forest moss. On Dorback Moor, inner groups nesting on the arable fields bred at a higher density than those on the adjoining moorland edges and rough pastures. In 1942 there were 27 pairs on 2.6 km^2, with 10 pairs concentrated on 6 ha. Small groups had territories on the farms and isolated pairs on a croft and moorland in Rothiemurchus. The only two pairs on my study area in Inshriach nested in mud flats on two well-separated bogs; lapwings did not then nest on the open or newly-afforested moors.

In 1975 Patrick found up to 26 pairs nesting in the rough pasture of a gently sloping hillside above our hamlet; two nests were only 7 m apart. This concentration was possibly due to the recent ploughing up and breaking in of fallow fields and old ley on the hillside and in the valley. Between 1976–84 there were nine breeding pairs in 1976, eleven in 1979, and seven in 1984. In no other year was there more than five breeding pairs. A freshly-broken field of 5.3 ha in the hamlet carried five breeding hens in 1981, one in 1982, but none in 1983–86. Are the furrows of newly-broken fields attractive as nesting places or does the plough turn up a rich harvest of invertebrates for food? The lapwings, however, still largely feed on neutral ground outside their new habitats.

Dispersion on another east Sutherland study area had a different pattern. An isolated pair nested on rough pasture, but a larger group of up to 10 pairs nested on grass-heath, sometimes in high density; we met with two nests less than 10 m apart.

K. G. Spencer (1953) suggested that 200 pairs nested on 2.6 km^2 in Orkney. On the other hand, E. M. Nicholson (1938–39) found only 2–3 pairs breeding on 4 km^2 near Oxford. On farmlands in Surrey there were usually 6–8 pairs/0.9 km^2 (M. D. Lister 1939). In 1930 A. W. Boyd recorded an average of 18 breeding pairs on 4 km^2 north of north Cheshire; and in Cornwall B. H. Ryves (1948) counted 10 breeding pairs on 1.4 ha of exceptionally suitable ground. On 21 April 1930, while passing a roadside field near Elsham in Lincolnshire, Arthur Whitaker and T. M. Fowler saw a flock of lapwings which they later discovered were nesting in exceptionally high density. In half the field of 5.5 ha they found 15 nests with eggs; thus suggesting a possible breeding density of about 30 nests/5.5 ha.

In Germany W. Schubert (*in* Glutz 1975) discovered a group in which nine pairs nested on 0.75 ha, with two nests just over 2 m apart. K. Kirchoff (1971) found that in 4.1 km², near Hamburg, 15.5% of the population was dispersed in groups containing over six pairs. In New Brandenberg, in a population of 125 pairs, 36 pairs nested in isolation; 61 in groups of 2–4; and 28 in colonies of 6–10 (H. Prill 1968).

How do lapwings determine their hierarchy? Are territories in cultivated fields more successful than those on the moorland periphery, irrespective of disturbance and destruction of nests during farming operations? Are groups self-perpetuating? How and from where do they attract recruits? Are isolated pairs, nesting in forest bogs or clearings or on open moor, of a lower social status than those with territories and living-space in the groups? The problems are intriguing and almost endless.

NEST, EGG AND CLUTCH

Nests are often in rough pasture, arable, fallow, stubble, grasslands, young corn and root crops; more sparingly in short heath or grass heath, peat bogs, old peat cuttings, swamps, forest bogs and clearings; beside rivers, and on stream shingle. They are also placed on sand dunes, saltings, machair, sea shingle, mud flats, sewage farms, breckland, industrial slagheaps, burnt *Nardus* and peat, gravel pits, beside sheets of open water, or on open moorland. Altitudinal levels in Britain range from a few metres to, exceptionally, 900 m or more ASL. Steep slopes or hillsides are avoided; but nests are occasionally within 50 m of occupied houses and exceptionally within 10 m of wire fences.

Lapwings sit tightly, usually flying or (particularly off hard-set eggs in the twilight) occasionally running from the nest whenever man or a ground predator approaches within 150–200 m. They nest in very low vegetation which usually enables the sitting bird to see its enemies from a great distance.

In the Netherlands the vegetation surrounding the nest varies in height from 6–9 cm in dense grasslands and up to 12–15 cm in growing corn (H. Klomp 1954). In south Bavaria vegetation grows up to 5–8 cm on their breeding habitats; and up to 15 cm on their roosting grounds. In more marginal habitats clutches are sometimes laid among taller plants, particularly in cultivated fields. C. Imboden (1971) records nests among plants 20–30 cm, exceptionally 45 cm, high; and Matter (*in* Glutz 1975) found nests in fields of rape with plants growing to a height of 100 cm, with an average of 54 cm for 15 nests.

The cock scrapes out the 'rocking' hollows, one of which both birds prepare, line and enlarge. Each cock usually 'rocks' on at least half-a-dozen scoops, two or three of which he particularly favours. A. Stiefel recorded cocks 'rocking' on 11 scoops at most; but in east Sutherland one male performed in over 20 different places in his nest dances. These 'rocking' hollows have a breadth of 9–15 cm and a depth of 2.8–7.0 cm (mean 4.9 cm) (Stiefel 1961). The scoop finally chosen is enlarged and becomes more rounded, averaging 14 cm in breadth. The hen almost invariably chooses and helps to line one of the cock's 'rocking' scoops; but in 1939 a Dorback hen laid in the old nest of a golden plover.

Nests may be markless on open ground; but they are sometimes situated beside cow pats, furrows, mud heaps, stones, clods of earth, etc. H. Lohscheller (1972) recorded a most exceptional nest-site on a flat roof 7 m above ground. The chosen nest is lined with bits and bents from the surrounding vegetation; straw, blades of grass, sprigs of heather, occasionally pine needles, small bits of wood and even on a thick bed of *Persicaria* leaves. The sitting lapwing continues to add material and restores or renews the lining of the nest if it is removed or blown away. If the surrounding ground is flooded, the sitting bird builds up the nest. Glutz (1975) records a nest which was raised to a height of 25 cm and not deserted.

The laying season varies from year to year and in different parts of the range. The earliest recorded British clutch (three eggs) was found on 23 February 1882.

Laying sometimes begins in the last week of March in northern Scotland; but in late seasons some hens do not complete their clutches until the first week of May. In 1941, in the Dorback Moor group, 17 hens laid out between 17–21 April, with a mean clutch-date of 18 April; in 1942 eleven of the hens in these territories clutched between 9–22 April (mean 15 April).

In 1975, Patrick found that 22 out of 26 hens in his Culrain study area had completed their clutches between 9–25 April (mean 20 April). In 1976 the nine hens laid out between 11 April–1 May (mean 18 April); and in 1977 the only hen laid a single egg on 23 April. In 1978 Richard found that the group consisted of four pairs, two of which completed clutches on 5 and 9 May respectively. When the group had increased to at least eleven hens in 1979, five clutches were completed between 13–30 April, a mean clutch date of 24 April.

Arthur Whitaker's Diaries contain data on 224 clutches of British lapwings' eggs. Calculated clutch dates varied from 24 March–9 May, giving a mean of 19 April. In Yorks-Derby, 175 clutches were completed between 27 March–8 May (mean 19 April); 25 hens in Norfolk-Suffolk were slightly earlier, with a mean of 14 April for complete clutches.

In West-central Europe the earliest lapwings laid up in the first ten days of March (Glutz 1975). R. Tolman (1969) records a laying season of 4–29 March in Holland, with a mean of 19 March for 72 nests. Klomp and B. J. Speek (1971) record a later laying season, with 90% of the hens starting to lay by 10 April. In Switzerland W. Fuchs recorded the earliest egg on 9 March 1961 (*in* Glutz 1962). S. Haftorn (1971) records a laying season ranging from early to mid-April in south Scandinavia. For Swedish Lapland, however, S. Svensson gives the peak as mid May; in western Siberia lapwings lay in the last half of May.

We have recorded the laying of 43 lapwings' eggs, at times between approximately 07.30–20.30, but have seldom seen any special behaviour. On 20 April 1959, however, an east Sutherland hen laid her second egg before 14.00; the cock then twice copulated with her and apparently became excited when he saw the second egg in the nest. He paused, made intention movements of brooding, then ran away and stood behind some rushes about 50 m from the nest; there he stayed for over an hour, periodically throwing bents over his shoulder.

Lapwings sometimes perform nest dances while there are one or two eggs in the nest. While laying, a hen sometimes tosses material; and she may brood incomplete clutches – particularly three eggs – at night. Hens also brood these eggs in heavy rain or hailstorm.

In some habitats many lapwings lay their eggs daily, but H. J. Beser (*in* Glutz 1975) and Klomp (1951) record that a full clutch is usually completed in five days. B. Laven (1941) noted that intervals of over two days between eggs were probably due to disturbance. G. L. Rinkel (1940) measured the laying intervals of 20 clutches; 13 hens laid their fourth and final egg on the seventh and two on the tenth days.

The Dorback groups, nesting about 360 m ASL, usually laid at intervals of 30–48 hours, but a few laid out in five days; three hens laid daily, completing their clutches on the fourth day. In 1975, Patrick found that one Sutherland hen took six days to lay the last two eggs in a c/3, and a second hen five days to produce her last three eggs; a third had a gap of three days between the third and fourth egg. Three other hens took four, five and six days respectively to complete their clutches. There are occasionally even longer laying intervals. In normal weather in Berkshire, for example, E. P. Chance (1930) noted a lapse of over a week between the laying of the second and third eggs.

Eggs are normally pear-shaped and unglossed. Ground colour ranges from olive, khaki and umber-brown to clay or stone-colour and, uncommonly, off-white. The eggs are blotched, capped, spotted, streaked, speckled and exceptionally dusted with black; some have zones at the heavy end. Rare types are blue, bluish-white, greenish-blue, dark or pea green or reddish-brown to light pink. In erythristic eggs, red-brown markings replace the normal black. After severe weather hens sometimes drop thin-shelled, blue to bluish-white eggs, sparsely speckled with black.

Although many outstanding types and varieties of lapwings' eggs have been recorded, these are rare. Francis Jourdain had a drawer of marvellous clutches, with reds, pinks, greens and blues; but many collectors for over half-a-century had contributed to his show of treasures.

Several ornithologists have measured lapwings' eggs. A hundred British eggs averaged 47.09×33.71 mm (Jourdain 1940). There are slight geographical variations. 1,097 eggs from Switzerland had a mean of 46.2×33.2 mm (J. Heim 1975); and 581 eggs from Leipzig averaged 46.1×33.2 mm (K. Grössler *in* Glutz 1975). J. Heim (*in* Glutz 1975) found that eggs in repeat clutches are usually smaller than those which they have replaced. Schönwetter (1963) weighed the empty shells of 500 eggs which ranged from 1.12–1.8 gm (mean 1.55 gm).

The weight of four fresh eggs is only about 46% of the hen's body weight (Table 2); this may partly explain the ability of a hen lapwing to produce up to four replacement clutches. R. K. Murton and N. J. Westwood (1974) suggest that food taken in different habitats influences egg weights. Sixty-five eggs from clutches on arable farmlands in East Anglia averaged 27.55 gm, 54 from pasture 26.26 gm, and 66 from breck 25.42 gm.

Lapwings normally lay four, occasionally three, rarely two or five eggs. Clutches of 6–8 eggs are exceptional and usually a joint laying by two hens. However, de Jonge (1959) and Efteland (1968) recorded eight eggs in a nest without seeing two hens. W. P. Hellebrekers (1964) saw six chicks hatch in a clutch of seven; and in Westmorland R. M. Band watched a pair with seven chicks about 2–3 days old. Gordon Douglas (1960) found c/6 in Surrey, with only two lapwings on the territory. In the Dorback group three different hens laid c/5 in 1939; at least one of these hens laid c/5 in all five previous years. The tendency to lay five eggs in thus possibly hereditary. Table 4 gives clutchsize in different locations.

Lapwings are single-brooded, but if the first clutch is lost some hens lay up to four replacements. The first egg of a replacement clutch is laid in a new scrape, 5–7 days after the loss of the clutch. These replacements are usually laid in the original territory, within 50 m of the lost nest. Twenty-three hens, all of which had laid c/4, replaced them with 20/4, 3/3 (mean 3.87 eggs) (Klomp 1951).

INCUBATION

Steady incubation starts with or shortly before the last egg in the clutch. Sometimes, however, a lapse of 12 hours, or exceptionally two days, intervenes before incubation begins.

There is no special nest-relief ritual, other than irregular copulation; but sometimes a hen tosses material sideways as she walks away from the nest. Both sexes incubate, but the hen's share is much greater and she alone appears to sit at night. The cock's brooding spells seldom exceed $1–1\frac{1}{2}$ hours and often last only a few minutes. The cock sometimes leaves the eggs before the hen has finished feeding. J. C. Wickens

(1948) only once recorded a cock sitting on eggs in at least 100 observations; but B. Tully (1948) found quite different rhythms at two nets in Northumberland. At the first nest the hen sat for 8 hours 27 minutes, the cock for 2 hours 50 minutes. At the second the hen incubated for 2 hours 54 minutes and the cock for 2 hours 53 minutes.

In sheep country, where sitting lapwings are frequently disturbed, the birds are sometimes off the nest for at least a third of the daytime. If she is undisturbed, the hen often sits for 1–3 hours, but if the cock fails to relieve her she leaves the nest and feeds for 3–40 minutes. The cock occasionally calls off the hen, escorts her to the feeding ground, and then returns with her almost to the nest. Some cocks sit less towards the end of incubation and on late replacement clutches. J. Heim (1974) found that brooding spells were longest in mid incubation but that the embryos are exceptionally resistant to cold weather and intensive sunlight. B. Laven and Stiefel recorded that particular eggs successfully hatched although incubation had been abandoned for up to two days. Bolotnikov and colleagues (*in* Flint 1973) found that in three nests the average temperature was 33°, 35°, and 37.8°, with average maxima of 38.0°, 38.3°, and 40.7°; and average minima 29.2°, 28.0° and 34.0°. Brooding temperatures rise slightly in the later stages of incubation. Stiefel noticed that if a bird had been disturbed and kept off its nest for a long time it then tended to carry out abnormally long brooding stints. This, however, did not always apply to the groups on the Dorback Moor, where there was so much interaction between pairs on adjacent territories.

Light sitting, and long periods off the nest by day, partly account for long incubation periods. In northern Scotland we have measured 41 clutches which have ranged from 24.7–34 days (mean 28.1 ± 12 hours). Most of our observations, however, were carried out in sheep country, where the sitting lapwings are constantly disturbed. In Wales, J. F. Thomas (1939) measured 15 periods which varied from 26–29 days (mean 27.4 days). Spencer (1953) timed 11 English clutches which averaged 27.5 (±1 day). In Holland, Klomp gives an average of 27.1 days for six clutches and Heim 26.8 days for 22 clutches.

Lapwings continue to incubate eggs long after the normal period of incubation. In 1943 a hen brooded a clutch, which was reduced to a single egg, for 88 days. Even then it did not desert the nest; the last egg was robbed by a rook. In the last weeks the cock had deserted her and the territory.

HATCHING

Some chicks start to squeak in the eggs at least four days before they hatch; the parents now call to them. They also use the 'all clear call' when returning to the nest after being disturbed. When the chick is emerging, the brooding lapwing – usually the hen – stands up and calls to it. The cock now also tends to squat close to the nest while the hen is acting as midwife.

In northern Scotland chipping periods have ranged from 36 (±2) to 96 (±9) hours in a sample of 31; those of 18 clutches lasted approximately 49–60 hours. Heim (1974) recorded that these periods in Germany varied from 2–6 days (mean 2.9 days). In England R. H. Brown (1946) measured five periods, ranging from 18–50 hours.

There are fascinating patterns of eggshell disposal. The sitting bird often lifts and flies away with large fragments of shell, drops them at any distance from 50–200 m, then turns and flies back to the nest. Sometimes, however, a lapwing alights, teases and possibly eats some of the shell. They deal in the same way with their own eggshells, or with those of domestic fowl, or of other species experimentally placed in or beside the nest during incubation.

Lapwings deliberately bury and hide small pieces of shell under the nest lining, thus enabling the observer to determine from an empty scoop whether a particular clutch has successfully hatched. There are, however, exceptions to these patterns. Brunhilde Laven watched a hen run away with a large piece of shell which she carefully hid in the herbage; and G. Charteris watched another disappear with a large fragment in its beak.

Addled or unhatched eggs are left in the nest; but lapwings have another method of dealing with damaged or broken eggs. In May 1942 a Dorback pair persistently mobbed a ewe and lamb which had approached their nest. The cock swept down and pecked both beasts, while the hen alternately raised her wings or lay on the ground flapping them. Before they had deflected the sheep, however, the lamb trod on the eggs. Immediately the cock went to the nest and flew away with a fragment of one of the broken eggs; this he dropped and then teased on the ground. The pair then rapidly removed and ate all the pieces of the broken eggs, including the well-formed embryos; within five minutes, the hen was again sitting.

In Culrain, between 1975–79, Patrick and Richard recorded 58 nests. Of these, 36 (62.1%) containing 144 eggs produced 97 chicks. The rest failed. Jackdaws and other predators accounted for 13 (22.4%), a mole for 1 (1.7%), and snow and severe weather for the remaining 8 (13.8%).

At Wangerooge, Germany, G. Grosskopf (1968) recorded that 594 eggs produced 485 chicks (81.6%); 12.5% of the eggs were robbed and 4.5% failed to hatch.

In a long-term study on farmlands in Switzerland, 1,021 chicks hatched from 1,803 eggs (56.2%). Farming operations destroyed 113 eggs (6.7%), other hazards 424 (23.5%), 207 eggs (11.5%) were deserted and 38 (21.0%) were infertile (Heim 1974).

YOUNG

Lapwing chicks have crowns mottled with greyish-brown and black and there is an irregular black line below, but not reaching, the eye. Nape, chin and throat are white, thus forming a white collar. The upper mantle is mottled with grey-brown, black and white; breast and underparts are white, with a black gorget above them. The bill is black, iris dark brown, but feet and legs vary from lead or slate-grey to greyish-pink; not the bright pink shown in several handbooks. Heim weighed 171 newly-hatched chicks which ranged from 14–21 gm (mean 17.1 gm) (Table 5).

The chicks can run soon after they are dry; but the older ones often stay in, or return to, the nest scoop for eight or more hours after they are capable of leaving it. If the last chick hatches in the evening, the parents usually brood all chicks in the scoop before leading them away in the morning. In severe weather in east Sutherland the chicks were recalled to the deserted scoop and were still there 41 hours after the last one had hatched.

On the Continent, however, adults sometimes quickly lead away their chicks, particularly when the nests are sited on flats with unsuitable heights of vegetation. Heim found that three chicks, about $8\frac{1}{2}$ hours old, had moved 200 m; and C. Imboden (1968)

recorded a day-old chick crossing a small canal 700 m from its birthplace. In another locality chicks covered 1,200 m in three days.

For most of the rearing period both parents accompany their chicks. The hen usually tends, warns, and leads them, while the cock feeds and stays on guard at some distance from the family. The hen regularly broods them for about a week and up to the twelfth day in severe weather; we have also seen cocks brood chicks during heavy rain and hail showers. The hen covers them for at least a fortnight at night. She leads her young over small ditches, stone walls, and other obstacles, flying to and fro and calling to urge them on. For the first four or five hours the chicks peck at and step over moving insects or other objects; they avoid ground beetles until they are about 14 days old (Glutz 1975).

When the parent gives warning cries, small chicks soon learn to squat or crouch but they often rise and run away before the danger has gone. Older chicks are more conscious of danger and more obedient to their parents' warnings; they squat for longer spells, but often end by rising and running away before 'freezing' again. Richard Perry (*pers comm*) watched lapwing chicks swimming strongly in their first 24 hours, and J. Ash (1948) saw a parent try to lift and carry a chick over a ditch.

Rearing patterns vary considerably. Some cocks, particularly those escorting late broods, desert their mates and territories before the young are free-flying. On the other hand, we have sometimes seen cocks leading and escorting large young after the hens had disappeared.

The young lapwings take a variable time to make their first flights, perhaps due to differences in the quality of the feeding habitats. We have made two fairly precise measurements. A single survivor of a late brood in the Dorback group first flew on its 39th day; and in 1958 the two survivors of a brood of four in east Sutherland flew on their 30th or 31st days. Heim recorded young lapwings flying between 35–40 days (*in* Glutz 1975); and Steifel watched a fledgling take off and flutter weakly on its 29th day. In Cumberland, Brown had records of 30 and 31 days; in Caernarvon, Thomas, and in Germany, Laven, recorded young lapwings first flying after 33 days. In Cheshire, on the other hand, S. S. Bates (1948) watched one make its first flight on its 42nd day.

In their study of population changes in the New Forest, Hampshire, in 1971–79, R. and J. Jackson (1980) found that newly-hatched chicks needed moist habitats in which to feed and to gain weight satisfactorily. In these groups fledging periods varied from 37–38 days in 1971–75, 50 days in 1976–78, but only 32–33 days in 1979.

Before most of the young are fledged and independent, small flocks already exist; these are probably composed of mature birds which have lost their eggs, or young together with mature or first-year birds which have failed to win mates. Rinkel (1940) considered that these groups formed the spearhead of the movement away from the breeding grounds. Parent birds, and their free-flying young, form late flocks and parties of 200 or more, which then go to the lower ground in late summer and early autumn. Later, other large flocks are made up of birds of the year. Perry recorded that his groups were on the water meadows and links beside the Spey from mid July to mid September. Finally, the lapwings depart for their winter quarters which are often on the coastlands.

DISTRACTION BEHAVIOUR

Lapwings' distraction displays are uncommon but sometimes elaborate. With raised and fully spread banners the sitting bird may run from its nest, almost to the feet or muzzles of feeding cows, sheep or lambs which are about to tread on the nest. These displays usually divert but do not stampede the mammals. Early and late in incubation we have seen a hen display against dogs and humans, squatting on a tussock less than 30 m from the nest and then stretching and shaking one wing and raising and lowering the other. One hen continued to squat until I was only 3–4 m away; then she crawled to about 5 m, fanning her tail and drooping her wings before lying flat with expanded and extended wings. Another displayed at a rabbit!

In twilight lapwings appear to treat humans as they would sheep or deer; a cock may now raise one wing and stretch and flap the other. These displays are particularly directed at cyclists. Other distraction behaviour in the half-light of late evening occasionally includes the rapid 'mammal run' in which the cock or hen runs rapidly from the nest. At other times, instead of flying away and wheeling about crying peevishly, the lapwing makes a short series of flights to lure away the predators. H. Lynes (1910) watched one running along, flapping its wings, a ploy which enticed a stoat over 400 m. Displacement feeding is another form of distraction; the bird goes through the motions of feeding exceptionally fast as it approaches its nest.

Cock lapwings often use a creaky call as if to warn the chicks; and then they run a few metres and rise in heavy flapping flight, calling excitedly, just as if flushed from a brood.

EGG-RETRIEVAL

In 1941–42 and in 1946 I carried out some tests to discover how lapwings reacted to unusual situations. I removed one or more of their eggs and placed these, along with 'egg objects' (small coloured wooden spheres, cubes and cylinders), 15–23 cm from the centre of the nests. Cocks and hens both retrieved their own eggs by rolling

them back between the undersides of their beaks and the upper breast. If the egg was within reach of the sitting bird it half-rose, extended its neck, and then rolled the egg back into the cup. If the egg was beyond its reach it retrieved it by means of several distinct movements. One hen, however, failed to retrieve two eggs which were placed beside her scoop.

Eggs were preferred to wooden spheres, spheres to cubes, and cubes to cylinders. Some birds retrieved but later ejected the foreign objects. At one nest the lapwings first concealed a wooden cylinder under the nest lining, but later ejected it. The most discriminating birds ejected all the introduced items.

I also tested the lapwings' reaction, during incubation, to the introduction of their own eggshells and those of other species. Almost every lapwing removed the shells, flying away and dropping them up to 200 m away. One hen flew to a favourite feeding place where she dropped the eggshell and then fed, prising out earthworms. When one of its own eggs, a pheasant's egg, and a large fragment of a domestic fowl's eggshell, were placed 15 cm from the centre of the scoop, the returning hen retrieved its own egg, but ignored the other two items; when flushed a second time it flew off with the eggshell; but it twice ignored the pheasant's egg. A second lapwing, faced with the same situation, hooked in her own and the pheasant's egg, but at first did not deal with the piece of eggshell. On being flushed, however, she returned and this time lifted and flew off with the shell fragment. The pieces of eggshell and the pheasant's egg were ignored when placed on a stone 5 cm above the level of the nest.

VOICE

(1) *Song and song flight*
The lapwing has a most evocative and haunting song flight. Rising with a few slow deep wing flaps, the cock quickly throws himself through the air in a series of exhilarating aerobatics; and he may repeat the performance twice or more before alighting on his territory. A lovely thrumming wing music accompanies the corkscrew phases when the bird swings madly from side to side. It sounds like *pwee-eee-weep*, then *wup wup wup* (wing music) and finally *pee-ee-eet wiluc-oo-wee*.

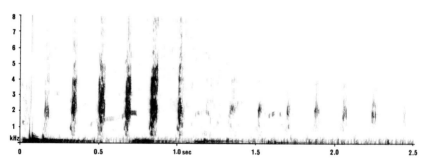

Lapwing, wing music of cock, Inverness-shire (Bill Sinclair)

In his analysis, Torben Dabelsteen (1978) describes a normal full song flight as having a sequence of seven phases: Butterfly Flight – Alternating Fight – Low Flight – Ascent – High Flight – Vertical Dive – Alternating Flight; with the Ascent and High Flying and Vertical Dives connected with separate song phrases.

'The Butterfly Flight seems to originate from the ordinary take off, while the Alternating flight originates from more or less aggressively motivated behaviour like fast take-off, chase flight and agitated flight, which normally occur as predator reactions and purely agonistic behaviour. Dives of type 1 and 2 have evolved from an attack dive. The origin of Low Flight is obscure. The Ascent may originate from the aggressive ascent to an air fight with other males. The origin of the High Flight is obscure. The Vertical Dive originates from an attack dive and the evolution has gone further than in the drive of the Alternating Flight'. The lapwing's song flight may thus give several different kinds of information simultaneously.

A variation shows the cock flying rapidly and giving the first two phases of the song. He also sometimes sings while on the ground in his arena, but his rendering is then much quieter and less audible from a distance. The peak of song flight activity occurs during the pairing and egg-laying phases. Thenceforward, singing steadily declines and almost ceases when the young are hatched and the territory is deserted.

(2) *Social contact calls*
(a) A loud rather wheezy *pee-wit* or *pee-wee*. Lapwings give this call in and outside the breeding season, and at night.
(b) A longer *pee-yee*, in rising pitch, is used as an alarm call. Single birds use it as do flocks in their roosts and resting places. A lapwing often calls in this way while making a short flight to re-join the flock.
(c) A flock or group join in a 'whining chorus' *pee-jee-pee-jee-wee-wee*. Groups of lapwings 'whine' when standing in the roost or just after putting down after a short flight (E. V. Cawkell 1949).
They also use a rather similar loud *pee-ee-a* which is repeated and used as an anxiety call in combination with (b).

(3) *Fear and anxiety calls*
(a) A loud *pee-ee-a*, continuously repeated, is used as an anxiety call in combination with 2(b).
(b) In slight anxiety situations lapwings give a rather thin but emphatic *pee-wip*, with strong emphasis on the first syllable. This call is not restricted to the breeding season. Chicks do not react to these calls.
(c) The alarm cry in flight is a loud and repeated *pee-eee-ir-ee-ir*, with the emphasis usually on the first syllable.
(d) During lure or distraction displays a lapwing sometimes gives wheezing cries. At other times is uses one of its normal cries.

(4) *Sex calls*
(a) In the early phases of display and sex-dances, a cock gives the scratchy *ur-ur-ur* while standing or running in the flock; he later uses this call during nest-dancing. Cocks give these calls at night as well as in daylight.
(b) Cocks in the arena give rather soft chittering cries while nest dancing and accompanying copulation.
(c) During nest dances, particularly when the sex rhythms of cock and hen do not synchronise, either bird may call a peevish *pee-wee*.

(5) *Nest call*
The hen calls *pee-wa* when she is about to leave the nest. Her mate then sometimes answers with the same call.

(6) *Calls to chicks*
(a) Chicks react to parent's soft *pee* call by freezing on the ground.

(b)   A soft *pee-wi*, a variation of the standard social call (3a) is used as the all-clear cry to the chicks. Stiefel (1961) records the hen calling and moaning *du-du-du* to the chicks. Matter (*in* Glutz 1975) describes these calls as *di-wu-di-wiu-di-wiu.*

(c)   Distraction cries sound hoarse and coughing.

(7)   *Chick calls*

(a)   While the chicks are hatching, the parent gives soft *pee* sounds. The chicks themselves have soft squeaks while in the egg. Later, when the chick is out of the nest, these soft squeaks are audible at a short distance.

(b)   Well-grown chicks give shrill screaming cries when in danger and in the absence of their parents.

(8)   *Anger calls*

Adults give loud ringing *pee-it-wai-owi* when attacking predators near the nest.

PREDATORS

Hooded and carrion crow, jackdaw, rook, common, herring and black-headed gulls, all rob lapwings' nests and sometimes kill chicks. Merlin, peregrine, sparrowhawk, and occasionally hen harrier, kill adults and sometimes take chicks. Fox, stoat, weasel and sheep dogs, and sometimes moles and hedgehogs, are other mammals which prey on eggs and chicks.

R. D. Elliot (1982) used experiments to discover that lapwings relied on active group defence against less dangerous predators like crows, and that they were favoured by nesting in groups or clumps, and passively through the dispersion of cryptic nests to reduce predation by more dangerous predators like the fox. They also avoided placing nests close to trees, particularly those in which crows were nesting.

FOOD

Feeding lapwings run a few yards, pause, tilt stiffly forward without bending their legs, and peck, pick and patter.

In south Sweden, Högstedt (1974) found that earthworms were the most important food while the hens were preparing to lay their eggs. 'The length of the pre-laying period was highly and negatively correlated with the abundance of Lumbricidae'. A comparable study in moorland and other marginal habitats would help to show whether this pattern is universal. While studying shelduck on the Clyde estuary and mudflats, during the severe winter of 1978–9, Bruin found that from December to February the lapwings particularly favoured tiny invertebrates, including the ragworm *Nereis diversicolor* and the small shrimp *Corophium volutator*. Towards mid February they leapfrogged over one another and some fed in pairs. Patrick, who studied lapwings on the Clyde estuary in the winter of 1980–81, noticed that in very hard frost they took the crustacean *Gammarus duebeni* from tidal debris as well as *N. diversicolor* and *C. volutator*.

Lapwings wintering on old pastureland in central England took mainly bill-sized earthworms (D. B. A. Thompson and C. Barnard 1984). Bruin found a strong positive relationship between lapwing flock-size and earthworm density. Golden plovers used lapwing flock-size and density to indicate the best place to start feeding.

Glutz (1975) has shown that lapwings feed on beetles and their larvae (Carabidae, Dytischidae, Hydrophilidae, Curculionidae, Chrysomelidae, Tenebrionidae, Cerambycidae, Byrrhidae, Scarabaeidae, Staphylinidae, Elateridae); ants (Formicidae) and larvae of other Hymenoptera, hover flies (Trichoptera), mayflies (Ephemeroptera); larvae of

Diptera, particularly craneflies Tipulidae; crickets and grasshoppers (Orthoptera), earwigs Dermaptera, spiders (Araneae), millipedes Myriopoda, woodlice Isopoda; moths (Lepidoptera), especially Noctuidae larvae; earthworms (particularly Lumbricidae); and small terrestrial and freshwater snails. Lapwings occasionally take small frogs and fishes and there is a record of one taking a jellyfish (Discomeduseae).

Seeds and grains of various farmland plants, including cereals and large quantities of maize and millet, have been recorded. Seeds of *Polygonum*, *Ranunculus*, *Spergula*, and bits of grass, moss and algae are also consumed. Most stomachs contain a number of small stones. In the stomachs were slightly digested worms and the indigestible remains of insects (especially beetles, *e.g.* Carabidae and Curculionidae). They take polychaetes (*e.g. Nereis diversicolor*) on mudflats and occasionally crustaceans and small molluscs on the seashore.

The stomach of a particular bird may contain a great number of one kind of insects, *e.g.* 139 *Tipula* larvae (Fallet 1962); 240 Dermaptera *Forficula* (K. H. Voous 1962).

There are records of chicks eating small white butterflies *Pieris rapae*, larvae of yellow underwinged moths *Noctua pronuba* and those of cabbage flies *Anthomya brassica*. Chicks are also recorded taking small black flies, wireworms *Agriotes* and an earthworm (R. H. Brown 1936). G. L. Boyle (1956) also watched a young lapwing of about a fortnight old taking tadpoles from a pool.

DISTRIBUTION AND NUMBERS

In the last 40 years lapwings have decreased in many parts of England and Wales, particularly in traditional habitats on the farmlands of southern England, where only small groups have survived from the very large pre-war colonies. They are scarce, but not entirely absent, in central Essex and in parts of south-west Suffolk, and are very scarce or do not nest in many parts of Pembroke and Cornwall. Fewer pairs also now nest on the rough marginal land or on hill farms about 300 m ASL in central and north Wales.

They are widely distributed in the north of England, but there, as in other parts of Britain, new methods of farming, conversion of pasture to arable, drainage and cultivation of rough pasture on marshland fringes, have greatly reduced and sometimes eradicated many good breeding haunts.

Lapwings have a fairly wide pattern of distribution in Ireland but there are some unoccupied 10 km squares in the midlands; and they are missing from much of the west and south-west. J. T. R. Sharrock (1976) records that they breed chiefly on marginal land and moorland edges where they are often associated with redshanks.

Many breeding groups were decimated, or they entirely disappeared from many haunts, in Scotland after the hard winters of 1941–42, 1946–47, 1962–63 and 1977–79. In Sutherland the lapwing population suffered particularly severely from the winter of 1962–63. There are many large groups in Easter Ross, both on marginal land on the lower hills and on the coastlands and saltmarshes. But in other parts, as in north-west Ross, there are none. This is partly due to the wet and rocky habitat which lacks mixed pasture and arable land. Worked crofts and old grasslands beside moorland edges, however, carry small colonies. Lapwings sometimes settle in fresh habitats, as in our north-west Sutherland study area; but these pioneering groups often disappear within a few years.

The overall picture in Britain is quite favourable, although little-understood climatic changes, with their possible influence of food, need further study. Between 1968–72 *The Breeding Atlas* observers recorded lapwings in 3,264 10 km squares (86%) in Britain and Ireland, with confirmed breeding in 2,814 squares (85%); probable breeding in

279 (9%); and possible breeding in 171 (5%). In 1972 the BTO Common Birds Census, directed by Ken Williamson, showed that there was an average of 3.4 pairs/km^2 on the farmland habitats investigated. One-fifth of this density, on all occupied 10 km squares, suggested a possible breeding population of 200,000 pairs in Britain and Ireland (Sharrock 1976).

This compares with an estimated 4,000 breeding pairs in France; a minimum of 4,000 pairs in Belgium; 1,500 pairs in Austria; over 2,000 pairs in Luxemburg; 125,000–165,000 in the Netherlands; 80,000–100,000 in West Germany, but with no firm estimate for East Germany. Switzerland had at least 730 pairs in 1970, with 13 new breeding haunts discovered by 1973. The declining Danish population is estimated at about 50,000 pairs; and the increasing Norwegian groups at 58,000 in 1981. There were about 120,000 pairs in Sweden in 1976; but possibly only about 26,000 pairs in Finland in 1958. (Cramp and Simmons 1983).

MOVEMENTS

Lapwings prefer a maritime to a continental climate. In Britain and Ireland, where they are partial migrants, they occupy their most northerly regular winter grounds although a few winter in West Germany and Denmark. Most wintering groups are found in the western maritime countries (British Isles and Netherlands to Spain and Portugal), on both sides of the Mediterranean, in wetter parts of the Middle East, and eastwards across the Oriental region.

In Britain some lapwings winter quite close to their nesting areas, but in the most severe winters many British and Low Country birds move south to south-west, some reaching North Africa and others crossing the North Sea and the English mainland to Ireland, whence they do not return until the usual period of spring passage.

A huge movement of lapwings overshot Ireland in 1927, with many hundreds success-fully flying the Atlantic and reaching Newfoundland and Labrador (Cramp and Simmons 1983).

Lapwings have a strong *ortstreue*. About 70% of winter survivors return to within 20 km of where they were hatched, thus possibly enabling pioneers to settle in new and attractive habitats and to restore or maintain numbers in suboptimal locations (Imboden 1974).

Surely one of our most exciting birds, the lapwing is a beautiful flyer with almost as many stunts at its command as a crack aviator. It is a fighter, always ready to challenge rival or predator. Less aggressive species nest close to it, almost seeking its protection. Still happily familiar to most of us, the lapwing survives in many different haunts. Those mournful cries, with the magic of its wing music, express the eternal spirit of the farmlands and the moorland edges.

5:   Moors and heathlands

In March and early April, with the pungent scent of peat reek and its blue-grey smoke rolling up corries and hollows of distant hills, our moors are exciting and attractive places. On the heather, red grouse beck, chuckle and strut, challenging one another; everywhere curlews are bubbling, and no Highland moor is ever complete without the mournful cries and wailing songs of golden plovers. The rare whimbrel, with its lovely silvery titter, is chiefly found on the grass-heath of Fetlar, Unst and Yell in Shetland. But our family has had the joy of watching them on a mainland firth where there are also curlews, snipe, lapwings, redshanks and dunlin; an assortment of groups and colonies of gulls and terns add to the clamour.

Leafing over our notebooks, we recall that each of our study areas has been subtly different. From the small lime-washed shieling on the Dorback Moor, on lovely days of bright sunshine, the surrounding moor was full of unforgettable sounds and sights. This was an outstanding grouse moor and a grand haunt of waders. In the 1930s and early 1940s golden plovers nested on the heathery flats and on ridges of low, rounded and dumpy hills. Curlews laid their large olive and red-brown blotched eggs in the open heather but seldom on the hill tops; they favoured rather taller patches of heather and sometimes used grassy hollows on the open moor or sheltered places close to stagnant burns.

A few well-separated pairs of redshanks were members of this moorland community. In 1935 a redshank and a golden plover nested barely 10 m apart in a small flow above the river. Snipe favoured wet hollows; in the evening the cocks quavered and bleated above mire and moor. Although most lapwings were concentrated on the edges and on the farm fields, some nested on the moor; in 1939 a lapwing laid her eggs in a nest bowl which the goldies had used in the previous year. Solitary woodcocks regularly chose adjacent belts of birch in which to nest. The roding flights of the cock often passed far over the moor and occasionally an eccentric hen laid her eggs quite far out in the heather. Common sandpipers wickered and flew their bat-flights where moor and river came together.

The waders had many neighbours on this moor. The small inconspicuous brown meadow pipit was the dominant bird in numbers, as in all parts of moorland Britain. Skylarks rose and sang above, and the hens made their nests in, short heather or on grassy edges. Wheatears bobbed in and out of the rabbit holes in which they later nested. More sheltered nooks close to the river were the choice of teal and mallard. This was not prime ring ouzel country, but high up on the crags and broken hillsides a few cocks piped beautifully in the evening and morning mists.

Few predators survived the gamekeepers. A pair of merlins sometimes laid their red-brown eggs in old hooded crows' nests in small stunted pines or on slopes carpeted by rank heather, but they seldom escaped. Kestrels, nesting in a rocky pass leading into the deer forest, were similarly persecuted. Wily hooded crows sneaked in and out to nests in clumps of pines in Abernethy Forest; and they regularly found and sucked curlews' and golden plovers' eggs on the nearby moor.

The attractive clearings west of Loch Morlich were quite different. In the 1930s solitary pairs of golden plovers nested in the forest-bogs and oystercatchers occasionally laid their eggs on bare patches of burnt heath. Before the heather grew tall and rank and the young trees sprang up, common sandpipers nested close to the few lochans. Curlews shared these haunts with the wonderful groups of greenshanks which have now disappeared.

While waiting for the homing flights of greenshanks, I sometimes watched brilliant scarlet Scottish pine crossbills lilt over forest and clearing to feed hens and broods in nests high up in the old pines. In openings close to river and loch, cock siskins, flying in exaggerated loops and circles, sang and fluttered with fanned tails above the trees. Blackcocks had leks on the clearings. In early morning and evening you also heard great cock capercaillies sneezing in their own leks on paths and openings among the trees. There were stonechats on heathery edges and whinchats in grassy places among burnt patches of juniper.

Here, sparrowhawk, kestrel and hooded crows were the chief predators. In 1956 a pair of ospreys sat on eggs in a great raft of sticks not far from the heathery clearings. In the 1960s goshawks nested successfully. Foxes skulked to their earths and herds of red deer, and solitary roe deer, often browsed in the evening.

In the early 1960s we camped in an old and dilapidated croft house in a lonely glen in south-east Sutherland. To the delight of the children, a pair of pied wagtails nested on a shelf upstairs and there were starlings in the chimney. Outside, on old grasslands, golden plovers fed morning and evening and roosted by night. There were sheep browsing and sometimes stags from the deer forest joined them on the pasture.

Here there are small gently-sloping hills with rock-studded slopes on which green-shanks occasionally breed; and dunlins sometimes nest in the blanket bogs. Lower down, skylarks perfectly mimic greenshanks and dunlins, often sending the bewildered hunter in the wrong direction. Golden plovers are the dominant waders, nesting all over the moors in moderate numbers and sometimes in grass-heath close to the old crofts. There are probably about ten pairs of goldies to each pair of greenshank.

Twite, wheatear, skylark and meadow pipits breed in high numbers. A few hoodies make their bulky well-hidden nests in clumps of small trees or on rocks on the higher ground. A buzzard often, and a golden eagle occasionally, sails overhead. In 'vole years' short-eared owls pitch on old stumps or fences. Foxes are the main mammal predators. Adders slide through the heathers; we all vividly remember the day when the keeper killed one just outside the cottage.

Golden plovers have very different neighbours in north-west Sutherland. One year they nested within 50 m of a greenshank which ultimately deserted its nest, leaving the plover in control then and in the next two years; but we never saw the two waders fighting. Common sandpipers nest on the edges of the blanket bog close to the river. Dunlins, 'the plover's page', lay their eggs in wetter flows, usually those having a complex of small pools; we often watched the dunlins following the goldies. There are a few red grouse and many meadow pipits in these plover territories. The snipe is usually a grassland nesting species here, but golden plovers are sometimes their neighbours. Greenshanks generally nest on rougher ground full of stones, boulders and pools. And in our long wader watches we have sometimes been delighted by red-throated divers flying into their tarns with a roar of wings and giving those evocative, wailing cries which are the very spirit of the flowlands.

In some ways the squat, dumpy hills of Orkney Mainland are the most exciting moorlands in all Britain. In the early 'thirties there were fine mosses where goldies nested in Harray at exceptionally high density. Curlews bred in fair numbers in dips and hollows. Now there are fewer goldies and far more curlews. There were many dunlins on the mosses, but these lovely waders can hardly be described as typical moorland birds.

The Orkney moors have long been famous for other birds beside waders. Now, as in the 'thirties, they carry a higher population and a greater density of hen harriers than in any other part of Britain. Short-eared owls, merlins, and, in some parts, ground-nesting kestrels, are among the predators of the moorland birds. Shelducks, and even wood pigeons, nest in cracks and hollows in the heather. Twites sing on the edges, but the ubiquitous meadow pipit is still the dominant passerine. Great moorland colonies of great black-backed and lesser black-backed gulls, as well as herring gulls, nest on the heather on some of the hills. On some Orkney moorlands, with Hoy still the main redoubt, bonxies and arctic skuas nest in good numbers. In the 'thirties corn buntings almost continuously jingled and corncrakes rasped in fields on the moorland edges; now both have disappeared or almost disappeared from the Orkney List.

The moors and grass-heaths of Shetland offer an equally exciting challenge. Whimbrels and curlews nest in particularly good numbers on Unst and Fetlar, with the whimbrels usually holding territories higher up the hill and the curlews occupying rushy croftlands and dips and hollows at lower level. Nowhere is there a better opportunity for studying the relationships of these two grand waders.

I first watched curlews in Surrey, where the commons grow on tertiary deposits. These fine heathlands have many bogs and fine breaks of gorse. Birches and pines grow around them and on some commons there are lines, clumps, and belts of solitary pines, in the valleys and on the hillsides. The curlews have quite different neighbours than those in northern England and Scotland. During April I used to watch woodlarks on dry patches of short heath, while the curlews were bubbling and joy-flying over the mires. How beautifully those woodlarks sang on soft evenings; and how thrilling to track down the pairs and at last watch the hen drop into the heath, with the little cock woodlark singing a soft sub-song from a nearby pine stump. On windless sunny days cock Dartford warblers song-danced and sneezed over the gorse; and hens, with stuff in their beaks, deftly plunged through the spiky bushes. Then, in May, I would sit on a bank and watch the fantastic aerobatics of courting hobbies or see them chase and catch dragonflies over the mires. In the evening, nightjars reeled and challenged all over the edges, seemingly changing gear in their churring. On the common, where I found my first curlew's nest, I saw a pair of wrynecks change over at a ragged hole in an ancient pine on the highest ridge of the common.

GOLDEN PLOVER

My first impression of the golden plover was in Orkney, in May 1932. I had just met John Douglas, a remarkable self-taught birdwatcher, who knew more about Orkney birds than anyone else of his time. We set out to visit hen harrier ground in the brown hills above his farm. On our way, he paused to show me a group of golden plovers nesting on his holding; their plaintive whistles were all around us. Striding slowly over the moss, Douglas showed me four nests in about 4 ha – a marvellous introduction to a grand wader. Yet I soon discovered that on the higher grass-heaths in Orkney golden plovers nested much further apart, usually with 400–500 m, and sometimes more, between their nests. The rough pasture around the farm must have had a great attraction for the goldies. When I returned to Orkney in 1971 I found that his wonderful moss, along with many others, had been drained, ploughed and re-seeded. Indeed, without a map, I would never have located the farm.

Back at Forsinard, in Sutherland, I watched small groups of golden plovers feeding on grassland pasture beside the hotel. In the evening some of these birds flew high up into the hills, or far away onto the flows; others apparently flew back to replace them. But I had little understanding of what was happening. I had come to Sutherland to hunt for greenshanks; these were my magnet. But in many greenshank haunts in the immense flows I met with goldies and had the good fortune to find a couple of nests by flushing the birds. One nest was in a typical greenshank place, with the eggs beside a large stone in a hollow on a stony flow.

My next memory of golden plovers was in Invereshie Forest, in mid April 1934, when I watched a cock sky-playing above a large and barren moor. High above the peat mosses and stunted heather he wailed his song *o-deah-o-deah*, as he slowly beat the bounds of his living-space.

Golden plovers are handsome birds, with short straight bills, gold and black spangled mantles, black underparts and belly. There are two races. The southern race *apricaria* is the predominant race in Britain. Nests of genuine *altifrons* are few and mainly restricted to the Cairngorms. The cock has a jet-black face and belly, with the distinctive white stripes running from forehead to flank. In 1979 Patrick watched a black-fronted bird of the northern type nesting on the dotterel grounds in the Drumochter hills. In the southern race the cheeks are sooty-black, the band from forehead to flank is often obscure, and the belly mixed with white and gold. There are, however, many different variations. Some *apricaria* males are very black in face, cheeks and belly; but the white band is the most important distinction.

The southern race *apricaria* regularly nests in Britain and Ireland, southern Scandinavia, south Finland, Baltic USSR, Denmark; and there are still a few pairs in West Germany. The northern *altifrons* is the dominant race. In greater numbers and with a more extensive range it breeds in north USSR, Norway and Sweden, Finnish Lapland, Iceland, Faroes, and occasionally in Spitsbergen.

Since the 1950s golden plovers have greatly declined, particularly on the southern fringes of their range – west England, Wales, Ireland, Belgium, Netherlands, West and East Germany, Poland, Denmark and south Norway. The causes are not precisely known, but probably an improvement in the climate, afforestation, and re-claiming of peatlands have contributed.

Golden plovers prefer flat or gently sloping ground, with short vegetation usually containing a few mounds, rocks, or hummocks as look-out posts. This habitat gives maximum visibility and enables the chicks to feed and run more easily than would longer and ranker vegetation.

Arthur Whitaker found that some golden plovers on the Derbyshire moors favoured blackened newly-burnt patches of heather, but this only occasionally happens in the Scottish Highlands. From 1935 onwards, on the Dorback and Revack Moors, and on the edges of Abernethy Forest, the goldies chose burnt heather moor and low, gently sloping hills with large tracts of grass-heath. A few isolated pairs also then nested in the forest bogs and edges of Rothiemurchus and Inshriach. In these years, in my study area on the Dorback Moor, golden plovers occasionally laid their eggs within 200 m of the cottage. In the western Cairngorms there were also large groups on Am Moine Mhor and on the slopes and flats of the fringe moss. The goldies were often neighbours of dotterel and ptarmigan on different habitats from those in the valley. This ground is not unlike the rounded tops and bumps of the East Drumochter in the central Grampians, where the golden plovers share ground with dotterel, dunlin and ptarmigan.

Golden plovers have always been present in our greenshank study areas in north, north-west and south-east Sutherland. Here we have learnt that the goldies nest at higher density in the drier grass-heaths of the south and south-east than in the vast blanket bogs and rocky flows of the north-west. Everywhere the goldies have given us much joy and many problems. From 1964 we have particularly studied their relationship and niches with the greenshank, as well as with those of dunlin, common sandpiper, snipe and lapwing.

Our friend Hugh Blair found golden plovers among pines in Sydvaranger; and S. Haftorn (1971) records nests on the edges of sub-alpine birch forest. In southern Norway, however, Ingvar Byrkjedal (*in litt* to Blair), found that very few pairs now nest close to isolated trees on the edges of forests. This is possibly because predators often favour isolated trees as look-out or hunting posts. Certainly the groups nesting on the edges of Abernethy Forest were frequently robbed by hoodie crows which sometimes found the nests by watching the birds.

Golden plovers are the first waders to return to the moors. In open springs they are back in mid February or even earlier, the males making their lovely advertisement flights in the group as well as singly. In early April I have seen a mixed party of 15 goldies, in which seven or eight cocks simultaneously started flapping and wailing high in the air, all the while singing their rippling songs.

By colour ringing some of the golden plovers in his Kincardine study group, Ray Parr (1980) discovered that some birds stayed together in the winter packs and arrived as pairs on their breeding grounds; the same two birds sometimes stayed paired for six or more consecutive years. In these groups many birds mated and nested successfully when they were only about 10–11 months old.

Each year, in Dorback, new pairs were formed on the surrounding farmlands. Single cocks then moved out of the groups and suddenly took wing, cleaving through the air with slowly flapping wings and singing plaintive *o-deeahs* high above. A sudden spurt of quick flying often followed spasms of song dancing before the singer flashed downwards, flying rapidly a few metres above the ground before re-joining its fellows. From time to time, a cock singled out a hen and, with rounded back, chased her until she flew. Or head, body and tail parallel to the ground he ran towards a rival with short quick steps, then raised his wings and jumped over him. You often heard the aggressive *too-roo* song as he advanced.

These early combats are quite fascinating. The rivals crouch, advance and retire so smoothly that they seem to be on rails. A cock also occasionally stands stiffly with black upper breast and belly feathers fluffed out; a posture which threatens rivals without physically attacking them. Pairs are formed in this phase. The two birds sometimes fly together far out on to the moor or peatland; or the cock goes first, establishes his territory, creaking from a hump or hummock in the moss before rising and performing his advertising flight above it. There are two distinct functions in these flights. When a cock flies high in his advertisement flight he often intrudes on the air space of other pairs; this possibly informs the group about numbers and dispersion. In the lower advertising flight, usually carried out less than 30 m above the ground, the singer is beating the bounds of his territory, indicating his living-space to others. Both forms of display flight help to achieve an equitable breeding density. Early in this phase they stand quite passively for long periods; their disruptive plumage makes them difficult to spot, unless they are 'creaking'.

A big snowstorm in late February or March upsets the rhythm of courtship and territorial establishment. All the birds re-assemble in packs and retire to the valley until sun and thaw enable courtship again to proceed.

In this exciting period of courtship and territorial combat two cocks may pair up, with the more subordinate bird in the normal role of the hen in ground and air displays. We have never watched two cocks copulating but this behaviour probably advances the sex drive of both birds.

TERRITORY

Cocks fight for territory. In March we have watched two of them contending for living-space. Time after time one attacked the other and knocked him off hump or tussock. The two rivals fluttered bill to bill or one flew at the other, hitting him so hard that the thud was audible for at least a hundred metres. Both birds periodically froze and later simultaneously carried out song flights over the disputed territory before switching earthwards and facing one another again. There was challenge after challenge, with the combatants fighting song duels or challenging one another while holding their wings high above their backs. At times they stood bill to bill; at others tail to tail. One started to form a nest bowl, holding his tail at an angle of 60°. A fortnight later there was a pair in this territory; but the hen laid her eggs about 200 m from the spot where the cock had made the scoop.

On 6 April 1937, after the deep snowdrifts left by the great March storm had started to melt, a trio of cocks courted and attempted to possess the same hen. Time after time the rivals fought, fluttered or leap-frogged over one another. At last the dominant cock separated the hen from his rivals, running behind her through the dubs and runnels and sometimes rising and fluttering above her. Twice, however, she turned on him, lunging with her bill and rejecting copulation. The episode ended when the hen rose, the dominant cock just behind her, and the two less-favoured suitors flying some metres in the rear.

We have also watched rivals challenge established or newly-forming pairs. Sex-flights are often dramatic and spectacular when the cock is in close pursuit of a hen. The two birds dip, climb and switchback before both flash downwards at high speed, skimming low over the ground for a hundred metres or more, before landing and starting to court again. Two or three cocks will chase a hen in this way, with the less dominant birds dropping out before the hen lands. Goldies often cover great expanses in their sexual pursuit flights, flying far beyond the bounds of the territory and may even disappear from the nesting grounds. A cock often song dances or flies in twists and turns just behind the hen. Before the pairs and territories are quite firm, you often watch exciting flights. The cock and hen cross and re-cross flight paths and perform spectacular synchronised turns, swerves and plunges. The two birds may then also roll or half-roll on their backs like excited ravens. Cocks also sometimes slide downwards, like impassioned swifts, with wings held almost vertically upwards.

After the goldies are firmly paired they periodically visit their territories, where they occasionally feed when crouching together and are then most difficult to pick up. For the rest of the day they feed on the fallows of adjacent farms. If a pair wanders onto a neighbouring territory the cocks fight, sing, and often leap-frog over one another. On 12 April 1937, after they had fought, two cocks stood 10–20 m apart before the intruding pair flew off, the cock slowly flapping behind his hen.

During territorial establishment cocks often define particular 'marks' – like hummocks or rocks – in their territorial centres or citadels. They now attack rival cocks and intruding hens or pairs, and sometimes other waders like lapwings or oystercatchers.

SEXUAL BEHAVIOUR

The sexual behaviour of golden plovers is not as dramatic as that of many other waders. A hen, standing close to the nest at which the cock is scrape-making, may suddenly run a few metres from him, give quiet subbdued cries, and then bend stiffly forward. The cock quickly runs up and copulates without any further display. In a different form of courtship, Parr watched a cock sit on a scoop as if moving the eggs and then stand up and turn round several times. The hen approached and the cock ran to her and mounted without further display. Hans Rittinghaus (1969) watched a cock preen and raise his nape feathers before he ran up to the hen and flew straight onto her back when about a metre away. I have also seen a cock raise and shake his wings violently before skimming onto his mate's back, but this is unusual. He usually takes her without any special display, sometimes flapping his wings to balance himself on her back. We have also watched a cock fly straight onto the hen's back, after she has signalled to him by tilting forward in the usual way of waders. She may do this unexpectedly and without any other invitation ploy. The coupling of goldies lasts from a few seconds up to half a minute; afterwards the two birds often preen and re-arrange displaced feathers before running or flying away. Coupling usually takes place in nesting territories, but occasionally on neutral or feeding grounds. Golden plovers copulate during incubation, but not so regularly or passionately as do lapwings.

I have twice watched a cock with two hens. I did not find the nest of the first trio; the birds disappeared from the ground, apparently without nesting. The two hens with the other cock laid the last and fourth egg of their clutches within a span of 48 hours, in nests roughly 100 m apart.

In other years, when there were more cocks than hens, it was possible that some were polyandrous; but I have never proved this. However, cock golden plovers appear to be quite capable of incubating and hatching eggs and rearing a brood.

Sequential nesting

Parr (1979) has greatly advanced the golden plover story. His study area on Kerloch Moor, Kincardineshire, 100 ha of well-burnt *Calluna* with patches of grassland, is bounded by farmland on its northern boundary. Between 1973–77 he found that golden plovers annually occupied 34 different breeding ranges and that there was a surplus of 1.20:1 of cocks over hens. By colour-marking a proportion of adults and young, and identifying others by distinctive facial and plumage characteristics, he discovered most unexpected breeding strategy. In addition to the off-duty birds, which regularly fed on the farmlands, there were other pairs consistently seen on the fields during the early part of the breeding season, but which he did not see on frequent visits to the breeding ranges. These apparently non-breeding pairs and groups contained birds which were waiting their turn to nest. Sometimes, within a few days of a pair losing its eggs or chicks in one of the breeding ranges, a new pair took over the territory, laid eggs, and reared a brood. Some ringed first-year cocks and hens paired and nested successfully and were not always later in nesting or subordinate to the older birds. Thus, two or three different pairs in succession sometimes bred, or attempted to breed, in the same breeding range in the same year.

This remarkable pattern is certainly not characteristic of all breeding groups; but it may well account for some of the late clutches discovered in late June and early July in more dense populations. On Dorback Moor sexual activity often revived in early July when several cocks sometimes simultaneously made advertisement song flights while chasing an off-duty hen. These pursuits often ended by the hen disappearing to her feeding ground and the cocks chasing one another before suddenly swishing down to their respective stances. In early July there is also sometimes a phase of 'false nest-site selection' in which robbed or possibly subordinate pairs make scoops without laying eggs.

Agonistic behaviour

There is formal agonistic behaviour in the spring flocks. Two cocks often stand opposite to one another in the high upright position, with breast feathers puffed out and head indrawn. At other times two cocks rush at one another, the less dominant slipping the attack which is then repeated. Another cock, with head and tail in line but with back humped, wings tight and tail partly fanned, chases a rival over the ground. At other times cocks fight song duels facing one another with wings held erect and giving bursts of trilling *too-roo* song. Sometimes the rivals fly or leapfrog over one

another before turning to continue the contest (*in* Cramp and Simmons 1983). In his study area in south-west Scotland, P. J. Edwards found that darker cocks were more dominant and aggressive, and more likely to invade the territories of rivals and to attempt to seduce their hens.

DISPERSION AND BREEDING DENSITY

The carrying capacity of different golden plover habitats varies greatly. D. A. Ratcliffe (1976) tabulates breeding density and spacing as follows:

Density	Average spacing (m)	Average area (breeding pairs/km²)
Very high	<250	>10
High	250–450	4–10
Moderate	450–850	1.5–4
Low	850–1650	0.5–1.5
Very low	>1650	<0.5

In the late 1930s the Dorback Moor groups ranged from moderate to high breeding densities, with the nests beside enclosed grasslands occasionally only 200 m apart. Between 1976–79, in our north-west Sutherland study area of 3,250 ha, the number of breeding pairs has fluctuated from 31+ pairs in 1976 to 15 pairs in 1978; a maximum of 0.9 breeding pairs/km². In these habitats, however, some territories are marginal, with golden plovers only breeding in one or more when greenshanks are absent. But in some of the flows small groups regularly nest 450 m, or ocassionally less, apart.

Density was moderate in south-east Sutherland in the 1960s; nests were spaced at intervals of 550 m apart, roughly 3 breeding pairs/km² The territorial centres in some Strath Helmsdale habitats in 1979 were roughly 450 m apart, with about 2–3 breeding pairs/km². In another part of north-west Sutherland, where we studied greenshanks in 1963, the breeding density of golden plovers was lower than in any other deer forest in which we have worked. There were only isolated breeding pairs at intervals of over 2 km. The moors and flowlands in Easter Ross and south-east Sutherland, where Bruin, Patrick and Richard worked, carry low to very low breeding densities, 0.5 breeding pairs/km² or less. On Struie Hill, Inveroykel and Braelangwell they also found small groups of goldies breeding at low to very low density.

On the high tops, 800 m ASL, or higher, golden plovers have bred in low to moderate numbers in the west Cairngorms; only occasionally in the central massif; and at low density in the east Cairngorms. On the Drumochter Hills the family has recorded low to moderate breeding density, with occasional pockets of high density on the eastern bumps and ridges. There is a very low density on the western tops where they have been studying the dotterel.

Breeding densities in other districts make an interesting comparison. Golden plovers, now scarcer in Wales, breed at generally low to moderate densities. In Montgomery, however, R. Longrove (*in* Ratcliffe 1976) recorded about 40 breeding pairs on 2,100 ha, a density of 5.3 breeding pairs/km². A handful of pairs nest on Dartmoor where A. Archer-Lock (*pers comm*) records them breeding at very low density. Breeding density in the Peak District National Park, where there were 380–400 pairs, varies from low to high. In 1970–73 D. W. Yalden (1974) gives an overall average of 1.93 breeding pairs/km², indicating a moderate breeding density.

Ratcliffe recorded a remarkably high density of golden plovers on the limestone grasslands of the north Pennines, with 18 pairs on 110 ha (16.4 breeding pairs/km²). Here nests were remarkably evenly dispersed and sited sometimes less than 200 m apart. The blanket bogs on Alston Moor also showed a high density, with nests about 400 m apart and 5.0 breeding pairs/km². Apart from Mallerstang and Alston Moor, many other groups in the north Pennines breed at moderate to occasionally high densities. The groups on the Scottish borders, however, show a low to moderate density. In the southern Uplands – in addition to the Moorfoot Hills – Spango Water, Cairn Table and the hills north of Gatehouse-on-Fleet, all carry moderate to high breeding populations.

In the south and south-west Highlands there is a low density on the Trossachs and Breadalbane Hills and low density with high populated patches on Rannoch Moor. In the east Highlands, including Clova-Caenlochan, Lochnagar, Glen Esk, Crathie, Upper Strath Don and Glenlivet-Cabrach, there are moderate to high numbers (Ratcliffe 1976). In one year Adam Watson (1974) recorded a density of 12.5 breeding pairs/km² in favourite habitats in Glen Esk. Parr recorded 34 breeding ranges, with about 40 pairs nesting annually in 1,000 ha on his study area in Kerloch, Kincardineshire (*c* 5.4 breeding pairs/km²). Density was highest close to the moorland edges adjoining the farms and grasslands where the goldies fed.

Numbers and densities are low to very low in Skye, but rather higher – low to moderate – on Rum. The Outer Hebrides groups have not been closely studied. In the Northern Isles goldies breed in much lower numbers and at a lower density than in the 1930s. D. Lee and W. R. P. Bourne (1975) give 0.7 breeding pairs/km² on 1,098 ha on mainland Orkney. Density on Fetlar, Shetland, ranges from low to high, with 67 pairs occupying 3,450 ha (1.9 breeding pairs/km²). Golden plovers have a very variable breeding density on Unst, which has ranged from low to high (G. Bundy *in* Ratcliffe 1976).

On the Continent there are many equally variable breeding densities. I. Byrkjedal (1978) compared densities and breeding schedules of groups on Jaeren, 300 m ASL, and on Hardanger Vidda, at about 1300 m ASL, in Norway. On Jaeren, in 1972–73, an average of 25 pairs bred on 9 km² (a mean density of 2.8 breeding pairs/km²). On Hardanger Vidda, in June and July, the predominantly *altifrons* groups had a breeding density of 0.9 breeding pairs/km² in a study area of 17 km². Rittinghaus (1969) found eight nests on the rocky heaths of Öland, north Sweden, in a study area of 10 km², at an average density of 0.8 breeding pairs/km². In the mosses of west Finland, Pihlasalo (1968–69) located 34 pairs in 3460 ha, a mean of approximately 1 breeding pair/km².

In south Waigatsch and the Samojeden tundra in north Russia, Uspenski recorded some high densities, with pairs only 200–300 m apart. E. Kumari *et al* (1974) recorded high densities in Estonia SSR, but here numbers and breeding density fluctuate from year to year. In 1952, for example, there was one breeding pair/80 ha and in 1959 one breeding pair/160 ha. In 1955 at least 120 pairs bred on 8300 ha on Muraka moss; and between 1968–72 an average of 51 pairs nested on Nigula moss (one breeding pair/40–70 ha). On the west Estonian moss of Koimaraba there was a density of one breeding pair/13.5 ha, in a study plot of 64 ha.

On one of the last refuges of the southern golden plover in lower Saxony in central Europe, a cock defended a rectangle of up to 100×700 m in which the pair held the centre most firmly; here the feeding grounds were 200–500 m away.

How do golden plovers regulate their breeding density? Recruitment in late summer and autumn and survival in winter is likely to determine the number of birds returning to a particular breeding area. The quantity and quality of food on the grasslands, fallows and other feeding grounds, while the hen is building up her resources for egg-laying, is clearly important. In Iceland, for example, golden plovers take large numbers of earthworms during this period and, judging from the long intervals sometimes recorded between eggs, the hens evidently have difficulty in producing them in hard springs. In some haunts suitable habitat is clearly scarce. In Kincardine, Parr showed that surplus pairs could not establish territories and breed until the territory holders had hatched their chicks or lost their eggs.

Breeding density is possibly determined by the advertisement song flights and early territorial fighting of the cocks and later of the pairs in the pre-laying period. The birds are then possibly able to assess the capacity of the habitat to provide sufficient food for the chicks and themselves. Many parents, when guarding their broods, still continue to fly away to feed on pasture, natural grasslands, or the fallows of farms and crofts, often at a considerable distance from their young. The chicks subsist mainly on invertebrates in heath or peat moss in or outside the nesting territory.

NEST, EGG AND CLUTCH

At first the cock makes unlined scrapes; but later, particularly after copulation, both birds alternately form and work at the nest bowl. While the hen is in the scoop the cock often stands close to her, giving his *too-roo* song, and occasionally jerks sprigs of heather or bits of moss sideways. One pair formed a nest bowl three weeks before the hen laid her first egg, but this is unusual. Ratcliffe (1976) in Britain and Kumari (1974) in Estonia SSR have measured nest scoops which vary from 10–14 cm in diameter and 3–6 cm in depth.

Nest linings are often scanty but some contain quite a large pad of adjacent vegetation. We have watched sitting goldies break off bits and pieces from around their nests, but they do this less habitually than some other waders. Out of the 179 scoops which Ratcliffe analysed in cotton grass *Eriophorum* communities, 172 linings contained the leaves of this plant; and 64 contained no other lining material. *Angustifolium* was also a component of many linings in these habitats and *Nardus* leaves were in bowls where this plant was dominant. Nests in *Calluna* heath or burnt heather contained heather twigs; and those found in limestone swards often had 'short tufts of sheeps fescue *F. ovina*'. Various species of lichen were also featured in 175 out of 273 nests, in 34 of which lichens formed the only lining. Reindeer moss sometimes formed a thick pad under the eggs. Ratcliffe tells us that the large tabular thalli of *Cladonia uncilla*, which golden plovers and dotterels often use as lining, is an excellent insulator. Kumari weighed the wind-dried linings of 17 nests, which varied from 6.5–13.4 gm.

On limestone turf Ratcliffe noted that nests were mostly placed on the crests, or on stony ground beside or between small bedded blocks or slabs. Golden plovers, nesting on the high tops close to dotterels, often make their scoops in carpets of *Rhacomitrium* on hummocks, on stony flats and slopes, and in wet grasslands. Apart from the grassland nest sites these are all typical dotterel habitats.

In the late 1930s single pairs chose the same general type of nest sites as the forest greenshanks. In 1935, for example, one golden plover actually laid in a greenshank's scrape of the previous year; and in 1986 Bruin found an addled egg in a greenshank's old nest scoop in our study area in Sutherland. Other pairs nested in forest bogs beside or below stunted pines. In Sutherland and Spey Valley golden plovers have occasionally laid in the same scoop in two or more consecutive years. R. Stokoe (*in* Ratcliffe 1976) found that a hen on Alston Moor in the Pennines used a scoop for six consecutive years; but this is unusual.

Golden plovers have varied laying seasons in different parts of their range. The Dorback groups usually had full clutches in the last week in April or in the first week in May. In Sutherland and Orkney early hens usually complete clutches in the first fortnight of April; but the north-west Sutherland groups, in our study area, have usually laid out in the last ten days of April and in early May. In late seasons, however, a few hens have not completed their clutches until the second week in May. In the western Cairngorms, 900 m ASL, the hens usually laid out two weeks later than those in the valley – early date 4 May. In some years clutch dates on the Drumochter tops are only slightly earlier than those of dotterel; seven clutches varied from 12 May–11 June. However, in 1977 Bruin and Patrick found one golden plover still laying on 16 June. Ratcliffe found that hens in the Pennines and south Scotland began laying in the last days of March; but most hens laid the first egg between 10 April–7 May, on ground up to 610 m ASL.

In the Netherlands, F. Haverschmidt (*in* Glutz 1975) records early April to early June as limits for first clutches, with the earliest date 3 April. In Iceland the laying season ranges from mid May to late June; and in north Finland L. von Haartman recorded the end of May to late July. Hens around the White Sea, USSR, start laying in the last ten days of May; but first clutches are also recorded in the first ten days of June and laying continues until the end of the month (Belopolski *et al* 1970).

On Jaeren, Norway, where the *apricaria* groups arrive in late March-early April, Byrkjedal (1978) found that the hens laid their eggs from late April to early May, with 2 May the average date for nine clutches in 1973. By comparison, the *altifrons* population of Hardanger Vidda, in southern Norway, arrived on its breeding grounds in early May and laid out about mid June, roughly one and a half months later than those on Jaeren.

Golden plovers' eggs are slightly glossed and their shape varies from pyriform to broad ovate. Ground colour ranges from pale greenish-olive to creamy-brown, deep red-brown, buff and stone colour. The red-brown eggs are exceptionally beautiful. Eggs are blotched, streaked, speckled and often capped with deep red-brown, blackish-brown and sienna. We have no records of erythristic or cyanic clutches. In severe springs, however, hens occasionally drop thin-shelled and almost immaculate blue eggs.

Hugh Blair (*in litt*) tells us that when a large series of eggs of *apricaria* and *altifrons* is compared there is a striking difference between them. If eggs of equal length are placed side by side they are seen to differ in outline; the greatest diameter is nearer to the upper pole in the egg of the northern race than in that of the southern. Eggs of *apricaria* thus appear to be more slender and those of *altifrons* more bulky. It is as yet uncertain, however, whether this distinction is constant, but 'it occurs frequently enough to call for comment'. Green tints, though unusual, also occur more frequently in series of the *altifrons*. Commenting on these interesting notes, Byrkjedal agrees that measurements of eggs from Jaeren appear to be broader relative to length than those from Hardanger Vidda. The material is possibly insufficient and as yet these differences are not statistically significant. 'The problem, however, is absolutely worth attention'.

Jourdain (1940) gives a mean of 51.77 × 35.88 mm for 100 British eggs; but 102 eggs from the Pennines, measured by D. A. Ratcliffe, were slightly larger, averaging 52.0 × 36.2 mm. There is little difference in the measurements of 92 Iceland eggs which averaged 51.94 × 35.2.

Table 3 gives the weights of freshly-laid eggs. Golden plovers' eggs are heavy in proportion to body weight. A clutch of four, averaging 73% of the hen's body weight, compares with 46% for clutches of lapwings' eggs (Table 1). Golden plovers usually rear their chicks on the moor or flow, whereas lapwings lead their chicks to richer grasslands (Ratcliffe 1976). These differences may also help to explain how lapwings can so easily and rapidly produce replacemanet clutches. M. Schönwetter (1962) weighed 140 golden plovers' eggshells (no race given) which varied from 1.40–1.90 gm (mean 1.68 gm).

The hens lay their eggs at almost any hour of the day, from early morning to 20.00. In the central Grampians in 1977, Bruin and Patrick recorded that the hen of an isolated pair laid her fourth egg some time between 15.00–20.00.

Golden plovers do not appear to have any special egg laying rituals or ceremonies. However, we have seen a cock stand close to the nest while the hen was laying her first egg. Both birds periodically cover, but do not incubate, first eggs; and they sometimes intermittently brood the first two eggs by day and at night. Incubation proper may begin between the third and fourth, and more exceptionally on the second egg, although many hens delay steady sitting until they have completed their clutches. Eggs are often laid at intervals of 48–60 hours; but, in the hard spring of 1941, we recorded intervals of 120 hours between the second and third eggs in two clutches, and 96 hours between the second and third eggs of a third clutch. In 1940, however, one hen laid her second egg between 30–36 hours after the first.

The details of one clutch laid in 1941 are worth recording:

2 May: Hen flew in alone to lay first egg at *c* 19.00 hours.

3 May: Pair close to nest; but did not appear to brood the egg.

4 May: Still one egg, 19.00 hours.

5 May: Second egg laid about noon (interval over 60 hours).

6 May: Still two eggs, 23.30; more material in nest.

10 May: Third egg laid about noon (interval over 120 hours).

11 May: Cock sitting on three eggs during afternoon.

12 May: Fourth egg laid just before noon (interval *c* 48 hours).

At Dalsland, Sweden, Lew Oring recorded a hen leaving her mate and laying her second egg between 06.00–09.00, 22.5–24 hours after the first; she then laid her third egg not more than 31.5 hours after the second. The possible richness of feeding, and the lateness of the season, may have contributed to these short laying intervals.

In harsher habitats, however, hens may have difficulty in building up resources before laying. At Hardanger Vidda, Norway, Byrkjedal (1975) found that five out of eight hens had eaten bones of small rodents about one month before laying. 'Two females collected some days prior to egg laying did not contain rodent bones, while one female, with an egg in her oviduct, had eaten a substantial amount of rodent bones'. Adults collected just after the young had hatched contained no bones. This interesting discovery complements that of S. F. Maclean (1974) who found that in Alaska bones from dead lemmings were possibly an important source of calcium for *Calidris* species. We have also recorded that greenshanks sometimes eat the bones of voles and fish.

A normal golden plover clutch consists of four eggs. Threes are not unusual, genuine twos rare, and a five exceptional.

The mean size for 126 clutches, examined in Inverness-shire and Sutherland by the family, is 3.85. Ratcliffe found the same average for a larger sample of 231 British clutches, and Arthur Whitaker's sample of 23 clutches averaged 3.52. F. Haverschmidt (1975) gives 3.78 as the mean size of 23 Netherland clutches (Table 4).

Golden plovers are single-brooded. Some hens lay replacements if the lost eggs are not too heavily incubated. Recorded replacements have been laid 12–24 days after clutch loss. These repeat clutches are usually laid in the original territory between 100–300 m from the robbed or destroyed nests. However, in view of Parr's observations on Kerloch Moor, students of golden plovers in high density populations around rich pasture or farmland would do well carefully to check egg types.

INCUBATION

Most sitting goldies fly from their nests when the intruder is anything up to 500 m away. Others, however, sit extremely closely, only quitting or running from their eggs a few metres ahead of the intruder. When disturbed the sitting bird sometimes flies very low, occasionally touching the heather or grass, and often spreading its tail in a modified distraction display. It puts down 200–250 m away and often only starts to call after a lapse of up to 15 minutes. We have also occasionally seen one start quite elaborate distraction displays, running low along the ground with drooped wings and spread tail. Ratcliffe also noticed that some sitting goldies allowed the intruder to pass the nest before flipping off it from behind.

During incubation the non-sitting bird usually feeds on enclosed or natural grasslands, often at great distances from the nest. Except at times of nest relief, you seldom watch both birds close to the nest. In north-east Sutherland D. A. Goode (*in* Ratcliffe 1976) noted a regular flight from bogs on the Knockfin Heights to croftlands around Achentoul Forest, a distance of 2–5 km. D. A. Humphrey also recorded a regular late afternoon and evening flight of up to 100 birds in Strath Halladale. The groups which we particularly studied regularly flew from the flows and bogs to enclosed grasslands up to 5 km away. Lack of natural grassland possibly accounts for the absence of nesting pairs on a large tract of apparently suitable flowland about 5 km long. In south-east Sutherland we noticed that the golden plovers fed on old croft pasture in the early morning and evening. Afterwards single birds flew out into the surrounding deer forest.

On returning to carry out nest relief, a cock goldie frequently makes a high advertisement song flight before swishing down to his nesting territory. He may later 'beat the bounds' of his territory in a flight performed much lower down. Two cocks occasionally arrive together and they then sometimes chase and sing against one another. Advertising flights may stimulate other cocks to start their own display flights and ground songs. For a few minutes the flow is alive with lovely sounds.

Before the change-over an incoming bird usually puts down 200 m or more from the nest, and only after a long interval approaches its sitting mate in a series of runs and short flights. Late in the summer three or more cocks sometimes chase a hen which has left her eggs; or they sing, song dance, and chase one another high in the air before flashing down to their stances. We have not seen a sitting bird wait until its mate reached the nest; it usually flies fast, low, and somewhat furtively, well ahead of the approaching mate.

Golden plovers have a wide variety of incubation patterns. At the nest within 150 m of the Dorback Moor cottage, the cock apparently incubated alone throughout daylight hours from the fifth day onwards. The hen covered the eggs on the third day and shared duties with her mate on the first, second and fourth days. After the fifth day the cock left the nest to feed 3–4 times daily, for meals lasting 10–30 minutes. He sometimes sang above the nest before returning; and once he left the eggs to chase away another cock which was pursuing his hen on a nearby hillock. Later that afternoon five other cocks came within 20 m of the nest but he did not drive them off.

On Öland in Sweden the cocks usually sat from 05.00 to 18.00 and hens incubated from the late evening until early morning; but Rittinghaus never actually watched a nest relief. Byrkjedal (1978) made two continuous 24 hour watches from a hide on Jaeren. Here the cock sat by day and the hen at night; brooding stints lasted 10–12 hours. At three nests on the Dorback Moor the cocks brooded more and more after the first week of incubation; but at two others cock and hen shared brooding duties during the hatch, changing over every 4–5 hours, or sometimes less. At two north-west Sutherland nests the cocks appeared to sit from early morning to evening and the hen incubated at night. On 29 May 1979 the non-sitting partner of a third pair flew in at 21.32; on the following morning nest reliefs took place at 08.59 and also possibly at noon.

Golden plovers have exceptionally long incubation periods. On a mixed sheep walk and grouse moor in Inverness-shire, in habitats where the birds were frequently put off their eggs, eleven periods ranged from 27.5 to 33–34 days. One Sutherland clutch hatched in 29 and two in 29–30 days (mean for 14 clutches 30.4 days).

HATCHING

The chicks start squeaking in the eggs before the first star or bump appears, and the sitting bird responds by calling to them. Eamonn tape-recorded the special calls given to the chicks while still in the eggs, and after they had hatched and were still in the nest scoop. In this phase cock and hen sometimes change over at frequent intervals; and, if the hen is sitting, the cock sometimes stays close by. Other pairs do not greatly change their behaviour during the hatch, although some birds return more quickly after they have been flushed from the nest.

Hatching sometimes takes place within a period of under six hours; but 24–40 hours sometimes elapse between the hatching of first and last eggs. Parr (1980) recorded hatching intervals of 9–10 hours between the eggs.

In 35 clutches Ratcliffe found only six unhatched eggs out of 135, a mean brood size of about 3.64 chicks. Analysis of 50 followed-up nests in the BTO Nest Records Scheme show that 31 pairs hatched at least one egg (62%) and 19 failed completely (38%). Predators robbed or disturbed 14 nests, two were deserted, two held infertile eggs and a sheep apparently trod on one. This estimate of 62% hatching success suggests that each breeding pair hatches an average of roughly 2.2 chicks. However, considerably fewer young ultimately fly.

We have known cocks and hens to continue to brood hatched eggshells for over six hours. Sometimes they place large portions on the edges of the nest before removing them. One cock flew away with a large shell fragment and then dropped it at a peaty pool where he dipped his bill in the murky water. Others have flown away with large pieces of shell which they have usually dropped in flight or occasionally after alighting. Another flew away, turned and flew back almost to the nest before dropping an eggshell. Small pieces are left in the nest or broken up during brooding; but some unhatched eggs are left in the scoop. However, Ken Williamson (1948) recorded that an infertile egg was possibly carried away.

YOUNG

In many ways golden plover chicks are the most lovely of all waders. The down on their crowns and mantles is golden brown spangled with black tips; their cheeks and throats are white; and breast, belly and underparts are greyish white. Their legs are dull leaden grey and irides are blackish brown. In the nest, or squatting outside it, they are not only attractive but are exceptionally difficult to see, so cryptic is their down.

Chicks are able to move out of the nest within a few hours of hatching; but their parents sometimes brood them in the scoop for 12 to 24, and occasionally up to 36 hours, or more. In the Faroes, Williamson watched a hen brooding the third chick and the last egg for 20 hours while the cock led away the two oldest chicks.

In their first week both parents periodically brood the young; and they also do so at night for over a fortnight and by day during heavy rain, sleet or snowstorm. How difficult it is to find the chicks which immediately freeze when their parents start to give warning cries or to carry out distraction displays. However, by playing a recording of the parents 'all clear' cries, Parr found that the chicks bobbed up again! In Kincardine he found that the parents guarded the chicks on the moor, standing 40–50 m away from them, but one by one they left the brood to feed on nearby farm fields. Golden plovers often ignore a car or other vehicle. In many years, when returning in the Snowtrac from our greenshank camp, we have watched parents and families running and feeding almost beside us. But once we left the machine the chicks immediately froze.

There are considerable differences in the movements made by the goldies and their families. Some Dorback broods were reared in their nesting territories and surroundings; but in north-west Sutherland we have followed particular families for over 1000 m and found that they sometimes moved on to ground on which we have never known them to nest during our 19-years study. The parents sometimes chivvied greenshanks away from grassy patches in the eroded peat.

In Kincardine, Parr (1979) discovered that golden plovers ceased to attack trespassers after the chicks had hatched, enabling new pairs to re-occupy and breed in their territories. 'The newcomers are not hostile towards other golden plovers with families, but they do attack and eject others which do not have chicks'. Breeding pairs thus appear to compete only with those that are nesting at the same time. Pairs with nests containing eggs, and those with chicks on the move, often combine to distract or mob possible predators. Several adults, including those with eggs, sometimes carry out distraction displays simultaneously in defence of a single brood (Parr 1980).

A golden plover family occasionally divides, each parent helping to rear one or two chicks, but at other times the pair works as a team. Before the chicks can fly, however, the hen sometimes disappears to join with others on neutral gound and the cock alone stays in charge of the family. On Hardanger Vidda, Byrkjedal (1978) found that the hens left the young and formed flocks where their moult could be completed in a less disturbed environment.

Young goldies are able to fly before they are fully grown; one chick flew in its fourth week. Heinroth (1931–33) recorded a period of 28 days as the time taken by a captive chick to make its first flight; but we have known as long as 32–33 days before a chick was fully grown and strong on the wing.

DISTRACTION BEHAVIOUR

Golden plovers have evolved a battery of complex distraction displays and behaviour patterns, but these are apparently restricted to particular individuals and are less regularly performed over eggs than with chicks.

(1) A close-sitting bird, after fluttering off the nest and almost touching the surrounding vegetation, flies low, with its tail depressed and partly fanned, and its legs dangling. It may occasionally pitch 100–200 m away, first holding out and shaking its wings and then, almost like a partridge, running in a crouch with head down, first drooping its wings and then wildly flapping them. A bird with eggs gives the full drooping only occasionally. Off eggs, she is more likely to use a modified display in which she droops and partly expands her tail, flaps her wings, and runs over the moss or grass-heath.

(2) When he was guarding small young, we have seen a cock lie spread-eagled on the ground, tail spread, head down, and flapping his wings.

(3) Cocks or hens flap over the ground, their wings used almost as levers; or they lie with heads almost to the ground, tails depressed and wing tips raised. This display reminds us of one in the dotterel's distraction battery.

(4) The 'mammal run' in which the goldie runs quickly over heath or flow looking like a small mammal.

(5) The hen depresses her tail and flaps over the ground, usually when she is about 50 m or more from nest or brood.

(6) A cock runs towards man or dog and then appears to stumble and hold out a wing.

(7) Parents with broods often make short flights, calling plaintively as they move away from the intruder, periodically alighting with wings raised and momentarily beaten vigorously. Each flight carries the distractor further away from the imperilled brood.

VOICE

The advertisement song flights of the cock golden plover high in the air, and the silvery evening chorus in early summer, are always most evocative sounds.

Golden plovers have two quite different songs. First the plaintive *o-deeah* or *per-pee-oo*, which the cock gives while slowly flapping his wings as he flies over hill, moor or flow, at heights ranging from 10 to 300 m above ground. His territorial marking flight is usually carried out much lower down and is restricted mainly to his territorial boundaries. We have watched a cock, flushed from a nest, start to flap his wings and start singing only a couple of metres above ground. Once a cock started to flap his wings and sing on the ground, but this appears to be most unusual. In our experience, cocks alone perform advertisement flights; but Rittinghaus twice recorded hens giving modified renderings.

The second song is an excited and throaty rippling *too-roo-too-roo*. Excited or angry cocks sing these songs on the ground, high in the air, sometimes after a spasm of advertisment song and display, and often during dramatic dives from a great height. Cocks frequently use this song during sexual and territorial fighting and sometimes while gliding or slowing flapping their wings. This form has several variations rendered in different tempos and in accord with different emotional simulii and it is often used by males in the flock. Towards the end of the breeding season some renderings are weaker and more faded.

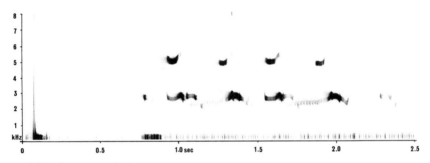

Golden plover, group of cocks singing too-roo *songs, Inverness-shire (Bill Sinclair)*

Golden plovers rely on several stock notes with subtle variations and changes of emphasis and timing. On 29–30 May 1979, Bill Sinclair tape-recorded nest-relief calls, with the incoming bird calling and the brooding bird answering softly from the nest.

Here is a brief analysis of a complex vocabulary.

(1)   The social contact call is a single ringing flute-like *too* or *ploo*, variations of which are given in different emotional situations. Standing alert on a hump or tussock, the off-duty bird often uses this far-carrying cry to warn its brooding mate. In both summer and winter golden plovers give these cries at their roosts or on feeding grounds; you often hear them answering one another from different parts of the moor. In the evening this distant silvery piping is always most attractive. Birds standing on the ground sometimes use these cries to call down others (Glutz 1975).

(2)   A disyllabic *too-ee*, with emphasis on the second syllable, marks greater excite-ment. The goldies use this when humans or dogs are passing through their territories.

(3)   A more excited or frightened bird also sometimes gives a series of slurred *toor-toor* cries as it rises and flies away.

(4)   Agitated *whee-whee-whee-oo* are given, particularly early in the breeding season.

(5)   During courtship we have heard cocks use rippling dotterel-like notes, but these are not so distinctive as those given by many other waders during courtship.

(6)   When a bird rises and flies from one part of flow or moor to another, particularly late in the evening, it sometimes gives *whee-whee* in a rising pitch.

(7)   Late in the breeding season we have recorded a plaintive wailing *way-way-way*.

(8)   A repetitive *weep-weep* in flight.

(9)   Towards the end of the breeding season groups are often very noisy in the evening. We have often listened to a long wailing *whee-whee*, with emphasis on the second syllable.

(10)   In May 1979 Eamonn tape-recorded the cries of a pair, first with chicks in the eggs and later after they had hatched but were still in the nest. While hatching was in progress the parents directed a series of *geek-ik-ik* cries to the chicks. They also warned them with high pitched calls.

(11)   A disyllabic *too-too* cautions the chicks to stay hidden.

(12   The 'all clear' cry *tee-too* informs the brood that danger has passed and induces them to rise and start moving and feeding again.

(13)   Parents use *ook-eeik* cries to call up their brood; and they sometimes possibly encourage them by means of a soft hoot (Eamonn R. C. Thompson).

(14)   Newly-hatched chicks have rather plaintive *whee* cries; and when the parent is away from the nest a hoarse whistling scream. Older chicks give dry or challenging cries *tuk tuk* or *wee-up* (Eamonn R. C. Thompson).

(15)   In the winter flocks birds about to take off use a combination of monosyllabic *tees* and *toos* (D. B. A. Thompson).

All these cries are part of the vocabulary of a most exciting wader and form striking contrasts to those of their neighbours on the moors and flows.

PREDATORS

Golden plovers have many predators. In his study of the prey of peregrines, in 1961–62, Ratcliffe found that goldies were the most victimised waders – 11 recorded in England, Wales and southern Scotland, 23 in inland and four on coastal areas of the Scottish Highlands. In the central Highlands, Douglas Weir collected 520 pellets and pluckings taken from the eyries of 23 pairs of peregrines between April–June in each year from 1964–75. Snipe with 35 victims and golden plover with 24 were the two most highly predated waders.

Hen harriers nest in many golden plover habitats, but do not appear to be formidable predators. Donald Watson (1977) found no golden plover remains in several of his Galloway study areas, although 15–20 pairs nested regularly in one of them. The same applies to Orkney and South Uist, where golden plover often breed on the same moors and bogs as hen harriers, but are seldom taken.

On many moors, crows – carrion in England and southern Scotland, hoodies in the Highlands – are oppressive egg thieves. In 1974 at least 17 pairs of goldies nested at high density at Mallerstang in the north Pennines, but only four hatched chicks from their first laying. In 1975 none of the 18 pairs hatched chicks and all nine known replacement clutches were also robbed. In 1973, on the Moorfoot Hills, a single pair of crows took the nests of at least four out of 20 pairs of golden plovers by 7 May (Ratcliffe 1976).

The Dorback groups, particularly those nesting on the moorland edge close to Abernethy Forest, suffered severely; in all years between 1935–42, hoodies robbed nests. They were particularly hard on those in which the golden plovers were laying. To find nests they flew low over the moor or discovered them by watching from trees on the edges of the forest. They may also have profited by watching my own movements as well as those of the birds! Small parties of rooks, which visited the Dorback Moor to feed on cowberries and blaeberries in late June and July, sometimes discovered and devoured clutches of golden plovers' eggs.

In north-east Sutherland common gulls are frequent predators; and in north-west

Sutherland crows frequently rob goldies' nests, apparently without greatly influencing numbers. Lesser black-backed gulls take eggs and black-headed gulls occasionally fly away with chicks in some districts.

Arthur Whitaker had an interesting experience on Derwent Moor. A lesser black-backed gull took off with a poisoned egg; but before the poison had taken effect it had flown 60 m and found a goldie's nest, swallowed one egg, and picked up a second which was still in its beak after the poison had struck. A third egg was still in the nest on top of a tussock of dry grass.

Foxes and sheep dogs occasionally rob nests and take chicks. Parr discovered, however, that, unlike redshanks and curlews, golden plovers apparently only have a weak scent when they are nesting, thus probably reducing predation by mammals.

FOOD

Golden plovers have their own way of feeding, running a few yards, pausing and then pecking. Philip Burton (1974) noticed that pauses frequently turned to feeding movements, either directly or after a further pause, with the head lowered down to the ground and bill pointed ahead; afterwards the bird usually pecked. Their short beaks generally lead to the goldies feeding on or near the surface. M. Fallett (1962) considers that hearing, as well as sight, is used in locating their food.

Glutz (1975) has summarised much about the food of the golden plover. The diet is largely animal, predominantly earthworms and various species of beetles, other insects and their larvae, and small snails, spiders and crustacea. In a systematic study of the summer food of golden plovers in Estonia SSR, Kumari (1958) recorded rove, click and dung beetles, weevils, ants, larvae, pupae and adult lepidoptera, bugs, dragonflies and grasshoppers in varying quantities.

Ratcliffe published Ernest Blezard's detailed analysis of the stomach contents of two males taken in July 1967 in Upper Teesdale, Yorkshire. One contained two larvae of broom moth *Ceramica pisi*, a carabid beetle *Feronia* sp and some rootlets, shreds of fibrous plant and grit. In the second there was an elaterid beetle *Agriotes* sp., a weevil *Otiorhynchus* sp. grit and a mass of grass and leaves, possibly accidentally taken while picking up other items of food.

Two species of cranefly *Tipula sub-nodicornis* and *Molophilus ater*, which emerge in late May and early June on blanket bogs, may also be an important food. On limestone grasslands sheep dung may lead to more earthworms, dung beetles and diptera, all probable food of the golden plover (Ratcliffe 1976). Earthworms are always important, particularly when the hens are building up before egg-laying.

In 1980–82 Bruin studied the winter ecology of golden plovers on farms near Nottingham where, in association with lapwings, they fed almost entirely on earthworms on old pasture. When feeding, they stood on average 2.35 ± 0.26 m apart (116).

The goldies were less inclined than lapwings to feed in pastures of less than 4 ha. In the three winters of intensive study, 2,000 lapwing flocks were located feeding in these small pastures, but groups of golden plovers were components in only four. In general, however, the goldies usually feed with the lapwings because the latter were more adept at locating fields with a high density of earthworms and were quicker to spot human and other potential predators.

Black-headed gulls were present in about one-third of the mixed flocks, from which they constantly stole the large earthworms which took the plovers longer to pull out of the ground. The association of the two plovers with the kleptoparasitic black-headed gulls, however, was not entirely one-sided. The gulls were exceptionally alert to possible danger, enabling the goldies and lapwings to concentrate more fully on worm hunting

(D. B. A. Thompson 1983).

Bruin found that in spring the main prey are beetles and earthworms. Both are taken mainly from the surface or probing down to 3 cm. He has shown that birds spend longer crouching (forward-bent posture preceding a peck) before taking large worms. This appears to be because the larger worms are deeper in the turf and therefore require greater degrees of assessment and orientation before a peck (Thompson 1983).

Ernest Blezard carried out a study of golden plovers collected on autumn and winter habitats in Cumberland. Various species of beetles were the main food, but three stomachs contained slugs *Agriolimax* sp. and two had univalve molluscs from the shore. A juvenile male from the Solway held a very small shore crab *Carcinum maenas*, fragments of bivalve molluscs *Tellina*, and the small univalve molluscs *Hydrobia* and *Littorina*. Another bird contained a weevil *Sitona* and fragments of a common mussel *Mytilus edulis*.

Burton also studied the food and feeding behaviour in winter and early spring in Essex, where they mainly fed inland and preferred leys in winter. The golden plovers also favoured ley grown over stubble in autumn, and fields of young wheat in spring. He recorded worms Lumbricidae, caterpillars of Lepidoptera, Carabidae and Staphylinidae adults and larvae, Hydrophilidae adults, Silphidae, and weevils *Sitona* and larvae, and spiders. The larvae of sandflies *Bibio* and the mollusc *Hydrobia ulvae* were favourite items. These birds also fed on small snails and 25 stomachs contained grass.

DISTRIBUTION AND NUMBERS

The Breeding Atlas Map shows the distribution of golden plovers in upland Britain and in the great blanket bogs of north-west and western Ireland. They breed in the Shetlands, Orkneys, Outer Hebrides, irregularly on Fair Isle and St Kilda; and, with the exception of the gaps indicated, southwards to the moors and grass-heaths of Yorkshire, Derbyshire and Staffordshire. During the last 50 years their range has reduced and contracted in Wales. A few pairs nest on Dartmoor in Devon, but they no longer breed on Exmoor in Somerset. In Ireland, where they are now much scarcer, they are to be found in the north, north-west and west (R. F. Ruttledge 1966). F. Steiniger

(1959) recorded a brood at Glendalough in Co. Wicklow in 1959, but in the last 50 years they have disappeared from haunts in Cork, Tipperary and Kerry.

Ratcliffe (1976) estimates a total breeding population of 30,755 pairs of golden plovers in Britain and Ireland. There are about 10 pairs in south-west England, 900 pairs in Wales and 7,500 pairs in north England; the southern Uplands carry 3,850 pairs. The bulk of the population breeds in the Scottish Highlands, where south of the Great Glen there are about 8,725 pairs and 6,820 pairs north of the Great Glen; a further 2,000 pairs nest in the Hebrides and northern Isles. Ireland, where it has decreased, carries approximately 600 pairs.

The highest densities are found mostly between 300–600 m ASL. In the northern and western Isles, however, some pairs nest almost at sea level, while in the east and west Cairngorms and central Grampians the goldies nest on the same tops as dotterels, sometimes at altitudes above 1,000 m.

Many of the estimates for populations abroad are indefinite. In Iceland the northern race is said to be abundant, but there has been no precise census. A single pair nested in the Netherlands in 1974. West Germany now carries only a few pairs of *apricaria* concentrated in lower Saxony. Numbers are apparently reduced in Jutland in Denmark, where afforestation and cultivation of peatlands has greatly increased; there are now a mere 10 pairs of survivors. J. Kålås and I. Byrkjedal (1978) estimated a population of 130,000 breeding pairs in Norway, with possibly some recent local increases. In south Sweden numbers have declined by 70%, due to reclamation and digging of peat bogs and afforestation of heaths. The total population is estimated at about 27,000–32,000 pairs. Numbers have greatly increased in Finland; O. Järvinen and R. Väisänen estimate 258,000 pairs in 1973–76.

Golden plover populations fluctuate in Estonia SSR, where S. Onno (1966) gives an estimate of 1,000 pairs. Latvia is said to be good for 400–500 pairs and Lithuania for 100–150 pairs. The bulk of the world population, however, probably nests in various parts of the Soviet Union.

This lovely wader is contracting in many former strongholds throughout Europe. Reclamation of peatland, afforestation, and climatic change has all played a part. Let us hope that wader watchers will always be able to enjoy the evocative evening chorus of golden plovers on the moorlands of upland Britain.

DW.

CURLEW

Long before I ever explored a moor – and what a challenge that was for a young birdwatcher! – I sometimes heard curlews passing over London on moonlit nights. I would peer out of my window and almost desperately look forward to spring. In those days quite half of the fun was in anticipation. I then little knew that a few pairs of curlews always nested within 25 miles of my home in Chiswick; and all I needed was a 2s. 4d. day return ticket to a heath where there were not only two pairs of curlews but two pairs of hobbies and small groups of Dartford warblers and woodlarks. First cultivate your garden and look around you, young man!

With its long beak and legs, and its brown back, the curlew is unmistakable. It is also one of our most romantic waders. The mudflats would never be remotely the same without those long whistles; and the moors would be barren without the glorious bubbling and barking in spring and early summer.

I first hunted for a curlew's nest in 1927, but without success. In the next year I had my first find. Soon I was learning how to track down nests and understand birds by watching. I located a pair of curlews on Chobham Common and saw one of them flying low and furtively far ahead of me over the moor. I hid up beside a clump of gorse bushes on a heathery slope and very soon my field glass was shaking in my hands. I could see the curlew running back in spurts and stops, often appearing to feed, but always moving steadily towards the heath where I thought the nest might be. It was not a really long wait but it appeared interminable; and then suddenly the long-billed grey-brown bird seemed to freeze and disappear in a patch of short heather. How patiently I waited until I had taken some marks, particularly tussocks of long grass, broken patches of earth, and tall clumps of heather. As I rose, I saw a moving blur and then watched the curlew flying low and away. It flew about 200 m before calling a few quiet whistling *quoi-quoi-quois*. I paused, picked up my marks, and moved on breathlessly. This time had I really found a nest? A few minutes later I was there, but casting around I saw nothing; and then I remembered to walk back along the line in case the curlew had run. And there they were – four large olive-brown beautifully speckled pear-shaped eggs. I dropped on my knees beside the nest and kissed the eggs! In the same year I found a second nest on the Common; this gave me almost the same thrill.

In the next few years, with Cecil Stoney, I was busy watching and hunting for other birds on the heaths and commons of Surrey and Berkshire. I had learnt to track down woodlarks and beat the gorse and long heather to flush Dartford warblers from their nests; and in late May and early June, while waiting for the hobbies to show up, we sometimes watched curlews back to their nests. It was always fun seeing them flying so low and in such a guilty fashion, hearing perhaps those quick anxious alarm cries and then later waiting to see the head and long bill appear and disappear, but always moving in roughly the same direction. We would hide behind bank, gorse bushes or trees, or crawl along a dip or ditch and then run out into the open when we thought, hopefully, that the curlew had returned to its eggs. Then, if we were lucky, we saw the bird fly off, almost always 200 m or more ahead of us.

Curlews have a wide variety of habitats. In winter they are often found on the mudflats of estuaries and the sea coast and on sands bared at high tide, where they rest on adjacent salt marshes and upper shores, as well as on the swampy edges of rivers.

They nest on *Calluna* heather, grass-heath, burnt and peat moorland, carpets of cotton sedge *Eriophorum*, fields of rough grass and wet pasture, forest bogs, sometimes the outskirts of golf links, bracken-covered slopes, sand dunes, occasionally on the fringes of large lochs and in clearings in old pinewoods. Many pairs are attracted to farm fields sown with cereals, turnips or potatoes.

On the Continent, nests are occasionally sited close to hedges, bushes, single trees and edges of woods, or, exceptionally, near well-used paths and railway lines; they have also been recorded in hay fields.

I never lost my love for the curlew. In the early spring of 1935, while cycling to the woods and forests of Spey Valley to watch pine crossbills, I first learnt the magic of the waders' home-coming. On the Dorback Moor, golden plover, lapwing, oyster-catcher and sometimes curlew – in that order – returned from mid to late February; and snipe in wisps, redshanks singly, in mid March. Then followed pairs and trips of ringed plover, greenshanks in early April, and last of all the home-coming common sandpipers about three weeks later. These were most exciting times for a young bird-watcher. Wonder came first, understanding took longer. The story of the courtship and breeding life of the curlew came in small bits and pieces, and only later started to become clearer in my mind.

TERRITORY

On the moor, where territories were about 300–400 m ASL, single curlews sometimes arrived in mid February; but the trips, possibly consisting largely of males, usually returned in the last week in February or in early March. They first went to the fields of farm and croft, where I sometimes noticed signs of early courtship, the cocks bowing to the hens and the two birds occasionally rising and tilting at one another. In the next phase they separated and started to establish display centres in territories on the moor or peat hags. The cocks, judging from their shorter bills, were usually, although not always, the first to isolate themselves.

In Rothiemurchus Forest the cocks sometimes took up territories in openings and clearings, or in forest bogs, from early to mid March. Here they immediately started to sing and give display-flight dances, as well as calling their many different cries of warning and alarm. One particular cock arrived, then paired, courted, and helped his hen to incubate the eggs and rear the young; and even after she had left the territory he stayed with the surviving chicks until they flew away, thus being in continuous possession of a territory from mid March to mid August.

During the first week several cocks rise one after the other and often song-dance quite close together; the boundaries of the territories are evidently not then fully settled. A little later two cocks sometimes fly up, calling, floating and tilting, almost side by side. I have seen similar homosexual associations in greenshank and golden plover. This behaviour probably stimulates the sex-drive of the two birds, particularly of the dominant partner.

On a still morning the moor soon rings with the marvellous bubbling songs and the air dances of different cocks. You often see a cock flying slowly and quite low above the moor and then climbing steeply on rapidly beating wings; and when he reaches a fair height he hangs, fluttering, before slowly gliding earthwards on expanded wings, and giving the thrilling bubbling trill. He might then land momentarily, holding up his silver-lined wings almost vertically above his head, or he makes several ascents and glides, singing each time; or sometimes he restricts his display to preliminary calls without the bubbling. These remarkable switchbacks often continue for 100–200 m or more. At other times a cock rises high in air where he soars head to wing, looking almost like some large but quite imaginary hawk. A hen occasionally accompanies him, singing, but not taking part in the aerobatics.

This tempo of display and territorial defence soon accelerates. A tenant cock flies towards a trespassing rival, sometimes singing and dipping as he approaches, and then jousts with him, his wings making a crumpling sound without actually buffeting the intruder. At other times both cocks float side by side with the territory-holder fluttering up and down, and later flying behind, speeding up, and actually striking the intruder. On the ground they fight more seriously. A tenant cock may raise his wings to show off the silvery undersides, and then, crouching forward, run towards the rival, holding his tail up and bill downwards. If this threat posture does not shift him, the tenant suddenly loosens his wings and fans out his tail to expose the white rump patch; a manoeuvre which sometimes succeeds in making the trespasser fly away. The aggressor then flies quickly behind the intruder, returning after he has reached the boundary of his living-space. I have also watched bill to bill flutter-jumping and sometimes leap-frogging, possibly between dominant members of a hierarchy.

In ritualised fighting on the ground between defending and intruding cocks, both birds lower breasts, raise heads and necks, and elevate slightly spread tails. They then sometimes start pulling up and dropping grasses while moving side by side and then doubling back along the same line. Defending cocks sometimes hit rivals with hefty wing thumps. Hens defend territories, but do not appear to lift and drop grass (O. von Frisch 1956). Curlews are, however, less violent fighters than many waders. Fighting with their long and easily damaged bills is probably selected against.

Song dances, advertisement, aerial chases, and active and psychological fighting on the ground, help each pair to hold and maintain a territory during the courtship, nest site selection, and egg laying phases. In many habitats each pair has a living-space containing several alternative nest sites, roosting places, refuges for small young, and reserve food sources for use in severe weather. Both sexes defend their living-space against any rivals which intrude on their air or ground space. The off-duty partner often feeds on neutral ground, but when on guard feeds in the territory while its mate is brooding.

Pairs on Dorback Moor and in south-east Sutherland start by rearing their chicks in the nesting territory; later leading them to farm fields when they have become more active and possibly requiring less dense cover. In some forest-bogs and clearings in

Rothiemurchus, however, the parents restricted their chicks entirely to the nesting territories, although they themselves sometimes flew away to farms or grasslands. When the parents of several broods are using the same fields, any fighting or skirmishing is concentrated round the broods rather than on fixed boundaries.

COURTSHIP AND SEX

The cock usually establishes his territory before the arrival of the hen; but I have watched pairs return together. The slow process of courtship and sexual adjustment then proceeds. In nuptial flights the two birds often glide side by side on bowed wings. I once saw a cock attempt to copulate in the air, floating with rapidly beating wings onto the back of the hen, but this attempt was probably unsuccessful. The cock chases the hen on the ground and in the air, but these pursuits are less dramatic than those of many other waders. Early in the ground courtship, when the cock starts to run behind the hen, she often turns and rebuffs him. On 9 April 1941, for example, a pair walked very quickly, but the cock at first did not directly follow the hen. Later she twice turned and raised her wings when he approached; the cock, which sang several times, moved after her without stretching out his neck.

When the hen has reached breeding condition the cock bows to her, with his tail elevated or fanned to display the white rump patch. He then approaches the hen from behind, but she often runs or walks rapidly away; and he follows more slowly, all the time giving his characteristic harsh and throaty *tree-tree-tree* copulation cries. The hen runs in circles, curves, ellipses, or sometimes in a fairly straight line; and, if not yet in full passion, she may turn and spar at her partner. The cock often partly raises and violently flaps his wings as he follows the hen; and she may periodically stop, peck at the ground, and generally appear indifferent. From time to time, when the hen pauses, the cock stands behind her, but just as he seems about to take her she moves forward again. When the hen is ready to mate she stands still, tilting slightly forward and loosening her wings to expose her white rump patch. Behind her the

cock still calls and beats his wings and pecks at her tail before finally jumping onto her back. The two birds then sometimes touch bills, or the cock bills her head or neck. He may take her more than once, either jumping down and then back again, or while still balanced on the hen's back. All the time he beats his lovely long wings. The cock stays on the hen's back for 1–4 minutes; once, Lennart Raner tells us, for 20 minutes. After copulation the two birds sometimes preen or fly away; or the cock may run to a patch of moss and start nest dancing, rotating, scraping, and sometimes pushing his head and beak into the scoop while waiting for his mate to join him. At other times he nest dances on his own.

Many curlews probably do not start to breed until they are nearly two years old. H. Greiner (*in* Glutz 1977), however, recorded that a cock reared in captivity copulated in his second calendar year. Some hens, identified by the peculiarities and shapes of their eggs, certainly return to the same territories in consecutive years. Gordon Douglas, for example, traced a Surrey hen which laid most unusual eggs between 1933–46.

DISPERSION AND BREEDING DENSITY

Breeding density varies greatly in different localities. The Dorback population was spaced at intervals of roughly 450 m; pairs in Rothiemurchus usually nested about 550 m apart. Paul Heppleston knew a locality in Orkney where there were 6 breeding pairs/10 ha; he once found two nests only 25 m apart. In north-east Sutherland we have found curlews nesting 450 m apart; but in the north-west, near Loch Stack, density is lower, with nests separated by 900 m or more. Around Culrain density has ranged from 300–1,000 m. Patrick recorded two pairs, in the grass-heath of a rough pasture, with nests about 450 m apart.

Density is high in the great Shannon Bogs in the Irish midlands, in parts of south-central Wales, and in Cumberland. In Carmarthen I watched several curlews simultaneously returning to nests which were on wet fields and less than 100 m apart; on these haunts two nests were sometimes separated by less than 50 m. Twelve pairs of curlews and 51 pairs of lapwings nested on 260 ha of farmland in Cumberland in 1937; and two pairs of curlews nested in a clover field of roughly 6 ha (R. H. Brown 1939). In one haunt in the Pennines, Ken Williamson recorded 14–18.5 breeding pairs/km².

In Bavaria, H. Greiner discovered that each pair dominated a living-space of 12.5–70 ha and that nests were occasionally only 100 m apart. In the marshes of Westphalia M. Kipp (*in* Glutz 1977) estimated a living-space varying from 6.9–38.1 ha, with an average of 19.3 ha for a population of 28 pairs; four unmated cocks were spaced out in an area of 8.8 ha. The average density of the group showed nests 384–477 m apart, a mean of 420 m for 132 nests with a minimum spacing between two nests of 110 m.

SOCIAL BEHAVIOUR

Curlews are social birds. Although they establish territories in the breeding season, only in most favourable habitats are nests found less than 100 m apart. On the other hand, isolated pairs sometimes occupy particular heaths, commons and pastures.

In high quality breeding habitats several pairs often move from field to field with their older families, without any serious fighting.

Groups feed and roost on fields and meadows. There were often parties of up to 20 on the Dorback fields, but no similar sociability in the population breeding in the forest bogs and clearings of Rothiemurchus Forest. In Cumberland, in May and June 1937–38, Brown (1939) watched groups of 50–60 curlews 'in derelict woodlands overgrown with peat and self-sown birch'. Were these low status birds which had not yet successfully established territories?

By means of colour marking, B. Ens and L. Zwarts (1980) discovered that some curlews of both sexes appear to be permanently territorial or non-territorial on the coastal lands all through the non-breeding period of July–March. Territorial birds annually maintain and defend the small winter territories of 0.3–1.0 ha which usually have natural boundaries. D. R. Phillips (1983) also recorded that some adults defended particular mussel ridges just after they had arrived on their breeding grounds.

NEST, EGG AND CLUTCH

The cock often forms many well-separated scoops in different parts of his territory. These 'scratchings' possibly indicate possession of living-space to rivals. In one of them the hen sometimes lays her first egg without adding any further lining. Some pairs very sparsely line the scrapes but others, particularly when nesting in fields, make a substantial and well-lined scoop. A few pairs choose the same kind of ground as do greenshanks. The Dorback curlews nested in grass-heath and sometimes in short or middle-height heather. In Abernethy and Rothiemurchus Forests the curlews nested in heather mixed with grass, occasionally at the foot of a stunted pine, and exceptionally in open clearings in the old pine forest. I twice found hens laying in the same scoop in consecutive years.

Some scoops are wide and deep. K. Hudec and W. Černý (*in* Glutz 1977) measured seven nests in Czechoslovakia which were 15–24 cm in breadth (mean 19.9 cm); and 3–12 cm in depth (mean 5.9 cm). However, the quality and hardness of the ground partly determines the depth of the nest scoop.

Most of the nests which Arthur Whitaker recorded on the Derbyshire and Yorkshire moors were in tussocks of grass; but on 2 May 1940 he found one in a large bed of 30 cm high *Calluna* heather, where the eggs could only be seen from above.

In mild springs the Dorback curlews were often on their territories for over 60 days before the hens laid their first eggs. In Rothiemurchus the pre-laying phase was a little less; but the cock was often singing and calling for up to 50 days before his hen started to lay. Much depends on the weather and the character of the habitat.

On the other hand, M. Kipp recorded that in Westphalia 18 cocks averaged 40 days and 14 hens averaged 38 days on territories before laying started. In Helsinki, in habitats further to the north, von Haartman and his colleagues estimated that the hens were on average only 21 days on territories before laying their first eggs.

Few pairs in Dorback, Rothiemurchus and Inshriach Forests completed their clutches before the last week of April; most were a little later. Twenty-six hens laid out between 21 April–19 May, with an average of 5 May. Between 1977–79 the hen which Patrick and Richard watched in Culrain laid her fourth egg between 26 April–3 May. Five nests in north Sutherland had an average clutch date of 7 May; and six nests in Radnor averaged 12 May. Twenty-five nests found on the Yorks-Derbyshire Moors ranged from 20 April–31 May (mean 3 May).

In central Europe, in early years, some curlews start to lay in the last ten days of March. The main laying season in north and east Europe starts on about 21 April. The earliest recorded clutch was found, with four partly incubated eggs, on 16 March 1961, at Oldeberkoop in Friesland (Bijstra 1961). A group in Bavaria completed clutches between 28 March–20 April. The earliest egg in Westphalia was recorded on 23 March, but Kipp found that 11 April–20 May was more usual. The laying season in Switzerland is similar to that in the north of Scotland, seldom beginning before 16 April (J. Heim *in* Glutz 1962). The groups nesting in Matsalu National Park in Estonia SSR lay their first eggs about 27 April, with at least one egg laid in half of the nests laid by 1 May (S. Onno). In Finland the laying season is partly determined by latitude, with distinct differences in timing for $60°–62°$, $62°–64°$ and $64°–66°$N.

Curlews' eggs are usually broad to pointed ovate but sometimes sub-pyriform. They are only slightly glossed and have exceptionally thin and brittle shells. The ground colour varies from greyish yellow, greenish olive-green to deep umber-brown. The eggs are spotted, flecked, streaked and sometimes blotched with umber, sepia and dark or reddish brown and have grey undermarkings. They are seldom heavily blotched at the heavy end but are streaked and spotted all over with rich reddish brown. Erythristic eggs, with a ground colour of reddish yellow, are on record. There are also a few examples of almost blue and greyish white eggs, but these are extremely rare. Whitaker found a particularly fine clutch in mid Yell, Shetland; all three eggs were pale bright green in ground colour and covered with unusual green blotches.

I once found a clutch containing an egg with a coating of lime over its ground colour and markings, this veil giving a lovely pink appearance. Our friend, Hugh Blair, considers that 'veiling' is unusual in waders' eggs; but he has examined two such curlews' eggs from different nests, one of which was blotched and spotted in attractive shades of lilac and violet on a pale lilac-grey ground.

One hundred curlews' eggs from Britain averaged 67.6×47.9 mm (Jourdain 1940). 273 eggs from Westphalia, at 67.5×46.7 mm (M. Kipp 1977), and 267 eggs from Bavaria, at 67.26×47.65 mm (*in* Glutz 1977), were slightly smaller. 155 Belgian eggs had a mean of 67.3×47.2 mm and 87 Netherlands eggs averaged 68.3×47.2 mm (Glutz 1977). von Frisch (1956) recorded a dwarf egg measuring 38.0×31.33 mm and another hen laid exceptionally small eggs with a maximum of 39.1×23.2 mm. Table 3 records the weights of freshly-laid eggs. Three hundred eggshells in north and central Europe varied from 3.78–5.70 gm (mean 4.75 gm) (M. Schönwetter 1963). The average weight of a hen curlew is 787 gm (Kipp) and the mean clutch weight is roughly 300 gm. A full clutch, therefore, weighs roughly 38% of the hen's body weight (Table 2).

Spey Valley hen curlews usually laid their eggs on alternate days, often at intervals of about 48 hours; but for others I have recorded intervals of 24–40 hours. In parts of Germany they usually lay daily, but sometimes with the lapse of a day between two particular eggs. In Westphalia, however, Kipp recorded intervals of 1.4–5 days, with an average of 1.85 days for 32 observations. Eggs are not laid at any set time. I have watched a hen slink in to lay her second egg at approximately 11.00; others have laid earlier in the morning and late in the evening.

Curlews are single brooded. A hen normally lays four eggs, occasionally three, rarely five. Genuine 'twos' have been recorded but most have probably lost an egg or two. Paulussen (1959) recorded a clutch of six eggs in Norway, all of which had apparently been laid by the same hen. Clutches of seven are probably due to two hens laying in the same nest. We have tabulated clutch size in Table 4.

The Dorback hens regularly laid replacement clutches, unless their eggs were taken or destroyed shortly before they hatched. These replacement clutches were completed 11–16 days after the loss of the first. Greiner recorded replacements in 8–14 days in Bavaria, but in ten years observations never met with a hen which laid a second replacement. In Westphalia, Kipp recorded intervals of 4–10 days between the loss of the clutch and the laying of the first replacement egg. Here, however, one hen produced a second replacement clutch from which three young flew in mid July. Replacements in the Spey Valley were normally laid in the same territory. Greiner and von Frisch met with hens which laid their replacement clutches in the same scoop; but a great amount of disturbance induces them to shift over 300 m from the original nest-site.

INCUBATION

Curlews often start steady incubation between the laying of their third and fourth eggs, but some pairs wait until the clutch is completed. I have flushed a curlew from two eggs at night, but do not know whether they then regularly brood incomplete clutches. In the evening one or both birds are often noisy when disturbed close to a nest containing a single egg. By day they brood two eggs for quite long spells but do not appear to advance incubation.

In the early days of incubation the cock seldom appears to take part, but he stands on guard on a stance; and he warns his sitting mate by excited cries whenever a human intruder is approaching. His warning cries almost invariably cause the hen to leave her eggs. She often runs a short distance before flying, or she launches herself in low flight, giving a few quick excited cries when she is well away from the nest. The two birds then fly around, *yaking* loudly, until the intruder has moved away. The non-brooding bird, judging from its calls when disturbed, often roosts quite close to the nest and sitting partner.

I have often watched the behaviour of nesting curlews while lying up on mounds and in clearings waiting for home-coming greenshanks. I sometimes built rough hides on the edge of the forest and from this saw a brooding curlew dozing on its nest while its mate fed fitfully on the grassy edge of a pinewood 75–100 m away. Nest relief came quite suddenly. The off-duty bird – a cock, judged by the shortness of the bill – ran up to the hen and gently touched her mantle feathers; she then stood up and allowed him to poke his head and beak into the nest. Afterwards the hen walked away rather stiffly, tossing sideways bits and pieces of vegetation, before going to the same part of the clearing from which the cock had started his run. Many pairs, however, appear to lack formal and regular nest-relief ceremonials; but the two birds sometimes bubble to one another as the incoming partner approaches. At other times, particularly if the off-duty bird has been feeding on neutral fields or pasture, the sitting curlew flies quietly away before its relief has reached the nest.

Curlews change over at different times of the day; some pairs relieve one another in late evening and early morning, but this is not a firm ritual. On one of the days that I was watching a nest containing deeply incubated eggs, the two birds changed duties at intervals of $3\frac{1}{2}$ and $4\frac{1}{2}$ hours. Philip Burton has had the same experience. In another territory the smaller-beaked bird took over after 21.00 hours on consecutive nights. W. Spillner (1971) recorded brooding stints of 3.6 hours. Other curlews, however, sometimes sit for much longer spells without nest relief.

The brooding curlew sometimes leaves the nest for spells of 24–40 minutes on warm days; but the eggs are seldom left uncovered for more than a few minutes in cold weather. I have watched an off-duty cock buffet his hen and drive her back to the nest and eggs from which I had flushed her.

A sitting curlew sits upright on the nest, periodically raising its neck to peer around. If slightly nervous it 'freezes', pushing out its long neck and beak along the ground. From time to time the bird half rises and pokes the underside of its beak among the eggs and shuffles them around with feet and lower breast. At other times the curlew fidgets with the surrounding vegetation, occasionally plucking blades of grass or twigs of heather and placing them on the edge of the scoop. Apart from spells of dozing, when the bird turns with its long beak stretched out along its back, a sitting curlew is alert, occasionally bubbling to the guard bird. Towards the hatch the sitter often broods more closely and its partner sometimes moves in and stands close by. There is now a great commotion if the pair are disturbed; the two birds agitatedly scream and shriek on the ground and in the air.

Keith Tayles told us about the curlews which he watched in May 1979. This pair, which nested on a burnt patch of moorland edge in Yorkshire, appeared to have reversed sexual roles. The cock – whose beak was at least 25% shorter than that of its mate – brooded during 24 out of the 26 hours of observations; and was sitting during the hatching of all the eggs. The long-billed bird – the hen? – guarded the nest from a hillside 150 m away, warned the sitting mate, and frequently chased intruding curlews from adjacent territories.

I have measured three incubation periods, in which the last egg hatched in 28, 28–29, and 31–32 days. In the third of these clutches the curlews, which were nesting on a sheep walk, were frequently disturbed. H. Noll (1924) and von Frisch (1956) give periods of 27–29 days from the laying of the last egg in a clutch to the hatching of the first chick. Kipp recorded 26–33 days for particular eggs, with an average of 28.8 days for 62 eggs.

HATCHING

A curlew converses with the chicks immediately they start to call in the eggs, sometimes answering their squeaks with loud and most unexpected hooting cries. Eamonn tape-recorded these at a nest in Culrain in 1979.

Young curlews take a long time to hatch; the eggs are 'bumped' or show a network of small cracks for 2–4 days before the chicks break free. At the Yorkshire nest, Tayles, who recorded a chipping period of 77 hours from starring to hatch, noticed that the sitting cock had some difficulty in sitting comfortably on the hatching eggs. After the chicks emerged the hen slowly came to the nest, taking 50 minutes to get within 60 cm of it. 'Two chicks scrambled out... but the remaining chicks stayed in the nest for another 10 minutes before joining them'. In the afternoon the hen stood about 6 m from the nest and the cock walked towards her. 'They faced each other, standing 10 metres apart and *bubbled*, their beaks clattering audibly before the cock began to feed and move away. Keeping away from the nest the hen quietly called the chicks... and they piped in reply but continued to wander'. At a nest in Inshriach Forest I watched a cock running in a curiously stiff and upright posture while following his mate back to the nest in which all four chicks were crouching.

Curlews are among the few waders which tend to leave eggshells in the scoop or immediately outside it. I well remember finding a curlew's nest by first seeing the large white interior of the eggshell before my eye took in the brooding bird. Selection has probably determined that it is more dangerous for a curlew to carry away its large eggshells, and thus give a clue to the nest, than to leave them in or around the nest. This is not, however, an invariable practice. John Markham and I have both seen curlews walk away with large portions of shell and drop them in water, before rinsing out their bills; and I have watched hens walk off and fly away with shells to a distance of 50–400 m. G. Tomkinson and O. R. Owen also found large portions of hatched eggshell well away from nests. The shell-removing impulse, however, may weaken after one or two shells have been carried away. But I have always found a quantity of shell debris in scoops in which the chicks have hatched and left.

Some curlews, as with the Yorkshire pair, continue to brood empty eggshells after the young have gone. The late Frances Pitt told me that a curlew she was watching from a hide failed to remove any shells; and when they were accidentally knocked out of the scoop the hen carefully raked them back and pushed them under her. When the chicks had gone the crushed shells remained.

Addled eggs are not ejected. In 1942 I experimentally placed a domestic fowl's eggshell in a nest in which the eggs were moderately incubated. The curlew soon removed the shell and dropped it about 35 m away.

YOUNG

Curlew chicks are gangling little creatures, with pink-buff eye stripes and creamy to pinkish white mantles, with patches and bands of brownish black dispersed over them. The sides of their necks and lower necks are reddish brown and their underparts light buff. Bills are dark blackish fawn, legs dark lead and feet leaden to greyish blue. Tayles particularly noted that they had blue beaks. Their irides are brown.

At first parent curlews usually brood the chicks under their wings in the nest scoop. The chicks are capable of leaving the nest within a few hours of hatching; but they are usually confined to the scrape, or recalled and kept there for 12–24 hours, and in one example for nearly 36 hours. As with greenshank, lapwing and some other waders, if the last chick or chicks hatch in the evening the parents usually brood them at night before leading them away in the morning.

The interval between the hatching of the first and last chick partly determines the period that the chicks spend in the nest and may take anything from 6 to about 24 hours. In Yorkshire, at the nest that Tayles was watching, the second chick was hatched 44 minutes after the first, but the four did not finally quit the scoop until about 18 hours later.

Sometimes the shrill cries of curlew chicks, while still in the eggs or after they have hatched, are audible from a distance of fully 50 m. Tayles noticed that chicks, which had moved about 2 m from the nest, froze when the parents gave their *yak-yak* alarm cries. This behaviour was markedly different from that of a brood which I watched in Inshriach Forest on 27 May 1941. There the two parents alternately flew around and flapped over the ground, shrieking dementedly. Despite their clamour, I heard faint almost ghostly answering *kourlis, kook-koos* and other alarm cries; after a search I found three chicks which were about 30 hours old. Their faint cries precisely mimicked those of their parents, to which they completely failed to react. One chick ran over my boot and I watched it feeding in gutters and taking midges from blades of grass. When caught, however, the downy started to scream and ran away immediately I put it down. I could hear the cries of these chicks when I was fully 100 m away; possibly the young take some time to react to their parents' warnings after they have left the scoop and its surroundings.

Curlew chicks can swim almost as soon as they can run. O. Heinroth (1927–28) noted that from about the fifth day they started to beat their wings and also 'froze' or made for cover in answer to their parents' alarm cries. When they are about two days old they make threat gestures, pushing out their short bills. Both parents periodically brood their chicks until they are about 10 days old. Sometimes the parents divide up the family, each tending two chicks.

After the chicks are well-grown, however, the hen frequently leaves the family in charge of the cock. The young curlews first attempt to fly when they are about four weeks old. Kipp recorded that 20 hand-reared young flew between 28–36 days, with an average of 32.3 days.

DISTRACTION BEHAVIOUR

R. H. Brown noted distraction behaviour in Cumberland directed against dogs and foxes. The parents now give elaborate displays, running through the bog, stumbling, and violently flapping their wings. These tactics certainly succeed sometimes in luring a dog from the brood. Several parents may also combine. In mid June Brown watched a fox searching a meadow for young curlews; this brought six curlews together. They all flew round the fox while the seventh – possibly the breeding hen – flapped along the ground ahead of it. Sheep and cattle occasionally trample on nests. I have watched a curlew attempting to distract or divert sheep by raising and flapping its wings, much in the same way as lapwings often do. Donald Watson (1977) once saw a pair of curlews turn a ewe aside by 'using both wings and bill to dunt its nose'.

VOICE

The haunting cries and the wonderful bubbling song of the curlew are among the most thrilling spring sounds in moorland Britain. Much stimulating research is ahead for the student who tries better to understand the voice of this lovely wader.

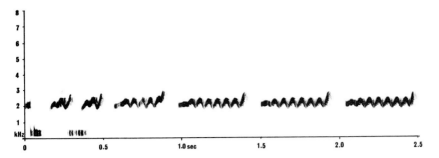

Curlew bubbling, Inverness-shire (Bill Sinclair)

Cocks alone appear to give the remarkable song dances, but both sexes sing in normal or gliding flights and on the ground. A sitting bird sometimes bubbles on the nest; or the two birds bubble and clatter their mandibles in greeting or in display to one another on the ground. On the moors you often hear curlews bubbling in the small hours and sometimes even in darkness. Curlews also sing in moonlight and on their autumn wintering grounds on the mudflats and estuaries.

Full song dance starts by the cock giving a series of long drawn out *oor-oor-oor* or *oog-oog-oogs*; and he then speeds these up and the calls merge into the bubbling *koor-lee koor-lees*, after which the singer gives almost the same cries as those used in the song's introduction.

Curlews have a large vocabulary.

(1)   The loud *koor-lee koor-lee* is a contact, warning, and mild excitement cry.

(2)   A cock chasing a hen, and violently beating his wings just before copulation gives characteristic grating *gree-gree-grees*.

(3)   A wailing call is possibly used by the cock to call the hen to the nest site (Glutz 1977).

(4)   One cock, in stiff upright posture, followed his hen to a nest with chicks while uttering deep loud gutteral *guck-guck-gucks*.

(5)   Fighting curlews utter growling calls while attacking one another. A cry of high alarm or excitement, a hoarse *craa*, is sometimes given by a bird 'jumped' from the nest, or by cocks when fighting.

(6)   *Koi-koi* or *kwoi-kwoi-kwoi* usually denotes slight alarm.

(7)   *Yak-yak-yaks* mark strong anger, alarm and excitement. Both birds use these barking cries near the nest or when chicks are in the heather.

(8)   A rapidly repeated series of *byuhuus* are cries of urgent warning to the chicks.

(9)   At the nest, curlews sometimes use tittering cries which faintly resemble those of the whimbrel.

(10)   In 1979 Eamonn tape recorded the loud hooting *hoo-hoo* of a parent talking to chicks squeaking in the eggs.

(11)   The chicks have several different cries:

(a)   a loud whistling *whee* which carries a suprisingly long distance.

(b)   a more excited *kwee-a kwee-a*, when standing up in the nest and beating its small wings.

We have already described how a chick of about 30 hours old showed no fear or reaction to the 'alarming' of their parents. They mimic these, giving faint whistling *koo-lees*, *kook-kook-kooks*, and other cries.

PREDATORS

Hooded crows were the most formidable egg predators of the Dorback and Rothiemurchus curlews. I often watched a single hoodie, or a pair, slowly flapping over curlew territory or carefully watching the moor from a tree on the edge of the forest. I never actually saw a hoodie find and rob a nest; but I sometimes found sucked eggs floating on pools. I saw a short-eared owl drop down in a forest marsh and fly away with a young curlew hanging in its claws. One of the curlews, calling frantically, followed it over the trees.

Peregrines are not predators in the habitats where we have worked; but in the central Grampians they occasionally take old and young curlews. In prey records for peregrines in 1961–62 D. A. Ratcliffe (1980) records 20 curlews, of which 11 were from inland and six from coastal sites in the Scottish Highlands. Between 1964–75 Douglas Weir (*pers comm*) found four adults and one young curlew in his April–June study of the food of 23 pairs of peregrines. Walpole-Bond (1914) noticed that curlews often foiled hunting peregrines by flying very low over land or water.

Eddie Balfour recorded that hen harriers in Orkney frequently took young curlews. In the Lowlands they apparently seldom do so; but R. C. Dickson (*in* Watson 1977) found two young curlews in a hen harrier's nest on a moor. There, and in Orkney, however, curlews frequently mob hunting hen harriers and sometimes breed successfully within 100 m of their nest. In his MS notebooks Edward Booth, the famous collector, noted young curlews among the prey which the handful of Spey Valley red kites took to their nests in the late 19th century. Glutz (1971) records golden eagles and goshawks as occasional predators.

The fox is always a likely enemy. I have found nests which they have robbed; they also hunt young curlews sometimes. Hungry sheep dogs are other predators.

H. Litzbarski (*in* Glutz 1977) watched the behaviour of a pair of curlews when a weasel had reached 6–7 m from the nest. Several times the curlews made excited threat flights above and over the nest, becoming increasingly agitated as the mammal approached. The curlews gave little jumps into the air, but did not attack the weasel or carry out distraction displays.

FOOD

Curlews peck, jab, probe and pick for their food, which varies according to its availability in a particular habitat. The differing size and shape of the bills of males and females sometimes leads to exploitation of different food niches. Near Teesmouth, for example, D. J. Townshend (1980) found that short-billed birds tended to feed on earthworms on pastureland while those with long bills sought *N. diversicolor* on mudflats. Glutz (1977) and Cramp and Simmons (1983) give comprehensive lists of recorded foods.

Inland breeding curlews feed on earthworms, Tipulid larvae, various species of dung and carabid beetles, larvae of other Coleoptera, grasshoppers (Acrididae), crickets *Gryllus*, earwings (Forficula), millepedes, woodlice (Isopoda), spiders (Araneae), small molluscs, and occasionally flying insects. I have watched them feeding on the berries of cowberry *V. vitis-idaea* and crowberry *Empetrum nigrum*, both of which Glutz records. They also take small fish, frogs *Rana*, toads, lizards, and occasionally young birds and small rodents. We do not know whether, like the bristle-thighed curlew, they sometimes rob eggs from other birds' nests. Curlews occasionally rob one another. Ens and Zwarts (1980) have also watched them steal food from oystercatchers, redshanks and turnstones.

In autumn and winter they take quite different food on the mudflats. They then eat small crustaceans like shrimps (Crangonidae), swimming crabs (Portunidae), occasionally shore crabs *Carcinus maenas*, ragworms *Nereis*, and also small molluscs. Mussels, cockles, tellins, clams (Midae), periwinkles (Littorinidae), gammarids, and sandhoppers *Talitrus* are sought and eaten quite regularly. The remains of Algae and Polygonum seeds have also been found in stomachs. On the Wash in East Anglia, J. D. Goss-Custard and R. E. Jones (1976) found that the most important foods taken were bivalve molluscs, polychaete worms and small crabs.

DISTRIBUTION AND NUMBERS

During the 20th century, curlews have spread quite dramatically in lowland Britain and Ireland. They now breed in every county, with the exception of Kent, Essex, Middlesex, Hertford, Bedford, Huntingdon and Cambridge (J. Parslow 1973). Curlews – and whimbrels – are colonising the vast peatlands of the Western Isles. In 1932 I found curlews breeding in good numbers on the peat mosses and low hills of Orkney; and Balfour (1968) suggests that they had greatly increased there in the 1950s and 1960s.

The greatest increase is, however, in the lowland counties of Scotland and England, where they are now firmly settled in rough pastures and in clover and cereals. Possibly they first started to breed in the breckland of East Anglia after the great floods of 1947. By the early 1950s A. W. P. Robertson (1954) knew of over a dozen pairs nesting on bracken heath; and he recorded a breck on which curlew, stone curlew, ringed plover and lapwing all nested. In the 1950s myxomatosis, which decimated rabbit populations, incidentally greatly expanded the breeding habitats of curlews in East Anglia, at the expense of traditional breckland birds like stone curlew, ringed plover and woodlark which shunned the longer grass. Curlews have also greatly increased in Durham and Westmorland where they have become adapted to breeding in crops of clover and cereals. In the 1950s they colonised the chalklands of the Lincolnshire wolds; and K. Williamson (1968) recorded 14–18 breeding pairs/km^2 on limestone country around Malham Tarn in Yorkshire.

Curlews continue to breed in fair numbers in most parts of upland Britain, but more pairs are probably now breeding in lowland pastures than in their traditional haunts on moors, heathlands and grass heaths.

The Breeding Atlas team recorded confirmed breeding in 1,870 10-km squares, probable in 542, and possible in 372 10-km squares. Assuming an average of 15–25 breeding pairs in each certain or probable 10-km square, 40,000–70,000 breeding pairs may now be nesting in Britain and Ireland (J. T. R. Sharrock 1976).

In western and central Europe numbers have fluctuated in this century. In France the curlew population has recently declined, but roughly 800 pairs still nest, of which 200–250 pairs breed in Alsace (A. Engel and P. Schmitt 1975). There is a greatly reduced population of 3,400–4,500 breeding pairs in the Netherlands, mainly due to loss of suitable habitats (C. R. Roselaar 1983). Denmark was colonised by curlews in 1934; 250–350 breeding pairs now nest there (T. Dybbro 1976). About 300 pairs nest in Belgium and there are a few pairs in Luxembourg. There has been a marked decline in the groups nesting in Switzerland, where there are now only 13–14 breeding pairs. In West Germany 3,000–3,500 pairs breed, with local fluctuations. East Germany has about 450 pairs, but drainage of habitats has led to a reduction. There are about 200 breeding pairs in Poland and roughly 100 breeding pairs in Austria. Czechoslovakia carries about 200 breeding pairs; and groups in Hungary and Romania are now also small. Curlews are said to be decreasing in European SSR; but Estonia SSR holds about 1,000 breeding pairs.

J. Kålås and I. Byrkjedal (1981) estimated the Norwegian population at 5,100 breeding pairs, with increases in the east and some coastal habitats. S. Ulfstrand and G. Högstedt (1976) estimated that 20,000 pairs now breed in Sweden, with fewer pairs in cultivated farmlands in the south and centre of the country. Numbers have greatly decreased in Finland since 1958, when Merikallio suggested a breeding population of 44,000 pairs.

At some of their roosts in autumn and winter, curlews sometimes form large flocks of up to several thousand birds. They migrate, however, in much smaller groups of seldom more than a hundred, and associate with other waders, such as oystercatchers, whimbrel, black-tailed and bar-tailed godwits. Those of us who know and love these wonderful waders on their breeding grounds are always saddened when they leave.

WHIMBREL

When waders first started to beckon to me, the whimbrel was always intriguing. But to travel to haunts in the remote northern islands was far beyond my means! In later years I thought of living in Shetland and devoting some years to a study of whimbrel and red-necked phalaropes, but that was not to be. I occasionally heard whimbrel passing over the foothills of the Cairngorms; their tittering whistles were unforgettable voices in the night. In the 1930s, A. H. Daukes discovered one or two pairs nesting near Newtonmore, Inverness-shire, but I never had the good fortune to come across them. I did not then know it, but whimbrels had recently passsed through half a century of withdrawal in the northern islands of Britain. It was nearly forty years on before I was able to watch breeding whimbrel on the Scottish mainland.

Compared to the curlew, the whimbrel is smaller and darker brown with quicker wing beats. The bills of cock and hen are less decurved than those of the curlew and there is less difference in their respective lengths. Seen at close quarters the pattern of the dark-brown crown, divided down the middle by a pale buff streak, is distinctive

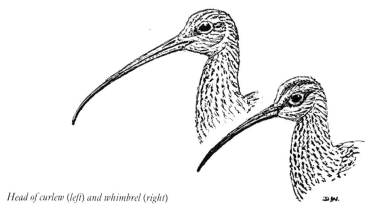

Head of curlew (left) and whimbrel (right)

although it is not always such a good field mark as one might expect; but their tittering calls and mellow silvery rippling songs immediately identify them.

The haunts of the whimbrel always have atmosphere. How lovely to hear those silvery whistles on a May morning in Shetland and to watch the cock hanging high above the moss. On Fetlar, snowy owls have sometimes carried young whimbrels to their young. There the largest concentrations of red-necked phalaropes in Britain are found among the dubhlochans. Bonxies and arctic skuas are neighbours and predators on the mosses of Unst.

Although whimbrel and curlew nest on roughly the same habitats in Shetland, and in parts of Norway, Finland and Estonia, the whimbrels tend to favour higher and more mesotrophic and oliogtrophic moors. Curlews prefer the lower eutrophic mosses, meadows, foreshores and overgrown pastures in the dips and valleys. Whimbrels often nest in short grassland only a few hundred metres from the sea. Both species are close neighbours in typical grassy heaths, with the whimbrels usually favouring drier patches and shorter undergrowth.

Finnur Gudmundsson noted that whimbrel and curlew shared breeding grounds at lower levels in Iceland; but the whimbrels often nested up to 700 m ASL on dry heath, lava flows and on sandy hills in the hinterland of small islands. In northern Scandinavia whimbrels nest on fell flats, on the edges of the pine forest, and on higher moors where mosses and dwarf shrubs are dominant. South of Trondheim they favour open crowberry heaths. Whimbrels nest in grasslands in the Faroes with snipe, dunlin, meadow pipits and oystercatchers as neighbours. They have special habitats on the rocky uplands, associating with ringed and golden plovers, purple sandpipers, oystercatchers, arctic terns and wheatears (F. Salomonsen 1935).

Wherever it nests the whimbrel has exciting and sometimes formidable neighbours. In the Pasvik, Norman Gilroy's first impression was of 'utter desolation and unfriendliness; of sheer silence and almost complete hostility'. But he later writes that 'the whole area seemed to be alive with whimbrels; wood sandpipers sang joyously high up in the clear sunshine and I heard a strange and unfamiliar clicking note, almost like the cantering of a horse on a hard road'. In those years, before the great marshes of the River Pasvik were drained, Gilroy and Edward Steward recorded finding 13 whimbrels' nests. Dusky redshanks in the mosses, bar-tailed godwits on the marsh, and sometimes waxwings and great grey shrike on the forest fringes are other neighbours of the whimbrel in the far north.

M. A. Skeel (1976) found that whimbrels of *N. ph. hudsonicus* were two years old when they started to breed. The oldest spring migrants of *N. ph. phaeopus*, recorded in Belgium, were at least 8, 9 and 10 years old when captured; and a banded hen of the Nearctic race was 11 years old when trapped. A whimbrel in Basel Zoo lived for at least 16 years. There has been no study on the nominate race with marked birds.

ARRIVAL, TERRITORY AND COURTSHIP

In late April whimbrels return to their nesting grounds singly or in small parties. Skeel (1976) discovered that if a pair survives they continue as partners in consecutive years.

Whimbrels are territorialists; challenging and fighting probably helps them to maintain a fair breeding density. In Iceland, in 1981, Patrick and his friend, Colin Galbraith, watched two whimbrels in a boundary dispute. One ran up to the other with tail raised high and the second bird flew away. In another haunt a single bird ran in crouched posture with fanned tail while chasing away a pair. Even late in the breeding season

they watched whimbrels with broods, fighting in the marshes. On 1 July there was a boundary dispute; the intruder was put to flight by the territory holder which ran towards him, head down and tail raised. Similar behaviour took place at another nest. In north Norway, W. G. Hale (1980) found that a defended chick territory ranged from 6–30 ha in heathland dotted with birch trees. Other waders, however, sometimes attack whimbrels which are feeding or running through their territories. On 16 May 1982 young Maimie, Donald Bremner and I watched a lapwing attack and expel a trespassing whimbrel.

The cock rises and circles high over the moor, rapidly beating his wings and giving soft *oo-oo* cries before gliding or spiralling downward and throwing out those thrilling silvery trills. At other times he soars high above ground with slightly decurved wings. Both cocks and hens trill in the air and on the ground; and they sing and call from the tops of trees and from stumps and posts. In song flight cocks sometimes hover head to wind, periodically shivering their wings below the level of their backs.

Whimbrels' ground displays are possibly less dramatic than those of curlews. L. Løfaldi (1983) watched a cock making scrapes and the hen walking up to him. He then rose and bowed, with his body tilted forward, tail up, and long bill pointing downwards. Later, when the hen was scrape-making, the cock stood beside her. Nest dancing sometimes led to copulation. At other times the cock walked or ran just behind the hen, sometimes moving his head up and down just above her back. When the hen stood still the cock lifted and beat his wings before fluttering onto her; she meanwhile loosened her wings and held her body horizontally. After mating, the hen leaned forward and the cock slid to earth. All the copulations watched by Løfaldi took place between 05.30–10.15.

Whimbrels are probably occasionally polygynous. Mike Harris and Stuart Murray (*pers comm*) recorded that in 1977 three whimbrels – probably a cock and two hens – were present on St Kilda. Six eggs were laid in the same scoop. On 12 May 1978 three whimbrels were again present. On 24 May a nest was found with four eggs; and there were seven on the 28th. The eggs were clearly laid by two different hens although only two adults were seen at the nest.

DISPERSION AND BREEDING DENSITY

A detailed study of the breeding density of whimbrels in Shetland would be well worthwhile. Two nests in Easter Ross, in 1971, were approximately 1,000 m apart. On Smøla Island, Norway, in 1980, there were 5.5 breeding pairs/km² on bogs, with only 1 breeding pair/km² on heaths. There are considerable variations in breeding density in Finland; south-west of Landes 0.2–0.3 breeding pairs/km²; north and east Oulu 0.1 breeding pairs/km²; north of Lake Inari 0.4 breeding pairs/km²; while north of Rovaniemi whimbrels only breed sporadically. In W. Estonia SSR, E. Kumari recorded a maximum density of 0.9–2.2 breeding pairs/km². The usual minimum spacing between nests varies from 800–1,000 m, but occasionally this drops to 200–300 m. Maximum density in White Sea habitats is two pairs per km as the crow flies. In Iceland M. Wink (1973) recorded a small wet heathland tract of 10 ha which held nine pairs of breeding whimbrels.

NEST, EGG AND CLUTCH

At first the cock and then both birds – one after the other – hollow out nest scoops, and thus lead to a number of unlined scrapes in different parts of the territory. In Easter Ross the whimbrels' nests were sometimes in short grass within 200 m of the high tide line. Ken Williamson recorded moorland nests in the Faroes close to small pools; and in Iceland Gudmundsson found that the nest bowls were usually sited in heath or grass beside dwarf birches. Among the nests that Gilroy found was one in which the eggs were laid in a deep hollow of a well-covered tussock and lined with dead grass and a few feathers; another, in a deep and dangerous bog, was beside a peaty pool. In Finnmark, Hugh Blair also found nests in crowberry, whortleberry and *Ledum palustre*; some contained large pads of lining material. Linings consist of tundra and heathland plants, particularly lichens (*Cladonia, Cetraria*), *Trichophorum, Eriophorum, Calluna, Vaccinium, Betula nana, Andromeda* and *Phragmites* (Glutz 1977). The sitting birds often add material during incubation. Dry grass contained in the lining is probably picked up within a metre of the scoop.

The contents of six nests, weighed by Kumari in Estonia, ranged from 8–31 gm. Scoops ranged from 15–18 cm in breadth and 3–6 cm in depth.

In Shetland whimbrels usually complete their clutches in the last week of May, but some hens do not start to sit until early June. On St Kilda, where whimbrels probably nested regularly from 1964–78, clutches were completed about 27–28 May in 1974 and 1978. Easter Ross groups have a similar laying season.

Four clutches in the Faroes were completed between 15–29 May (mean 23–24 May). Twelve Iceland hens laid out between 12–31 May, 60 in June, and five between 1–13 July; the latest fresh clutch was completed about 26 June. Laying is delayed in backward years; and in exceptionally cold springs some whimbrels in Iceland fail to breed (Gudmundsson 1957). In Jaeren south Norway, Blair found that many whimbrels were sitting in the second half of May and the first half of June. Further north, round the Trondjhem Fjord, some hens laid their first eggs as early as 13 May or as late as 9 June. The lateness of spring and the snow cover partly determines the laying season in Finnmark; but Blair found four full clutches before the end of May. In the Pasvik marshes, in 1928, Gilroy saw many pairs on 25 May and recorded the first clutch of fresh eggs on 30 May. Hens in arctic Sweden tend to lay later, usually in the first week of June. In Estonia SSR, however, some complete their clutches before 16 May; and in Archangel the laying season ranges from 15 May–11 June (mean 27 May) (Belopolski *et al* 1970). Most clutches are laid in late May and early June on the Kola Peninsula and in White Sea habitats.

Whimbrels' eggs are pointed ovate, broad ovate, and occasionally pyriform. In Finnmark, Gilroy recorded a pygmy egg in an otherwise normal clutch. Ground colour varies from pale olive to dull dark brown but a few are bluish or bright green. The eggs are boldly blotched and spotted, particularly at the heavy end, with sepia and umber and have lavender-grey undermarkings and sometimes black squiggles. They tend to be more heavily marked than those of the curlew.

Jourdain (1940) gives measurements of 58.43 × 41.64 mm for 100 eggs from Britain and the Faroes. 83 Iceland eggs had a slightly larger mean, 59.17 × 42.18 (Timmermann 1949), and 40 eggs from the White Sea, USSR, were smaller, 57.5 × 40.3 mm (E. P. Spangenberg and D. V. Leonovich 1960). An average clutch of four eggs at 200 gm weights approximately 50 per cent of the hen's body weight (Table 2). P. Rosenius (1937) weighed 189 blown eggshells which ranged from 1.89–3.2 gm (mean 2.55 gm).

Clutch size is given in Table 4. The normal clutch is four, three is occasional, and genuine clutches of two or five are exceptional. Daukes (1933) recorded a nest with two eggs in Inverness-shire. Gudmundsson knew of clutches of six and seven eggs in Iceland, but these were the joint layings of two hens; similarly, clutches of six and seven eggs in 1977 and 1978 on St Kilda were laid by two hens in the same scoop.

Whimbrels are single brooded. In Iceland and Easter Ross some hens are known to have laid replacement clutches; but Gilroy found none in Finnmark. In Iceland two golden plovers laid eggs in whimbrels' nests (Gudmundsson 1957).

INCUBATION

Most hens delay steady incubation until the clutch is complete. A few sit from or just before the laying of the third egg. Incomplete clutches are also periodically brooded.

On Yell, on 21 May 1933, Arthur Whitaker watched two whimbrels show little excitement when an arctic skua was blown almost over the nest which he had not then found. But once the hen started to sit on her four eggs the cock chased away every gull or skua which invaded his territory.

Both cock and hen sit; but the hen incubates for longer periods, particularly during the early stages of incubation. At a Shetland nest, watched by Ralph Chislett, one bird sat from 10.55 to 13.53 before relief. Harold Lowes recorded a nest where one of the partners brooded for 3–4 hours before the exchange took place. An off-duty whimbrel spends much time on humps or ridges from which it can overlook the nest, warn the sitting bird of danger, and chase any possible predators.

Like curlews, whimbrels often slip off their nests at a long distance from a human nest hunter. Ken Williamson noted that they sometimes quit at a distance of 800 m. A few, however, sit extremely closely, allowing the observer to stand almost beside them while they crouch like greenshanks with flattened backs, heads low and forward, and long bills touching the ground. Many sing and scold at the intruder. Most observers find that whimbrels return to their nests much more quickly than curlews, but some fly right out of sight. During the hatch both sexes have been recorded sitting on the eggs.

On Faroe, M. Danielson (1946) noted an approximate incubation period of 27–28 days; and in Iceland, Gudmundsson (1957) measured a period of 26.5–27.5 days.

HATCHING

Some eggs take long to hatch. Williamson (1946) recorded periods ranging from 90–220 hours (with a minimum of 40–75 hours at one particular nest), from the first squeak or bump to the release of the chick from the eggshell. In our experience, the long chipping period of 220 hours has only been exceeded in waders by that of particular common sandpipers at nests in north-west Sutherland.

The first egg usually has the longest chipping period, thus enabling all the brood to leave the nest at the same time. The interval between the hatching of the first and last egg varies greatly. All four chicks were hatched almost simultaneously at one nest; at another they emerged in pairs, 16–38 hours apart; and at a fourth nest the first and fourth chicks emerged within the space of 44 hours. In Estonia, on the other hand, Kumari records a period of 1–2 days for the entire brood. M. M. Tremaine (1974) watched a sitting whimbrel of the Nearctic race use its bill to assist a chick emerge from the egg.

Eggshell disposal by whimbrels poses many interesting problems. Chislett recorded that the three large eggshell fragments were removed but that the fourth large portion was still in the nest when his observations ended. Williamson also found that large fragments of the earlier hatched eggs were invariably removed when the chicks were dry. In Inverness-shire, however, Daukes noticed that a considerable amount of shell debris was still in the scoop along with the two old chicks.

This pattern, which differs greatly from that of the curlew, probably arose from the balance of risks. Whimbrels often nest in short herbage and curlew in longer vegetation. Predators are more likely to notice the white interiors of eggshells in open than in more sheltered nest sites.

Addled eggs are usually allowed to stay in the nest; but Williamson reported that a parent probably removed a broken egg.

Between 1942–48 the 14 nests recorded by Williamson in the Faroes had an average hatching success of 76.9%. Predators destroyed 11.5% of the eggs and infertility accounted for a further 5.8%.

YOUNG

Individual hatching patterns differ. Both parents usually take part, but at a nest which G. K. Yeates was watching the cock took the principal share in brooding while the chicks were emerging.

The chicks usually stay in or close to the nest until all members of the broods have hatched. Older chicks sometimes stay up to 40 hours in the scoop; others leave after a few hours. In an unusual experience, Kumari watched parents repeatedly lead a chick back to the nest for brooding which apparently continued for 3–5 days. Chislett and Williamson both watched one parent lead away the two oldest chicks while the other brooded the third chick and hatched out the last egg. The second parent is sometimes torn between chick and egg which it broods alternately.

The parents later divide the brood, each particularly brooding, tending and guarding one or two chicks. Whimbrels are extremely noisy and excited when they are guarding young. One parent often acts as sentinel while the other feeds on the ground close to the brood. In Easter Ross an adult called frantically from a wooden post while its chick scuttled around and fed fully 150 m away. In the second and third weeks the parents each tend one or two chicks; one usually moves away with its portion of the family, but the two groups sometimes join up. Whimbrels sometimes move up to 3 km from where they were hatched in Faroe habitats.

Young whimbrels have a long fledging period, probably only making their first flight after five or six weeks. In Estonia the first young whimbrels fly early in July, in Iceland in mid July, and in the forest bogs of northern Europe usually not until late July.

DISTRACTION BEHAVIOUR

Whimbrels use aggressive flights and rather poorly developed distraction displays to drive away or lure enemies from their nests or chicks. In rather spectacular aggressive flights they fly low and straight at the head of the intruder. A Yell hen, which had not then started to sit on her full clutch, flew straight at Whitaker, trilled loudly and dropped down on a tussock about 12 m away from him. Here she 'lowered her head and stood with wide open beak calling loudly', and then walked away false feeding. Lure displays are poorly developed; a whimbrel may merely run away without any elaborate display. On the Faroes, Williamson recorded others leaving their nests or hatched chicks and moving with spread wings 'in a series of leaps and bounds over the rough ground'. Another whimbrel ran off hatching eggs with half-spread wings and tail partly spread. In answer to the distress calls of chicks parents sometimes flutter up and 'collapse', giving high screaming barks. Colingwood Ingram (1942) watched one sweep its wings through vegetation to make 'swishing noises'.

VOICE

Cramp and Simmons (1983) give a full analysis of the variations of song and cries of the whimbrel, largely based on M. A. Skeel's fine study of the Nearctic race *hudsonicus*.

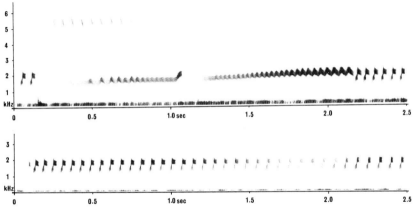

Whimbrel trilling, Ross-shire (Bill Sinclair)

(1)   The silvery trill follows a rapid series of rising common curlew like *koos*. Both sexes sing in ground courtship but the cock uses the aerial song as an advertising weapon. This bubbling trill is also used by sitting birds and by those about to exchange at the nest. To some ears it resembles the bubble of the hen cuckoo.

(2)   During nest dances and territorial assertion both sexes use a harsh whining call, unlike any used by common curlew.

(3)   Copulation calls of the male are a series of soft low *tu-tu-tus*.

(4)   A rapid hoarse whistling *worlip-woworlip-woworlip-lip-woworlip* is used in aerial chases and pursuits.

(5)   As the bird settles on the nest it gives a soft call *whoo*.

(6)   The anxiety call is a shrill quick *whip*.

(7)   Alarm cries sound like *whip-ip-ip-ip*.

(8)   When flying at ground predators or human intruders, whimbrels give quick series of *klik-lik-liks*.

(9)   Anger notes include a sharp barking call and low *pwohs-pwohs* (Williamson 1946).

(10)   Scolding trills sound like *guck-gucks*.

(11)   An alarmed bird escorting chicks gives a series of *quak-quaks*.

(12)   The chicks have at least two different calls; but it is not known whether, like young curlews, they mimic the full battery of their parents' alarm calls.

(a)   In the egg and after hatching the chick gives soft *peeps*, probably as contact notes with its parents and siblings. A hoarse plaintive *whee-ee* is rather similar but stronger than those given in the eggs.

(b)   Young whimbrels five weeks old, but unable to fly, greet their parents with adult whinny calls.

(13)   The characteristic call of passage whimbrels are quick tittering *titti-titti-tittis* or *bibi-bibi-bibis*. These serve as contact notes and are principally used outwith the breeding grounds.

(14)   Passage birds have a hoarse cry *kahiyah-kahiyah* similar to that of an alarmed curlew.

PREDATORS

Whimbrels have many enemies on their northern nesting grounds. A particularly high concentration of possible predators nest around the few pairs breeding in Easter Ross. Colonies of great black-backed and herring gulls, and smaller groups of common gulls, all nest close to the whimbrels. Our friend, Donnie Macdonald, watched a herring gull fly down and carry away a whimbrel chick. Hooded crows and many jackdaws are also persistently on the hunt for eggs; they robbed three nests which we had hoped to watch. The eggs were broken and sucked with large gashes on their sides. Foxes, seldom seen, are other possible predators.

Arctic skuas are deadly enemies in Shetland. Bonxies and the larger gulls, together with many hooded crows, also make living difficult for waders on the mosses. On Fetlar the famous cock snowy owl probably took young whimbrels to the nest. A note in one of the watchers' log books records, '3 curlews or whimbrels'.

The gyr falcon is a likely predator in Iceland, as well as arctic skuas, large gulls, hooded crows and arctic foxes. Goshawks, hen harriers, hawk owls and other northern owls, long-tailed skuas and foxes are all predators in the forest marshes of northern Europe. So artful are the hoodies at nest finding that it seems almost a miracle that whimbrels and other waders still thrive.

FOOD

In Easter Ross we have watched whimbrels feeding on unidentified insects on short grass, but no special detailed study of the whimbrel's food and feeding behaviour appears to have been carried out on their Scottish breeding grounds.

Kumari (1958) analysed the food contents of stomachs of 20 whimbrels breeding on the Estonian marshes. 53.5% consisted of cranberries *V. oxycoccus* (two had also been eating crowberries *E. nigrum*); 33.4% consisted of beetles. Like greenshanks in north-west Sutherland, they greatly favour *Plateumaris* leaf beetles of which 224 were counted. 4.0% consisted of caddis flies and there was a smaller quantity of spiders, moths, flies, dragonflies and bugs; lizards *Lacerta vivipara* were found in six stomachs. The stomachs of four coastal birds in autumn contained many *Gammarus*.

G. P. Dementiev and N. A. Gladkov (1951) analysed three stomachs in summer in USSR. These almost exclusively contained vegetable food including crowberry *E. nigrum*, cowberry *V. vitis-idaea*, cloudberry *Rubus chamaemorus*. Gudmundsson analysed the food of 20 birds collected in Iceland, 19 of which held remains of crowberry *E. nigrum*, blaeberry *V. hermaphroditum*, *uligonusum* and *myrtillus*. In spring and early summer the whimbrels had fed on the previous year's berries. Thirteen stomachs contained insects, particularly beetles (Coleoptera) and flies (Diptera); there was one moth larva and an unidentified insect pupa; four held pond snails. P. Beretzk *et al* (1959) recorded that two stomachs, from birds taken in Hungary during autumn, contained grasshoppers *Ailolopus thalassinus* and *Conocephalus dorsalis*.

Coastal whimbrels feed on marine animals like *Lymnaea balthica*; and one bird had eaten molluscs *Littorina obtusata* and *Nucella lapellus*. These birds do not appear to probe deeply for their food, which they usually extract from the upper soil and from plants. They drag small crabs *Uca* from their burrows, crushing small ones before eating them and cracking the larger by striking them with their bills (Glutz 1977). In the Faroes whimbrels move from nesting grounds in the hills to partly cultivated ground below, to feed on tipulid larvae and earwigs (Forficula) (Williamson 1946).

DISTRIBUTION AND NUMBERS

In the last 100 years numbers of breeding whimbrels have varied greatly in Britain. In 1921–22, for example, no whimbrels nested on Hascosay in Shetland where, in 1897, O. A. J. Lee had found 16 nests of the 22 pairs breeding on that island. Richard Perry suggested that the last known pair nested in Noss in 1922; and in the early 1940s they apparently ceased to nest on Yell, which was formerly one of their strongholds. Even Unst, the great Whimbrel island of Shetland, had a lapse in 1938 when J. Peterson could not locate a single pair. In the late 1940s, however, possibly coincident with a cooler climate, the whimbrels started to revive and stretch south, as did some other boreal birds. L. S. V. Venables and U. M. Venables (1955) recorded that in 1949 at least 35 pairs bred on Unst and seven pairs also nested in two different locations on Mainland Shetland. Thenceforward the whimbrels have thrived. Fetlar and Unst are the headquarters, but they also now nest on Yell, Whalsay, and on different parts of the north Mainland of Shetland.

Whimbrels periodically nested in Orkney, particularly Hoy and Sanday; there was a brood on Hoy in 1889. After a very long lapse they returned to Orkney and bred on Eday in 1968 and 1974. Whimbrels have also nested on Fair Isle and St Kilda and they have successfully colonised the flows and peatlands of north Lewis. Stray pairs nested in Sutherland in 1961 and 1973; and at least from the late 1960s a small group has nested regularly beside a firth in Easter Ross.

J. T. R. Sharrock (1976) concludes that 'the present population is certainly under 200 pairs (30% of this total being on Unst).' M. Herfst and M. G. Richardson (1982) estimate that 105–135 pairs breed on Mainland, 70–75 pairs on Unst and Fetlar, and 15–20 pairs on other islands in the Shetland group, 260–305 pairs in all (Thom 1986).

Böhme and Reiner (1973) estimated the Faroe population at 22 pairs – five on Mykines, 11 on Vágar, and six on north Streymoy. In Norway there are small but irregular nesting groups in Dovre, Roros and Kvikna; but their main habitats are further north where J. Kålås and I. Byrkjedal (1981) estimated a Norwegian breeding strength of approximately 10,000 pairs. S. Ulfstrand and G. G. Högstedt (1976) give 5,000 breeding pairs for Sweden; and in 1958 Merikallio calculated from his transects that about 43,000 pairs nested in Finland. Dementiev and Gladkov (1951) assert that whimbrels are not plentiful in USSR; but around Leningrad, in 1963–70, S. Maltschewski knew of six high moors which held up to 100 breeding pairs. Whimbrels are scarce in Latvia; but Kumari gives a breeding strength of 250 pairs on 15 high peatlands in Estonia.

As we write, these whimbrels, with their lovely flights and magic trills, seem to have a rosy future in their Shetland homelands. But the clash in Fetlar, between conservation of nesting habatats and drastic improvements in crofting, will only be solved by good will and hard thinking on both sides.

6:   Flows and peatlands

The flows and peatlands of Sutherland have been the happiest of our many hunting grounds for waders. In the north-east, between the Halladale, Dyke and Helmsdale Rivers, there are huge blanket mires and complexes of pools, hummocks and dubh-lochans. To reach these you pass through drier heath and deer grass where you may flush a teal from a pool and sometimes listen to the becking of red grouse. Arriving at the wet flows you explore the bogs at your peril, stepping warily from tussock to tussock and always trying to avoid the softest and most oozy places. You move slowly, stopping to listen to the wild triple calls of a greenshank disturbed from a dubhlochan or perhaps one that is feeding beside a distant loch. Over the maze of deep acidic pools cock dunlins purr and challenge one another or chase hens in quick twisting flights. On drier parts golden plovers greet you with mournful cries of alarm and warning; or perhaps you watch a cock rise high, slowly flapping his wings as he sings his plaintive song in time with his wing beats. Snipe *scaap* harshly as they zig-zag away, or a cock bleats above the edges; curlews bubble on the periphery.

On many days you squelch forward through misty rain; the waders are often silent and the peatlands stretch endlessly ahead, like a grey desert. The Highland drizzle soon chills to the bone and your clothes become sodden with moisture. At other times, the Great Bog, now more friendly and inviting, may even be prepared to hint at its treasures. In the distance, close to a large bump of old sandstone, a golden eagle plunges and rises above the cliff where it has an eaglet in the eyrie. It was here that I saw my first eagle's eyrie in 1932. In more recent years Donald Bremner has joined us for some memorable eagle-watching days; and young Maimie has had the thrill of being lowered on a rope to an eyrie with an egg. The grey bog is now often pregnant with challenge and excitement. When the clouds scud fast and the sun shines briefly, silvery loch waters show in the far distance. This is country – big country – fit for any hunter.

Black- and red-throated divers are in the flows and a few greylag geese nest close to large lochs. Wood sandpipers have called and sung on several different flows here, but so far no one has recorded finding eggs or chicks. Just beyond the Sutherland march, on the bogs of south-west Caithness, greenshanks and dunlins are in good numbers. In wet mires teal and wigeon lay their creamy eggs; and in these peatlands they have a few scoters as neighbours. There may be still greater treasures in the future. In late May 1974 a pectoral sandpiper – a North American wader – sang and displayed over peatlands near Altnabreac on the Caithness-Sutherland march.

The huge expanse of flow north of Altnaharra is historic wader country where the old trophy seekers and egg collectors so often hunted. Here there are wide horizons, formerly clear and treeless, but now – alas! – with many plantations of bottle green conifers growing steadily higher on well-drained edges. There are no large hills until you reach Ben Hope and Ben Loyal in the north. In their splendid isolation these two fine hills are much more impressive than their heights suggest. Ben Loyal is crowned by curious and characteristic tors; Ben Hope, with its broad back and ridges, always encourages the dotterel hunter to search strenuously. Golden eagles nest on both hills; sometimes more than one pair favouring Ben Loyal. The waders are spread out on undulating ridges and hillocks and on immense flats studded with tarns. Solitary pairs of dunlin nest on the flows; golden plovers are here in low numbers; and greenshanks' nests are sometimes spaced out at about 1,200–2,000 m apart. On soft evenings, shortly before the greenshanks' eggs are due to hatch, you may hear four or five different cocks song dancing, possibly to warn neighbours of their presence and movements. In late May 1962, I also came across a Temminck's stint, which almost certainly had eggs; but, exhausted from a difficult – and unsuccessful! – greenshank hunt, I failed to find the nest. At that camp greylag geese fed and honked beside the deserted cottage in the early morning. A little further north, in flows bordering Caithness and nearer to the sea, powerful bonxies have started to colonise.

Another flowland haunt in north Sutherland has greenshanks, redshanks, and occasionally wood sandpipers. One pair of greenshanks hatched out their chicks in a scoop beside a grey hummock of sphagnum in one of the wettest flows in the district. Dunlins sometimes lead their chicks from the flows to overgrown edges, morasses and lagoons; golden plovers nest in the drier flows and curlews in the grass heath.

Set in some of the wildest and roughest country in all Britain, our greenshank study grounds in north-west Sutherland hold a mosaic of different kinds of peat. The winding salmon river runs for nearly five kilometres between great hills. Above its east bank there is a long bulky massif with narrow strips and expanses of peat bordering the river below. Along this, snipe court and nest in small numbers; and greenshanks often feed at pools to which they later herd their broods, although we have not known them to nest there.

The bogs and flows along and above the west bank are wider, wetter, more individual, and always full of character. There are large morasses of blanket bog rich in deep ruts and wet holes, perilous, and sometimes quite impossible to explore. Strangely, this vast bog holds no dunlins and only a few snipe; the greenshanks nest around the edges and on the hillsides above. On the stonier flows, arranged in layers on the slopes, greenshanks also have nesting territories. Further west there are flats and hillocks on the ankle of a great amphitheatre in the gneiss. In some years a solitary pair of goldies nest on the same flow, within 400 m of the greenshanks. The four large stones, with which Derek Ratcliffe marked a golden plover's nest in 1970, are still to be seen as you scan the ground through your field glass.

In some ways these are the most remarkable greenshank grounds in Scotland. What a fantastic range of flowland habitats they contain. Here, in their own special niches, dunlins nest in small communities as well as in isolated pairs; and golden plovers breed at higher density that in the river flows and on the hill flanks below. Here, two pairs of greenshanks once had nests less than 200 m apart. Snipe are scarce, but a few nest in wet and soggy flows in the middle gneiss; and cocks regularly bleat and their hens lay their eggs on the edges of more grassy habitats. There are memorable days when all these waders are calling almost simultaneously; and all from different niches in their vast living-space. But more often the grey wilderness is dead and silent, with perhaps only a distant golden plover piping monotonously. Then there is just the sigh and bump of the wind among the rocks and hollows.

The waders have many attractive neighbours in the valley. Dippers divide the river into territories and on soft days the bluffs and corries come alive with the songs and piping of ring ouzels. Two or more pairs of merlins regularly hunt the hills, usually nesting on broad ledges of high cliffs rather than in more orthodox nest sites on the steep flanks of heathery braes; in one year they nested on top of a huge isolated erratic. In 1981 a peregrine falcon hatched two young on one of the merlin bluffs. Another year, a tiercel peregrine terrorised the greenshanks and other waders. I watched it quarter a corrie like a harrier, and finally drop down and disappear into a bunch of rank heather from which it emerged with a wheatear in its claws.

But the most successful bird in the flows and grasslands is the little brown meadow pipit with its attractive song flights and those soft *peeps*, sometimes the only sounds heard by the wandering naturalist throughout a long hard day.

Glen Einich, in Spey Valley, is a wide and wind swept glen terminating in a loch, with the cliffs and huge bluffs of Brae Riach in the east and the challenging precipices of Sgoran Dubh in the west. At about 500 m Glen Einich harbours one, and sometimes two pairs of greenshanks, the further territory of which is one of the highest in Scotland. These greenshanks lay their eggs beside pine stumps or between old roots in sparsely vegetated peat. An occasional snipe bleats over the bog and sandpipers and dippers defend well-spaced territories along the river. Teal, mallard, red grouse and the ubiquitous meadow pipit are other neighbours. Up above, on the broken flanks of the high hills with their massive granite scree fields, are wheatears and ring ouzels. In early summer and late spring the faint piping and occasional scolding cries of ring ouzels are always attractions in this grand Cairngorms glen. Still higher, and far above Glen Einich, is the vast and often mist-bound peat bog of Am Moine Mor – The Great Moss – a country of high winds and grey mist with outcrops of granite on steep hillocks or on flanks below the beautifully sculptured massifs. Brae Riach, Monadh Mor, Carn Ban, and Sgoran Dubh Mor rise above a stony wilderness on which there are mosses and lichens and vast tracts of shallow bogland containing tongues and patches of drier and more stony ground. Small communities of dunlins nest in the bog. In mid May you watch exciting pursuits and erotic behaviour, the cocks whistling shrilly as they hover over the peat which they share with golden plovers. Above the flats, on the moss-and-lichen-covered bumps and ridges, the lovely dotterel is the dominant wader.

The eastern Drumochter hills often have dunlins in the high peat mosses, almost beside dotterel. We have found their nests less than 10 m apart. Golden plovers also haunt the high ground. Lower down, but still over 600 m ASL, the few snipe choose soggy patches of hillside. There are more dotterels on the whalebacks of the west Drumochter, but far fewer dunlin and golden plover. Here the family has heard snipe drum over a large moss, well above 750 m. Isolated pairs of greenshanks nest beside primeval pine roots in the morainic drift country below the hills; and oystercatchers and common sandpipers are scattered along the river. Golden eagle, peregrine, merlin, hoodie crow, and fox, are among the predators.

When I visited the north mainland of Orkney, in 1932, the mires held some marvellous assemblies of dunlins and fine concentrations of golden plovers. Many of these haunts are now reclaimed and seeded with grass; but many more curlews now bubble in wet dips between the brown and dumpy hills where hen harriers, short-eared owls and merlins hunt for their living. There are some grand peatlands in Shetland, particularly in Unst, Fetlar, Yell and north Mainland; whimbrel, dunlin and snipe breed in good numbers. Here, in various bogs, are fine colonies of bonxies and arctic skuas.

For some, the isolation and loneliness of the remote peatlands lead to a sense of infinite smallness; the great bogs seem almost terrifying in their vastness. But love comes later. Soon these huge open spaces become the grandest of all hunting grounds for the wader watcher.

THE GREENSHANK

Greenshanks live in wild country; we have camped close to them in the great flows of Sutherland and formerly in the forest bogs of Spey Valley. They have colourful courtship and displays, exciting song dances, and a most tantalising breeding life.

You often hear the pure triple whistles of a slightly excited greenshank long before you see it. If you are lucky, you may hear the passionate song, given by a tiny dark midge-like thing *yo-yoing* high above the flow. Later, when you watch the bird at closer quarters, you note the lanky olive green legs, longish uptilted bill, grey mantle, and the wedge and rump patch of startling snowy whiteness. The greenshank is a grand flier, covering the ground fast with strong clipping wing beats.

Greenshank habitats in the Scottish Highlands are all subtly different. In our study area in north-west Sutherland most territories are separated by various physical obstacles like steep ridges, hill flanks or streams. Some pairs favour soggy blanket bogs; others prefer rocky gneiss-studded flows and hillsides. But all have look-out rocks, and many pools, gutters and lochans to which the parents at first lead their young. Further west, where the valley broadens, a few dunlins harbour in the river flows or among clusters of dubhlochans. Above the west bank the next four – occasionally five – territories are placed at various distances and heights above the river. One is sited in a vast rocky hollow with tons of peat and blanket mire scattered among morainic drift, offering many choices for the greenshanks to use and the hunter to search. The next territory, higher uphill, has grey stony flows and huge blocks of gneiss on its flanks. In a third, the greenshanks have recently chosen a wet, broken and stony hillside where they made scoops beside embedded rocks and by stones close to gneiss erratics on which the incoming bird often pitches and *chips* before exchange with its mate. Dunlin, golden plover and snipe are usually absent from these territories. In a small gorge lower down, and closer to the river, a pair of greenshanks nested within 300 m of its nearest neighbours. Up above, on the lip of the corrie which mounts to a vast gneiss field, is another regular territory. The broken expanses of peat and gneiss are finally dominated by the cliffs and bluffs of a high and formidable hill.

The flows around Forsinard and between Kinbrace and Syre in north-east Sutherland are still fine greenshank habitats, although conifer plantations are now growing on some of them. In the south-east of the county, where we worked in 1961 and 1965, the grenshanks feed on the river and beside small lochs; but they nest on the flanks of rolling brown hills and on big flats in the deer grass country, as well as in stony flows in boglands higher up the valley where their breeding density is markedly higher.

Further south, a few pairs meet and court beside the Kyle of Sutherland and cocks song dance high above farms and planted conifers before flying six kilometres, or more, to settle down among rough flows and dubhlochans. Here, two pairs sometimes nest within 800 m of one another on newly ploughed peatlands. Red-throated divers give ghostly moans on small lochans and cackle strangely as they fly across country. Golden plovers nest in well-dispersed territories on wet heath and common sandpipers and dunlins display and nest close to a small loch. Sometimes two pairs of hen harriers and, in vole years, up to ten pairs of short-eared owls nest in the plantations; kestrels and merlins are not far from the edges.

There are fabulous sites in west Inverness-shire where some greenshanks meet and court on the shores of large lochs, but nest on stony flows at about 80–460 m ASL and from 5.5–8.0 km from the lochsides where they had paired. Here, as in most Scottish haunts, greenshanks almost invariably lay their eggs beside rocks or stones, but occasionally on the tops of furrows in land newly-planted with spruce and sitka.

Much of the greenshank country in Spey Valley was more akin to that in Fenno-Scandia and USSR. These greenshanks nested in large clearings in the old pines and in small forest bogs in which warped and stunted pines had escaped successive forest fires. In some years, 6–7 pairs met and courted around Loch Morlich and later pushed out into different nesting haunts in Rothiemurchus and Glenmore Forests, ranging from 150 m to over 4 km from the lochside where they met and mated. In Abernethy Forest the birds paired beside the river Nethy and by the Dorback burn; but their nests were placed in openings in the old Caledonian pines and in small bogs full of pine roots and peat ruts. An occasional pair nested on rough patches of heath on the Dorback grouse moor. In at least three years a solitary pair nested at 600 m ASL on a steep and stony flank of the Geal Charn. Apart from the groups nesting on the clearings west of Loch Morlich, the Spey Valley pairs were well spaced out on wet moors with an occasional pair choosing a dumpy morainic hillock close to the railway line in the grim Drumochter Pass.

Greenshanks in northern Europe favour large forest marshes dotted with small and large lakes and many pools and expanses of water. In parts of Norway, S. Haftorn (1971) found that they tended to nest on ridges in well spaced pine forest and in stunted spruce and birch in the clearings; the scoops were often in peat mosses or close to large sheets of open water. On the marvellous forest bogs of Hardanger Vidda greenshanks are the commonest waders, nesting in boggy meadow clearings far out in birch woodlands. A few Norwegian spruce and some scattered pines grow in this exciting country where greenshanks have wood sandpipers and green sandpipers, ruff, lapwing, red-necked phalarope, curlew and common snipe as neighbours. On Dovre Fjell they nest on flat morainic tops with a lichen cover and a few pines.

Further north, in Finnmark, dusky redshank, bar-tailed godwit, whimbrel and golden plover regularly nest out on the peat; common snipe, jack snipe, broad-billed sandpiper and reeves prefer wetter marshes. These are wonderful bird grounds; besides the waders there are pine grosbeaks and crossbills, Lapp or Siberian tits, Lapland and occasionally rustic buntings, bluethroats and Siberian jays. In some years the greenshanks also have fascinating waxwings and great grey shrikes as close neighbours.

Many haunts in northern Sweden are on drier ridges in the pine and birch zone. They also favour large clearings in the pine forest when these are associated with lakes and pools. Wood sandpipers, great, jack and common snipe, ruff, and broad-billed sandpipers often nest in different niches of the same habitats.

In Finland greenshanks nest in openings and clearings in the forest marshes, often far from their main feeding grounds. Here they favour dry ridges and the edges of peat bog and swampy forest lands. In Finnish Lapland, where they are scarce, they sometimes lay their eggs close to small bogs in dry forest with a carpet of *Calluna*. Habitats in the vastness of the Soviet Union usually range from forest clearings to wet bogs and marshes, sometimes surrounded by cultivated fields.

The greenshanks usually arrive on their Scottish Highland breeding grounds in late March or early April. The cocks return ahead of the hens, but this is occasionally reversed; exceptionally a pair arrives together. In some haunts the greenshanks court and mate beside a large loch, river or firth several kilometres from their nesting territories. Other pairs mate, re-mate, and court, not far from where the hen later lays her eggs. On 16 April 1986, a late season, Bill Sinclair and I watched a flock of 9 rise and fly together over a firth in north-west Sutherland.

In 1983 the first greenshank arrived in our study area on 26 March – an early date for the district. When Bruin and young Maimie checked seven territories on 8 April they found cocks were singing and contending in six; in only one was there a pair. Over the years we have come to know by a special name every territory in our wonderful greenshank valley.

Territory

Greenshanks establish mating, nesting, food, and sometimes chick territories. A mating territory enables a cock to establish and maintain its status in the breeding hierarchy, courtship to proceed with minimal interference, and is a meeting place for partners when they are temporarily separated. Before and after the eggs are laid cocks feed in their mating territories, defending favourite pools, dubhlochans, and parts of loch and river shore against rivals. In a district like Glen Garry in Inverness-shire, greenshanks court and mate on defended territories close to large lochs, but nest on wet stony flows several kilometres away and sometimes 250–300 m higher up the hill.

Chosen nesting territories provide a variety of nest sites and contain prominent command posts such as rocks, boulders, mounds, stumps or trees, as well as a number of pools, tarns or shallows which the sitting bird can use for snacks and homing birds as staging posts. These territories also provide feeding places near the nest for the newly-hatched brood.

In north-west Sutherland chick territories are often flexible. In 1967–74 a well loved bird *Old Knoll*, and her different mates, annually shepherded the chicks to the same complex of pools, peat runnels and water saucers which were situated about 400–800 m from her different nests. Before reaching these nurseries the chicks had to swim across quite a large stream. A second pair, which nested on an adjacent flow, shared this ground, each pair defending its own part. On the disappearance of an established hen, the newcomer and her mate sometimes choose entirely different nurseries. *New Knoll*, for example, moved uphill with her family and settled in a portion of a neighbour's nesting territory after these chicks had moved elsewhere.

Some greenshanks, in Spey Valley and in parts of Ross and north Sutherland, herd their chicks to the grassy shores of large lochs, thus providing suitable food and feeding territories for both parents and chicks at comparatively close quarters. Adults often favour different food and feeding grounds from their families, one or both old birds periodically leaving the chicks and flying to loch or river, though usually still within voice-range of the family.

Numbers and topography help to determine the general pattern of the greenshanks' territorialism. Presence, calls and subtly different song dances all play a part in acquainting pairs with their neighbours' movements.

COURTSHIP AND SEXUAL BEHAVIOUR

Immediately a hen arrives on the breeding ground the cock flies to her. Then, for a few hours, there is a hub-hub of noise and excitement, the cock chasing the hen in passionate twisting flight pursuits or occasionally switch-backing and singing high above her and then attempting to copulate when she settles on a rock, on the ground, or on a tree top. After these hours of tension and passion the two birds may separate or they start to settle down as a pair. New partners usually provide the longest and most thrilling courtship displays. The cock runs after the hen in a tortuous chase which may also roughly follow a straight line; or the two birds occasionally run in loops, circles, and figures-of-eight. These chases are less continuous and sustained than those of redshanks; the roughness of the ground possibly helps to restrict them. Established pairs synchronise their sex rhythms with less passion and commitment.

The cock's full display before copulation is often breathtaking. He stalks towards the passive hen which signals her readiness by bending slightly forward. The cock then approaches, often slowly goose-stepping up to her and uttering loud harsh and throaty cries while he violently flaps his wings. Before mating he sometimes holds his wings vertically upwards or he ducks forward, fanning and raising his tail to expose his brilliant white rump patch and white tail feathers; and he may walk round his mate, bowing and holding a wing over her. He then floats onto her back, sometimes touching her nape or bill with his. After coupling he drops off or she shakes him off; or he may again bow round her on taut legs and hold a wing above her. The two birds then sometimes go through the motions of feeding and preening before they fly away, usually together.

At other times the act of love is less spectacular. The cock merely jumps or flutters onto the hen's back on the loch shore, or he drops onto her while she is perched on top of a dead tree or stump. Once the cock of a long-established pair stood on a tussock in the marsh calling up his hen and merely slightly fanning his tail. She then squatted in the mud where he stepped straight onto her back without any special wing play.

The nuptial flight of a pair of greenshanks is exceptionally dramatic. The cock starts by chasing the hen in the usual twisting pursuit low over the ground and then the two birds suddenly rise high, sometimes up to cloud level where they turn, swerve and circle in perfect harmony, first one leading and then the other. After a few glorious minutes, when you only faintly hear their passionate cries, both suddenly dive steeply to pool or loch shore or onto stumps or rocks. Two cocks in pursuit may pass from an orthodox pursuit flight into this remarkably exciting performance, first one and then the other leading in the sky dance. The flight usually ends by pursuer and pursued parting and each flashing back to its own living space.

During incubation a pair sometimes takes off on a nuptial flight. For several minutes you watch frantic gyrations high in air and strain to hear their cries. If the flight takes place during a break in incubation this may lead to nest relief, with the incoming bird dropping down and giving peals of *chipping* cries before making its nestward run.

Agile and graceful flyers, greenshanks sometimes achieve spectacular feats of flying. In Scotland, both Richard and I watched cocks attempting to copulate with flying hens, the two grey birds fluttering their wings like butterflies and the hen arced her wings downwards as they momentarily came together.

Cocks are occasionally promiscuous, successfully cuckolding rivals. A cock may attempt to copulate with a hen almost immediately after she has arrived on his mating territory; but these attempts do not appear to be complete or successful. Passion is at its height a few days before the hen lays her first egg; and we have watched apparently successful coupling the day before a third egg was laid.

A cock sometimes displays to, and attempts to mount, a hen or even an intruding cock which his own mobbing cries have attracted to the territory. This kind of coupling during incubation is, however, particularly characteristic of forest groups where the cock is possibly stimulated by the sight of his mate dipping forward to balance herself on a branch or top of a tree. Once I saw a hen fly onto the back of a cock which had himself already twice attempted to take her; but this abnormal behaviour was probably caused by agitation, as I was close to the nest from which the hen had just left to feed.

Polygyny

Cock greenshanks are occasionally bigynous. In 1868 Edward Booth recorded two double clutches in Ross and Sutherland, one of which contained seven eggs and 'a downy chick just released from the shell'. In *The Greenshank* (1951) and *Greenshanks* (1979) we have described other trios of greenshanks. The famous Spey Valley triangle of *George*, *Fanny* and *Elizabeth* is the best documented. In 1926 the two hens had nests 4 m apart, with their clutches closely synchronised; in 1932 the two clutches were laid in scoops on different hillocks 150–200 m apart; and in 1931 and 1933 the two hens laid all eight eggs in the same nest. In Sutherland we recorded triangles in 1974, 1975 and 1981, in one of which the two nests were less than 100 m apart. In another triangle the dominant hen, *Eamonn 1*, possibly broke her rival's eggs which were less than 80 m from her own nest.

From his photographic hide in north Sutherland, Derick Scott also discovered that a cock greenshank had two hens and nests. The cock exchanged with his mate and sat on the eggs for a short stint; and then he flew across the tarn and changed places with a second hen on another nest which Scott had not previously located. In 1981 Gordon Ireson found and photographed a nest with five eggs in Ross. His transparency clearly shows that there were three eggs of one type and two of another. The double clutch was at that time probably incomplete, but Ireson was unable to check at a later date.

Roger Powell and Barry Larking, two other greenshank enthusiasts, met with another most interesting trio in west Inverness in 1979. On 10 May a scoop, in which a pair had successfully hatched eggs in 1978, was apparently untouched. However, 75 m away and hidden from the previous year's nest by a spur of the hill, they found a nest with four eggs, one just laid and still wet with mucus. These had similar markings but a slightly darker ground than the eggs laid nearby in the previous year and might have been laid by a daughter.

On 11 May, to their great surprise, the 1978 scoop now held a single egg; judging by its shape and markings it was probably laid by the hen of the previous year. The clutch of four eggs was completed on 17 May, the hen having laid her last three eggs on alternate days. Meanwhile, on 13 May, one egg had disappeared from the new 1979 site. Further observations led to the conclusion that these two hens were bigamously mated to one cock. 'The triangle relationship appeared to cause a lot of strain to the female on the 1979 site. When the male and female visited the old 1978 site she would anxiously call and occasionally leave the nest and walk to the top of the ridge in order to see them'. It might have been during one of these absences that one of her eggs disappeared. Is it also possible that she or the cock ate one of their own eggs, or that the second hen raided the nest?

DISPERSION AND BREEDING DENSITY

Spacing between greenshanks' nests varies greatly in different habitats. Some of the vast gneiss flowlands of the Scottish Highlands usually produce maximum breeding density in Britain:

Density	*Average spacing between nests*
Very high	<0.5 mile (<0.8 km)
High	0.5–0.75 mile (0.8–1.2 km)
Moderate	0.75–1.5 miles (1.2–2.4 km)
Low	1.5–2.5 miles (2.4–4.0 km)
Very low	>2.5 miles (>4.0 km)

In north-west Sutherland we have studied annual fluctuations in an area of 3,250 ha. Here the population has varied from 6–7 breeding pairs in 1966 to 20–23 breeding pairs in 1976 (Figure 1). Breeding density thus ranged from 0.2 breeding pairs/km² in 1966 to 0.7 breeding pairs/km² in 1976. In suitable habitats in Spey Valley there was a maximum breeding density of 0.9 breeding pairs/km² in 1937, but that was an exceptionally good year for greenshanks.

There is less data on breeding density of greenshanks in Fenno-Scandia. In the 1920s, however, there was the high density of 2.4 breeding pairs/km² in the Pasvik marshes in Finnmark. Recently, Roger Powell recorded two nests 2.5 km apart on the Hardanger Vidda, Norway; and, in north Finland, L. Saari (MS) estimated the low

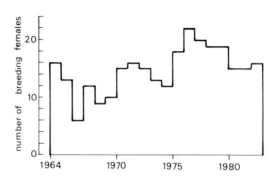

Fig. 1   Number of breeding female greenshanks found in north-west Sutherland 1964–82.

density of 0.01–0.05 breeding pairs/km². J. Kålås and I. Byrkjedal (1981) suggest that greenshanks in Norway are breeding at a density of 1 breeding pair/km² in the south and 0.5 breeding pair/km² in the north.

There are marked differences in the spacing between nests in our study area. In 1981, for example, five nests on the river flows ranged from 700 to 2,300 m apart, with a mean of c 1,200 m; whereas in the middle and high gneiss five nests were placed at intervals varying from 80 to 900 m, with a mean of c 650 m.

The tract of wild country in north-west Sutherland, where we worked in 1963, carries a fair population of greenshanks with nests 1,650–2,400 m apart. In the flows of north Sutherland, where Gilroy and so many other enthusiasts have hunted, nests are exceptionally only 800–1,200 m apart.

NEST

In the first phase of nest site selection the cock independently explores and tests many niches in his territory, shuffling in hollows and sometimes uttering special sobbing cries before song dancing high above flow or clearing. Later, following a display of song dancing and high flying, he may flash back to loch or river and later lead his hen to the niches he has already looked over. If you are well placed you may now watch the two graceful birds at work. The cock often runs ahead and then squats in a hollow; or he stands on a rock, hummock or stump while the hen shuffles, scratches and rotates and sometimes picks up bits of grass and lichen which she throws sideways or over her shoulders. If she does not choose a particular site or complex of niches the cock leads her to another part of his territory where the process of site selection starts all over again. But probably all that you are now likely to hear are those sobbing cries; or you may catch a distant flash of white as the hen 'upends' and rotates on a possible scoop. Once she has chosen the scoop the pair flies away even if the hollow is unlined or is still only an almost invisible depression. The scoop may now be abandoned for 3–5, or exceptionally up to 10 days, before the hen lays her first egg.

We watched and listened to a cock in 1979 going from spur to spur, standing on rocks and examining possible nest sites one after the other while giving sobbing *tyawan tyawan* cries. One scoop, in which he shuffled and left some down from his breast feathers, was in a most unusual place, previously selected in 1976; this time, however, the hen did not finally lay in it.

Most hens annually select different nest sites in different parts of the same territory; but a few lay their eggs in the same scoop in 2–3 consecutive years, or they may return to an old scrape after a lapse of one or more year. In one territory a particular hen laid in a hollow in the dry bed of a dubhlochan in 1964; and three other hens have chosen the same nest site, one in 1970, the second in 1975 and 1976, and the third in 1986.

In the north-west Highlands a hen usually lays her eggs beside or close to a 'mark', normally a stone or rock. A few others occasionally lay on open heath or on peat devoid of any mark. Less usual sites are in long heather near or beside pools or dubhlochans. One nest was placed on a small islet of peat entirely surrounded by water of a small dubhlochan. In 1970 a favourite hen, *G*, chose a cleft in a big rock where her mantle was extremely cryptic (Fig 2).

Nests in the clearings of Spey Valley were usually placed beside fragments of dead wood; a few beside or between the roots of an old pine in a bog, or exceptionally at the foot of a tall mature pine tree just inside the forest.

We have recently met with pairs placing their nests on the tops of furrows in ploughed peatland in south-east Sutherland. This kind of nest site has also been recorded in

Beside or between stones or rocks	92
In clumps or tufts of longish heather	20
In or beside hummocks or tumps of moss	13
In clefts of embedded gneiss	14
Beside small pools	6
In rough quartzite gravel or stones	6
In upturned lump of eroded peat sheltered by heather	2
Beside stone close to small loch	1
In burnt grass heath but not beside stone or rock	1
On small islet of peat in small tarn	3
	158

Fig. 2   Greenshank. Nest marks in north-west Sutherland 1964–82.

north Sutherland, Wester Ross, Spey Valley, Argyll and southern Norway. A few pairs regularly nest beside discarded snow fencing and sleepers close to the railway line in north-east Sutherland and north Perth. In northern Europe, Lennart Raner and E. S. Steward have occasionally found that greenshanks and dusky redshanks use one another's old scoops.

A greenshank often lays her first egg in a shallow unlined scratching; further material is added during egg laying and incubation. In the north and west Highlands the lining usually contains varying quantities of *Molinia* grass, with additions of *Sphagnum* moss, bog myrtle *Myrica gale*, a little heather *Calluna*, and bog cotton *Eriophorum* fluff. Some Spey Valley nest linings contained quite large quantities of pine bark; others had pine needles, cowberry *Vaccinium vitis-idaea* and blaeberry *V. myrtillus* leaves, and lichen. Several times there were rabbits' and mountain hares' droppings in the lining. Eggs were also occasionally laid in scoops on burnt blackened heath sparsely lined with bits of charred wood.

LAYING SEASON

Between 1964–82 the average date for full clutches in our north-west Sutherland study area ranged from 4–14 May (mean 7 May). Some hens, however, annually laid earlier or later than the group average. For example, between 1967–74 *Old Knoll* completed her clutches between 26 April–3 May (mean 29 April); and in 1971–76 *Heather Point* laid her eggs between 28 April–1 May (mean 29 April). Late hens included *Broken Egg* who completed her clutches in 1972–77 between 8–19 May; and *Great Day* who clutched on 16 May in 1976, and 15 May in 1977 (Fig 4).

The laying season in Spey Valley, between 1931–42, ranged from 28 April–16 May, with an average of 10 May for the 12 years. Here too there were considerable individual differences. In 1940–42 and 1946 *Old Glory* laid out between 28 April – 3 May (mean 1 May); and in 1938–41 *Castle* laid the last eggs of her clutches between 23 May–3 June (mean 26 May).

In Fenno-Scandia the laying season partly depends on the annual snowlie. In southern Norway, where Roger Powell found two clutches of fresh eggs on 30 and 31 May 1979, the majority of hens start to sit between the third week in May and early June in most years. Two clutches were laid on 5 and 9 July, but these were probably replacements. Twenty clutches in Finnmark were completed in the last week of May and nine in the second week of June; the earliest hen laid up about 24 May and the latest on 14 June. In 1928 Gilroy and Steward found six fresh clutches in the Pasvik between

31 May–14 June; other hens hatched broods from eggs laid in late May. Hens have full clutches from late May until mid-June in north Sweden. In the Muonio marshes, for example, John McNeile records eight clutches completed between 31 May–14 June; other hens also had chicks from clutches laid in the last week of May.

Most hens in Finland start to sit between 20 May–10 June, with a peak in the last few days of May. The earliest recorded clutch was completed on 19 May and the latest had fresh eggs on 20 June (Hildén MS). J. Baldwin Young found four fresh clutches near Ivalo, between 20 May–1 June. Greenshanks in USSR have fresh clutches from late May to early June onwards. The earliest clutch, recorded in the Darwin Reserve close to the River Kolva, was completed about 20 May.

Timing of breeding and breeding performance

D. B. A. THOMPSON

In general birds lay earlier in spring when the weather is warm and dry, and food is abundant. The laying season is timed so that chicks hatch when food is plentiful. That is not to say, however, that birds can predict precisely when their chicks will encounter most food, and so time the precise date of laying appropriately. Rather, birds appear to use early spring cues (*eg* air temperature, snow cover, daylight, rainfall and available food) to breed as early as possible. Nesting schedules differ between and within seasons in response to a combination of environmental and biological factors. In understanding the underlying patterns we can learn a great deal about the evolution of nesting seasons and when and how natural selection appears to operate on the birds themselves.

Year to year fluctuations in laying date and breeding performance are summarised here, a fuller story is presented by Thompson *et al* (1986). The average date of clutch completion in our study area was 7 May. In years when April and May experienced high soil temperatures, greenshanks bred earlier (Fig 3). This appeared to be due to the main prey – adult chrysomelids, molluscs and small fish – becoming active sooner in years when early spring was mild. Laying date was independent of weather conditions in June. Fresh egg weight (which correlates with chick size and, in some cases, viability) was heaviest when early spring was warm. Again, abundant food early in the season may facilitate the production of large eggs. Clutch size rarely deviated from four and was unaffected by any changes in weather.

Hatch success was not affected by laying date, but was lowest in years when May was cold and wet. Perhaps harsh weather conditions during the incubation period resulted in birds having to spend longer periods away from the nest in order to feed. Clutches, in turn, were more likely to chill or to be predated (especially by hooded crows and foxes). We looked at the number of birds returning to breed and number of new territories occupied in the following two years as an indication of the population's breeding success. As in most studies of waders, we could not measure fledging success with any accuracy. Fewer birds (of both sexes) returned to breed and fewer new territories were established when the two preceding years were characterised by: (i) harsh weather in June, and (ii) poor breeding success (product of average fresh clutch weight and number of breeding females. Presumably the effect of harsh weather in June arose because fledging success was lowest when weather conditions were cold and wet.

Taken together, these results suggest that the greenshank's breeding schedule is shaped by climatic conditions throughout spring and summer. Bad weather early in the season affects laying date and egg weights; later in the season it appears to affect hatching and fledgling success.

The story is complicated, however, by marked differences amongst birds and habitats. Two characteristics of females affected laying date. First, older hens laid earlier in

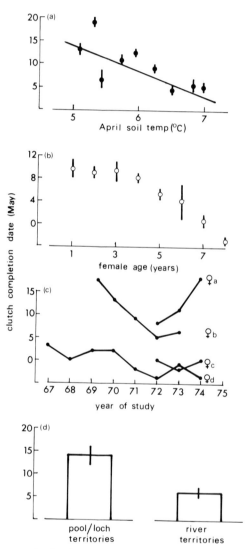

Fig. 3   Four factors associated with timing of breeding in greenshanks. For date of clutch completion, zero = 1st May. Points give mean ± standard error. Analysis performed on original data (which **are lumped** *for presentation). Statistics: (a) r = −0.513, F = 35.7, p < 0.001, n = 106; (b) r = −0.464, F = 19.2, p < 0.001, n = 64; (c) data for 4 individual females; (d) t = 5.09, p < 0.001, df = 62. (Thompson et al 1986).*

the spring (and laid lighter eggs) (Fig 3). Second, there were consistent differences between hens. Hens could be typed according to eggshell pattern and colour (see Baerends and Hogan-Warburg's 1982 study of herring gulls). Every year some were consistently early, others late (Fig 3). Perhaps older birds laid earlier because they were more skilled foragers or had experience of good feeding sites. Individual differences in laying pattern may be inherited or learned from parents. Heritable components of laying date, egg size and adult body size have been found in great tits *Parus major* by Van Noordwijk *et al* (1980, 1981). With the exception of a study of red-necked phalaropes (Hildén and Vuolanto 1972) there is no evidence for heritability in laying date of waders. In greenshanks we attempted to compare the effects of April soil temperature, female age and individual differences on laying date. Analysis of covariance indicated that 12%, 9% and 26% respectively in laying date variance were attributable to the three variables. Clearly, we need much more information about the individual differences in females, for they appear to exert important effects on timing of breeding.

A final factor affecting laying date was habitat (Fig 3). Birds breeding in territories bordering the river nested an average of eight days earlier than those in gneiss flow territories containing small streams, numerous dubhlochans and larger lochs. Apparently, invertebrates are active sooner in the river and river flows than in the slightly higher (and cooler) oligotrophic pools. Interestingly, females did not move between territories; maybe familiarity with a given area outweighs the benefits of moving to areas where earlier breeding is possible?

AGE

We have insufficient data to ascertain whether greenshanks often breed in their first year. One male did so in 1979. In each year there has been a small non-breeding surplus. One cock, colour-ringed as a chick in *Eamonn 1* territory in 1974, returned and nested in *Big Moss* territory, 1,000 m away, in 1977. Figure 4 summarises the identity of known hens and dates of complete clutches in north-west Sutherland between 1964–83. The annual breeding life of a hen was 3.3 years, approximately the same as in the groups studied in Spey Valley. The two hens with the longest breeding lives were *Old Knoll* in Sutherland, who nested in the same territory for eight years; and *Elizabeth* who laid her eggs in the Lochan Deo territory in Rothiemurchus from 1921–33.

EGG AND CLUTCH

Greenshanks' eggs are amongst the most beautiful of all waders'; their ground colour varies from stone or off-white to buff or deep reddish brown, pale olive-green or bluish green. The eggs are pear shaped, elongated ovate, and fairly glossy. They are blotched, capped, spotted and streaked with shades of deep red, chocolate-brown and sometimes purple-red, with a few sepia scratchings, and have undermarkings of brown, grey, lavender and lilac. Each hen lays eggs of roughly the same shape and general colour pattern in each year, unless she suffers from disease. In 1957 a Spey Valley hen had laid an unmarked blue egg as the final egg in the last clutch that she was known to lay. Patrick and Maimie found a dwarf egg in *Pygmy's* 1973 clutch. It was perfectly marked and had the same colour pattern as the rest of the clutch, but contained no yolk and weighed only 9 gm.

In Spey Valley the eggs of *Green Bands* – each one zoned by a broad band of green – were always diagnostic. *Old Glory* laid dumpy buff-coloured eggs heavily blotched with various shades of brown and red; and *Glorious* had long pointed eggs with exceptionally heavy and most beautiful lavender-grey and lilac undermarkings.

territory	1964	1965	1966	1967	1968	1969	1970	1971	1972	1973	1974	1975	1976	1977	1978	1979	1980	1981	1982
Loch West	A 27/5	A 2/5			B 5/5	C 10/5	D 9/5	D 6/5		E ?	F 4/5	F ?	G 15/5	H 15/5	I 24/5	I 26/5	I 5/5	?I	J c30/
Big Moss	A 2/5				B 7/5	C 3/5	C 4/5	D 7/5	C 7/5	D 11/5	E 11/5	C 15/5	C 9/5	F 27/5	G 4/5	G 18/5	?		
Beauty	A 2/5	?A 1/5	B 9/5	B 7/5	?B	B 9/5	B 8/5	B 7/5						C 9/5					
Eamonn 1	A 8/5	B 9/5			C 7/5	C 10/5	C 9/5	D 4/5	D 1/5	D 4/5	D 1/5					B 11/5	?♀	♀ from 10/5 HT 1978	(E)
Eamonn 2	?♀								?A 1/5			B 30/4	B 1/5	B 5/5	B 10/5				
HT	A 3/5	B 30/4					C 7/5				?♀ 13/5		D 5/5	D 7/5	(E) 13/5				
HP					A n=b	A n=b	A 29/4	?A 30/4	A 28/4	A 1/5	A 28/4	B 23/5					C 4/5	C 8/5	C 7/5
Knoll	unmated ♂	?♀ 3/5	?♀ 3/5	A 30/4	A 2/5	A 2/5	A 29/4	A 26/4	A 28/4	A 25–26/4	B 12/5	B 2/5	B 10/5	C 6/5	♀E from HT 1978				D 13/
Pygmy						?♀ 2/5		?A	a 9/5	A ?	A 18/5								
Tiger	A 4/5	A 6/5		A shift 7/5		B 19/5	C 13/5	C 9/5	C 7/5					D 12/5	E 10/5	E 16/5		F 14/5	
RON	?♀								♂			A 12/5	B 14/5	B 18/5	C 14/5	C 22/6	D 5/5	?D 6/5	?♀ 6/5
R with 3				A 6/5					B 13/5										
Broken Egg		?♀ 4/5	?♀ 7/5						A 8/5	A 11/5	A 19/5	A 15/5	?A	A 19/5	B 13/5	B 5/5	?C	D 10/5	
G	n=b.	?♀ 3/5	?♀ 5/5	?♀ 9/5		A 3/6	A 6/5	A 2/5	A 6/5	B 3/5	B 15/5	B 11/5	C 9/5	C 14/5	C 19/5	C 7/5			
ROR	?♀		A 3/5		?♀ 4/6	B 7/5	B 5/5	B 5/5	B 5/5	B 5/5	C 6/5	C 14/5	C 14/5	D 13/5					
DB				?♀ 2/5	A 9/5	B 20/5	B 13/5	B 9/5	B 5/5	B 6/5	C 2/5	C 11/5	C 8/5				?D		
Cigar													A 12/5	A 9/5	B 18/5				?♀
Great Day													A 16/5	A 15/5	♂ n–b	B 21/5	B 13/5	?♀ 16/5	
Speckles															A 11/5	A 18/5	A 14/5	A 9/5	A 8/5

Fig. 4   Greenshank. Laying season, identity of females and dates of complete clutches in north-west Sutherland 1964–82. Capital letters indicate females.

Eggs in our north-west Sutherland group have been much more variable. *D/B* laid long pointed eggs, strongly blotched with purplish red. *Great Day* laid some of the most beautiful eggs that we have ever seen in the field, with huge red-brown blotches at the blunt end on a light pale brown ground.

The mean measurements of 100 Scottish eggs, 51.45 × 34.8 mm (Jourdain 1940), is larger than that of 117 Swedish eggs, 49.61 × 32.63 mm (P. Rosenius 1937). In Table 3 we give weights of freshly-laid eggs from our north-west Sutherland study area between 1972–82. In 1974, a year of heavy greenshank eggs, a particular clutch weighed 145 gm and the hen 200 gm – 73% of the bird's body weight. On average, however, the proportion is probably slightly lower; with an average egg weight for a clutch of 124 gm and that of a hen at 178 gm, the proportion is 69.9%.

Eighty-eight blown shells from Scotland varied from 1.42–1.68 gm (mean 1.58 gm) (D. A. Ratcliffe and R. Hodgson *in Greenshanks* 1979). Rosenius (1937) weighed 118 blown eggshells from Sweden which ranged from 1.21–1.70 gm (mean 1.46 gm); and eight from Finnmark, Norway, varied from 1.38–1.49 gm (mean 1.45 gm).

In the 1930s I was sometimes able to forecast correctly, by the behaviour of the birds, how many eggs there would be in unfound nests. This is always a most satisfying and exciting experience, the success of which greatly depends on an intimate knowledge of particular pairs. Edgar Chance could often accurately forecast the number of eggs that would be in an unfound nest of red-backed shrike; and Jim Vincent, the great Norfolk self-taught ornithologist, successfully performed this feat at an unfound nest of marsh harriers.

Cocks tend to behave in subtly different ways when their mates are laying the earlier and later eggs of the clutch. When she is about to lay her first egg the cock sometimes stands on a tree or rock waiting for her; and afterwards the two birds fly away together. For the second and third eggs he frequently escorts her to the nest, but usually leaves before she has laid and brooded the egg. For the final egg the hen often flies in and departs alone.

Evelyn Meek is one of the few watchers who has had the patience and good luck to watch a hen greenshank start her clutch. At 06.50 on 19 May 1981 she was watching the birds on a north Sutherland flow. 'For 10 minutes both greenshanks stood quite still, silent, and alert. Then one of them seemed to settle on the ground and I could see its head sticking up. The other bird started *chipping* and walked slowly round the other. It finally stalked off the mound and disappeared, only to show up on a rock a few seconds later, when it again started *tewking* and continued doing this for about 5 minutes. It then walked back to the sitting bird which rose up and both then seemed to look down at the ground. The greenshank which had been sitting then picked up little pieces of grass or heather and tossed them over her shoulder before settling down in the same place as before, with the other bird standing close by; both were quite still for about 10 minutes. Then the standing bird became excited and started *tewking* and circled the other again. At 07.55 both suddenly flew off, calling loudly as they disappeared towards the river. I now found that a single egg, still warm, was lying in a slight depression beside a small rock'.

Some greenshanks do not visit their nests during egg laying; others, both cocks and hens, cover and brood earlier eggs at night and occasionally briefly visit and add material to nests during the day. While so doing, they often throw bits and pieces of vegetation sideways or over their shoulders. Before laying her last egg the hen some-times broods the first three eggs and appears to prepare a space between them for the last.

Greenshanks usually lay their eggs on alternate days, occasionally at intervals of up to 70 hours or *c* 24–30 hours (average for 26 eggs in Spey Valley and Sutherland,

44 hours). In 1912, Macomb Chance was possibly the first to record that greenshanks laid on alternate days. The Glen Einich hen laid her first egg at 06.00 on 6 May; at 18.00 on the 10th there were only three eggs, and the clutch of four was complete on the 12th.

A hen greenshank normally lays four eggs, occasionally three, and exceptionally two or one. In 1978 the hen *HT* sat on one egg; and in 1928 Gilroy recorded two apparently completed clutches of one egg in Finnmark. There are at least three records of clutches of five eggs; one in Spey Valley, one in Ross, and one for which we have no details. The c/5 in Spey Valley was taken by Aeneas Stewart, a keeper in Abernethy Forest, on 10 May 1912. Three hundred and seventy-three completed Scottish clutches averaged 3.92 eggs. In north-west Sutherland, between 1964–83, we found 158 clutches of which 146 were complete (mean 3.89 eggs). Table 4 compares clutch sizes in different locations.

In Scotland, when greenshanks lose their eggs during the first fortnight of incubation, they are usually replaced. In Spey Valley, 27 hens laid replacements. Of these 21 had at least one, four had two, and two had three repeat clutches. In north-west Sutherland seven nests were lost during the first fortnight; but we have only found two repeat clutches, both completed 13–14 days after the loss of the first. Intervals between first and replacement clutches have ranged from 10–21 days, with an average of 13 days for 15 replacements. The distance between first and replacement clutches has varied from *c* 50–950 m (mean *c* 325 m for 29 replacements). In 1932 *Fanny* laid her third replacement in her original first-clutch scoop.

INCUBATION

Greenshanks usually start steady incubation shortly after the hen has completed her clutch. Only one hen in Spey Valley started to sit continuously before she had finished laying. In north-west Sutherland, however, a few pairs began to incubate between their third and fourth eggs; the two birds occasionally changed over before the clutch was complete. Both cocks and hens usually share incubation; many cocks sit at night and their hens by day. In Spey Valley a few cocks – possibly strongly-sexed – apparently took no part in incubation; but they sometimes called and sang their hens off the eggs and escorted them back to the nest after they had fed beside a loch or river or in a pool. This happened 1–4 times daily and the hens were off for less than 5 or up to 40 minutes. Hen greenshanks sometimes leave their nests during their brooding stints and walk to a pool close by to feed; at other times they fly away to dubhlochans, lochs or rivers.

Most pairs change over twice daily at the nest, the first relief taking place in early morning, often between 06.00–08.00, and in the evening between 18.00–20.00. In Sutherland, however, some pairs have carried out their nest reliefs later in the evening, changing over between 20.00–22.00; and once, in the south-east of the county, we heard the characteristic exchange cries of a particular pair at midnight and at noon. A Spey Valley pair once changed over four times in 24 hours; so there is always plenty to intrigue and puzzle the greenshank watcher.

The exchange, which has many patterns and variations, is always thrilling and eagerly awaited by the watcher. An off-duty cock sometimes becomes agitated and extremely noisy before he starts his homing flight. He may take off from 200 m away; or, particularly when unsuitable habitats separate the feeding grounds from the nest, as far away as 5.5 km or more. Some pairs have special feeding niches at a large loch from which they fly to the nest in stages, first dropping down to a pool or dubhlochan; each pair has its own style. The nest is occasionally below, but more frequently a few metres, or up to 300 m, higher than the feeding ground.

Before nest relief, cocks or hens sometimes wait beside a river or lochan, warning their sitting mates by giving a few brief songs, calls or *chips*. A little later the relieving bird flies silently to the vincinity of the nest, usually first alighting on a big rock or tree stump, before starting peals of those famous *chipping* cries which are so welcome and encouraging to the hunter. At this point the greenshank often flies from rock to rock or from tree to tree, alighting a little lower on each flight, bobbing and curtseying, movements that indicate a clash of drives, before it finally flies or runs to the nest. The sitting bird usually slips silently away and flips low over the ground on its way to feed; only occasionally, particularly late in incubation, does it wait until its mate actually reaches the nest; but one cock bent forward, partly fanning his tail, while the hen stayed glued to her eggs. A second jostled his mate; and two others touched their mates' heads or backs before inducing them to leave.

Exchanges in the early morning are sometimes silent, the outgoing cock singing briefly when he is well on his way to the feeding ground; his hen then drops silently and stalks up to the nest.

We have measured 21 incubation periods in north-west Sutherland which have ranged from 22.9–26.1 days (mean 24.4 days). Twelve pairs of greenshanks in Spey Valley hatched their chicks in periods varying from 22.9–25.1 days (mean 23.9 days). Disturbance at the nest, thus allowing the eggs to cool, sometimes lengthens the incubation period.

At ten nests in north-west Sutherland the chicks took over 100 hours to hatch from the appearance of the first bump. Nineteen chipping periods have varied from 48–172 hours (mean 92.2 hours). In Spey Valley seven chipping periods were less, ranging from 38–98 hours (mean 61 hours).

HATCHING

Hatching patterns vary considerably. In forest groups many cocks perched almost continuously on tree tops not far from the nest, where they gave burst after burst of insistent chipping and warning cries and were always ready to chase passing hoodies. Sutherland birds behave rather differently. Many stay beside the river, or at a dubhlochan several hundred metres from the nest ridge, but always maintaining continuous contact with the sitting hen. At 54 nests, 21 cocks shifted to rocks close to the nest only on the day of hatching. A few pairs, however, change over more frequently than earlier in the rhythm. If the hatching period is protracted, with the last one or two chicks emerging up to 24 hours later than the others, the cock may hatch the last egg or eggs while the hen leads away the rest of the family. The sitting greenshank sometimes enlarges the hole through which the chick is emerging, eating or tossing away small bits. For several days before the chicks hatch the brooding bird answers their squeaks with loud explosive gruffs or grunts. In the *Heather Point* territory, on 25 May 1975, Richard and Eamonn were very excited when three of the four eggs exploded almost simultaneously and the three chicks started to struggle through from the shells. If chicks hatch late in the evening, or on a rough day, the parents usually restrict the downies to the scoop, often leading them away early next morning.

Greenshanks deal with hatched eggshells in many different ways. Some brooding birds fly away with large fragments almost as soon as the chicks have left the shells. Others drop the main portions over the edge of the nest before lifting and then releasing them 45–450 m away. A few also drown the shells in stagnant pools, afterwards rinsing their bills, or they pulverise them on rocks and then eat the small pieces. In 1984, from a hide in south-east Sutherland, David Whitaker watched one of the greenshanks,

while standing close to the nest, break shell fragments into tiny pieces. Egg caps are carried off one by one and usually dropped well away from the scoop. Small pieces are eaten, flicked over the brooding bird's shoulder, dropped out of the nest, or pushed firmly into the lining.

YOUNG

Some chicks scuttle away from the nest within four hours and are then usually gruffly recalled by the brooding parent. It is lovely to see a chick emerge from under its parent's wing and perhaps end by standing on its back; or the combined family actually lift their parent from the scoop.

The soft colours of the chicks vary considerably. Their bills are bluish grey with black tips; irides dark brown; shins of the legs olive-green to greenish yellow, with partly encircling silvery rings; calves are yellowish green and soles a rather sickly yellow. About a week later the chicks' legs are greenish yellow. Eighty-eight of these downies, which the family has measured in north-west Sutherland between 1972–82, weighed from 18–26 gm (mean 21.0 gm) (Table 5).

In their first 10 days the parent greenshanks periodically brood their chicks by day, particularly in rough weather, and regularly at night. On 3 June 1975 we watched a hen fly over and brood a couple of chicks on which the cock had been sitting, a movement which closely resembled a nest relief.

At Loch Morlich, Spey Valley, parents first led their chicks to small tarns before shepherding them to the rough grass-heath edges of the loch, in different parts of which several pairs attempted to rear broods. The movement of broods from nest to loch varied from 150 m to over 1.6 km. In some years, when special food for the chicks appears scarce or missing, the cock often scouts out new feeding grounds to which he leads hen and brood, sometimes moving 800 m or more in the course of a single hour. In four river-flow territories in north-west Sutherland, studied between 1964–81, the parents led their broods into a maze of pools and dubhlochans higher uphill and in the middle and upper gneiss. Sometimes a pair herds its brood to or through the nesting territory of another.

Some of these journeys are remarkable. In 1981 young Maimie found that a chick, ringed at a nest in the *Tiger* territory, had moved 3.5 km within its first 48 hours. In this long trek parents and chicks had climbed at least 100 m higher into the rough gneiss and passed through the nesting territories of four other pairs, in at least one of which a parent and chick were still present. Chicks were ringed mainly to help us to plot such movements. But one of the four *Knoll* chicks, ringed in the nest by Eamonn on 4 June 1982, was recovered on 18 September 1983 at Mulroy Bay, Co. Donegal, Eire.

In Sweden a greenshank was seen to lift and carry a chick for about 100 m, but we have not yet witnessed this in Scotland.

Towards the end of a fledging period of 25–31 days, one of the parents, usually the hen, deserts mate and brood. Early pairs, however, sometimes stay with their families; in 1982, for example, we watched three pairs all with well-grown broods. On 21 June 1981, Geoff Bates saw a pair escorting two flying young.

DISTRACTION AND AGGRESSIVE BEHAVIOUR

Most greenshanks sit extremely tightly, often waiting until the hunter's foot is almost upon them. Then, *chipping* excitedly, they fly, often rather awkwardly, from the nest. *Beauty* in Sutherland, and *Old Glory* in Spey Valley, were two very special hens. Both would allow us to fondle them and sometimes lift them off their nests. The children used to kneel beside *Beauty* and gently touch and tickle her throat feathers. Occasionally, however, a particular bird sits lightly, rising and flying from the nest when the searcher is 200 m, or more, away. In southern Norway, Powell recorded two nests where the greenshank sat tightly, flushing only when he clapped his hands 20 m from them.

Once flushed from the nest, most greenshanks career erratically overhead with clipping wing beats, flying in circles and elipses. Calling excitedly and *chipping* furiously, they periodically alight on stone, rock or stump, and the cock often rises high to song dance over his territory. The excited bird may now fly away to a distant feeding loch or river shallows, returning with its mate. We have then sometimes watched a cock try to chivvy the hen back to her eggs.

Some greenshanks are exceptionally aggressive. In the *Eamonn 1* territory in Sutherland, one cock regularly rose about 20 m ahead of us and dashed at our heads. In north Sweden, Lennart Raner watched an even more unusual greenshank which habitually rose and flew straight at his head from a distance of over 200 m.

A few give extraordinary displays, running a few metres while partly fanning out their tails and showing off the brilliant white rump patches. Or one stumbles and shrieks as it runs towards you, raising and violently beating one or both wings.

The *Eamonn 1* bird discriminated between children and adults. On 29 May 1973, when there were small chicks in the territory, the guarding greenshank flew at Richard and then pitched on the moss and ran to within 3 m of him, all the time shrieking while raising one wing and stretching out the other. Yet, when I approached the nest, the bird did not react.

VOICE

The voice of the greenshank is always most special to the wader watcher. There are long silences on the flow only broken by the tremulous song of a meadow pipit. Hours pass while you watch and shiver and almost despair of hearing a greenshank. Then, far away or perhaps just beyond a ridge, a cock starts to sing or gives loud insistent peals of *chipping* cries. All your senses tingle and you become instantly alert. Rising with strong wing beats to a height of 60 m, or often much more, the cock starts his song dance, flying in giant switchbacks, gliding down with wings set below the level of his body and then furiously lashing his wings to regain his pitch. From time to time he soars and circles, occasionally tumbles almost like a raven, or allows one or both legs to dangle below him. Sometimes he climbs so high that he disappears into a cloud; and all the time he sings his rich disyllabic *too-hoo too-hoo* which is sometimes broken by rather dry *kluk-kluks*. Subtle nuances of the song dance convey different messages. A cock seeking a mate, or replacing a lost one, may add a series of sobbing *tyawan-tyawans* to the song. In other emotional situations, for example shortly before the pair chooses the nest site or just before the hen lays her first or second egg, the cock dances high, making exceptionally steep dives and climbs, presumably to forewarn neighbours or potential intruders. These song dances tend to space out the pairs and to curtail energy-wasting territorial fighting.

Cocks and hens both sing, but the hen seldom performs the more impassioned song dances; her dives and climbs are noticeably less acute and are enacted at a lower height. Each pair, and perhaps every individual, probably learns to recognise the songs and dances of its neighbours. At other times the two greenshanks may sing from the tops of nearby trees or rocks and occasionally in duet.

When leaving the nest after a change-over, or when flushed from eggs, the bird often gives a few very quick and excited songs – a form of emotional release – as it speeds away towards loch or river. Cocks may also song dance high in the air when flying from the loch to make an exchange; and they often sing from a perch while the hen is dealing with the emerging chicks. Cocks invariably song dance while leading hen and brood to new but already explored feeding grounds, thus warning other pairs of the movements of their families. These song dances are usually performed in quick time and at a modest height above ground.

Greenshanks sing in many other emotional situations outwith their normal flight dances; as in nest site prospecting, before copulation, and in challenges involving two cocks. They often give quick songs just before dropping down at a loch or in the shallows of a river. In the evening, cocks frequently sing loudly in short bursts before taking off on their homing flights and they may sing to announce their arrival at the dubhlochan or river bend from which they make their final approach flight to the nest. This enables the sitting bird to give warning cries if it has noticed a possible predator in the territory. Cocks and hens both occasionally sing on the nest.

(1)   *Basic calls*

(a)   In all seasons the ringing *tew tew tew* calls, often given in threes, are the stock social contact signals. Greenshanks give these cries when they have been mildly disturbed, but we have occasionally known them used in place of *chipping* during nest relief.

(b)   The sharp, rapid, continuous and insistent *chip chip chip* is the characteristic excitement cry in the breeding season. These calls are rendered in different rhythms and intensites (*Greenshanks* p. 77), and are uttered in the air, on the ground, or from perches.

One special rhythm of *chipping* is usually restricted to a bird about to exchange or return to a nest with eggs. Hearing this, whether in the distance or nearby, always makes the hunter's pulse race wildly. While *chipping* from perch or ground, greenshanks frequently bob and curtsey; and they sometimes stand still or move towards the nest in a final run full of short stops and starts. The bird often continues to *chip* until it is within a few metres of the nest, when it stops suddenly and runs or walks onto the eggs.

Greenshanks give quick bursts of *chipping* cries during sexual or territorial fighting, when attacking human or natural predators, and sometimes while prospecting nest sites. These are also often used during sexual displays, while cocks are guarding mates on the feeding grounds, or before either bird starts its homing flight.

The use of special and detectable rhythms of *chipping* during nest relief is puzzling. Why has selection favoured such a loud and penetrating cry which, on calm days, is audible from a distance of 800 to possibly 1600 m? There is clearly a balance between risks and advantages. These cries inform the sitting mate of the approach of its partner, thus enabling the bird to warn the 'homer' of potential danger. *Chipping* also informs neighbours, at least twice daily, of the continuous presence of the pair in their nesting territory. Neighbours are thus prompted to join the nesting pair in defence of eggs and young. On the other hand, it alerts predators to the approximate position of the nest, although the sound may be difficult to locate precisely.

While guarding or shepherding broods, parents use variations of these *chipping* cries.

(2) *Sex calls*
(a) Cocks have several distinctive cries while displaying to receptive hens. A grating *woorp-woorp*, not unlike the gruff used to re-assure chicks, and an insistent *kumeer-kumeer*, both of which assist cocks to approach hens.

These cries, which have fair carrying qualities, although not easy to locate, inform neighbours of what is happening and probably do little to help predators.

(b) The sobbing *tyawans*, used independently or among peals of *chipping* or bursts of song, show that a cock with a strong sex drive is trying to entice a hen. They are also given during nest site selection. These carry a good distance but are not easy to locate.

(c) We have also heard greenshanks using twanging and chuckling cries in their ground displays.

(3) *Cries of stress, warning and anxiety*
These are given on the ground, from a perch, and sometimes in flight, but they offer weak locatory clues.

(a) A single redshank-like *tyoo* or more urgent slurred *tyoors* are habitually given by birds guarding small chicks and occasionally when warning a sitting mate.

(b) Monotonous *town-towns* are used by parents to maintain contact with the brood as it moves through the flow. A parent – or pair– which has left the young and flown to feed beside loch or river continuously give these cries to stay in touch with their chicks.

(4) *Anger calls*
(a) In situations of great stress and anger a cock or hen sometimes utters a screeching *kree* or *kreejee*. We have heard cocks give these screeches while chasing rivals or when a fox is close by. A perched cock, watching a nest containing a clutch or an incomplete set of eggs, may also screech with anger at the sight of an intruding human. We have also heard unreceptive hens using this violent cry when chased sexually by a strange cock.

(b) A cock, flying from a look-out post close to a nest, periodically gives high-pitched hawk-like *krik-kriks* to attack an intruding cock.

(c) Parents use different mobbing cries when chicks are in the nest or flow. These include a quacking *kluk-kluk* or *ker-ker* and a high pitched shrieking *tyeeagh*. All these cries are full of menace as the bird rushes at, and occasionally touches, the intruder with its wings.

(d) A few greenshanks give most unusual calls, probably caused by a clash of fear and anger. These have sounded like *kwee-kwa-kwa* or still more strident *kweea-kwow-kwow*. Two of the birds giving them were hens flushed from chipping eggs, but a third hen had only just started to sit.

(5)   *Nest calls*

The brooding greenshank occasionally gives *tyoors* to warn its incoming mate, which it may call up by special *chips*. Just before its relief arrives at the nest, the sitting greenshank sometimes utters soft little cries.

(6)   *Hatching calls*

(a)   While the chicks are squeaking in the eggs and hatching out, the brooding bird talks to them with deep harsh-sounding *gruffs*. These calls, which are probably difficult for a predator to locate, are so surprisingly loud and menacing that they possibly frighten away small ground mammals.

(b)   A parent returning to nest and chicks often gives loud dry angry-sounding *kluks*, singly or in short sequences.

(c)   A brooding greenshank has many other special cries restricted to hatching.

(d)   In these critical hours we have also heard curlew-like cries and some not unlike the *pooks* of blackbirds.

(e)   When about to lead away its chicks, the parents give *cluking* calls similar to those of a domestic fowl leading chicks to food; and as the brood moves away it is shepherded to the sounds of quickly repeated *kwik-kwiks*.

(7)   *Cries of parents to chicks*

While flying around the nest the parents have several different high-pitched squeaks with which they warn the chicks to freeze. When they give these warning squeaks to unhatched chicks they fail to silence them. However, soon after the chicks have left the scoop they usually respond immediately by silence and freezing.

(8)   *Chick calls*

The cries of chicks are extremely difficult to locate on heath and flow. This is particularly true when two or three of them are squeaking one after the other.

(a)   The main cry of the unhatched and hatched chick is a squeaking *whee*.

(b)   A second cry, *pee-pee-pee*, given in the egg and after hatching, is probably the precursor of the parental *chip*. We first discovered and tape-recorded this sound in 1967.

This is only an outline of the greenshank's remarkably large vocabulary. In *Greenshanks* (1979) we show 59 original Sonagrams made from our Sutherland tape-recordings.

PREDATORS

Greenshanks have many predators. Hooded crows and foxes are common to almost every occupied habitat in the Scottish Highlands; both are potential predators in our study area in north-west Sutherland. Peregrine, merlin, buzzard, common and great black-backed gull and arctic skua also hunt in the valley. In 1983, Bruin and Maimie watched the *Broken Egg* pair chasing a buzzard; and in 1978 they saw a merlin unsuccessfully try to cut down a greenshank which was guarding a brood, but the greenshank out-flew the predator. On 11 June 1984, Bruin and Maimie watched a tiercel peregrine stoop at high speed at a cock greenshank which was *chipping* and singing above a brood. The greenshank dropped behind a rock, just before the peregrine attacked and soon re-appeared when the falcon had missed and passed on. Why have these noisy demonstrations over broods not been selected out, when their clamour and song dancing clearly attracts predators? Possibly, however, their uses as dispersion mechanisms

outweighs these dangers. Bonxies, presumably from Handa Island, have recently started to harry waders and divers in the middle and higher gneiss.

Between 1966–72, predators destroyed two out of 44 (4.4%) of known greenshank nests; but in 1973–77 they took 14 out of 56 nests (25%). Some territories are possibly more vulnerable than others. Between 1969–76, for example, nests of *Loch* pair were predated in four different years; and in 1964 and 1969 one of the adults was killed in this territory.

Peregrines are also deadly predators sometimes in north-east Sutherland. Jon Hardey and David Whitaker each reported particular tiercels and falcons killing and carrying greenshanks to their eyries. Hen harriers and short-eared owls nest in new conifer plantations in north Sutherland. The hen harrier is a particularly dangerous predator and one known to carry greenshanks to its broods. J. G. McNicol (MS) found that the common gull was a rapacious egg robber around Forsinard and that foxes and wild cats were other predators there.

In Spey Valley hoodie, sparrowhawk, fox and now possibly goshawk, hunt some of the greenshank haunts. However, predators had much less influence than man on the loss of the fine greenshank groups in Glenmore and Rothiemurchus Forests. Misuse of habitats around Loch Morlich helped to destroy this grand population. Douglas Weir found the pluckings of seven greenshanks in his peregrine study area in the central Grampians. In inland Highland habitats, Ratcliffe (1980) also recorded seven greenshanks as prey of peregrines between 1964–75.

Murdo Matheson watched a peregrine continuously stooping at a greenshank in west Inverness which only escaped by diving and hiding under a bank. In that lovely district buzzards, foxes, badgers, otters and pine martens are other possible predators. Here, Roger Powell watched a pair of greenshanks with chicks mobbing a short-eared owl.

Yngvar Hagen (MS) recorded a peregrine killing a fully grown greenshank in south Norway. He considers that merlin, kestrel, rough-legged buzzard, hen harrier, short-eared owl, Ural and eagle owls are other possible predators. Hugh Blair recorded goshawks and possibly hen harriers, hoodies, Siberian jays and occasionally pine martens as likely predators in Finnmark.

Ants of different kinds sometimes trouble sitting greenshanks. In 1979 two of our Sutherland greenshanks' nests were placed on ant hills, from one of which the birds rolled their eggs away. At a north Sutherland nest in 1979, S. Lythe watched a sitting greenshank make quick dabs at the peat and then move its bill through its wings and mantle feathers. The bird was possible 'anting', but this was not proved. In south Norway, in 1979, Roger Powell found that wood ants were swarming over a sitting greenshank which was only able to sit for about 10 minutes at a time. 'When returning she made regular frenzied attacks on the ants in and around the nest, pecking at them and often flicking them over her back. In the end the nest and eggs were deserted'. In another part of the forest, wood ants also overran two bramblings' nests which were also later deserted.

On 11 June 1986, Bruin had the thrilling experience of watching a pair of greenshanks luring a fox away from their chicks in a Sutherland flow. The two greenshanks 'danced', ran, jumped and flapped their wings, to distract the fox which followed them for nearly 300 m. At the height of the commotion a third greenshank joined them and also very briefly gave a lure display on the ground. A pair of dunlin, which had chicks nearby, crouched behind a bank while the greenshanks were distracting the fox.

FOOD

In winter, greenshanks favour gobies *Pomatoschistus microps* and crabs *Carcinus maenus*, less frequently they take ragworms *Nereis* and Shrimps *Crangon crangon*. In the Clyde estuary Bruin watched them feed in pools and take *Gammarus* and *Carcinus*. Greenshanks take parr and fry of salmon *Salmo salar* and trout *S. trutta* in summer and eels in estuaries in winter; they probably take more fresh fish than any other European wader. We have watched them capture newts *Triturus*; and we have found the remains of frogs *Rana* and small lizards *Lacerta* in summer pellets.

Hens probably require extra calcium to form their eggshells in hard springs. This may account for the presence of the teeth of small voles and the vertebrae of medium-sized salmon and trout in pellets from our study area. However, the greenshanks in north-west Sutherland particularly favour *Plateumaris discolor*, a tiny leaf beetles, usually found on water plants. The many vivid colours of the elytra of these beetles shine out in the pellets. In these habitats they also catch large carabid and dytiscid beetles, as well as adults and nymphs of dragonflies *Libellus*, mayflies (Ephemeroptera), water bugs *Corix*, pond skaters *Gerris* and whirligig beetles *Gyrinus*.

Greenshanks make quick dabs or pecks in the shallows, often running through the water with outstretched wings and beaks half-open. Sometimes they take high steps, almost as in courtship, and they may dance through standing pools, turning, twisting and rotating while pursuing elusive pondskaters and whirligig beetles. We have seen them probing deeply in shallow pools, bringing up beaksful of water weed which possibly contain some of the animals that they are pursuing. They also sometimes dab themselves with water weeds. Greenshanks run over wet heath, swerving, or moving in circles, semi-circles, figure-of-eight and ellipses, while rapidly dabbing from side to side as they pick up insects, or they occasionally tackle frogs or lizards on drier heath. A greenshank stands sometimes on a stone or rock just above the river surface, deftly picking up adult mayflies or nymphs as they sweep past. Mowing movements are used to prey on hatches of stone flies *Plecoptera* as they emerge from under the stones. Other insects are picked up from vegetation on river banks, but they do not work these habitats as thoroughly as do common sandpipers.

In 1978 an unusual cock greenshank frequently settled in the middle of a small loch, where he swam around just like a phalarope, moving his head from side to side as he picked up flying insects. He also had a special bathing pool in the corner of a tarn where he sometimes spent almost an hour washing himself after feeding, half-plunging under the surface with partly raised wings and his white tail feathers fanned and fluttering. He frequently emerged with weed in his bill, dabbing it under his wings and on his breast and belly. Afterwards he went through grotesque contortions while he preened and dried himself.

DISTRIBUTION AND NUMBERS

Greenshanks have a restricted breeding range in the British Isles. On the mainland of Scotland they nest regularly in Caithness, Sutherland, Ross and Cromarty, Inverness, Perth, Argyll, and in very small numbers in Aberdeen. The 1924–25 record from the Lammermuirs on the borders of Berwick and East Lothian must be discarded. Ian Lyster, of the Royal Scottish Museum, has confirmed that the two alleged greenshanks' eggs were those of golden plovers. Stray pairs have possibly nested in Northumberland and Yorkshire, but there is as yet no acceptable record.

A pair of greenshanks bred on Hoy, Orkney, in 1951 and a pair nested on mainland Shetland in 1980; earlier records for Shetland are not acceptable. In the Outer Hebrides, where Professor William MacGillivray found a nest on Harris in the 1820s or 1830s, greenshanks have re-colonised and thrived from the 1950s onwards. They nest in good numbers in Lewis and Harris; smaller groups breed in Benbecula, North and South Uist, and probably occasionally on Barra. In the Inner Hebrides greenshanks have nested on Jura, Tiree, and possibly Mull; but the only known regular breeding groups are those in south and central Skye.

R. F. Ruttledge told us that greenshanks nested in Connaught in 1972 and 1974. These are the most westerly known breeding records.

In northern Europe they nest in Norway, Sweden, Finland, occasionally in Latvia, and in USSR. Their haunts in Norway are in the coniferous forests, birch, and in the lower limits of the willow zones. In the west the greenshank is an upland species, nesting at over 1,000 m in the great marshes of Dovre and Langfjell where it is well distributed. Trondelag also carries a good population. Draining of the fine Pasvik marshes in Finnmark has reduced breeding waders, but greenshanks are still in good numbers in suitable habitats. In northern Sweden they breed west and north of the line north Vårmland – Vårmland – north-west Angerman – Kusfors – Edefors – Niemis. In 1962 they nested in Medelpåd, in 1975 in north-west Gastrikland and they have occasionally bred in Gotland and other parts of south Sweden.

Finnish habitats include Kilpisjärvi in the north, Enontekiö in fell-Lapland, Inari and the birch zone of Utsjoki. Further south, they nest in the boglands of forest Lapland. The southern boundary in western Finland is the line Isjoki-Honkajoki – Parkano – Kuru – Ruovesi. Many greenshanks nest north of Jyvåskyla. There are very few acceptable breeding records from south-west Finland, but a few pairs nest almost to the frontier in the east of the country.

The great forest marshes of USSR hold most of the world's greenshank population. Here they nest in north-east Estonia SSR; on the northern fringes of the Murman Sea; up to 66°N on the River Pechora; and to 66°39′N on the Lower Ob. They nest in Jenissej and eastwards to about 65°N on the Rivers Lena and Kolyma, and in the forest zone of the Lukovaya channel of the west Anadyr. The breeding range in east Siberia has not been fully studied, but greenshanks nest in Kamchatka, on the southern edges of Lake Ochotsk, south to the Santar Islands, and possibly in forest marshes along the lower Amur. In the west they have breeding grounds on spurs of the Stanowoi Mountains, and to the north of Lake Baikal. Greenshanks nest north of the Anjari and close to Tomsk, Tara, and Tobolsk in west Siberia. Their most southerly boundaries touch west Sajan, Novosibirsk and the Baraba steppe. They are scarce in the middle course of the River Ural, but breed in forest marshes close to the Rivers Kama and Belaia in Baschkir. Above Moscow and the upper Dnieper they range northwards to Pskov and thence to the Gulf of Finland on the north-west borders of Estonia.

In *Greenshanks* (1979) we suggested that roughly 800–900 pairs bred in Britain. Since then, further correspondence with enthusiastic watchers suggest that we may have under-estimated the population in some districts.

Between 1977–79 Roger Powell and Barry Larking surveyed breeding groups in four different parts of west Inverness. They assess the total greenshank population for these areas to be in the region of 25 pairs in 1978, possibly dropping to 12 pairs in 1979. Our friend, Andrew Currie, who has been taking a keen interest in greenshanks in Skye, estimates that there may be up to 15–25 pairs breeding there.

It is almost impossible to make an accurate breeding census of a bird nesting in such huge, rough country, and with a population which fluctuates so markedly from year to year. Possibly an estimate of a little less than 1,000 breeding pairs is the best approximation at the present state of our knowledge.

On our first visit to the greenshank valley, in May 1964, we could not possibly know of the exciting experiences that lay ahead. We have returned year after year, spending in all 490 nights in the small fishing but between 1964–84, as well as making many daily visits. We have found 159 nests in the valley. Some of our hunts have been tense and thrilling, although by no means all have been successful. The original *Tiger, Knoll, Beauty, Eamonn 2* and *Great Day* hens were all very special greenshanks that we have loved and will always remember.

COMMON SNIPE

School holidays in the 1920s, on the farm beside Amberley Wild Brooks, in Sussex, led to an early acquaintance with common snipe. I soon learnt where to look for their nests which I found by hard hunting and searching rather than by watching. At first the song dance puzzled me. The small brown bird rose on fast beating wings which it then partly closed and quivered and dived and rose time after time. I then heard, for the first time, the goat-like bleating. Lapwings, redshanks and snipe nested in different parts of the wet and rushy fields which were divided by deep dykes.

The common snipe is easily recognised in the field by its long straight bill, richly barred and mottled reddish brown mantle, and particularly by the harsh *scaap* cries as it rises from marsh or ditch and zig-zags away before climbing steeply and making off. In the hand you find that its legs and feet are greyish green and its tail is white at the sides and barred with black and tawny-brown.

Leslie Tuck (1972) has carried out the most thorough long-term study of a race of snipe. His subject, the Wilson's snipe of America – a nearctic race of *Gallinago gallinago* – is distinguished by 'the narrower width and constant number of the outer tail feathers and a more intense barring on the axillaries'. Faroe snipe *G. c. faeroensis*, which nest in Iceland, Faroes, Orkney, Shetland and St Kilda, have redder breasts, throats and under tail coverts, and the nape and scapulars are much more orange-red. This race cannot be safely distinguished in the field from *G. g. gallinago*.

Most races of common snipe are probably capable of breeding when about one year old. In Wilson's snipe, for example, Tuck found that banded yearlings tended to breed late in the season when about 14 months old. In Heligoland, where 14 common snipe chicks were ringed before they could fly, seven were recovered in their first year, one in the second, and three each in their fourth and fifth years. The oldest Heligoland bird was at least 12 years old (F. Goethe). Finnur Gudmundsson (*in* Glutz 1977) recorded details of several Faroe snipe recovered after being ringed as chicks. Sixteeen were in their first year, seven in their second, one in its third, four in their fourth, and one in its fifth year. Two other banded Faroe snipe were 7 years 6 months and

7 years 3 months old respectively. Robert Spencer (1961 and 1969) also recorded snipe which had carried rings for 11 years 7 months and 10 years 3 months (Table 1).

Snipe have always belonged to the wader communities in the haunts we have worked. In Co. Antrim, on misty moonlit nights, I heard them bleating over wet fields but found that they moved away before nesting. Snipe courted and nested on the edges of rough peatlands and in moist hollows of the heather on Dorback Moor; a few pairs also laid their eggs on soggy flanks alongside the burn. In Abernethy Forest there was a wonderful confluence of rills and streams just outside the old pines where, on many evenings, I watched amazing aerial stunts performed by courting snipe. At Loch Morlich a few pairs regularly bred in tall grass among the stumps of burnt pines not far from where the greenshanks nested. In one particular forest bog a solitary pair of snipe nested every year. There are still more exciting habitats on the dotterel hills of west and east Drumochter where the family have recorded snipe drumming over the bog at least 750 m ASL.

In later years, particularly since 1978, we have been learning a little more about the behaviour of snipe in habitats in our greenshank study area in north-west Sutherland. Here a few pairs are scattered over natural grassland in the peat bogs and on the edges of the gneiss flows where their numbers fluctuate from year to year.

ARRIVAL, COURTSHIP AND TERRITORY

It is always exciting to watch snipe arrive and disperse in their nesting haunts. Cocks arrive up to a fortnight ahead of hens. At first they are quiet and inconspicuous, but soon start to bleat, particularly in the twilight of warm evenings when they display over large expanses of bog. When other cocks arrive and also start to drum the movements and song flights of the territory holder are contracted. On the other hand, if no cock arrives to challenge him, and no hen visits his arena, the displaying cock deserts or enlarges his original territory.

I have never watched the arrival of a hen, but the behaviour of a cock soon shows what has happened. There are now great chases and sometimes magnificent exhibitions of stunt flying. The cock often pursues the hen, perhaps gliding over her with his wings acutely raised above his back almost like the approach of a cock swift to a hen in mid-air. These flights are seldom high above ground, but are given by the cock when he is flying after a hen. There are other great moments. A cock suddenly flips over on his back, sails upside down for a few metres, or dives and hovers over the hen, perhaps fluttering above her, dangling his legs and raising his wings.

A cock snipe excitedly courts a hen on the ground. He walks towards her, perhaps encircles her, droops his wings and erects and fans his tail. The hen then sometimes responds by giving similar displays; or she stands motionless in front of him. If a second cock challenges the courting pair excited and erratic flights follow, with the territory holder apparently trying to shepherd his hen back to his arena. At other times a cock flutters over a hen after she has returned and time after time swoops at her head.

DISPERSION AND BREEDING DENSITY

Between 1978–81, 6–10 pairs of snipe have annually nested in our north-west Sutherland study area of 3,250 ha – a breeding density of 1 breeding pair/541 ha. This estimate, however, does not give a true picture as snipe in the valley are largely restricted to marginal grasslands and are absent from many apparently suitable peatland habitats.

In the fens and wet meadows of East Anglia, F. Ogilvie (1920) estimated a breeding density of 1 pair/10 ha; and in 1957, a good snipe year on Hirta, St Kilda, Ken William-son (1960) recorded 40 pairs breeding on 22 ha.

Some haunts in the Netherlands carry a high density; for example, 5.1–10 breeding pairs/100 ha in an expanse of 4,800 ha near Hilversum (Alleyn *et al* 1971). Breeding density is high in some small flats in Schleswig-Holstein where H. J. Lepthin (*in* Glutz 1977) found two nests 15 m apart and up to 1 breeding pair/ha. Suitable habitats in the USSR also carry a high breeding density of snipe. At Kirgizia, for example, Yanushe-vitch *et al* (1959) recorded an average of 1.9 breeding pairs/ha in their study areas; and on floating islands of vegetated peat on the River Volga, E. M. Vorontsov and N. Khokhlova (1963) recorded 2.2 breeding pairs/ha in the first year after a reservoir had been created.

NEST, EGG AND CLUTCH

Soon after pair formation the nest site is chosen. I have only twice seen this, but on each occasion a single bird – presumably the hen – formed the nest site, hollowing out a depression in a tussock of grass in rough herbage. At one of these we also flushed a second bird close to the scrape at which its mate was working, but it appeared to take no part in the scoop formation. Both site-selecting birds allowed me to approach quite closely before crying harshly as they zig-zagged away. During egg laying and incubation the sitting hen adds grass to the nest; by twisting grasses together she also sometimes forms a small tent over the eggs.

The nests are placed in tussocks and hummocks in the grass, rushes or heather and are lined with various grasses and sometimes a few dry leaves. In USSR, Elizabeth Kozlova (1962) found that the scrape measured 9–19 cm across and was 2–7.5 cm deep, and K. Hudec recorded breadths of 8–12 cm (mean 9.2 cm) and depths of 2.5–5.0 cm (mean 3.8 cm) in Czechoslovakia. During flooding, J. H. Owen, and others, discovered that snipe built up their nests to avoid their eggs being swamped.

F. G. Penrose (1912) recorded that snipe occasionally started to sit from early to mid March in Wiltshire. In early years, R. C. Britton likewise found full clutches in West Sussex in the last ten days of March. On the Amberley Brooks, in West Sussex, however, we recorded the completion of 27 clutches between 10–18 April (mean 15 April). Ten Surrey hens clutched between 11 April–9 May (mean 21 April). In the rough grazings, moors, and marshes of Yorkshire and Derbyshire, Arthur Whitaker recorded 45 clutches completed between 12 April–15 June (mean 30 April). Whitaker also found ten nests in the Norfolk and Suffolk brecks where the hens had laid up between 6 April–1 May (mean 20 April). In Spey Valley the weather determined consider-able differences, but most hens were down between 25 April–7 May. C. F. Mason and S. M. McDonald (1976) recorded that most clutches were started in the latter half of April and many also in May (average date for 174 clutches, 30 April).

In central Europe the earliest hens go down between late March and early April. In central Sweden and south Finland snipe occasionally complete their clutches in early May, but the average laying season ranges from late May onwards. R. Väisänen (1977) gives 11–12 June as the spot date for full clutches in central and north Norway. In Estonia National Park the average laying season starts from about 12 May.

Timmermann (1949) gives the end of May and the first half of June, and very occasio-nally mid May, as the laying season in Iceland of *G. g. faeronsis*. Williamson (1960) records laying in May/June in the Faroes and from mid May onwards in the Outer Hebrides.

Snipe have occasionally laid their eggs in nests of black-tailed godwit, common sand-piper, lapwing and redshank. Tewnion and Thomis (1975) photographed a nest in which a snipe and laid her eggs in a redshank's nest on which the hen redshank was sitting.

The eggs are fairly glossy, pyriform or pointed ovate. Ground colour is usually greyish to olive-brown, less frequently yellow-brown or buff. Scarce varieties have starling blue, grey-blue or green on olive-green ground colour. Complete clutches of unmarked blue (cyanic) eggs are on record. Snipes' eggs are usually spotted or boldly blotched, particularly in a zone round the heavy end, with sepia and deep red-brown, and they have violet, purple or ash-grey undermarkings and a few almost black squiggles.

In Britain 100 snipes' eggs averaged 39.3 × 28.6 mm (Jourdain 1940). This figure differs only slightly from measurements for Sweden 40.0 × 28.65 mm (247) and for Norway 39.15 × 28.60 mm (44) (Glutz 1977). Sixty eggs of *C. g. faeroensis* at 40.0 × 28.4 had no significant difference (Jourdain 1940). W. P. J. Hellebrekers (1950) weighed 100 blown eggshells, in the Netherlands, which ranged from 0.70–0.99 gm (mean 0.84 gm). Sixteen freshly-laid eggs from Germany averaged 17.2 gm. Although the eggs look large for the bird's size, a clutch of four weighs only about 61% of the hen's body weight.

Hens do not consistently lay their eggs at any special time of the day. Most lay at intervals of 24–30 hours, but there is often a lapse of two days between the second and third egg.

The usual clutch is four, occasionally three, and exceptionally two or five. Six has been recorded but was possibly due to two hens laying in the same nest. Table 4 analyses clutch size. Williamson (1949) recorded a mean of 3.7 for Faroe snipe on St Kilda and the Faroes. Tuck (1972) recorded a mean clutch-size of 3.8 for Wilson's snipe in Newfoundland, Canada.

Judging by eggs, identified by peculiarities of shape and markings, common snipe complete replacement clutches in 14–17 days. W. M. Congreve (1942) recorded a replacement clutch which was completed in 16 days. Whitaker, who had taken a half-incubated clutch of unusual eggs on 11 May 1943, found the hen sitting on a 'repeat' of four fresh eggs on 28 May.

INCUBATION

The hen starts to sit steadily at some time between the third and fourth egg, or soon after she has laid the last egg in c/4. She alone appears to incubate. Hens usually sit extremely closely and are most difficult to spot when they are brooding. At intervals of 3–4 hours, and sometimes longer, the hen leaves her eggs to feed, flying to some favourite place in the marsh or moor anything from 50–150 m or more from the nest. After feeding for 25–35 minutes she makes her way back in different ways. She may first drop down in the bog and then make a second flight before finally flying to the nest. Or she may rise and tower and then dive straight back to the nest where she re-arranges the eggs before settling down to incubate.

In Wilson's snipe, Tuck discovered that the cock's drumming display greatly diminished after the hen had been sitting for about 10 days. However, 4–5 days before the chicks hatched, he again started to bleat in the early morning and late evening, but these spasms lasted only 2–3 minutes in each twilight period. We have recorded similar behaviour and noted that the sounds of the cock's bleating are now extremely weak or faint. We have occasionally flushed both birds from the side of a nest during the hatch. Tuck watched a cock Wilson's snipe crouching on the edge of the nest with partly opened wings, or 'clucking softly' and hovering just beside it after the hen had left to feed. The chicks' squeaks apparently stimulate his weak but latent incubation drive.

Most hens leave their eggs, giving a harsh *scaap* of alarm, when the searcher is less than 5 m away. Even when she is sitting on quite fresh eggs a hen sometimes waits until a foot is about to descend upon her. At least one unfortunate hen was killed on her nest in this way. She had previously towered and then dived steeply back to the nest, but she did not rise when the boot was coming down. While hunting a Lancashire marsh on 6 June 1926, Whitaker noticed that 'the bird had had a narrow escape as my foot went on to the edge of the nest and broke two of the eggs'. An exceptionally hard-sitting hen may even allow herself to be lifted from her eggs.

The last egg in an Abernethy clutch of four hatched after approximately 19 days incubation. In the Faroes, Williamson recorded two full clutches hatching on the 18th and a third on the 19th day after steady incubation had started on the third egg. In Wilson's snipe three clutches hatched in 19 days and a fourth in 19.5 days after the fourth egg was laid.

HATCHING

The chicks squeak in the eggs for at least one whole day before they hatch. On Dorback Moor, and in habitats in USSR, there are records of chipping periods lasting from eight to 60 hours. Tuck records 1–6 hours, and once less than 30 minutes for Wilson's snipe. The intervals between hatching of the chicks at six different nests of Wilson's snipe ranged from 4 hours 20 minutes to 7 hours 45 minutes (mean 5 hours 45 minutes).

F. Ogilive (1920) recorded that common snipe carried away their eggshells, one by one, as they were hatched, but this is certainly unusual. In our experience, most hens leave the larger portions of hatched eggshells in or just outside the scoop. A domestic fowl's eggshell, placed in a Dorback nest containing unchipped eggs, was at first ignored but later carried away. J. H. Owen found that all four shells were left in some nests but larger fragments were removed from others. Williamson (1949) noted that Faroe snipe sometimes removed the shells of the first two chicks and allowed later fragments to lie in the scoop. Wilson's snipe leave hatched shells in their nests (H. Mousley 1935 and L. Tuck 1972).

YOUNG

Young snipe are a mixture of red-brown, black and silvery stripes and blotches. Their irides are dark brown. Legs, feet and shins are dark grey with patches of green and their calves dark grey with pink patches. They have dark brownish grey bills. This colourful uniform blends admirably with their marshy habitats and makes them extremely difficult to locate once they have left the nest.

After the chicks have hatched, cock and hen may divide the family, the cock brooding and leading away the two oldest and the hen the two youngest. This sometimes results in the break up of the family as each parent may lead chicks to different feeding grounds up to 500 m apart (Tuck 1972). The parents brood chicks under their wings.

W. J. Nash (1916), M. Casement (1948) and D. F. Parmelee (1954) all record that common and Wilson's snipe occasionally carry their chicks. However, with his wide experience, Tuck had no evidence of this and suggests that some examples of carrying were possibly accidental. For our part, we have never watched a snipe carry a chick.

Cock and hen both carry food in their bills for chicks which are still unable to fly. On 3 August 1940, for example, the two parents flew in with food and alighted periodically on an old fank on the Dorback Moor. Young snipe flutter strongly when they are about a fortnight old. Kozlova recorded sustained flights at 15–18 days and

Williamson watched chicks flying strongly at 21 days. In Newfoundland a young Wilson's snipe could flutter after a fortnight and occasionally flew quite strongly for 300 m when 17–18 days old. However, it was more usual for a chick to be 20 days old before flying over 100 m. Young snipe are not fully fledged until they are about 4–5 weeks old (Williamson 1960; O. Heinroth 1972).

In an analysis of results for 234 British nests, Mason and Macdonald (1976) recorded that at least one egg hatched in 59% of the nests but that 41% failed completely. This shows a gross average of 2.2 chicks per nest, with a mean of 3.5 chicks for each successful or partly successful nest. Of the 56 known failures, 56% were robbed, 25% destroyed by trampling – usually by cattle – and 11% were deserted.

DISTRACTION BEHAVIOUR

After a hen has been flushed she often flies away twisting and zig-zagging before dropping into the fen well away from the nest; but some perform elaborate distraction displays, crawling away with spread wings and expanded tails. Snipe also occasionally flutter over the ground with their tails depressed and one wing beating and the other slightly trailing over heather or grass. E. Selous recorded a hen spinning round with her bill parallel to the ground and crouching with neck fluffed up and slowly raising her rear and fanning her tail. Williamson (1950) gives a good description of the distraction behaviour of a Faroe snipe. The hen's tail was spread widely 'showing a beautiful blaze of reddish-chestnut feathers mixed with creamy-buff'. She carried her tail in a horizontal position and ran directly away from the observer. From a side view the tail seemed to be tilted upwards and the fan extended vertically; several times she closed and then snapped open the fan. All the time she moved in a crouch, with sunken head, and her long bill pointing downwards at an angle of about 45° while she gave low harsh *kwaars*. Bleating flights are also probably sometimes used as forms of distraction behaviour.

VOICE

(1)   The famous instrumental bleating or drumming of snipe has two different functions. It is used by the cock to attract a hen and also to repel intruders from his territory. Tuck (1972) describes bleating as 'primarily a sexual display over the home-range'. Hens also periodically bleat during pair formation and sexual flights and after they have laid their first and second eggs. The rapidly vibrating wings accompanying the bleating probably help to give the characteristic tremulous quality.

(2)   The usual call given by snipe flushed from ground or nest is a hoarse-sounding *scaap*, often uttered at intervals of one to two seconds as the bird zig-zags away.

(3)   Cock and hen have a throbbing *chipper-chipper*, notes of excitement and sex, which are given on the ground or on the wing.

(4)   *Yik-yak* or *chuk-chee* is another call common to both sexes during sex chases and and ground displays as well as in the air.

(5)   The cock *clucks* softly when crouching over eggs.

(6)   In distraction displays on the ground the hen sometimes gives harsh throaty cries.

(7)   Parents use soft *chirring* cries to disperse chicks and 'soft coaxing calls' (Hosking and Newberry 1940) to recall them.

(8)   Chicks squeak in the eggs and also continue to do so after they have hatched.

PREDATORS

Snipe have many different predators. In Sussex, carrion crows sometimes found and sucked eggs as did hooded crows in Sutherland. Foxes are other likely enemies in both these locations. At different times, in Spey Valley, we have watched a short-eared owl and a buzzard drop into a forest bog and rise holding a well-grown young snipe. Douglas Weir found the remains of 35 snipe in pluckings at 22 peregrines' eyries in the central Grampians. Ratcliffe (1980) also gives snipe as frequent prey of peregrines in inland and in some coastal districts of Britain. Donald Watson (1972) recorded snipe in hen harrier kills in Galloway; and at winter roosts in Kintyre Dugald Macintyre identified snipe remains in hen harriers' pellets. D. H. MacGillivray watched a harrier increase speed to catch a low-flying snipe which a dog had flushed from a habitat in Arran. Merlins occasionally pursue and cut down snipe in mid air and kestrels have been known to do so; J. H. Owen recorded snipe as prey of sparrowhawks. In marshes close to their colonies, jackdaws are robbers of chicks and eggs.

A. C. Bent (1927) lists goshawk, Cooper's hawk, peregrine, American kestrel, marsh hawk and horned owl among the predators of Wilson's snipe in North America. The marsh hawk is possibly the most deadly. Tuck watched them taking 17 Wilson's snipe and found their remains in the stomach of five others. He also saw a red-tailed hawk take a snipe on the wing; and boreal owls attacked the heads of snipe caught in mistnets. In Newfoundland, S. A. Temple (*in* Tuck 1972) found Wilson's snipe in four pigeon hawks' nests sited close to bogs, but they were absent from 18 other nests in dry uplands. In all, snipe accounted for 10% of the prey taken.

Other dangers to snipe are cattle, horses, and man trampling on eggs; flooding and farming activities frequently destroy their nests. But the greatest hazard is the reclamation of nesting fens or marshes.

FOOD

The snipe's long bill with its sensitive tip helps it to feed on moist ground of different kinds, particularly peatlands, in the breeding season.

In Europe, animal food has included small land snails (Helicidae: *Viviparus, Valvata, Bulinus* and *Planorbis*). Snipe also feed on small crustraceans (Isopoda) and various oliogochaete and polychaete worms – including earthworms, mostly less than 10 cm long and at largest 25 cm. They also feed on polychaetes in the mud and leeches on soil or mud. Insects include Chironomidae, Culicidae, Tipulidae, Tabanidae, Syrphidae, Ephemeroptera and Trichoptera, small caterpillars of moths, beetles (Carabidae, Dytiscidae, Staphylinidae, Elateridae, Hydrophilidae, Curculionidae and Scarabaeidae) and ants. Plant material is frequent in diet and includes seeds of *Rumex, Polygonum, Vicia hirsuta, Myosotis caespitosa, Sonchus arvensis, Solanum dulcamara, Potamogeton, Scirpus* and *Carex* (Glutz 1977).

Stomachs of 48 snipe collected in the Ukraine contained 48 Diptera (principally larvae), 190 beetles, 12 snails and 10 small frogs; six held bugs (Heteroptera) and moth caterpillars. Five stomachs contained the remains of mayflies, four had hover flies, three had leeches and small crabs, and one had spider and dragonfly remains. There were also 457 seeds (O. B. Kistyakivski 1957).

Between March and April, R. Stadie (1933) examined 14 stomachs from Baltic coastlands. These contained plant remains, one with seeds and one with two worms; one with three millipedes and one with eight mandibles of *Nereis diversicolor*. Eleven stomachs from the coast of Schleswig-Holstein contained much plant material such as moss, grass fibres and fragments of rhizomes. Unidentified seeds were recorded in seven stomachs, unidentified molluscs in two stomachs, fragments of *Nereis* in five, *Arenicola* probably in three, earthworms in two, beetles in seven, and one had Diptera larvae.

In seven stomachs, collected in France between August and November, five held insects (larvae of *Eristalis*, small Carabidae, Staphylinidae, Dytiscidae (mainly Laccophilus), and one held 40 small caterpillars).

Leslie Tuck has made a careful study of the food and feeding behaviour of Wilson's snipe in North America. Insects averaged 59% of known animal food in the various habitats; but in the peatlands and fens the proportion rose to 80%, dropping to less than 20% in tidal waters. The proportion of Diptera ranged from 8–75% and Coleoptera from 15–80%. In some habitats plants contributed between 17–45% of the stomach contents. Most contained grit, much probably accidentally taken while probing in wet ground.

C. F. Tubbutt watched snipe catching worms and taking them one by one to the water's edge where they first washed and then swallowed them. Snipe, like other waders, produce pellets containing indigentible matter.

DISTRIBUTION AND NUMBERS

There has been no significant changes in distribution in the last 50 years, except where suitable habitats have been drained or afforested or parts of lowland farms reclaimed. J. T. R. Sharrock (1976) recorded that snipe bred in Britain and Ireland in 1,760 confirmed, 1,010 probable, and 360 possible 10-km squares. Assuming 30–40 breeding pairs in each confirmed or probable squares, he estimated a total British and Irish population of roughly 80,000–110,000 breeding pairs.

The estimates of numbers given in Glutz (1977) and Cramp and Simmons (1983) indicate a fairly regular decline in numbers outside Britain, due to the draining and reclamation of marshes and of other breeding habitats. Populations are estimated at 300–350 breeding pairs in France, 80 in Belgium; 100 in Luxemburg; about 5,000 in the Netherlands and over 16,000 in West Germany (with 10,000 pairs breeding in Schleswig-Holstein and 5,300 in Lower Saxony). Denmark is said to have a population of about 2,000–4,000; Norway 55,000; Finland possibly 90,000; and Estonia SSR 1,000 breeding pairs. There are also small breeding groups in other parts of Europe; under 100 pairs in Austria, 10–20 pairs in Hungary and less than 200 pairs in Spain (Cramp and Simmons 1983).

The snipe form a fascinating group of waders. In Britain we have no opportunity to watch and study the intriguing lek displays of great snipe or to probe the breeding life of the mysterious jack snipe about which little is known. But the drumming and sex displays of common snipe on soft spring evenings and early summer mornings, and their many patterns of sexual behaviour, are always wonderful consolations.

DUNLIN

Early on 25 April 1929 Jock Wapole-Bond was showing me how to find ringed plovers' nests on a rather public beach near Hove in Sussex. Small boys with dogs frequently disturbed the returning plovers, but while we were waiting for them to move away a wisp of small waders, with a flash of whitish underwings, flew low over the Channel and landed briefly on the pebbles. These homing dunlins were quite lovely to see. Small waders, with reddish brown mantles and large blotches on their lower breasts, they had whitish wing bars and rather long and apparently straight bills. It was to be many years before I had the joy of watching them on their breeding grounds.

Dunlins have attracted many fine ornithologists, each of whom has contributed to our knowledge of their behaviour. Edgar Chance's data cards, for Orkney, are invaluable to anyone studying the dunlin. An ornithologist with a great love of hill birds, R. H. Brown, watched dunlins on the Solway saltmarshes and on the high fells of the Pennines, where their neighbours were quite different from those in Orkney. Brown's paper, published in 1938, is full of warmth and first-class observations. More recently, R. Heldt and M. Soikkeli in Europe and R. T. Holmes in North America have all chosen the dunlin for special study.

The damp machair grasslands of the Outer Hebrides provide some of the richest dunlin haunts in Britain. What a paradise for waders and watchers these machairs are! Lapwings, oystercatchers and snipe are almost everywhere; ringed plovers are on sandy and newly-ploughed ground; and redshanks and sandpipers nest on the wet edges of lochs as well as on the machair.

In 1932 I first met with breeding dunlin at Forsinard in north-east Sutherland and around Loch Harray on mainland Orkney. Very few dunlins nested on the low ground of the upper Spey Valley; indeed I only knew isolated pairs around Lochs Morlich and Insh. But on the high west Cairngorms and on the east Drumochter hills there were groups and solitary pairs which nested close to dotterel and golden plover. Since 1964, while watching greenshanks in north-west Sutherland, we have become increasingly interested in the small clusters of dunlin in the gneiss and in isolated territories in other parts of our study areas. Although our main work has been with the greenshank, knowledge of the fascinating little dunlin has slowly accumulated over the last 20 years.

During his fine study in Finland, Soikkeli (1973) found that most first breeders returned to their birth haunts and that all pair-faithful adults bred in successive years within 0.3 km of their former nest sites. Of the hens which had taken new mates, 90% nested within 1 km of the previous year's nest. The average age of a new breeder was 1.8 years.

Dunlins' nests are often difficult to find, unless they are nesting in good numbers on short mossy ground or on machair grass. Cock and hen often sit extremely tightly on well incubated eggs, only rising at the feet of the searcher. Off-duty birds, particularly cocks, sometimes warn the sitter which then slips off its eggs and flies to the side of a tarn or loch. Others run from their nests well ahead of the hunter or they flick off, anything from 10–300 m ahead. A dunlin sometimes leaves its nest, fluttering over the nearby vegetation in tremulous flight, almost like a sandpiper, and with its tail downstretched and often touching the vegetation. If one fails to see exactly where the bird has risen it is best to mark the nearest point and return from another direction about an hour later.

COURTSHIP AND TERRITORY

In late seasons in the valley the earliest dunlins feed for a few days along the river before moving up to their normal breeding grounds in the gneiss. Once settled, unmated cocks display over their territories, continuously drawing attention by remarkable flights and piercing whistling songs. If a hen is not attracted, the cock makes many song flights above his old territory and if he is still unsuccessful he prospects and sings over many different flows, periodically hovering, gliding, and singing. One cock sang over ground 4.5 km from his old nesting site and sometimes displayed over flows in which dunlins were never known to nest.

The dunlin's advertising song flight, used by both cock and hen, is always attractive. The bird rises steeply to a height of 10–50 m and then glides, hovers, rises and drops,

at times holding its wings vertically or at others beating them very rapidly in an almost moth-like action. Time after time the displaying bird gives his loud shrill scream and pulsating whistle, with the hen's trill markedly slower and more fragmentary (Holmes 1966). Early in courtship and territorial establishment the cock displays regularly and the hen occasionally does so. Cocks also sing shrilly while walking through the flow. In habitats where there are other courting cocks they sometimes leave their own living-space and take part in chases. A cock periodically flies past a hen and sings in front or beside her as well as behind her. Then the two birds swish down to the bog where they briefly run rapidly with one or both wings held vertically above their backs.

Dunlins are territorial birds, defending boundaries which vary considerably in different districts. The song flight is used to advertise possession of territory as well as to attract mates and to maintain pair bonds. On the gneiss, west of the river, we have often watched cocks from adjacent territories respond to advertisement flights, with the pursuing cock periodically holding his wings upright. Dunlins are also aggressive

on the ground; a cock often briefly raises and lowers one or both wings before repelling an intruder.

Scrape ritual plays an important role in pair formation. The cock now attempts to stimulate a hen by running ahead of her, occasionally fluttering a few metres into the air, or pausing at a tussock in which he starts to scratch out a scoop, rounding it with his breast rather like a lapwing. In this display he shows off his white under-tail coverts and when the hen walks up to him he steps out of the scoop, holding his wings upright, and she then continues to scrape and brood in the scratching. The hen tosses bits of grass or moss sideways and, from a distance, you see flashes of white as the birds are working. Dunlins often form many scrapes within a small radius of the ultimate nest.

We have only once seen dunlins copulating. The hen bowed slightly forward, and the cock flew a few yards towards her, hovering in the air before settling on her back, whirring his wings to keep his balance. At other times the hen has moved and rejected her suitor.

Dunlins appear to recall favourite landmarks. In an isolated territory in north-west Sutherland a pair laid their eggs within a radius of 30 m in four consecutive years. Three other hens laid their clutches in old scoops in consecutive years.

We have no reason to believe that there was a sizeable floating population in Sutherland, with some members prevented from breeding by inability to establish territories. At Barrow in arctic Alaska (71°20′ N) and probably on the River Kolomak (60°30′ N), however, Holmes proved, by removal experiments, that fresh pairs occupied the vacant niches thus artificially created.

DISPERSION AND BREEDING DENSITY

Spacing and breeding density vary greatly even in the same area. Between 1964–81, in north-west Sutherland, in 1.6 km^2 of predominantly schist habitats in blanket bog east of the river, 1–4 pairs nested annually, at a density of 1 breeding pair/160 ha to 1 breeding pair/40 ha. Spacing between nests ranged from 820–950 m (mean 910 m). In this period greenshanks had roughly the same breeding density; but between 1979–81 no greenshanks, and at most only one pair of dunlin, nested in these habitats. West of the river, in the large complexes of pools and dubhlochans on the gneiss, 15–20 pairs of dunlin have nested in 740 ha, with a density of 1 breeding pair/37 ha to 1 breeding pair/49 ha. Spacing ranged from 630–1,180 m (mean 410 m). Another study area in north Sutherland, which we worked in 1980, carried five breeding pairs of dunlin in 20 ha (1 breeding pair/4 ha) and the average spacing was less than 200 m.

In 1981, B. Etheridge (1982) recorded at least 43 breeding pairs in 14 ha of machair grassland on the Outer Hebrides, the equivalent of 315 breeding pairs/km^2. Several nests were only 20 m apart with a few separated by only 7 m. In a further study, in 1983, Etheridge (1984) estimated that 400 pairs nested in moist machair grasslands around Loch Bee, South Uist. A study plot of 6.7 ha held 25 pairs (3.7 breeding pairs/ha). In these haunts nests were often sited in clumps at an average distance of 45 m apart. Density on the English saltmarshes is much lower. M. E. Greenhalgh (1969) estimated a breeding density of 0.1 breeding pairs/10 ha in Morecambe Bay, Lancashire, a southerly breeding haunt of dunlin.

In arctic North America, R. T. Holmes (1970) recorded breeding densities in his study areas varying from 1 breeding pair/5.5 ha to 1 breeding pair/7.5 ha (mean 1 breeding pair/6.5 ha).

S. M. Uspenski (1975) found that nests in the Anabar tundra, USSR, were from 400–500 m apart, but usually 200–300 m; and in the Arangastach valley there was only one pair in a stretch of 15–20 km. On Jamal Peninsula, however, V. V. Leonovich and Uspenski (1965) discovered some stretches of late snowmelt where there was the high density of 1 breeding pair/ha. At Pori, in south-west Finland, Soikkeli recorded 24–27 breeding pairs on 60 ha (4–4.5 breeding pairs/10 ha). In parts of Norway, where dunlins nest in pockets of swamp in the high fells, the Cambridge Expedition of 1980 recorded 1 breeding pair/44 ha in their census area of 4.4 km^2 at 1,075–1,255 m ASL. On the high fells, as well as on lower marshes, J. Kålås and I. Byrkjedal (1981) estimate densities of 0.5 breeding pairs/km^2 in south Norway and 1.0 breeding pairs/km^2 in the north. In Schleswig-Holstein, in years of high numbers, R. Heldt (1966) found that 2–2.6 pairs bred in 10 ha, with a minimum spacing of 20 m between two nests. Some small flats in Iceland carry high density populations. M. Wink (1973) found 10 breeding pairs/8 ha on sedge-rich marsh, 8 breeding pairs/10 ha on dwarf shrub, and 3 pairs/10 ha on lava fields which carried 70% plant cover.

NEST, EGG AND CLUTCH

The hen probably lays her first egg in one of the scoops prepared during nest dance ritual. But we do not know whether – as with dotterel and red-necked phalarope – there is sometimes an egg ceremony in which one of the birds indicates the chosen scrape, or whether the hen drops her first egg haphazardly in the last scoop prepared after she is ready to lay. Before and after laying her first egg the hen briefly sits on the scrape as if incubating and then sometimes adds the first bits of lining.

Heldt (1966) measured 10 nests which averaged 89 mm in breadth and 49 mm in depth. In Iceland, Timmermann (1949) recorded breadths of 75–80 mm and depths of 30–55 mm, differences probably partly due to the kind of habitats selected. The neat little scoops are lined with fine grasses and a few leaves or with bits of *Salix* or *Vaccinium*.

In the west Cairngorms and Drumochter hills, at heights varying from 720–820 m ASL, the laying season varies according to snow cover and temperature. Most full clutches are laid from about 27 May onwards. In 1907, Chance found that over 100 Orkney clutches were completed in the third week of May. We have records of 21 clutches in Sutherland completed between 9 May–10 June (mean 25 May). Brown recorded the earliest full clutches on the Solway Marshes on 10 May; but he also found day-old chicks on 27 May from a clutch that must have been completed on 4–5 May. Arthur Whitaker found two nests on the Yorkshire-Derby moors which had clutched between 15–18 May; four in Orkney varied from 12–24 May; and four hens in the east Drumochter hills had completed their clutches between 31 May–11 June. At Barrow, Alaska, between 1960–63, Holmes (1966) recorded clutches laid between 6 June–6 July, with a peak between 12–18 June.

J. Strijbos (1936) recorded that the earliest clutch found in the Netherlands had three eggs on 14 April 1906 and that the latest held four eggs on 9 July 1935. Heldt (1966) recorded that the earliest egg from Schleswig-Holstein was laid on 14 April, with the latest clutches deposited between 8–18 June. The average laying season starts there about 1 May. In Finnmark, Norway, in 1924–25, Hugh Blair recorded that five full clutches were completed between 6–28 June. In his study area, at Pori, Finland, Soikkeli found that laying usually started when there was an average temperature of 6°–9° C at the end of April. Egg laying began between 24 April–4 May and finished between 24 May–10 June. Established pairs started laying about five days earlier than the mean date for the bulk of the population. Hens laying for the first time tended to lay later than those that had bred previously. In particular years he found that the latest clutches were hatched *c* 20 June; about two-thirds of the mid June hatches belonged to genuine first layings. Dunlins in Iceland start to lay from the end of May onwards, with the earliest full clutch recorded on 24 May, but most hens lay in early June (Timmermann 1949).

Dunlins' eggs are attractive, thin-shelled, slightly glossy, and ovate or sub-pyriform in shape. The ground colour ranges from creamy white and buff to pale olive-brown and bluish green. Blue (cyanic) eggs have been recorded. The eggs are spotted, blotched and streaked with rich red chestnut-brown and have purple-brown, ash-grey or lilac undermarkings. On many the rich red blotches are concentrated on the large ends, but a few show spiral markings.

The mean of 123 British eggs is 34.84 × 24.78 mm (Jourdain 1940). There is little difference between this measurement and those of 177 Finnish eggs (34.5 × 24.5 mm) and for 177 eggs from Schleswig-Holstein (34.41 × 24.63); but 44 eggs from the Netherlands were slightly smaller, averaging 33.5 × 24.4 mm (W. P. J. Hellebrekers 1950). Shell weights range from 0.38–0.56 gm (mean 0.49 gm) (M. Schönwetter 1963).

In north-west Sutherland we have weighed 34 freshly-laid eggs which varied between 10–11 gm (mean 10.1 gm). This compares with Heldt's measurements of 16 eggs from Schleswig-Holstein which averaged 10.06 gm (Table 3). The average weight of a breeding hen is 55 gm; a clutch of four eggs thus weighs approximately 75% of the hen's body weight (Table 2).

Two hens in our study area laid their eggs on alternate days at intervals of at least 36 hours. However, in Orkney, two hens laid on consecutive days at intervals of less than 30 hours. Guy Charteris (1927) also recorded that dunlins laid daily in the Outer Hebrides, although he did not give precise intervals. Holmes found that in Alaska dunlins also lay daily. In Finland, where there is a longer breeding season, Soikkeli found that most hens laid at intervals of about 36 hours with the clutch completed in 4.5 days; in six nests the intervals were less than 36 hours. Heldt (1966) also gives 1.5 days as the interval between eggs and a clutch period of 5.5 days.

Dunlins usually lay four, occasionally three, and rarely two to five eggs. At least one clutch of six is on record (Brown and Jourdain 1924). On 21 May 1927, Charteris found a nest in South Uist which contained six eggs. However, these had clearly been laid by two hens, three by each. This nest was destroyed and the eggs sucked. Two days later Charteris found that both hens laid two more eggs, this time in different nests; each therefore laid five eggs on consecutive days. In Sutherland, 21 out of 24 nests contained four eggs and the remainder three, with an average clutch of 3.87 eggs.

In Schleswig-Holstein, Heldt (1966) recorded an average clutch of 4.0 eggs between 24 April–10 May; but later clutches averaged less, with 3.3 eggs between 1–13 June (Table 4).

If the eggs or small broods are lost early in the season, some hens lay again; but clutches destroyed in early June are seldom replaced. Repeat clutches are usually sited quite close to the first nest. Heldt discovered that the first egg of a replacement, in Germany, was often laid three days after the loss of the original. In Finland, Soikkeli found that only three out of eight hens laid repeats in 1963, but in 1966 most hens repeated.

Heldt in Germany, Soikkeli in Finland, and Holmes in Alaska all recorded that hens occasionally start a new clutch after the first has hatched. The new pair is usually formed through the hen mating with a surplus cock breeding for the first time. In two clutches the first egg of the new clutch was laid 8 and 13 days respectively after the hatching of the first brood.

INCUBATION

Norton (1972) compared the incubation schedules of four species of *caladrine* sandpipers at Barrow, Alaska. 'The nests of dunlin were generally the least continually attended of the three species investigated during egg-laying. Two nests of semi-palmated sandpipers and one of Baird's sandpiper were brooded for 90 minutes in a heavy rain shower. On the other hand, dunlins failed to sit on two eggs when snow completely filled the nest and covered the eggs. However, all four eggs hatched'. Norton suggests that resistance to chilling damage appears to be greatest during egg laying before steady incubation begins. In dunlins' nests with four eggs the birds continuously covered them for $97.55 \pm 0.25\%$ of the incubation period. Clutches of Baird's sandpipers' eggs were covered for $96.5 \pm 0.47\%$ and those of pectoral sandpipers for $84.99 \pm 0.54\%$. Incubation of clutches holding only two or three eggs was erratic. Overall attendance at these nests was $88.73 \pm 2.4\%$. The success of these small clutches was lower than average; two chicks from c/3, one from c/2, and three from c/3 hatched.

We have found that before the clutch is completed both birds sit for short spells, the cock sometimes from one egg onwards. Steady incubation usually starts on the final egg, but sometimes begins between the third and fourth. Heldt (1964) and Soikkeli (1977) found that hens usually incubate at night and the cock by day; but Norton (1972) and others have had different experiences.

In Alaska, Holmes (1966b) found that hens appear to take the greatest share in incubation during the early stages, but that the cock's share increased as incubation advanced. We have recorded cocks sitting for short stints during the early phases of incubation. We have watched change-overs; one of these was tape-recorded by Bill Sinclair at 07.55 in our Sutherland study area.

Two incubation periods, measured in the Cairngorms, varied from 21.5–22.2 days.

Soikkeli gives 20.5–23.7 (mean 21.5–22 days) for 23 clutches, and Heldt recorded periods of 20–22 days. However, in the exceptionally dry summer of 1984, John and Trina Barrett (pers. comm.) recorded two long incubation periods in Sutherland of 25–26 and 24–25 days. The first clutch, completed by 19.00 on 17 May, had two eggs chipping at 20.00 on 7 June, four chipping at 20.30 on 9 June, with all four eggs hatched by 17.15 on 11 June. The second c/4, completed at 16.00 on 8 June, had one egg chipping at 11.30 on 30 June, four eggs chipping at 14.00 on 1 July, and three eggs hatched – with the fourth chick breaking shell – at 12.00 on 2 July. During this hot summer did the incubating dunlins take frequent spells off the nest and thus allow the eggs to cool? The chipping period of the first nest at *c* 90 hours was protracted; other timed chipping periods have seldom exceeded 48 hours.

HATCHING

Some broods hatch synchronously and may leave the nest almost as soon as they are dry. Like other waders, however, if hatched in late evening or during cold wet weather, the chicks stay in the nest until the following morning or even longer. Richard found a dunlin brooding the oldest chick, at least 48 hours old, in the scoop. Like greenshank, curlew and other waders, the brooding dunlin uses special harsh calls to converse with chicks in the eggs; and it recalls them if they attempt prematurely to leave the nest.

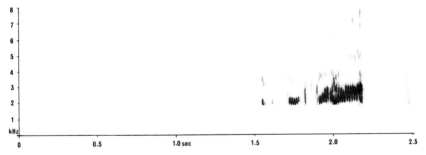

Dunlin, sitting bird purrs on nest, Sutherland (Bill Sinclair)

A brooding dunlin lifts and carries away large portions of hatched eggshell, but sometimes drops the caps in a nearby pool. On 11 June 1981, for example, Richard noted that the main portions of three hatched eggs had disappeared, but he found two caps floating in a pool a few metres away from the nest. Small pieces of eggshell are crushed in the nest lining. R. C. Thin watched a dunlin, which was nesting close to a redshank, pick up and fly away with one of the redshank's eggshells which had been dropped nearby.

YOUNG

Dunlin chicks have yellowish brown foreheads and tawny coloured crowns bordered by light buff. Ear coverts, cheeks, and neck sides are off-white, upper breast is brownish buff, and lower breast and upperparts white. The eye stripe is yellowish white and the nape deep chestnut-brown spotted with yellowish white; irides are brownish black. The newly hatched chicks have blackish brown feet with a tinge of olive which become blacker as they grow older. At four of our nests in north-west Sutherland, however, all chicks in the broods had pinkish legs.

We have weighed eight freshly-hatched chicks which ranged from 5.5–7.5 gm (mean

6.7 gm). Near the White Sea two one-day old chicks weighed 7.8 and 8.7 gm (mean 8.2 gm) (Belopolski 1970). J. Innes (1980) recorded that 14 chicks on Hardanger Vidda, Norway, weighted from 6.3–8.4 gm (mean 7.3 gm). In south-west Finland, 194 freshly hatched chicks averaged 7.0 ± 0.03 gm; only three of these chicks weighed 8 gm or more and only four were less than 6 gm (Soikkeli 1967) (Table 5).

Brown found that the parents periodically brooded their chicks for about a week, with the hen taking the greatest share and the cock mostly guarding them. Three times he watched a cock and hen alternately brood their chicks. He also saw a solitary adult, flushed from a brood of six young, begin beating along the ground with hunched back and trailing wings and tail and periodically uttering strident alarm notes. In a short time, 'six or seven adults arrived on the scene and began running ahead, falling or flying around, and gliding or hovering'. One adult landed and held its wings upright to display the silvery white banners.

Dunlins occasionally adopt the broods of others. Soikkeli watched three cocks and two hens in succession brood the same group of chicks. Similar behaviour has been recorded in Kentish plover (H. Rittinghaus 1961).

Towards the end of the fledging period, and before the young are flying freely, many hens leave their broods in charge of the cocks. Once, when the cock died before the chicks had hatched, the hen alone tended the brood for nine days; and in another territory the cock took over rearing duties after the hen had gone south. Another time a brood joined up with a neighbouring brood, the chicks in which were about a day older, leaving eight chicks to be brooded (Soikkeli 1967).

R. Casen and Soikkeli (1967) recorded a young dunlin fluttering less than 1 m when it was 19–20 days old; but Heldt (1966) gives a flying period of 21 days and others have recorded 24–26 days. Heinroth (1927–28) reported a 28 days fledging period for a hand-reared young dunlin.

In south-west Finland, between 1962–69, Soikkeli (1967, 1970b) recorded a total of 472 chicks to 374 adults, an average of 1.26 young per adult. His study area, however, sometimes suffered heavy nest predation. In 1963–66 the rate varied from 1.24–1.72 for each pair; but in 1967–69, with a higher level of predation, it dropped to 0.83–1.04 young per adult. Seventy-eight per cent of all nests and 69% of all eggs produced chicks.

DISTRACTION BEHAVIOUR

Dunlins carry out distraction behaviour and displays from the laying of the first egg, and continue to do so when the young are on the wing. The distractor sometimes runs hunchbacked with tail fanned and drooping wings, or it creeps through moss or grass almost like a small mammal. From time to time they raise one or both wings, or they rise and hover in the air giving screeching cries. After the chicks have left the nest the cocks become more and more excited and carry out frantic distraction displays.

VOICE

On the big whalebacks of the central Grampians and west Cairngorms and on the lonely flows of Sutherland, so often silent on cold, grey, windy days, it is stirring to hear the vibrant trill and strident whistling climax of a cock dunlin advertising his holding and perhaps seeking or courting a mate. The dunlin may have a less varied and beautiful vocabulary than that of many waders, but the *purr* and shrill whistle always have poignant memories for us.

Both cock and hen sing, but the hen's song is less protracted and regular. Cocks also sing as a form of distraction display; but they sing much less after the eggs are laid or when chicks are in the flow. As the hunter splashes through dark pools and by-passes deep dubhlochans a dunlin sometimes rises well ahead, giving a short shrill *twee*; or, if you approach too closely, a more prolonged twittering *twee-ee-ee*. If the watcher is lucky he may also hear the courting trill, a series of harsh frog-like wheezes (Cramp and Simmons 1983). A little later, while a pair nest dance and prepare the scoop, you hear another low-pitched trilling which Heldt (1966) describes as a trisyllabic *wi-wi-wi*.

Brooding dunlin have special variations of the trills and rattles before exchanging at the nest. These are less harsh than the trills of courtship; and they also use purring *wooer-wooeers*. Piercing squealing cries are given during bouts of distraction behaviour.

Dunlins also have special, loud, harsh cries, dry *kluk-kluks* and explosive *kok-koks* among them, to communicate with chicks already squeaking in the eggs; these cries later help to control the chicks' movements in and out of the nest. Several cries, like *koy-koy-koy*, express different degree of alarm and excitement while the young are moving through the flowlands. When especially alarmed and excited they give a series of rattling and angry *kree-kree-krees*. Another cry resembles the screams of swifts in their aerial chases (Glutz 1975).

The chicks have a variety of cries which require tape-recording and careful analysis in the future. Soikkeli recorded a thin *siii* and a flatter more buzzing note.

PREDATORS

Etheridge (1983), in his study on South Uist, describes the common gull as a significant egg predator, but none of his marked dunlin nests were known to have been robbed. On the other hand, Charteris found that it was dangerous to look at a nest because it would attract the attention of these predatory gulls.

In north-west Sutherland, possible predators of the dunlin include arctic and great skua, the larger gulls – particularly common gull – hooded crow and occasionally perhaps raven. Kestrel, peregrine and merlin are other potential enemies, although we have not found dunlins among their kills.

Ratcliffe (1980) mentions that peregrines in the Pennines, and on the coastal and inland Highlands, sometimes take dunlins. Douglas Weir records dunlin as prey of peregrines in the central Grampians where these small waders are uncommon. Hen and marsh harriers, gyr falcon, kestrel and sparrowhawk are other occasional predators. Foxes are a danger in many habitats and stoats in others. At Pori, stoats switched from field voles to rob and eat birds' eggs including those of dunlin. Kestrels, carrion crows and probably vole rats *Arvicola terrestris* were other predators on the ground.

In five consecutive years Soikkeli recorded that hatching success in Finland was reduced by nest predation to 73%, 58%, 75%, 85% and 55%. Merlins and *Mustela* species were among the most significant predators. In Alaska, Holmes recorded a lower loss, about 25%, in his years of study on the dunlin. In these haunts lemmings were among the known predators.

FOOD

Dunlins find their food by eye and touch. Philip Burton (1974) observed three different methods of feeding on the Essex coast:
(1)   pecks in which the bird's beak just touched the surface;
(2)   probes in which they inserted their bills just below the mud; and

(3) 'stitching', a quick succession of shallow probes close together.

Burton analysed 26 stomachs, seven of which contained 40 polychaetes (mainly *Nereis*); four had amphipod shrimps (200 *Talitrus salator*); and in twenty-two there were molluscs (600 *Hydrobia*).

In years of late snow and cold wet weather in north-west Sutherland, where dunlin are the latest waders to lay, we have found that particular birds first feed on gravel beside the river before establishing their territories in blanket bogs and gneiss flowlands above. This is probably because the necessary amount of essential insect food is at first unavailable to hens which are building up their reserves before egg-laying. In north Alaska, S. F. MacLean (1970) discovered that hen dunlins consumed bones and vertebrae of lemmings before their laying season in June, presumably to provide the extra calcium needed to form the egg-shells and the bones of the chicks.

Dunlins feed almost entirely on animal food, principally adults and larvae of small insects and occasionally the pupae of Tipulids. The main food on the breeding grounds consists of dipteran flies (Chironomidae and Tipulidae) supplemented by beetles Carabidae, Staphylindiae, and Curculionidae, wasps and sawflies (Hymenoptera), caddisflies (Trichoptera), mayflies (Ephemeroptera) and spiders (Arachnidae). Holmes (1966 and 1970) found that dunlins in Alaska fed mainly on larvae and adults of Diptera, particularly Tipulids and Chironomids 5–7.8 mm long, with an average wing span of 3 mm.

Uspenski (1965) recorded Chironomids and the larvae of Diptera and carabid beetles as dunlins' food in Anabar tundra and on Waigatsch Island. Insects have an important place in the diet of migrating dunlin in the Bay of Bothnia and in Norway, and are supplementary food in the western Baltic and on German and Netherlands mudflats. Polychaetes predominate in dunlin stomachs collected on the French coast. In the Persian Gulf, gastropods (Prosobranchia: *Hydrobia, Rissoa, Littorina* and *Theodoxus*) and bivalve (*Macoma* and *Cardium*) molluscs are taken.

On the south Swedish sandbanks, Sven-Axel Bengtson and B. Svensson (1968) collected dunlins which mainly fed on *Nereis diversicolor*, and little stints which took insects. The dunlins foraged close to the water's edge and in shallow water by probing in the sand, while the little stints were restricted to narrow strips above the water line where they found and took food by sight. Their research showed how two closely related species both survive in the same habitats by exploiting different food by different means.

DISTRIBUTION AND NUMBERS

Dunlins have been assigned to six different races. The nominate, *alpina*, breeds in north Scandinavia, including inland habitats in Norway, and north-west USSR east to the River Kolyma. *Schinzii*, which is the race we have watched in Scotland, also nests in other parts of Britain and in Ireland, in south-east Greenland, Iceland, and in very small numbers in the Netherlands, east to the Baltic, north to south Finland, south Sweden and the coasts of south and south-west Norway. *Arctica* breeds in north-east Greenland. *Sakhalina* nests in north-east Siberia, Chuckchee Peninsula and north Alaska. *Pacifica* breeds in west Alaska and north-east Canada and *arcticola* in north Alaska.

K. H. Voous (1960) considers that the dunlin's isolated breeding range on the Baltic coast and in Britain and Ireland is probably a relict of its distribution in an earlier phase of the post-glacial period. In other respects the dunlin's range is almost circumpolar arctic.

In Britain the main concentration of breeding pairs is found in the high mosses of the Pennines and Grampians, on the vast blanket flows of Sutherland and Caithness,

particularly in the machairs of the Outer Hebrides, and in some of the peatlands of Orkney and Shetland. In the central Grampians many pairs haunt rough wet places from Glas Maol and Carn na Tuirc and thence to Glen Clova and Lochnagar. In the west Cairngorms sizeable groups nest on Am Moine Mor where they outnumber dotterel and golden plover. They breed sparsely on the Caiplich hills and on the heights around Invermark, Glen Muic and Balmoral as well as on the Ladder Hills and the tops of north Argyll. Dunlins are well distributed on the bumps above Gaick and on the east Drumochter hills where they share the high mosses with golden plover and dotterel. Some of the best dunlin haunts are the complexes of pools and dubhlochans in Caithness and around Forsinard in north-east Sutherland. There are also good dunlin breeding grounds in south-east Sutherland and Wester Ross, but fewer in Easter Ross.

Small groups or solitary pairs nest in the hills of central and south-central Wales; and the handful of pairs breeding on Dartmoor are the most southerly in the world. In this century fewer pairs have nested on the saltmarshes of north-east Scotland and northern England, but they are still to be found from south-east Sutherland south to the Ribble estuary in Lancashire.

In Ireland dunlins seldom nest on open moorland, but usually on the grassy edges of lochs and bogs, particularly in Connacht and on the estuarine marshes, west to north-west from Mayo to Donegal where they previously shared the same habitats with red-necked phalaropes.

J. T. Sharrock (1976) recorded confirmed breeding in 245, probable breeding in 155, and possible breeding in 137 10-km squares. Breeding numbers possibly range from 4,000–8,000 pairs in Britain and Ireland.

Dunlins are probably the most abundant nesting waders in Iceland; but Ken Williamson recorded that only a few pairs bred on the Faroes. Loss or changes in West Germany habitats has led to a diminished population of 50–70 breeding pairs (Glutz 1975). Reclamation of habitats has led to a decline in East Germany, where G. Klafs and J. Stübs (1977) estimate a maximum population of only 160 pairs. Numbers have also dropped in Poland where the population now stands at 30 + pairs (L. Tomialojc 1966). There has been little change in Estonia SSR which carries 1,000–1,500 breeding pairs. Drainage of marshes has reduced numbers in Denmark where T. Dybbro and O. H. Jorgensen (1971) estimated a population of 600 pairs. Kålås and Byrkjedal (1981) give a figure of 35,000 breeding pairs for Norway. Many good habitats in Norway have been drained but numbers have increased in the south. S. Ulfstrand and G. Högstedt (1976) suggest that 26,000 pairs nest in Sweden.

The dunlin will always attract the researcher. Recently, Kålås and Byrkjedal (1983) in Norway, and Bruin and young Maimie (1985) in Sutherland, have been able to explain the 'plover's page syndrome'. The dunlin is not the 'plover's page', but almost a parasite. It uses the great wariness and extra height of its larger cousin to enable it to feed with concentration and without interruption while the goldie gives timely warning of danger from predators.

Drainage of marshes and afforestation, which has already destroyed so many habitats in modern Europe, has also affected dunlins in Britain, particularly those on the salt-marshes and on the north-west coast of Britain. In many of its haunts, however, dunlins are still breeding in good numbers. It would be wrong to stop progress, but only a carefully selected series of Reserves can give these attractive little dunlins full and absolute hope in the future.

7:   Loch, river and stream

Large sheets of water, called lochs in Scotland and lakes in other parts of Britain, shining in the sunlight or dull-grey and uninviting in rough weather, are always a challenge to the watcher. Many Highland rivers are equally inviting, roaring or purring – according to the strength of wind and rain – as they pass through wild country to the sea.

Our special Sutherland river flows fast, often changing its depth at alarming speed. Lying huddled on the floor of the hut, with the wind howling and the river rising, is not a pleasant experience, but there are always good days coming. Many of our happiest hours have been spent on the bank outside the hut.

Greenshanks often start their homing flights from the river in early morning and late evening, unless the bays and shallows of their shingle-stretches have been swamped by a deluge of brown peaty water; other pairs are thirled to lochs in the gneiss above. Common sandpipers have much the same pattern and dispersion. Every year dominant cocks and pairs divide the river into territories and spread themselves along it, expelling rivals and chasing trespassers passing through their living space. There are nights when the loud, compelling, passionate displays of the cock sandpipers have kept us awake. Later, when the chicks are hatched and their parents rearing them along the river, all the hours of daylight are full of shrill cries.

Fairly evenly spaced, with the hubs of their territories about 400 m apart, lovely dippers with dark brown mantles and snow-white throats and breasts, bob up and down on stones and rocks, almost as if they had hinged legs; and they rise to chase rivals which have encroached on defended stretches of river. A pair sometimes nested in front of the hut; we have seen the parents carry away the droppings of their young and rinsing out their bills in pools almost below the nest. There are a few scattered pairs of pied wagtails; one cock regularly flew over 800 m from its nest to visit us at the hut and feed on our few crumbs. Dainty grey wagtails are extremely scarce; in only one year have we found them nesting on our stretch of river.

Red-breasted mergansers, the drakes pursuing the ducks, usually follow the course of the river, but sometimes cut across and fly overland. The ducks lay their brownish-coloured eggs in rank heather on river islands. It is always a joy to watch mergansers courting; the duck lies low on the water with her neck outstretched and the drake swims around her, dipping his beak in the river and tossing his head up and down. During coupling he sometimes siezes her mane.

We have other delights while watching over the river. An osprey arrives, hovering again and again over the water like a giant kestrel before plunging down with a great splash, or it hesitates and then re-gains its pitch. Once a golden eagle swung down from the crags above, causing the osprey to give those musical tinkling cries which we have come to know so well at the nest. Solitary herons often work the shallows, giving hoarse shrieking cries as they move from pool to pool. We have watched otters plunging from the bank into the water leaving a trail of bubbles on the surface. Salmon, on their way from sea to loch, occasionally make great splashes when passing through a shallow pool. All these sights, and many others, delight the watcher on the bank.

In the valley red-throated divers are birds of the dubhlochans and small lochs in the upper gneiss. Their evocative calls are the very spirit of the wild. On a big loch, partly surrounded by huge crags and cliffs, a pair of black-throated divers lay their eggs. We have seen the pair with a chick, but seldom hear their unforgettable wails and screams. In the corries above there are soft evenings when cock ring ouzels sing and challenge one another. Their territories are about 400 m apart; we have occasionally found nests in old heather on the river bank. After mild winters we heard the *chacking* exchanges of stonechats which nested in heather and grass heath along the river, but by 1979 they had almost disappeared.

A favourite camp in the early 1960s was in a fine sweep of country with a river winding beside an untarred road; sandpipers wickered and dippers cut corners or followed the stream. Close to our tent a pair of redshanks nested and in June the chicks often hid in nettles beside an old sheepfold. Sometimes we have wakened, cold and shivering, to find snowflakes blowing around us.

On some of the tops and flanks are pools and dubhlochans where, in 1961, an unusual greenshank nested beside a grey mound of *Cladonia*. Common sandpipers are spaced out fairly regularly, with nests about 500 m apart; curlews and golden plovers are in well-dispersed territories on the moor and there are dunlins in the wetter mires. Magnificent black-throated divers nest on two of the lochs, on one of which a pair of great black-backed gulls laid their eggs on a small islet.

In 1980 Patrick returned to this happy hunting ground to find the wader groups much as we had known them twenty years before. He also heard common terns calling beside one of the lochs where they were nesting. Kestrels, buzzards, short-eared owls and hooded crows were all predators on the river and lochside birds in this glen.

The Dorback burn, flowing sluggishly except when in full spate, winds through grouse moors, sheep walks and farmlands on its way to join the Spey. On the river shingle oystercatchers dominated in the 1930s and 1940s; but several pairs of ringed plovers, nesting between 330–390 m ASL, held well-spaced territories, usually laying their eggs on rather finer gravel. Here, and at Loch Morlich, I spent many happy hours watching the courtship, displays and nesting of the ringed plovers. How exciting it was to see the cock goose-stepping up to the hen and 'marking time' with exaggerated steps behind her and later to watch them changing over at the nest. Other waders were on the river. Common sandpipers flew their bat-like song flights; and isolated pairs of greenshanks sometimes fed in the shallows, with the cock occasionally rising high and 'song dancing' above the moors. On the heathery edges of the river shingle golden plovers and lapwings also occasionally nested.

Loch Morlich was the most important bird loch in Spey Valley and one of the best in all Scotland. I used to sit on a small heathery mound about 50 m from the loch and absorb it all. In the 1930s and 1940s up to 6–7 pairs of greenshanks, now rare waders in the eastern Highlands, fed and courted in bays and inlets of the loch and made their wonderful song dances high above. You could watch their reactions to the 2–3 pairs of redshanks which nested annually. There were several pairs of oyster-catchers, 6–8 pairs of lapwings, up to 5 pairs of common snipe, 2 pairs of dunlin and 4 pairs of ringed plovers, one of which, I remember, often nested in the sawdust of an old mill. There were also sometimes as many as 30 pairs of common sandpipers which wickered and flew like bats on territories fiercely held on the shores of the loch and beside small lochans. Woodcock roded over soggy birch trees and a few pairs of curlews fed around the loch and nested in forest bogs. Mallard, teal, wigeon and goosanders were in good numbers, and gadwall occasionally nested.

In June 1979 I returned to Loch Morlich and was saddened by the changes. Around the loch there was almost complete silence. I could find only one pair of common sandpipers nesting in an area which had previously held five pairs. Adam Watson carried out a survey of the birds of Loch Morlich and adjacent ground in May 1985. He recorded 'no greenshanks, redshanks, curlews, lapwings, oystercatchers, dunlins, ringed plover, golden plover and snipe, and only 3–4 common sandpipers. There were three pairs of mallard, one pair of teal and several goldeneyes. A pair of goosanders was seen flying over the loch en route from the River Luineag up to the burns above the loch. Other birds seen on the loch only on one occasion, and therefore probably in passing, were a drake wigeon, a duck gadwall, and a pair of tufted ducks' (Watson and Nethersole-Thompson *in press*).

I watched lovely red-necked phalaropes in Ireland in the early 1930s; but they are missing from all the lochs we have worked in Sutherland. Their main Irish colony is in Co. Mayo where they nest in wet grasslands on small holdings in the estuarine marshes. Cecil Stoney used to say that he always found dunlins nesting along with red-necked phalaropes, but unfortunately not the reverse! Their few haunts in the Outer Hebrides are among pools in the machair grassland. In Fetlar, Shetland, they choose marshy ground pocked with old peat cuttings. Whimbrels and curlews sing and display over the small hills above as they divide the habitats. Great and arctic skuas, not to mention snowy owls, constantly hunt the ground.

Red-necked phalaropes are members of different communities in their various habi-tats. On the mainland of northern Scotland Charlie Young, a keen bird watcher, noted that red-throated diver, dunlin, greylag goose, arctic skua, teal, occasionally scoter, mallard, common gull and meadow pipit are their neighbours. Arthur Whitaker found a red-necked phalarope sitting less than 1 metre from a skylark's nest in a sodden hayfield in North Ronaldsay, Orkney.

O. Hildén and S. Vuolanto (1972) describe a different assortment of habitats and neighbours at the Norrskär group of islands in west Finland, where the phalaropes choose dry nesting sites at a considerable distance from water. Scaup, eider and red-breasted merganser are the most abundant ducks and turnstone the most significant wader. The phalaropes site their nests among loose colonies of arctic terns, evidently to benefit from their aggression, defence mechanisms and alarm cries. Turnstones regularly rob the phalaropes' nests. In East Greenland, E. M. Nicholson noticed that red-necked phalaropes nested close to ptarmigan, birds sufficiently aggressive to drive off or distract arctic skuas.

The main haunts of redshanks in Britain are in moist grasslands, wet heath and pasture, rushy fields, water meadows, sand hills and salt marshes, where they sometimes nest at very high density. The estuarine marshes of the Ribble in Lancashire carry great nesting groups of redshanks. On the other side of the sea wall, on habitats so different from those in the Highlands, there are many lapwings' nests. Out on the marsh colonies of common terns have their 'dreads'.

When I knew the Norfolk Broads, in the early 1930s, redshanks yodelled and bred on the rough marshy edges of these grand sweeps of reed and water where bitterns boomed; bearded tits built nests in the sedge, and cock harriers – marsh and Montagu's – passed food to their mates high in the air.

We have watched solitary pairs and small groups of redshanks close to lochs and rivers in Inverness, Ross and Sutherland. Some of these haunts are very special. At a grassy loch in Inverness, beautiful Slavonian grebes, with their red-currant eyes and fine red-gold ear tufts, dab water weeds on to their brown-stained white eggs before they slip off into the water. One lovely summer's day we watched an osprey plunge down and rise with a fish in its claws, almost beside a boat-load of fishermen.

We often sit over a favourite Sutherland loch where the bird sounds are always haunting. Greenshank, redshank and wood sandpiper all lead their broods to the thick vegetation around the lagoons. On an island, magnificent black-throated divers nest and a pair of red-throats lay their large brown-speckled eggs beside a small tarn in the peat. Despite the torturing clouds of midges, every watch is memorable.

COMMON SANDPIPER

While watching red kites in south-central Wales, in the 1920s, I often saw common sandpipers and listened to their cries as they flew along the fast-running streams below the wooded dingles, but I never allowed myself to enjoy them.

A small olive-brown-backed wader, with a pure white breast and wing bars, the common sandpiper has exceptional grace and charm. It usually flies low over river and loch with fast flickering shallow wing beats and brief glides – an unmistakable jerky flight – and as it flies it gives shrill excited cries. On the ground it is equally its own bird, continuously 'teetering', bobbing head and tail up and down almost like a wagtail.

Many of my early observations were made in Spey Valley. On 2 May 1934, I was on the move early, hoping to find the nest of a pair of greenshanks which had been courting on 29 April. As I crossed a rickety wooden bridge at Loch Morlich, shortly after 05.00, I found the place alive with exciting sounds and sights. Two cock greenshanks were sky-dancing higher up the loch and a pair was feeding quietly in a little bay. Further on, I heard crested tits 'sneezing' in old pines and blackcocks *roo-kooing* in a lek out on the flats. A redshank was yodelling by the water's edge and a ringed plover called softly near the shore. But the sandpipers were the star performers. All along the loch, standing on stones and rocks and sometimes flying up in their inimitable song flights, these graceful little waders were almost continuously on the move. In Abernethy I also had particular watching places along the Dorback burn. On many days the sandpipers were silent or almost passive; but on a few, shortly before they started to lay, they were small bundles of excited passion.

We have watched common sandpipers on different habitats in Sutherland, often along rivers as well as beside large and small lochs. Since 1976 we have concentrated on a 4.5 km stretch of river in the valley in north-west Sutherland, where they share some of their feeding niches with greenshanks. Over the years, as the family began to take up the reins of the wader research, I was frequently dispatched to watch the sandpipers.

As they nested fairly close to the hut, and thus cut out those long, tiring, sweat-sodden marches over flow and gneiss to the greenshanks, I most happily agreed! It was always a joy to sit over a sandpiper's nest or to have chances of watching their exciting and beautiful courtship.

The weather generally determines the dates on which sandpipers return to their breeding grounds. In 1975 we watched pairs copulate on 4 and 5 May; but in 1976 we only located a single bird on 1 May and did not hear one singing until the 5th. Pairs were calling noisily on 30 April 1977. After the cold and wet April of 1979 no sandpipers had arrived by 5 May. However, the birds returned early after the dry April of 1980; we saw a small trip of three – possibly cocks – on 3 May. On 4 May the cocks were in full song and song dancing over the river.

TERRITORY

In mild springs the cocks almost immediately start to establish territories, singing and displaying over river and lochs, and approaching any other sandpiper which flies through its living space or alights on a stone by the river or on its bank. Each cock dominates a stretch of water containing at least one fairly large tract of shingle. They now soon start to chase away rivals and apparently recognise hens by their subtly different reactions.

Fighting cocks also face and leapfrog over one another. On 12 May 1980, I watched two cocks fighting on a broad stretch of shingle which appeared to contain their territorial boundary. The two birds occasionally flew at one another or ran forward with wings raised and met with bills stretched downwards; and then they fluttered up a few metres, continuing this bill fighting under the river bank and in a hollow just below. In fluttering, their feet occasionally touched the water of a pool starting circles of ripples. Then, breaking away, one bird false-bathed and occasionally dipped his bill in the river. When a third sandpiper flew downstream the cocks parted, and the territory holder chased the new intruder.

The song flight is a weapon of advertisement which has more territorial and dispersion significance than sexual importance. Towards the climax of courtship the cock makes display flights over his territory, occasionally rising to 30 m or more above the river, flying with tremulous wing beats, twisting, turning, and swerving almost like a bat; and all the time singing his *kitti-needi* songs in different rhythms. Sandpipers occasionally continue these flights for 10 to 15 minutes and carry them out in moonlight, in the small hours of early morning, and late into the evening as well as by day. They also sing from rocks and stones and from the banks and shores of river or loch.

When a cock is chasing a hen in quick swerving flight the two birds sometimes fly through the territory of another which may then rise and chase them; but he usually returns when the courting pair has passed out of his defended living space. Pursuing cocks sometimes retard and then raise their wings, almost like swifts, or they hold them down in an inverted arc. During sexual pursuits the two birds may give trilling cries. Both sexes sing, but chiefly the cock.

We have often seen a sandpiper rise from its feeding bay to chase and follow briefly a greenshank which was flying low over the river and thus through the sandpiper's territory. Sandpipers and dippers occasionally dispute over living space. On 11 May 1980, for example, Bruin watched a sandpiper, which had pitched on a rock in its own territory, being dispossessed by a dipper.

A Common sandpiper's territory fulfills several different functions.

(1)   Mating: A cock pursues and attempts to mate with any female which alights in or flies through his territory.

(2)   Nesting: The nest is placed adjacent to or a short distance away from the defended stretch of water.

(3)   Feeding: In our study area sandpipers feed mostly on or immediately around the river, particularly on tracts of shingle, muddy or vegetated edges, grass heaths on the banks, and in the shallows of tributary streams.

(4)   Nursery: The brood is largely reared in the territory. This leads to parents of two broods disputing and driving away others which have intruded on their living space. Much the same pattern obtains on territories on large or small lochs where the cock or pair dominate a stretch of shore and surrounding habitats of the larger lochs and the entire shortline and surroundings of a small loch.

COURTSHIP

On stretches of river shingle a cock, all bunched up, runs forward with quick steps, occasionally rasing his wings vertically; and the hen runs equally fast, sometimes partly fanning her tail sideways or raising both her wings or the one that is nearest to him. The two birds then turn and confront one another, jumping into the air, bill to bill, with fluttering wings; or perhaps they leapfrog over one another. A cock sometimes flies over a grounded hen, holding his wings at an angle of about 60°. The coupling of sandpipers is sometimes very lovely. In May 1980 I watched a cock rise and beat his wings at high speed before he fluttered over the hen like a large grey moth and then alight gently on her back.

Other sexual moments are often less dramatic. When she is ready to pair the pursued hen stands still or slows down and the cock flutters onto her back. Afterwards the pair may preen, false-feed, bathe, or make pulling movements. At other times the cock takes the hen without any special ritual, as on 4 May 1974, when the cock fluttered onto the hen's back as she ran over the gravel; previously both had run in fast bursts, sometimes one and then the other taking the initiative. On 9 May 1980, Eamonn watched a cock flutter onto the back of a hen which was standing on a rock in the river, raising and beating his wings while balancing himself on her back; a second cock was on the bank nearby.

A hen which is not ready to copulate behaves rather like the subordinate rival in a ground pursuit, periodically turning to face her partner, tilting forward with head and bill down and sometimes partly spreading and raising or twisting her tail. Elevation of a single wing appears to indicate less emotional excitement than the raising of both. Ritualised wing raising in display probably originates from a clash of the conflicting drives to attack or to flee.

In some years there were trios during the early courtship period, with two cocks pursuing the same hen; we have assumed that the cock dominates the courtship. However, in 1980 one hen completed two clutches, each of four eggs, at an interval of nine days. She and her mate sat on one clutch and the other cock apparently alone incubated the second; the nests were roughly 200 m apart. The first clutch was hatched on 1 June and the second on 10 June. This was the only hen which we proved to be polyandrous.

DISPERSION AND BREEDING DENSITY

Breeding density varies greatly in different habitats. In our north-west Sutherland study area there has been an average of 1.5–2.2 breeding pairs/km on 4.5 km of river. On a 1.9 km stretch 6–8 pairs have bred annually and there is usually a non-breeding surplus. The complex of small lochs in south-east Sutherland, which Patrick investigated in 1980, were 100–350 m long and separated by 400–1,500 m. The three smaller lochs each held a single pair of common sandpipers and the largest at least two pairs. In north-west Sutherland the minimum distance between nests was 100 m and in south-east Sutherland 500 m.

Around Loch Morlich, between 1934–56, there was sometimes 30 plus pairs in a circumference of 4.6 km (6.2 pairs/km). In the late 1930s there were up to eight pairs in a 1.4 km stretch of the River Dorback (5.6 breeding pairs/km). On the Upper Spey, by comparison, Richard Perry estimated an extremely large breeding population near Newtonmore, with at least 20 pairs on a stretch of 800 m. On the River Dorback,

	period	area	numbers	density	minimum spacing	authority
NW Sutherland	1975–80	32.5 km²	19–34 pairs	0.58–1.04 pairs/km²	100 m	Nethersole-Thompson family
„	1975–80	4.5 km of river	7–10 pairs + surplus	1.5–2.2 pairs/km²	100 m	„
SE Sutherland	1980	4 lochs 100–350 m long, 400–1500 m apart	single pairs on 3 small lochs, 2+ pairs on the largest		500 m	P. S. Thompson
Loch Morlich, Inverness-shire	1934–56	4.6 km	30+ pairs	6 pairs/km	60 m	D. Nethersole-Thompson
R. Dorback, Spey Valley, Inverness-shire	1938–42	1.4 km of river	6–8 pairs	4.2–5.6 pairs/km	120 m	„
R. Spey, Newtonmore, Inverness-shire	1950s	800 m of river	20+ pairs	25 pairs/km	?	R. Perry MS

	period	area	numbers	density	minimum spacing	authority
R. Esk, Midlothian	1962–66	400 km of river but only 90 km colonised	41–51 pairs	0.2 pairs/km; 0.55 pairs/km of occupied river		C. N. L. Cowper (1973)
Sedbergh, Yorkshire	1939–51	96.5 km of river	101 pairs	1.05 pairs/km		E. I. Cuthbertson *et al* (1952)
N England and Wales	1974			0.83 pairs/km		BTO Waterways Survey (1974)
English Midlands	1974			0.1 pairs/km		,,
Bavaria		43 km alpine streams with breadth of 10–50 m		0.7–1.0 pairs/km		E. Bezzel *in* Glutz (1977)
Rivers Isar and Lech, Bavaria		with breadth of river 50–150 m		0.3 pairs/km		,,
Graubünden, Lower Rhine, Germany		7.5 km of river with breadth of 30–220 m	15–20 pairs	2.2–2.7 pairs/km		W. Müller (1975)
Lower and upper Rhine, Switzerland		83 km	35–40 pairs	0.5 pairs/km		,,
Sense, Berne, Switzerland		12.5 km of river with breadth of 20–30 m	10 pairs	1.3 pairs/km		*in* W. Müller (1975)
NE Slovakia				up to 5 pairs/km		W. Makatsch (1966)
Lake Lagoda, USSR				0.6–1 pair/km of river bank		N. S. Ivanova *in* Glutz (1977)
Oblast, Smolensk, USSR		20.7 km of river bank	12–15 pairs	1.4–1.7 km	700 m	Djakov *in* W. E. Flint (1973)
Pamir, USSR				not more than 1 pair/km		R. L. Potapov *in* Flint (1973)
E Caucasus, USSR				1.0–1.5 pairs/km of river		L. S. Stepanjan (1957)

Fig. 5   Common sandpiper. Breeding density in Britain and Europe.

two nests were spaced at 120 m apart and at Loch Morlich two nests were separated by 60 m. W. Müller (1975) recorded an exceptionally high density on a river island on the Rhine, where at least four pairs had nests 18–25 m apart.

Our own records, along with those of others in Britain and central Europe, are compared in Figure 5.

NEST, EGG AND CLUTCH

We have twice watched a bat-flying cock go to the ground and start to make scoops in the presence of the hen. Both birds then rotated and pressed themselves briefly on to the ground. Afterwards, the cock ran a few metres tossing bits and pieces sideways. Near the lodge at Loch Stack, Sutherland, on 8 May 1963, cock sandpipers periodically flew up on to ledges of the banks where they shuffled and then flickered down in inverted arcs; a display apparently to entice the hens. One of two cocks in a trio which we watched on 12 May 1980 also behaved in this way. The hen adopted one of the second cock's scoops on which she shuffled and later laid her eggs. A steep bank, as in this case, possibly curtails more orthodox ground displays.

Sandpipers choose many different nest sites in a variety of habitats. In our Sutherland study area nine were in short grass-heath, five beside large stones or small rocks on ridges of steep hillside, three in short heather among stones, and three in a mixture of heather, bog myrtle and cotton sedge; one was on a hummock of sphagnum, one in a patch of rank heather, one in short heather on a river island, and another in a clump of rank vegetation in river shingle.

The brooding bird later adds grasses, bracken, leaves, and bits of heather from the adjacent vegetation to line the scanty nest. A few nests contain quite substantial pads of dead grass and leaves.

None of the sandpipers on the river territories studied had nest sites on its bank. Five were 1–10 m, five 11–20 m, three 21–30 m, three 31–40 m, two 51–60 m, five 90–100 m, and one between 111–120 m from the river.

On the 1,600 m stretch of the Dorback especially studied, most hens laid their eggs in nests in tussocks of vegetation in river shingle and on steep grassy banks which were seldom more than 5–15 m from the water's edge. One nest was in a small cavity or pocket sheltered by a flat stone projecting over it; the cavity was barely large enough to hold the sitting bird and her nest and eggs. On Loch Morlich most nests were sited on marshy ground 30–80 m from the waterline, but some pairs nested among the sodden pines, birches and alders which surrounded the loch; their leaves and pine needles were often found in the linings.

In north Sutherland we have also found nests on the edges of pine and birch woods, and on small river and loch islands. Arthur Whitaker and I found a nest near Inchnadamph which was completely hidden under a small triangular projecting rock on a steep grassy bank close to the roadside. We saw the bird fly up to the rock, disappear, and when we went forward, come running out. I have also twice found nests on railway embankments near Forsinard.

E. P. Chance and O. R. Owen made notes on 21 common sandpipers' nests found close to rivers and streams in Radnor and Hereford. Ten were placed beside plants or flotsam in river gravel, four beside or below dykes or banks, one in short grass close to a railway line, and one in a small depression in dry grass beside a hump. Two were open nests, a few metres from the river; one was in an unlined scoop on a high bank and the other in a clump of heather. In May 1899, Macomb Chance located nine nests in Roscommon, Ireland, three of which were on grassy banks, two in grassy tufts or hummocks, one in a bunch of rushes and one on a railway embankment.

Two of these nests were in open sites – one 30 m and the other 40 m from water.

Arthur Whitaker's diaries give details of 20 nests in Derbyshire, Yorkshire and West-morland. Nine, in different years, were on islands on a dam where they were usually placed under brambles or rhododendrons. Six were in slight hollows in long grass on steep banks, two in wheat fields (one under stalks of *Brassica*), one in rough tussocky grass on rising ground, one under a dock leaf in a weedy ploughed field on the edge of a wood, and one under a small frond of bracken below a stone wall. The nests were all 5–7 m from stream or reservoir. M. D. Crosby found a nest in a most unexpected situation, on top of a flat rock over a metre high and just above high water mark. In the Peak District, P. K. Holland and his colleagues (1982) recorded that all 98 nests were within 50 m of the water. Forty were in a mixture of short grass and rushes, 15 in bracken, two in heather and two in nettles.

On the Continent of Europe there is an equal diversity of nest sites and habitats. Von Haartman *et al* (1963) recorded that 70 out of 122 nests in Finland were under small trees or saplings; 24 were in spruce woods, 13 in juniper, nine in pine, five in alder, five in birch, three in willow, two in rowan, and nine among unidentified shrubs; 23 were in dwarf *Calluna, Vaccinium* and *Empetrum*; 16 were in grass, five under the fallen branches of trees, two in shrubs, one in moss and one under a fern. Glutz (1977) records less usual nest sites in maize fields, on pollard willows, dead stumps standing in water, rabbit holes, one in an old ring ouzel's nest, and a few close to 'carriage drives' to country houses.

Nests on the Continent are seldom far from the water line. On the lower Rhine, W. Müller (1975) recorded 24 nests between 1–32 m from the river (mean 9 m). Nests in Norway are at most 80–100 m from water; but, in USSR, N. S. Ivanova (1966) found that, in habitats subject to flooding, nests were sometimes sited 300 m from the river.

A common sandpiper's nest scoop is usually quite small; outer dimensions 11.5 cm, inner dimensions 8.5 cm, and depth 3.5 cm (Stecher *in* Gladkov 1951). A. Karlstrom measured five nests in Norway which averaged 8–10 cm for their inner dimensions, with a depth of 3.6 cm.

In the British Isles and Ireland few hens complete their clutches before 10 May. In north-west Sutherland 30 clutches were laid up between 10 May–22 June (mean 21 May). Twenty-seven clutches in Spey Valley ranged from 15 May–2 June, with 23 May the average date for the start of incubation.

Whitaker has notes of 19 full clutches in Yorks-Derbyshire between 12 May–12 June (mean 23 May). E. I. Cuthbertson and his colleagues (1952) recorded clutches around Sedbergh in Yorkshire varying from 19 May–1 June in 1950 and 14–23 May in 1951 (mean 19 May), with a mean of 23 May in 1949–51. In Radnor and Hereford, Chance and Owen found that 22 pairs had laid up between 10 May–28 May (mean 20 May). John Walpole-Bond (1938) noted that many clutches in south-central Wales were completed between 15–20 May; and in 1899 Macomb Chance found 12 completed clutches in Roscommon between 19 May–2 June (mean 25 May). In the Peak District, Holland *et al* (1982) recorded the start of incubation in 49 clutches between 6 May and 24 June, with the average period between 15–20 May.

Laying dates in central Europe are slightly earlier; a clutch was recorded in France on 26 April and others, in Switzerland, were completed in late April and early May. On the lower Rhine a pair had one chick on 15 May (Wille 1968) and in north-east Slovakia there were chicks on 17 May 1964.

In south and central Sweden the laying season is comparable with ours, starting about 10 May. Clutches in north Sweden, however, are not completed until the end of May. In Finland ten hens started to lay between 11–20 May and 44 between 21–30

May. Newly-hatched chicks were found on 20 July 1877, but these were probably hatched from a replacement clutch. On the Dneiper, USSR, laying starts in early May and flying young have been seen in the first ten days of June. On the Murman Coast sandpipers lay up towards the end of May; and in north-east USSR and throughout northern Siberia the laying season normally lies between late May and early June.

Three hens in our Sutherland study area laid their eggs at intervals between 24–28 hours and another the last two eggs of her clutch at 30–32 hours intervals. Two others laid their third and fourth eggs on alternate days. On the River Oder in Germany, G. Stein (1928) found that the sandpipers usually laid daily although occasionally on alternate days.

There is no set time for laying but some hens periodically brood the first one or two eggs; and they often stay on the river close to the nest. In four replacement clutches, for which we have records, the first egg was laid 7–9 days after the first clutch was lost.

Many eggs look rather like small toy tops. They are pointed ovate to sub-pyriform in shape with ground colour varying from creamy buff to reddish brown and occasionally to olive brown, exceptionally greyish white to bluish grey. The eggs are highly glossed, and spotted, speckled, streaked and blotched with reddish brown and sepia, particularly on their blunt ends, and they usually have pale violet or slate grey undermarkings.

One hundred British common sandpipers' eggs, measured by Jourdain (1940), averaged 36.40×26.27 mm. This mean was slightly larger than that for 217 eggs from Sweden, 36.28×26.17 mm (P. Rosenius 1973); 67 from Norway 35.21×26.03 mm (Haftorn 1971); and 47 from Finland 35.9×26.1 mm (von Haartman 1963–66).

We have weighed 34 fresh or slightly incubated eggs in Sutherland, ranging from 10–15 gm (mean 12.0 gm). This small sample is slightly heavier than that measured in the Peak District where 16 eggs averaged 11.8 gm (Holland 1983) (Table 3). A clutch weighs 96 per cent of a hen's body weight (Table 2). Rosenius (1937) weighed 216 blown eggs varying from 0.40 to 0.72 gm (mean 0.56 gm).

Table 4 gives details of clutch size. A normal clutch consists of four eggs, occasionally of three. We have never found five eggs in any Scottish nest; but on 25 May 1928, Edgar Chance found a sandpiper sitting on c/5 near Knighton in Radnor. Clutches of six or eight eggs in the same scoop are likely to be the joint layings of two hens. In 1957, Abraham photographed a double clutch; and F. Venzlaf recorded eight eggs in Bavaria (Glutz 1977).

INCUBATION

Some common sandpipers do not start to sit until they have completed their clutches, but six hens in Sutherland began steady incubation soon after laying their third eggs in clutches of four. This led to intervals of up to 16 hours between the hatching out of the third and fourth chicks. Four Sutherland clutches had incubation periods ranging from 21.5 to 23.3 days (mean 22.2 days). Incubation periods at two nests in Spey Valley lasted from 22 to 22.5 days; and Holland recorded that two nests in the Peak District both hatched in 21 days. Glutz (1977) cites records of seven incubation periods of 21 days and five of 22 days.

At four Sutherland nests, which we specially watched, the cock carried out most of the earlier incubation; but later rhythms varied greatly. On 2 June 1980, the cock left the nest twice between 16.35–22.10, at intervals of 2 hours 26 minutes and 2 hours 22 minutes; each time he was off the eggs for approximately 5 minutes. At the same nest, on 3 June, the sitting cock did not leave between 16.41–21.05; and on 5 June there was no movement between 16.37–20.37. At a second nest the sitting bird incubated without interruption between 18.55–21.45.

Exchanges between cock and hen usually take place without any special display. The sitting bird sometimes leaves the eggs, flies to the river bank or loch shoreline, and its mate immediately flies to the nest and starts to sit. At other times, the incoming bird flies, or partly runs and flies, to the nest and the change-over takes place immediately. At 16.45 on 29 May 1980 a sandpiper suddenly left the river and flew 120 m with flickering wings before landing on a hump. The sitting bird then left the nest and flew to the river where it started to feed.

Common sandpipers sometimes sit extremely closely, only running or flying from the nest at the last moment; or even exceptionally allowing themselves to be touched or stroked while they are sitting. If the nest is on a high bank or a steep hillside the bird often leaves in a characteristic inverted arc flight; or it flutters off, screaming, with depressed and fully fanned tail. The off-duty bird sometimes calls its partner from the nest as soon as it sees a human. At other times the incubating bird rises and slips off, irrespective of whether the nest is in short or long herbage. In warm weather the brooding bird may periodically leave the eggs unattended for 4 minutes or more, first running or flying from the nest and afterwards returning straight to it. The non-sitting bird often roosts on or under a bank within 50–100 m of the nest.

The eggs have long chipping periods, seldom less than 60 hours and often as long as 100. At one nest in Sutherland all four chicks hatched from a clutch which had carried bumps or chip marks for 277 hours; but this was exceptional and probably due to some defect in the eggshells.

HATCHING

When the chicks are hatching out, or are still in the nest, the sandpipers often give wonderful exhibitions of excitement. The parents make those shrill *swee-ee* cries as they run and flounder almost at your feet. Time after time they make short flights and then start those swift runs again. We have twice watched a cock encircle or run past his sitting mate. On 22 June 1980 a cock in north Sutherland did this while his mate was brooding three chicks in a scoop under a bank. Flying a few metres from the loch he pitched on the road, ran past his mate with the quickest of steps, and continued running some 50 m uphill before returning on the same course and taking wing just before he reached the road. Even more unusual behaviour sometimes takes place when the hen is sitting tight. John Markham watched a cock lie on the top of a brooding hen which had failed to quit her chicks and hatching eggs.

Many sandpipers' nests are exceptionally clean after the hatch. Both cock and hen lift and carry away the larger portions of hatched eggshells and the brooding bird also breaks up and eats some of the smaller fragments. In Radnor, Owen watched a sandpiper peck at a large piece of hatched shell and then carry it about 25 m before dropping it in the river. At Dorback, on 17 June 1944, I placed a large piece of red grouse's eggshell in a sandpiper's nest containing four eggs. The returning bird immediately picked it up and flew about 45 m to a small stream where it pecked at the shell and then dipped its beak in the water. F. C. R. Jourdain (MS) noted that after two chicks had hatched the pointed ends of the two unhatched eggs were wedged into the larger portion of the hatched shells. This occasionally happens in most waders.

In our Sutherland study area 71 out of 81 eggs hatched from 21 nests; a success rate of 87.6%. Two nests disappeared, one hen deserted during laying, and one clutch was trampled, probably by a red deer. In the Peak District, of 88 nests, 78 (89%) hatched and 10 failed. Humans probably robbed three and caused desertion of a further two nests; predators robbed four. Out of 367 eggs, 279 hatched, 34 failed, and the fate of 36 was unknown. Cuthbertson and his colleagues (1952) recorded that chicks hatched in 24 out of 30 nests investigated, a loss of 20%. Carrion crows robbed at least two of these nests and one was flooded out. Ivanova (1966) recorded that 72 out of 84 eggs hatched in 23 nests (85.7%) in habitats around Lake Lagoda, USSR. On the lower Rhine, Muller (1975) recorded that three out of 24 nests were destroyed, one through flooding.

YOUNG

Sandpiper chicks are dainty little creatures. Crown, forehead and upper mandibles show different shades of grey tipped with sooty black, and the sides of their necks, lower throats and underparts are all white. They have light green legs and feet with yellowish patches on their calves. Beaks are blackish brown to horn colour and irides dark brown.

We have weighed four newly-hatched chicks from two nests, which varied from 8–9 gm, with an average of 8.2 gm. This compares with Heinroth's (1927–28) measurements of 9 gm, and 7.8 gm for seven chicks weighed by Holland *et al* (1982).

Young sandpipers are capable of leaving the scoop within two or three hours of hatching, although they often stay in the nest for up to 16 hours. The sitting bird may keep the brood in the nest if the last chick is hatched in the late afternoon or during rough weather. However, this does not invariably happen. At a Sutherland nest, in 1972, the fourth and last chick hatched before noon and all four chicks were in the scoop at 17.45; but by 20.30 they had gone and were not to be seen around the site.

The chicks can swim quite strongly on their second day and are remarkably adept at hiding themselves under stones or stumps or in patches of vegetation. No small wader chicks are more difficult to find, unless one happens to see them with their parents as they run across a road or over river shingle. Both sexes assist in their rearing. Cocks often alert hens and broods by giving warning cries or singing and bat-flying.

Holland *et al* (1982) record that out of a small sample, fledging success varied from 24–35 per cent. Glutz (1977) summarises the observations of Continental ornithologists who have discovered that young sandpipers can fly 12–15 m on their 13th day and about 100 m on their 20th day. In Britain, P. A. Rayfield (1961) found that one young sandpiper flew on its 16th day and that a second was flying quite strongly when it was 19 days old. Young sandpipers in the Peak District also fledge when they are 18–20 days old and weigh about 40 gm.

P. Christison (*in* Bannerman 1961) watched a parent fly down, pick up a large chick between its legs, and carry it for about 25 m. The youngster then continued to fly on its own.

SITE AND MATE FIDELITY

There are still many discoveries to be made about these attractive little waders. Holland and his colleagues have already pointed the way. Forty-seven returning birds were found in their old territories in successive years, and only eight had changed. Two pairs breeding in 1979 again mated in 1980; but three cocks, still holding the same territories, had different mates in 1980, though their partners of the previous year were still in the breeding population. The birds in two 1978 pairs split between four different pairs in 1979.

DISTRACTION BEHAVIOUR

Common sandpipers have a remarkably mixed assortment of distraction displays.

(1) During incubation the sitting bird sometimes flies in an arc from a high bank, dropping down and then rising – always a hopeful sign to the nest hunter.

(2) A brooding bird often fully fans and expands its tail to display its white outer tail feathers and couples this with flickering or whirring wings and screaming cries.

(3) Fast running over bank or shingle with, or usually without, drooping wings, and to the accompaniment of long shrill cries, is characteristic of common sandpipers with chicks.

(4) Fluttering over the ground, with spread tail and flapping wings, the sandpiper utters screaming or chittering cries. On 9 June 1979, Patrick watched a sandpiper, flushed from highly incubated eggs on a small island on a large loch, start its distraction displays on land and continue them in the water where it thrashed along the surface with fanned tail. On the shore it gave strange and most unusual calls.

(5) In twilight, behaviour is sometimes quite different. At 21.45 on 6 June 1980 a cock rose slowly from well incubated eggs and first walked in upright posture, then ran a few metres with its tail depressed and mantle fluffed, out, looking almost like a small mammal. It then rose silently with laboured flight, its tail partly spread and hanging down. On the same night a second bird behaved much in the same way although its ground display was less elaborate. In daylight the cock at the first nest always ran off its eggs and disappeared well before the watcher reached the nest.

VOICE

The songs and cries of common sandpipers are always part of the wonderful atmosphere of loch and stream. Their different rhythms of song are evocative of soft evenings and early mornings on the river, with the cocks bat-flying or teetering on rocks while they pour out excited *kitti-needie kitti-needie* or *willy-wicket willy-wicket*. These lovely little waders possibly have a smaller range of calls than many others; and their cries are rather thin, depending on emphasis for their function.

(1) The sandpipers sing in display flights and from stones or rocks by loch or river. On 9 June 1980 Eamonn tape-recorded beautiful examples of a cock singing on well incubated eggs.

(2) When the bird is disturbed and rises from the waterside, the most characteristic call is a trisyllabic *tee-titi-titeee*.

(3) The usual anxiety cry is a thin high-pitched *see*. In situations of greater emotional stress this is doubled into *see-ee*, with emphasis on the second syllable.

(4) Particularly when they are escorting small chicks, they give long-drawn *see-ee-er* anxiety cries. *See-ee* is also sometimes used during sexual chases.

(5) During distraction displays on the ground, or exceptionally in the air or on water, the sandpiper gives loud screaming sounds or occasionally *teer-teers*.

(6) *Hatching calls*
Only those who have sat over a hatching sandpiper can appreciate just how varied are the cries and signals between parent and chicks. Here are descriptions of some of these remarkable interchanges, all of which Eamonn tape-recorded on 9 June 1980 while the cock was sitting on the four hatching eggs.

(a) Deep *kluk-kluk*.

(b) *Ik-it-it*.

(c) *Coic*, and a subdued and a thin *hee*.

(d)   Long drawn out *wheet*, rather like one of the dotterel's calls.

(e)   *Whee-zik*, possibly a combination of (b) and (d).

(f)   Successions of twittering cries.

(g)   Double squeaks directed to chicks in the eggs.

(h)   When three chicks had hatched and the last was starting to break free, the cock gave a sharp *tyook*, followed by a high pitched *coroc* call to the chicks. Later he gave cries which we interpreted as *korok-korok-kok-kok*, followed by a series of squeaks. The *korok* cries are not unlike the 'wire twanging' calls of a pair of dotterel during nest-site selection.

(i)   *Kok-koree*, not unlike the sound of a rod being pulled over iron railings.

(j)   A succession of songs and *whees*, possibly encourging cries.

(k)   A loud explosive *kuk*, possibly to discipline chicks.

(l)   Very loud long *pee-ee*.

(m)   Loud whistles *whee-whee-ee*, as Eamonn approached the nest.

(7)   *Chick calls*

The chicks have a variety of different calls as they rhythmically tap in the eggs.

(a)   An almost precise replica of the parent's single or double *titi-titi*. When the egg is hatching they sometimes give this call almost continuously.

(b)   Long drawn squeaks.

(c)   *Wheep-wheep*, which is distinctly weaker than that of the parent.

(d)   A succession of high-pitched, almost lisping, screams.

PREDATORS

Common sandpipers' nests are occasionally flooded out when placed too close to running streams and rivers. Predation does not appear to be high in north-west Sutherland. Merlins are the most likely hunters; we found the skull and bill of a common sandpiper in one of their pellets. At least two pairs of kestrels nest in the valley, but we have no evidence that they are taking sandpipers' eggs or chicks. Hoodie crows and common gulls are likely to pick up eggs or chicks from time to time. Red deer certainly trample on nests occasionally and foxes are other likely predators. On the Dorback, a well-keepered grouse moor, merlin, sparrowhawk and hoodie were potential enemies; but fox, stoat and sheep dogs possibly did more harm.

In the literature, peregrine, kestrel and merlin all appear among records of raptors which prey on sandpipers. Derek Ratcliffe (1980) occasionally found sandpipers in the pluckings of peregrines in the Southern Uplands and inland districts of the Scottish Highlands.

FOOD

In Sutherland common sandpipers feed along the river edges, occasionally wading and often picking up water-borne insects, making little runs and dabs as they do so. They also hunt river gravel or shingle some distance from water, as well as the edges of streams, and pick up insects from and between stones and below rocks. The sandpipers exploit patches of ooze and mud, often probing and prodding, and also catch insects on the surface or in the root systems of aquatic plants. We have watched them work under river banks and explore the middle and upper parts of steep banks clothed in grassy heath or eroded peat, sometimes going over the same patch time after time, fluttering into the air and trying to catch small moths. Under the banks and on the

shingle they occasionally find and rapidly feed on hatches of insects. We have watched a sandpiper run down a large boulder, head first, picking up insects as it went.

Greenshanks are the only wader regularly sharing and probably competing with common sandpipers on the river, but the greenshanks often take larger items of food and they regularly wade deeper into the water. The two waders compete on the water line and on shingle bars and stretches but the sandpipers have a large complex of feeding niches. They seldom attack one another, but while feeding on the water line a sandpiper sometimes rises to chase a passing greenshank. When nesting close to lochs, around which they feed, we have often disturbed them from pools and tarns, but they do not work these as regularly as do greenshanks.

Common sandpipers feed almost entirely on animal matter, seldom on plants. Glutz (1977) has summarised what is known about their food. They take Coleoptera (click beetles Elateridae, ground beetles Carabidae, weevils Curculionidae and water beetles Hydrophilidae). They also feed on different groups of Diptera, *e.g.* horseflies (Tabanidae), craneflies (Tipulidae) and mosquitoes (Culicidae). We have seen them chasing and capturing small moths. R. J. Waters (1974) recorded the small fox moth *Aglais urticae* as prey. In his study in the Peak District, D. W. Yalden (1986) discovered that the main food items were carabid beetles, weevils and adult flies. 'Earthworms, click beetles, larval carabids, stone fly nymphs, spiders and staphylinid beetles also each occurred in 25% or more of the samples'. The sandpipers fed mainly on grassland but the stony edges of rivers and streams were other important feeding places. Common sandpipers are also known to take grasshoppers (Orthoptera), mayflies (Ephemeroptera), water bugs *Corixa*, hover flies (Phrygaenidae), ants (Hymenoptera), millipedes (Myriapoda) and occasionally water spiders *Argyroneta*.

Along the coast sandpipers take small sea crustaceans, *e.g. Talitrus, Gammarus, Carcinus, Platyonichus* and occasionally various Polychaetes and small molluscs. Worms are sometimes extracted, and small frogs and tadpoles, and occasionally fish spawn, are eaten. Nichols recorded small decayed fish and Fitzpatrick watched a sandpiper eating small bits of apples. In rough weather in north-west Sutherland one ate crumbs and crusts at the door of our hut.

In Africa their food is sometimes exotic and unexpected; they feed on insects and possibly ectoparasites on the backs of hippopotami and extract food from between the teeth of crocodiles.

DISTRIBUTION AND NUMBERS

In the Palearctic zone common sandpipers breed north to 71° in Norway, thence to north Finland, and to about 68°N in northern USSR. A few pairs have bred in Denmark and they also nest irregularly in the Netherlands. Common sandpipers are few in East and West Germany and they are also scarce, but well-distributed, in Poland (L. Tomialojc 1976). They are scarce breeders in Hungary and Albania and are decreasing in Austria and Switzerland (B. Bruderer and W. Thönen 1977).

Small groups nest in the Iberian Peninsula, northern Italy, occasionally north-central Greece, Crimea and Caucasia. Its breeding distribution in Asia extends from Siberia south to north and east Asia Minor, northern Iran, Afghanistan, Kashmir, Tibet, and east to China and Japan. Pairs have occasionally nested in Kenya and Uganda in East Africa.

L. J. Yeatman (1976) estimates that between 1,000–10,000 pairs breed in France. Our friend, Alfredo Noval, estimates that there are 3,000–4,000 nesting pairs in Spain. In Norway, J. A. Kålås and I. Byrkjedal (1981) estimated a population of 150,000 breeding pairs; S. Ulfstrand and G. Högstedt (1976) give an even healthier total of 300,000 breeding pairs for Sweden. Olavi Hildén (*in* Cramp and Simmons 1983) suggests a breeding population of 200,000–300,000 pairs in Finland.

Between the 1930s and 1960s numbers fell and the range contracted in south-west England, Wales and the English Lakeland, east Scotland and Orkney. Common sandpipers are now scarce or absent from much of south-west and east England. They are abundant in the Hebrides, but scarce or absent in many parts of Orkney and Shetland. On the Scottish mainland sandpipers nest around sea loch inlets and on shingle bars, and they do so on coastal shingle ridges in Ireland.

Their breeding range in Ireland contracted between 1900–1960. Common sandpipers are now scarce in Carlow, Kilkenny, Waterford and Wexford; more recently they have decreased in Kildare, Louth, Meath and east Cork (J. T. R. Sharrock 1976). They are more widely distributed and nest at greater density on loughs and lowland river streams, particularly in the midlands, Connacht, River Shannon, and County Clare.

In *The Breeding Atlas* survey breeding was confirmed in 1,262, probable in 319, and possible in 277 10 km squares. Sharrock (1976) suggests a possible breeding population of about 50,000 for Britain and Ireland, but this can only be the roughest of estimates as, judging from our own study areas, numbers vary greatly from year to year.

The charm of the lively little sandpiper partly belongs to its haunts on loch, river and stream, many shared with dippers and grey wagtails. We remember with joy long warm nights in May, lying in our sleeping bags in the hut, and listening to their sounds of courtship and rivalry.

RED-NECKED PHALAROPE

Well over 50 years ago John Walpole-Bond, in his inimitable way, introduced me to the red-necked phalarope when I was staying with him in Sussex. He slowly opened a small box, unwrapped the cotton wool, and displayed four small rather pointed olive brown and buff-speckled eggs. 'Red-necked phalaropes from Benbecula', he muttered lovingly.

Red-necked phalaropes are small, dainty, colourful waders with a reversal of courtship roles, size and plumage. The hen is slightly larger and distinctly brighter than the cock and she dominates in courtship and pairing behaviour. On their breeding grounds they have slate grey crowns and mantles, white chins and bellies, rich chestnut brown bands and patches on their necks and upper throats, and thin black bills. In winter they have white crowns, necks, breast and bellies and dark grey backs with white streaks.

In 1936, when I was studying the dotterel in the Grampians and Cairngorms, Jourdain sent me his copy of *Ardea* with Niko Tinbergen's fine study of the pairing and egg laying of red-necked phalaropes in East Greenland. There are many similarities between these two fascinating waders, both having reversed courtship, but there are also many differences.

These are birds of the estuarine marshes and grasslands, rough grazings with plenty of natural or man-made pools and peat cuttings. They also nest not far from larger lochs with small islands in a country of small peaty tarns. Cecil Stoney used to tell me of his hunts in coastal flats and grazings near Belmullet in Co. Mayo, where he once found 20 nests within a few days. Single pairs of these lovely little waders also nested in Co. Donegal from 1916 until the late 1920s. In the Outer Hebrides, red-necked phalaropes are often associated with base-rich water and bogs in calcareous machair. Arthur Whitaker gave me an account of his experiences in North Ronaldsay, Orkney, where the phalaropes haunted sparse pasture and thin hayfields bordering Lochs Hooking and Ancombe. In Fetlar, now their British headquarters, the phalaropes nest among flooded peat cuttings and move to new haunts when these are overgrown.

Tinbergen's studies in East Greenland were made among small fresh-water pools at sea level. In Finland, O. Hildén and S. Vuolanto (1972) studied a coastal population from 1966–1972. This island group nested at Norrskär in the Gulf of Bothnia where the main concentration of habitats was a small island of 28 ha consisting partly of bedrock and sand and stones, and clothed in very short sheep-grazed vegetation.

Dates and arrival patterns of phalaropes differ. Venables and Venables (1955) found that the hens were the first to arrive in Shetland, with 23–27 May the earliest dates; but the bulk returned in the first ten days of June. They arrive in Iceland in the second half of May, with 15 May the earliest recorded date. G. Timmermann (1949) found that the birds stayed in flocks on salt water until the inland pools and small tarns and lakes of their nesting haunts had thawed out. In 1933, in East Greenland, Tinbergen noted that the first birds – hens – returned on 17 June; in hard springs pairs may be formed on inlets of the sea before their breeding grounds are clear of ice. Hugh Blair recorded that the earliest phalaropes arrived on the Varanger Peninsula, Finnmark, between 28–31 May 1926; but in the late summer of 1924 the birds first paired on sea water. Between 1966–72, at Norrskär, Finland, Hildén and Vuolanto found that there was no consistent pattern of arrival. In Alaska, however, the hens in E. O. Höhn's study area usually arrived a week ahead of the cocks.

TERRITORY AND COURTSHIP

Red-necked phalaropes are not strictly orthodox territorialists. They appear to tailor their behaviour to meet local needs and possibly defend territory more consistently if, for example, suitable pools are scarce. Wilson's and grey phalaropes are likewise unorthodox in their territorial behaviour. Hen Wilson's phalaropes choose particular cocks which they defend against other hens wherever the cock goes. The bird, not the plot of land and water, is the defended object. If a strange pair passes by, the hen threatens or attacks the hen only, ignoring the cock (Höhn 1967). Similarly, grey phalaropes do not defend particular areas but have developed different dispersion mechanisms. On Victoria Island, for example, David Parmelee and his companions noted that aggressive grey phalarope hens chased cocks in fluttering flights; 'at times two hens fought furiously in the presence of a cock, fluttering up and facing each other in mid-air'.

While watching a pair of red-necked phalaropes swimming around their nesting lochs in North Ronaldsay, Whitaker and Tom Fowler observed that other pairs frequently flew in and dropped down close to them, lingering briefly, almost as if they were paying social calls. The four birds then fed amicably for a few minutes until the visitors flew off. Once or twice the residents flew away, 'possibly to return their neighbours' call'. Behaviour was rather different in a Scottish mainland haunt where Charlie Young watched a trio – a hen and two cocks – on an acidic flow. The hen followed the brighter cock and from time to time drove off the other, which was apparently in less colourful first-year plumage.

In East Greenland, however, the phalaropes which Tinbergen (1959) was studying did establish territories and form pairs in an orthodox manner. After feeding, the hen would rise from the pool, loudly rattling her wings and calling harsh *wit-wit-wit* cries, fly a few metres and again settle, now calling *wedü-wedü-wedü* while 'swimming or lying on the water with an extremely long vertically-stretched neck and alertly looking around it'. This display, the hen's method of enticing possible mates, and repelling rival hens, was repeated time after time whenever another cock or hen approached the defended pool. If the advertisement flight failed to shift the intruder, she swam towards it, head lowered, beak pointed forward and plumage ruffled; if necessary, she would peck her rival. This physical and psychological behaviour usually succeeded. Occasionally, however, a trespasser avoided the attack without quitting the pool, which it subsequently shared with the dominant hen, although each kept to its own corner. 'Our hen thus had a territory of varying size centred round one corner of the pond and including part of it. But the boundary was never sharply defined since the hen often tolerated intruders at the periphery where she drove them off at other times'.

Several different hens defended territories in this way, but Tinbergen never saw a cock doing so. All the defended areas were parts of pools with suitable nesting habitat around them. When cocks alighted in the territory the hen approached them in the same way as rival hens, rattling or whirring her wings. Silent or calling, she would then fly to them, alight, and swim forward in aggressive posture, without physically attacking them. After a few days the hen approached the cocks more closely, rattling her wings in front of one of them. Both then rattled, behaviour which usually preceded copulation. The cocks, however, usually left when the hen advanced, often flying away in a low tortuous flight, the hen in hot pursuit. Occasionally a mated or unmated cock would turn around, wings whirring, and attempt to copulate with his pursuer. At other times he hid from her, lying motionless on the water among tufts of vegetation bordering the pool.

Tinbergen robbed the nest of another pair in the evening and by morning found that the unmated hen had paired with this cock. Before pairing, she periodically went to land to form a number of scrapes. On the morning after the nest was robbed the hen stopped making her advertising flights and the two birds stayed in a sheltered part of the water. Soon they were feeding together and copulating. The hen swam towards the cock, 'suddenly rising before it and whirring her wings, then turning away from him and lying in a characteristic flat attitude on the water, motionless for up to 10 seconds, and when the cock did not respond turning again towards him with vertical neck and immediately turning away again and lying in her attitude of readiness'. The cock, in turn, also rattled his wings and then copulated, first hovering in the manner of a cock redshank, which is about to alight to mate with a hen. During coupling, the hen sank into the water and afterwards chased the cock for several seconds. The hen now ceased her wing rattling and pursuit flights. In all, Tinbergen saw 15 successful and many abortive copulations which the hen, but occasionally the cock, had initiated. All copulations took place on water. It is interesting that red-necked phalaropes almost exclusively copulate on water. Grey phalaropes copulate on land as well as on water (H. Løvenskiold 1964) and Wilson's phalaropes mate on dry land or standing in shallow water (Höhn 1967).

After copulation the hen red-necked phalarope left the water and started to form scoops. The cock followed and changed places with her and also made scraping movements. At times he swam to the land alone and formed his own scoops, occasionally pausing to raise his neck and give the very same cries as the hen had uttered in advertising flights. A few days later the pair co-operated at the same scrape, working together for up to 10 minutes. The two birds would often stand in the scrape in a stooping posture, uttering a soft rhythmic sound while making rapid downward pecks with their bills, without touching the ground. The pair also had spells of 'sideways building'; the bird sitting in the scoop picked up grasses which she placed beside or behind her. They also changed places at the nest, the outgoing bird walking away and tossing grasses over its shoulder. During this phase the pair made scrapes in many different places but showed no special interest in any one in particular.

On the fourth day the hen again started to make advertising flights, rising abruptly from water, calling and rattling her wings. Each time the cock followed her. Then she alighted and sat in one of the scoops at which the cock joined her. She now visited four of her old scoops one after the other. In the fourth she laid her first egg. 'She looked down into the nest, pecked in the cup and then the cock changed places and did the same. Then he walked away, throwing straws as he went, but he soon returned to her again looking down under her and pecking but then walked away. Once more he left and returned about 20 times, sometimes first standing next to the hen, sometimes sitting down after pushing her off the egg and neither bird scraped any more'.

Gales prevented Tinbergen from watching the laying of the second and fourth eggs but a similar egg ceremony preceded the laying of the third. This exciting account of the red-necked phalarope egg ceremony particularly interests us as we have watched almost precisely similar behaviour by some pairs of dotterel while laying the first and second eggs in a clutch, but not before the third and final egg. Other hen dotterels laid their eggs without any special behaviour. Over forty years after Tinbergen's discovery, Olavi Hildén reports that some pairs in Finland perform these egg ceremonies for the first three eggs, but apparently not over the fourth and final eggs in the clutch.

Polygamy

Species with reversed sexual rôles, size, and plumage, are always likely to evolve unusual breeding patterns. If there are more cocks than hens, and hens take no part in incubation or rearing of young, a system of successive polyandry is likely to produce more young. Successive polyandry has occurred in the red-necked phalarope. Leslie Montgomery watched a trio of two cocks and a hen in Co. Mayo, and later discovered two nests, containing almost identical eggs, only 10 m apart; one clutch was fresh and the other slightly incubated. The same hen had clearly laid both clutches (Nethersole-Thompson 1951).

In East Greenland, although proof was lacking, Tinbergen suggested that successive polyandry was possible. Later, Hildén and Vuolanto (1972) proved that there was successive polyandry in their colour-marked Finnish groups. In 1966 and 1970, single unmated cocks mated with hens whose original mates were sitting on their first clutches. These hens laid second clutches which their new mates then incubated. In 1971 three surplus cocks also successfully mated with hens which had already laid clutches on which their first mates were already sitting. The intervals between the first and second clutches were, respectively, 5, 8, 9, 19 and 22 days. In a small colour-marked colony in Sweden, consisting of four hens and six cocks, Lennart Raner (1972) proved that two hens provided clutches for the two surplus cocks. In some colonies with an unbalanced sex ratio, therefore, successive polyandry is possibly normal.

Female Wilson's phalaropes are also sometimes polyandrous. In Alberta, T. E. Randall (1959) recorded hens successively mated to two different cocks. In one locality the only phalaropes present were a trio – a hen and two cocks. This hen laid two clutches, each of four eggs, in nests roughly 100 m apart; the second clutch hatched 11 days after the first. Höhn (1967), however, recorded no example of polyandry in the groups studied in another part of Alberta.

Polygyny, which sometimes occurs when there is a surplus of hens, is likely to be selected out in species with reversed sexual roles. However, it probably occurs occasionally in red-necked phalaropes. W. M. Congreve and S. W. P. Freme (1930) found more hens than cocks in some Iceland groups. One cock copulated with two hens, one after the other. Congreve later discovered two nests, each containing eight eggs. Had two hens simultaneously laid their two clutches in the same scoop and left the cocks to incubate them?

DISPERSION AND BREEDING DENSITY

Hildén in Finland, Raner in Sweden, and J. M. Dymond in Shetland all met with red-necked phalaropes breeding in loose groups, sometimes in association with colonies of arctic terns; the phalaropes quickly reacted to their alarm cries. At other times isolated and solitary pairs were located.

Hildén and Vuolanto (1972) recorded that the closest nests in Norrskär were 2, 3, and 5 m apart and, in another part of Finland, S. Ulfstrand and G. Högstedt (1976) recorded a density of 2.5 pairs/km². In northern Siberia, A. A. Kistchinski (1975) noted a density of 0.3–0.5 breeding pairs/ha in polygonised tundra and a slightly more consistently higher density of 0.5 breeding pairs/ha when this habitat was divided into willow thickets.

NEST, EGG AND CLUTCH

In northern Scotland, Charlie Young watched the hen going on to the land close to a dubhlochan, but he did not see the elaborate nest site selection displays described by Tinbergen. Charlie found one nest on an island in a tarn in a large flow; two others were within half a metre of a dubhlochan. Nest sites in Orkney were in deep tussocks of grass or beds of sedges. One nest was in a tuft of grass between two small clumps of buttercups. Whitaker and Fowler (MS) recorded that the nests were 11–60 m from the lochside.

Hildén and Vuolanto (1972) found that nests at Norrskär were usually sited on dry ground. Fifty five out of 70 nests were placed in low vegetation in positions from which the brooding cock had a good look out. Thirty-one were in grasses (*F. ovina, F. rubra, D. flexuosa, Puccinellia* sp), 21 in *Eleocharis uniglumis*, 10 in sedge *Carex* sp., and 6 in *Trifolium repens, Potentilla anserina* and *Empetrum* sp. Four nests were within a metre of the water line, 14 between 5–15 m, 21 between 5–20 m, 26 between 20–50 m, and 9 over 50 m away. F. Salomonsen (1951) recorded that nests in Greenland were almost all well hidden in different species of sedge. Herbert Brandt (1943) measured 22 nests in Alaska which were 6–10 cm across and 2.5–3.8 cm deep.

While sitting, the cock toys with grasses and adds them to the lining. Fowler described one peering about, pulling up bits of grass in his beak, tossing them over his shoulders, and looking round to see where they had fallen.

Venables and Venables (1955) recorded that 11 Shetland broods hatched from clutches completed between 3–23 June, and one each from those completed on 29 June and 7 July. In 1921, Whitaker and Fowler recorded six clutches in Orkney laid up between 1–14 June, with a mean date of 8 June. On the Scottish mainland, Charlie Young tells us that apparently the same hen completed her clutch on 17 June 1978 and on 23 June 1979.

Salomonsen gives a laying season of 3–29 June in Greenland. In their seven-years study in Finland, Hildén and Vuolanto recorded that the hens started to lay between 31 May–6 June. Older and more experienced hens, which have nested at least once in a previous year completed their clutches between 31 May–21 June (mean 7 June), and 1-year old hens between 10–21 June (mean 14 June). In pairs in which one bird was mated to an older bird the date of egg laying was usually brought forward. Inexperienced or young birds, however, took longer to pair, establish territories, and possibly for the hen to build up reserves for laying.

In northern latitudes waders which arrive late tend to start laying remarkably quickly. Hildén (1972) found that broad-billed sandpipers in Finland laid their first eggs a week after they had arrived. In Finnish Lapland Erkki Pulliainen (1971) recorded that the first two dotterels arrived on 30 May and that the hen laid her first egg on 6 June. However, in Scotland, there is usually a longer interval between the return of dotterel and the laying of their first egg.

Hen red-necked phalaropes only take 3–4 days to form and lay their first egg in favourable years; but after severe winters they occasionally take as long as 10 days.

Hildén and Vuolanto recorded red-necked phalaropes laying eggs at intervals of 24–30 hours (mean 26.5 hours). The minimum laying intervals, involving two hens, were at most 23.5 and 24.0 hours; and the maximum intervals were those of two hens which laid their eggs after lapses of 38 hours. A third hen, disturbed when about to lay her third egg, took a further 49 hours before laying. Raner also recorded that eggs in Sweden were laid daily and clutches completed in four days. Whitaker and Fowler found that one Orkney hen laid her eggs daily.

Jourdain (1940) describes the eggs as 'ovate to sub pyriform in shape'. The ground colour varies from buff or stone buff to olive brown or olive green and they are rather pointed and have little gloss. A few eggs are grey to greenish. Markings are in the form of speckles and spots with blotches of dark to blackish and reddish brown on the heavy ends. One hundred British eggs averaged 29.9×21.0 mm; max: 33.3×21.2 mm and 32.5×22.1 mm; min: 27.7×21.3 mm and 29.0×20.0 mm (Jourdain 1940). Thirty-five Iceland eggs averaged 29.5×20.9 mm (Haller *in* Glutz 1977). M. Schönwetter (1963) measured 150 blown eggshells which averaged 0.34 gm. He calculated that the weight of a fresh egg was 6.3 gm. Twenty-four females in Finland averaged 35 gm. A clutch of four eggs thus weighs roughly 70% of the hen's body weight.

A clutch usually consists of four, exceptionally of three eggs. Clutches of 8–12 are due to two or three hens laying in one nest. In Finland, Hildén and Vuolanto recorded 71 clutches: 1/3, 70/4 (mean 3.9) (Table 4). In Orkney, Whitaker and Fowler recorded five clutches: 1/3, 4/4 (mean 3.8); and in northern Scotland, Charlie Young gave us records of four clutches: 1/3, 3/4 (mean 3.8).

Cocks which have lost their clutches occasionally re-pair with the same or different hens and thus incubate replacement clutches. At Norrskär four out of 18 cocks, which had lost their eggs during incubation, later sat upon replacement clutches. Three of these cocks were identified. One re-mated with his first hen and two with new hens. The intervals between nest loss and laying of the first replacement egg in four clutches was 3, 3, 4 and 3.4 days (mean 3.2 days). Hildén and Vuolanto also mention five other cocks which again paired up and repeatedly copulated but without the hens laying replacement clutches.

INCUBATION

In East Greenland the cocks started to sit from the second egg onwards, leaving to feed every 20–30 minutes. Steady incubation begun before clutch completion is irregular. On 10 June 1921, Whitaker and Fowler noted that a cock was not sitting on a nest with three eggs. In Finland a cock may sit on a nest from the first egg onwards. However, Hildén and Vuolanto record a cock only visiting a nest with two eggs once in two hours; but he sat for spells of 15 minutes on the third egg. When he starts to sit steadily on a full clutch the cock is on and off the nest for roughly equal periods of 15–30 minutes, but he soon sits for longer spells, incubating for about 50 minutes and feeding for less than 10 minutes in each hour. Tinbergen, Whitaker, and Fowler all noted that the cocks usually fed only a short distance from the nest. However, one of the Orkney nests was 400 m from the feeding tarn. If the nest is some distance from his feeding pool or tarn he sometimes returns to it in fast low flight over the bog, looking almost like a large swallow. This is a wonderful sight and not easy to mark as the cock dips down to the nest without any preliminary hesitation.

Hildén and Vuolanto measured 20 incubation periods, ranging from 16.8 to 20.7 days from the laying of the last egg to the hatching of the last chick. Twenty-seven per cent of these periods lay between 17–18.5 days (mean 18 days). As in dotterel (Nethersole-Thompson 1973) and dunlin (Soikkeli 1967), late or replacement clutches sometimes hatch after shorter than average incubation periods, possibly because the sitting bird has already developed its full brooding heat or the warmer air temperatures prevents the eggs from cooling while the bird is off the nest.

Höhn (1967–1969) estimated that Wilson's phalarope had incubation periods of 20–21 days and J. Johns (1969) recorded 16–21 days and 15–18 days for 10 eggs hatched in an incubator. Estimates of incubation periods of grey phalaropes varied from 15 days (C. B. Worth 1940) to 23–24 days (F. Salomonsen 1950).

Male red-necked phalaropes continue to brood infertile and addled eggs long past the normal incubation period. At Norrskär particular cocks sat on their nests for 24–31 days.

HATCHING

A brood usually takes 4–12 hours to hatch (mean 8 hours for 9 Finnish hatches). The chicks stay in the nest from 3–6 hours, provided that the brood hatches in the morning. Like other waders, however, chicks hatched in the afternoon or evening, or in rough weather, are often brooded in the nest overnight.

Cocks fly away with large fragments of eggshell.

In some habitats breeding success is apparently low. Höhn (1968) recorded that only two chicks hatched in eleven nests in Alaska. Two nests were deserted and seven robbed; at least one by a long-tailed skua.

On the Scottish mainland, Charlie Young tells us that only one young hatched from c/3 in 1979. In 1980, although the four eggs hatched, only one flying young survived. A pair which laid four eggs on St Kilda in 1972 reared three young.

YOUNG

In the hand, newly-hatched chicks are lovely little objects looking little larger than bumblebees. Their underparts are paler and eye-stripes and mantle brighter than grey phalarope chicks at the same age. The cocks usually sit quite tightly, leaving their nests only a few metres ahead of the searcher; and they occasionally allow themselves to be lifted off the nest.

Eighty-six newly-hatched chicks at Norrskär weighed 3.2–4.8 gm (mean 3.9 gm). Höhn (1968) weighed four chicks in Alberta which weighed 3.6–4.0 gm when they were less than 24 hours old. Young red-necked phalaropes have increased their weight almost five-fold by their ninth day, compared to young dunlin which, in the same number of days, increase their weight by little more than three times (Hildén and Vuolanto 1972) (Table 5).

At first, most cocks move with their broods up to several hundred metres in a day before finally choosing their nursery. They brood the chicks for short spells until the sixth day, and continue to do so at night and during severe weather. The precise time span is uncertain, but Hildén and Vuolanto found that the cock left the young unattended after about a fortnight.

At Norrskär small chicks were not seen swimming; but in Lapland broods in sedges close to pools swam behind the cock, almost like ducklings. These different patterns have possibly evolved because chicks would be likely to drown in rough sea water. Johns (1969) watched Wilson's phalarope chicks swimming when they were little more than one hour old.

About half the hens demonstrated at nests in Norrskär during hatching periods, but these birds were not always the mothers of the chicks. 'Of six individually marked hens, four had laid the clutches from which the chicks had hatched, two others were foreign, and on two occasions four hens were close to a nest during the hatch, all calling anxiously'. Like dotterels, however, cock red-necked phalaropes often drive away the hens. At one Norrskär site the hen attached herself to a male and brood for two days, making scrapes when attacked. Another time, a hen successfully invited the cock to copulate; dotterels have similar behaviour. Noisy and active guardian cocks attract hens with still unsatisfied sex-drives. On Spitsbergen, Sven-Axel Bengtson (1968) watched hen grey phalaropes court cocks with broods; and Johns (1969) recorded hen Wilson's phalaropes joining cocks and broods. However, this practice is unlikely to be selected in, as the second parent tends to attract attention to the brood without contributing much to its defence.

The age at which the chicks start to fly is difficult to measure, but has been estimated at 18–20 days.

Red-necked phalaropes do not appear to be long-lived birds. However, Hildén and Vuolanto followed up a colour-ringed nesting hen in at least four consecutive years. The oldest Iceland bird, recorded by F. Gudmundsson, was 3 years and 7 days. Glutz (1977) records another which was at least 5 years old (Table 1).

Elaborate distraction behaviour does not appear to have been developed by red-necked phalaropes. A guarding cock flies around a human intruder, calling noisily, and periodically landing in the marsh. Cocks also produce lure displays in which they partly raise their wings.

VOICE

As yet, there is no full analysis of the red-necked phalarope's vocabulary, but various observers have expressed in words what they have heard in different situations. Some of these calls have been recorded on tape and rendered as sonagrams (Cramp and Simmons 1983).

(1)   The cock appears to have a twittering song in courtship which has been likened to those of the swallow and ringed plover.

(2)   The usual cry on the wing, or when settled on land or water, is a low-pitched *wit-wit*. Jock Walpole-Bond likened this sound to two pieces of gaberdine rubbed together.

(3)   A characteristic cry of the bird on the ground, in the breeding season, is an abrupt chirping *prek* or disyllabic *cherrp* (P. J. Sellar 1983).

(4)   Tinbergen recorded a harsh *with-wit-wit* given by the hen while rattling her wings in advertising flight. Different versions of this call are given in other situations.

(5)   On alighting on the water at the end of a sexual flight, a female calls *weedü-weedü* and the cock also uses this call when nest dancing. At other times the pair gives these cries as means of re-finding one another (Tinbergen 1935).

(6)   In joint nest dances cock and hen give soft and continuous *wee-wee* calls.

(7)   When feeding or in sexual situations the birds use quick 'slightly ascending phrases *pri-ri-rip-pri-ri-rip* interspersed with brief nasal squeaking *wü* notes' (P. J. Sellar 1983).

(8)   G. A. J. Schmidt (1965) recorded the hen using a disyllabic or trisyllabic *bit-tit* or *bitt-itt-itt* when warning cock or brood.

(9)   Schmidt (1965) recorded anger or fear cries, during situations of great excitement with chicks, as urgent *vaats* or *daits*.

(10)   After danger has passed the cock gives soft cries to re-assemble his brood.

(11)   The cock gives sharp *kluk-kluks* in answer to the cheeping of chicks; and a captive bird gave 'soft rasping squeaks when handled' (S. R. Leffler 1966).

(12)   1–2 days old chicks, while swimming and feeding, gave cries like a yellow wagtail's flight call (J. N. Dymond 1983).

(13)   Unfledged chicks have contact cries described as *syht* or *buit*.

(14)   At 8–10 days chicks call shrilly while held in the hand (Schmidt 1965).

PREDATORS

Arctic skuas are particularly dangerous predators in Shetland. Bonxies, the larger gulls – especially common gull– merlin and hooded crows are others. In the Outer Hebrides common gulls are probably the most deadly enemies of the phalaropes. Foxes are predators in some habitats and cattle sometimes trample on nests.

At Norrskär, Hildén and Vuolanto found that red-necked phalaropes often nested in colonies of arctic terns and these possibly acted as monitors and protectors. Turnstones were frequent egg robbers.

FOOD

In their nesting habitats, and also on passage, red-necked phalaropes feed largely on small insects and their larvae, particularly Diptera, which they usually take on or just below the water surface or from overhanging grasses and other vegetation. The diet of insects is occasionally varied by a possibly accidental ingestion of seeds, sprigs, and leaves of water plants.

A. A. Kistchinski and Y. I. Tchernov (1973), in a detailed study at Indigirka, USSR, found that the phalaropes' main food changed with the passage of the season. In early June they took many springtails washed up on the lakeside, and pupae of Diptera on vegetation beside the lakes. Around mid June they turned to Tipulids which they took from grass; later in the month, Diptera were taken from the water surface; and from mid July onwards Caddis flies provided their main diet.

Hildén and Vuolanto (1972) concluded that early swarms of Chironomids *Tantytarsus gracilentus*, following a rise in temperature to 8°C, stimulated the hen's ovary and induced her to start laying. Later in June other Chironomids and their water larvae, water fleas, tadpoles, and occasionally small fish, provided abundant food.

In feeding, red-necked phalaropes use the well-known spinning trick in which they twirl round on the water to stir up small pupae. The Orkney pairs fed close together, picking up food from thin growths of mares tails and other water plants. Whitaker watched one hen apparently feed her mate. Other methods of feeding include 'upending' while swimming, small jumps from the water surface, and occasional fluttering like black terns.

DISTRIBUTION AND NUMBERS

The red-necked phalarope is a holarctic species with many of its most populated haunts lying on the northern mainland and islands of European and Asiatic USSR. In the nearctic zone it breeds freely in suitable habitats from Alaska, Aleutian Islands, and the Yukon to north MacKenzie, Central Keewatin, James Bay, North Ungava and Greenland.

H. Schiemann (1972) estimated a population of over 200,000 breeding pairs in Iceland, where they are really numerous in many places. Red-necked phalaropes have decreased in the Faroes (D. Bloch 1983). J. Kålås and I. Byrkjedal (1981) give 9,500 breeding pairs in Norway in 1979 and S. Ulfstrand and G. Högstedt (1976) give a breeding strength of 50,000 pairs in Sweden.

M. J. Everett (1971) traced the decline of red-necked phalaropes in Britain and Ireland. There were probably over 100 pairs in the 1920s, about 70 pairs in the 1940s, and approximately 45 pairs in 1970. Red-necked phalaropes nest in Shetland, with Fetlar as their headquarters, where there was a total of 28-plus breeding pairs in 1970. In 1972 a pair also successfully nested on St Kilda.

The Breeding Atlas (1976) records confirmed breeding in 13, probable breeding in three, and possible breeding in the 10 km squares. J. T. R. Sharrock estimated that 10–16 pairs bred in Shetland in 1974. In 1977 nineteen, in 1978 nine, in 1979 ten, and in 1980 18 clutches are believed to have hatched successfully in Shetland. In 1981 a total of 24–38 pairs still nested in Britain at six different sites – five in the Outer Hebrides and one in Shetland (Sharrock *et al* 1981). Breeding still continued. In 1984 19–21 pairs nested on Shetland, three pairs on the Outer Isles, and possibly one on the Scottish mainland – a total of 22–25 pairs (Thom 1986).

From the late 19th century onwards collectors visited red-necked phalarope haunts in the Western and Northern Isles, but it is unlikely that their predation decisively lowered numbers. Change of land use, such as drainage of marshes, grazing of cattle and a slightly warmer climate, are more likely to have been responsible for their decline in Scotland and Ireland. There the red-necked phalarope is breeding on the fringe of its range, with the Irish haunts the most southerly in the world. Long may it maintain this small toe-hold.

COMMON SANDPIPERS in agonistic displays. They use uplifted wings both in courtship and in aggressive situations. (Photo: Tapani Räsänen).

RED-NECKED PHALAROPES, a species with reversed sexual differences, courting in mosquito country. (Photo: Seppo Keränen).

REDSHANK about to incubate. Frequently, redshanks weave a canopy over the nest.
(Photo: Dennis Green).

RINGED PLOVER pair changing over at nest. Both sexes takes turns to sit, usually for short intervals. (Photo: Eric Hosking).

GREEN SANDPIPER sitting on eggs in a tree nest. A rare photograph. No one has yet found a nest with eggs in Britain. (Photo: P. O. Swanberg).

REDSHANK

I first watched breeding redshanks on the Amberley Wild Brooks in Sussex, and the Cooling marshes of the Thames Estuary in Kent. Here I found nests and listened to their songs and calls, but it was many years before I started to study their behaviour.

A restless and noisy wader, of medium size, the redshank has longish orange-red legs, red-orange bill base, a white rump and tail coverts, and broad white wing bars.

On passage redshanks visit marshes, sewage farms and edges of reservoirs, but their main winter grounds are tidal estuaries, mud flats and sea shores.

In Britain redshanks breed in damp grassy marshes, grass heaths beside lochs, rough rushy pastures, water meadows and, particularly in Scotland, on the edges of hill moors. In only two of our study areas have we found redshanks and greenshanks in the same breeding community of waders, and never in the bogs and clearings of the old pine forest. We have known nests of redshank and golden plover less than 10 m apart on a small flow. Snipe and curlew are also nesting neighbours sometimes, but curlews usually choose longer herbage and snipe rougher or wetter heath.

Early this century Julian Huxley studied the pairing behaviour of redshanks on the estuary of Cardigan Bay in Wales. Much later, in north Germany, G. Grosskopf researched them in the Wangerooge Reserve which is a mixture of dunes and salt marsh. Professor Bill Hale, a most enthusiastic wader watcher, and his equally dedicated students, have worked in the salt marshes of the Ribble Estuary. Their intensive long-term research has greatly advanced our knowledge of the redshank's breeding behaviour.

The Ribble marshes on the coast of Lancashire contain one of the greatest spreads of salt marsh in Britain. In summer they are full of wet ditches, pools, depressions and moist grasslands. Here, where Patrick studies redshanks along with Chris McCarty, they sometimes nest alongside common and arctic terns and black-headed gulls. In two instances, in 1983 and 1984, redshanks nested within a metre of a common tern's nest.

In Lancashire some redshanks are on the estuary throughout the year, and they are present on their breeding grounds on the marsh from February onwards. At Wangerooge, Grosskopf (1959) found that it was usual for the cocks to arrive first, but occasionally a hen preceded her mate. Exceptionally a cock and hen arrived simultaneously, but it was impossible to prove that they had travelled together.

On the Dorback Moor, cocks usually arrived first but I have known pairs and small trips to come in together. On arrival, the cocks fed on pools on squashy moorland edges before starting to call from fences, dykes and sheep fanks. From time to time they rose high in the air to perform those wonderful switchback display flights, with wings held below their bodies; and then, by setting their wings, they rose and fell in a series of gigantic inverted arcs. During these flights they gave a succession of single, loud, sweet calls *tü-tü*, which became more rapidly uttered towards the climax as the bird floated towards the ground. These displays were also often accompanied by yodelling *taweeo-taweeo* songs, given in both normal and undulating display flights.

TERRITORY AND COURTSHIP

There has been much discussion about territorialism in redshanks. In his study area, Grosskopf (1963) found that cocks established territories close to former nesting sites over which they made display flights which were not, however, restricted to the narrow limits of the defended area. They also defended this living space by calling from ground or perch and by making fierce attacks on intruding cocks. These rudimentary territories helped to disperse nests fairly uniformly, and in time the various cocks learnt to recognise one another, with dominant birds tolerating their nearest neighbours. Cocks, but not hens, actively assailed dummies placed close to nests during incubation.

The picture was broadly similar in Dorback, although the numbers were small. Soon after their arrival dominant cocks drove off rivals from feeding pools close to nesting sites and thus promoted dispersion. In the Lancashire groups, on the other hand, Hale (1956) found that redshanks apparently lacked territorial drive and did not even attack dummies placed beside their nests. Patrick also saw no sign of territorial behaviour from incubating birds on the Ribble. However, he watched several fights between adults with chicks when two broods were apparently moving along the same ditch.

At the beginning of the season there is often confusion, with particular cocks chasing and attempting to copulate with more than one hen. If the hen's sex drive is not at full strength there are often many lengthy ground pursuits. The cock chases the hen for several minutes, and often longer, running with partly outstretched neck in a series of loops, semi-circles, circles, ellipses, or occasionally in figures-of-eight. In these pursuits he fans his tail and pokes his head sideways to keep the hen in view. She may abort by flying or running away and the ploy has to start over again. If, however, the hen stops and perhaps bends slightly and stiffly forward, the cock marches slowly towards her with short steps, changing to a high-stepping 'mark time' as he approaches. All the time he beats his wings so fast that they eventually lift him from the ground onto her back. While taking the hen, the cock continues to beat his wings, partly to balance himself; and he sometimes holds or touches her nape or mantle with his bill. Then, after a few seconds, he dismounts or the hen shakes him off.

During copulation the cock uses special rolls of continuous rattling cries, partly caused by quick vibrations of the lower mandible; and, as the coupling reaches its climax, both redshanks often sing very fast yodelling songs before separating and then preening. Another form of sexual display is for the cock to approach the hen head on, bowing low to her before and after the act. In full passion the pairs dispense with long ground pursuits; the cock then omits every sexual action except the ecstatic wing beating.

Hale and Ashcroft (1982) described the functions of advertising flights and alighting ceremonies. 'The early display flight of an unmated cock is designed to attract the hen into the air'. If a cock is joined by an unmated hen, which glides alongside or in front of him, one and sometimes both trill as they glide towards the ground. Up to four cocks may try to attract a single hen by this means. An alighting ceremony helps to maintain the pair. 'Some 30 or 40 metres from the point of intended landing the bird or birds stop beating their wings and depressing them at an angle of some 45° and glide down singing the musical *talüdal-talüdal-talüdal* song'. They usually stop singing on landing, but sometimes continue for up to three minutes. The bird in the air usually begins the singing and the one on the ground joins in and sometimes raises its wings. Throughout incubation the two birds also use this alighting ceremony to greet one another.

After the cock has accepted a hen he makes scrapes, running from tussock to tussock, sometimes selecting a scoop which he has already started. He now rotates, presses his breast down, wings partly drooped, and holds his tail at an acute angle to show off his white rump patch. Simultaneously he scratches vigorously with his feet and periodically broods the scoop. When the hen slowly approaches him he rises to make room for her, or she may even jostle him out of the scoop and herself start to scrape. He then often bows low, drooping his wings and fully fanning his tail, always positioning himself in such a way that his spread tail and white rump are exposed to her. Later the hen also gives a similar deep bowing display directed at the cock. There are many variations and elaborations of these fascinating sequences of sexual excitement.

Patrick watched a pair nest-site selecting on the Ribble marshes. 'The cock ran

with his tail fanned, using a quiet continuous call as he ran up to a scrape; the hen then flew in and joined him. He left the scrape in an upright posture, with head slightly turned, and the hen took his place.'

Polygamy

Different forms of polygamy occasionally occur. Ken Williamson (1938) recorded that a particular cock apparently mated with three different hens in the space of about a fortnight. Norman Gilroy (*in* Walpole-Bond 1938) found a nest with eight eggs in Sussex – two clutches laid by different hens. J. Reynolds (1948) also recorded a double clutch at Pagham Harbour in Sussex. On 24 April the nest held two eggs, on 27 April six, and on 29 April eight eggs; two hens were clearly laying in the same nest. Unfortunately the eggs were destroyed before the case history was complete. Hale and Ashcroft (1982) had three nests with five eggs and two with six eggs, each clutch probably containing eggs laid by two different hens; but there was no proof that the same cock had fertilised them.

When a hen deserts, leaving her mate to incubate and hatch the eggs, she occasionally mates with a second cock and produces a second clutch. Patrick proved this on three occasions in 1984. He also had 18 instances of pairs which had successfully hatched their eggs and were then found 12½–19 days later with second clutches. The chicks in their first broods had presumably died.

There were three examples of what Patrick calls 'combination pairs', involving four birds. A cock from one nest and a hen from another joined up to form a new pair. In two instances they had apparently deserted their first nests, leaving one adult to carry out parental duties. In the third example a cock, caught on 3 June 1984 at its first nest, was later found sitting on a second nest in which the clutch had been completed between 10–12 June. This cock apparently had two mates simultaneously. Grosskopf also found that paired cocks often coupled with surplus hens.

DISPERSION AND BREEDING DENSITY

Redshanks are waders with remarkably diverse patterns of breeding density. In some coastal saltings and salt marshes they nest almost in colonies. Hale (1980) estimated that there were sometimes 77 breeding pairs/km^2 on the Ribble estuary. In good years, as in 1984, Patrick suggests that breeding density may have exceeded 100 breeding pairs/km^2.

On the Wash in East Anglia there is also a high density, with an average of 160 breeding pairs in a 10 km square (J. T. R. Sharrock 1976). Arthur Whitaker described a salt marsh near Boston, Lincolnshire, where, after a high tide had flooded their marsh, 'there was literally scores of pairs, all calling, flying and singing, but we could not find a single nest as the birds had evidently not yet had time to re-lay'. On the Essex salt marshes the breeding density is probably lower – about 55 pairs in a 10 km square (Sharrock 1976).

On Amberley Wild Brooks, in Sussex, nests were seldom less than 150 m apart. Similarly, on the moorland edges of Dorback the few nests were often spaced as widely as greenshanks, at intervals of 400–1,600 m or more. On some salt and loch marshes in Ross and Sutherland pairs are also quite widely spaced; but small dips and hollows in the hill, up to 2 km from a firth, sometimes carry half a dozen or more pairs, forming a group which collectively mobs possible predators.

These dispersion patterns pose many challenging problems. Why, for example, do we never find greenshanks nesting close together, except when two hens are mated to the same cock? Yet redshanks, in areas of high density, occasionally have nests within a radius of 10 m.

Some habitats on the Continent also carry dense groups, with a maximum of 93 breeding pairs/km^2 in Friesland in the Netherlands, and up to 80 breeding pairs/km^2 at Rinsumageest. P. Robien (1929) also recorded 12 breeding pairs in 15 ha of inland marsh in West Germany. Density is much lower on pasture and moorland, as in Britain; sometimes 2–3 breeding pairs/km^2; and 0.5–1.0 breeding pairs/km^2 on sand dunes in the Netherlands (van der Ploeg 1976). In Schleswig-Holstein large flats may carry only 0.2–2.0 breeding pairs/km^2; and in many coastal hinterlands and river marshes density is as low as 0.1 breeding pairs/km^2 (Glutz 1977). In 1959, 90 pairs nested on 18 ha in the Wangerooge Sea Bird Reserve. Average breeding density was then

5 breeding pairs/ha, with a peak of 10–12 breeding pairs/ha. These birds nested about 1 km from their feeding grounds on mudflats and were well away from cattle and nest predators (Grosskopf 1959).

SEXUAL MATURITY AND PAIR FIDELITY

Twenty-seven per cent of breeding redshanks caught on the Ribble marshes in 1984 proved to be first-year birds. Five chicks, which had hatched before mid June in 1983 returned to breed in 1984. Patrick suggests, however, that chicks hatched in late June and July may not be sufficiently mature to breed in the following season.

By 1984 five marked pairs had been together for four years, two of them consecutively. Three pairs had been trapped together over five years, though not consecutively. Others, on the contrary, had been caught with 4–5 different partners. Divorces have been recorded within and outwith the same season. At Wangerooge, 38 pairs were known to retain their pairings for two or more years.

NEST, EGG AND CLUTCH

In short grass habitats redshanks delay laying until the grass grows sufficiently high to give cover. They also sometimes nest between small stones or in marram grass on sand dunes. Nests are placed on dry as well as on moist ground. S. Haftorn (1971) recorded that eight nests ranged from 8–12 cm in diameter (mean 10.5 cm) and 3–7 cm in depth (mean 6 cm).

The hens sometimes lay their first egg before the scoop is fully formed and then add material during egg laying and incubation; lining largely consists of grasses from the surrounding vegetation. Many redshanks weave a kind of canopy above the eggs,

possibly an adaptation to prevent flying predators from spotting them. Patrick suggests that this canopy, which is sometimes prepared before the eggs are laid, also helps to prevent the eggs being washed away by high tides.

In Spey Valley, at an altitude of over 300 m, the redshanks seldom laid out before 7 May, thus roughly synchronising with the laying season of greenshanks. Walpole-Bond (1938) found that a few Sussex hens completed their clutch between 9–16 April, but that the earliest clutches were not usually laid before 20 April or a little later.

The laying season greatly varies in other locations. In southern England a few pairs nest at the end of March and early in April, but most do not complete their clutches before 20 April. Arthur Whitaker recorded 13 clutches in Yorks-Derby, with a mean of 5 May for full clutches. Twenty-seven clutches in the Norfolk and Suffolk breckland had an average clutch date of 1 May; and ten clutches from Scotland ranged from 24 April–17 May (mean 2 May).

On the Ribble, where nesting is spread out from mid April until late June, the two earliest clutches found in 1983 were completed between 18–19 April; and the latest between 25–26 June. In 1984, a slightly later season, one pair completed their clutch between 17–18 April, a full week ahead of the rest. A bird found with very small chicks in late July must have laid out between 22–23 June. One redshank, ringed as a chick on 17 June 1983, was caught sitting on a nest on 2 May when only $10\frac{1}{2}$ months old. As a rule, first or second year birds, nesting for the first time, lay later in the season than do older birds.

In southern Fenno-Scandia laying starts in early May and in the north in late May and early June. The laying season in the north thus roughly coincides with that of the dusky redshank. The earliest completed clutch in the Netherlands was recorded on 8 April 1921; in Westphalia on 29 April; and in Switzerland on 21 April. On the north German sea coast the earliest clutches were not usually laid until early May.

At Wangerooge, Grosskopf recorded the earliest date as 20 April and the mean for first eggs in his 13-year study was 29 April. An increase in temperature in the middle of the day stimulated egg-laying activity. For example, in 1961 the earliest eggs were laid 12–14 days earlier because April was unusually warm. First-year hens tended to lay their first eggs 2.5 days later than those that had nested previously. Firm pairing only slightly favoured early laying. In their first breeding year pairs tended to lay five days later than those in which one bird was breeding for the first time and the other was over four years old. The laying date was not affected when the cock was the older bird (Grosskopf 1959). The older mate in the pair determines the date on which the first egg is laid, probably because it has a greater knowledge of the qualities of the territory and feeding habitats. If a young and inexperienced bird is mated to an older bird it profits from its senior's knowledge and is then able to synchronise its breeding rhythm. This is not, however, a universal practice. We have found that some hen greenshanks, irrespective of partners, annually lay earlier or later than the mean for the population.

I was present when two Dorback hens were laying their first eggs, one in the afternoon and one in the evening. On both occasions the cock was nearby, once at a pool, and once perched on a fence post waiting for the hen to lay; each time the hen was on the nest for over an hour.

Patrick considers that on the Ribble marshes laying generally takes place in the early morning and in the evening. He found that freshly-laid eggs were sometimes covered by a white mucoid substance, making them very sticky to touch. Using this indication, he estimated that 10 eggs were laid between 06.00–noon; 16 between noon–18.00; and two between 18.00–24.00.

Grosskopf (1963) watched a hen lay her third egg. After she arrived and turned the eggs she sat for 25 minutes without moving and crouched low over them, then 'lifted herself up and stood for five minutes with neck stretched out, back and tail horizontal'. She then made egg-turning movements, lifted straws towards the nest, and brooded for 25 minutes. The cock stayed close to her while she was laying and flew off with her. Grosskopf (1959) carefully studied laying times at ten nests, each containing a single egg. There were two main patterns. (1) Second eggs were laid in the morning up to noon; third eggs at night; fourth and final eggs before or slightly after noon. (2) Second eggs were laid in the evening or at night; third eggs before noon; and fourth eggs at night or early in the morning.

At Kirr Island, Germany, A. Stiefel and H. Scheufler (1984) recorded that the first egg in one clutch was laid at 14.00. Second eggs in two clutches were deposited between 14.00–17.00 respectively; and the third egg in two others at 10.00 and between 22.00–08.00. The fourth egg in another clutch was also laid at *c* 18.00.

In Spey Valley we found that most redshanks laid their eggs on alternate days. On the Ribble two hens laid eggs at a minimum of 20–24, 33 at 24–28, 7 between 28–32, 1 between 32–36, and 3 at 40–44 hour intervals. Young hens breeding for the first time and hens aged 10–12 years were responsible for the longest intervals, thus suggesting that laying caused them some stress (P. S. Thompson).

J. F. Thomas (1942) met with a hen which laid her first two eggs within 50 hours and then had a lapse of 51 hours before laying her third. Grosskopf records a mean interval of 38 hours between eggs. The eggs in ten clutches which he specially studied were laid at intervals of 35–43 hours. The longest recorded interval on Kirr Island was 6 days between the second and third egg, the same hen apparently having laid all the eggs in the clutch (Stiefel and Scheufler 1984). It would be fascinating to discover why there are such great differences in egg laying intervals between the Lancashire hens and those breeding in apparently similar salt marshes in Germany.

The eggs are pear-shaped, ovate or long-ovate, and slightly glossed. Ground colour ranges from brownish clay, yellowish brown or reddish ochre-brown to bluish white or pale greenish white. Each egg is spotted, streaked and sometimes blotched or capped with dark reddish brown and has purple or lavender undermarkings. Markings are occasionally in the form of scrawls and hair lines. Immaculate white eggs are on record. Patrick met with a hen in 1984 which laid a long thin egg, 56.5 mm long, shaped rather like a fat cigar; this was the first egg in the second clutch of a very old bird. On the Ribble in 1983 some clutches of outstanding shape and colour pattern were noted. These were again found in 1984 before trapping confirmed that the same hen had laid them.

One hundred British eggs averaged 45.18 × 31.55 mm (Jourdain 1940). Patrick measured samples of all four eggs in Ribble clutches:

91 first eggs	averaged 45.26 × 31.86 mm
89 second eggs	averaged 45.11 × 32.07 mm
91 third eggs	averaged 45.23 × 32.06 mm
90 fourth eggs	averaged 45.34 × 31.59 mm

He found that the fourth egg in a clutch is often significantly the smallest and that the third and fourth eggs are likely to hatch out in that order.

Grosskopf records 366 eggs averaging 45.21 × 31.33 mm. South-west Finland is responsible for the smallest recorded mean size. R. A. Väisänen's series of 308 eggs averaged 44.45 × 30.56 mm.

Eighty fresh eggs from Wangerooge ranged from 19.0–26.0 gm (mean 22.3 gm). The heaviest of these thus overlap with the lightest greenshank eggs. In 20 examples, clutches weighed 58.3–73.0% of the hen's body weight (mean 66.4%) (Table 2). The weight of empty eggshells ranges from 0.84–1.35 gm, with a mean of 1.15 gm for 400 eggs (M. Schönwetter 1963).

Other waders have occasionally laid their eggs in redshanks' nests. These include lapwing, dunlin, black-tailed godwit, common snipe, marsh sandpiper and common sandpiper.

A redshank clutch usually consists of four, occasionally of three, and exceptionally of five eggs (Table 4). Clutches of six or more are usually the product of two hens; and those of one or two have possibly lost two or more eggs. Single eggs are seldom, if ever, incubated. While pairs were brooding the Ribble, single eggs – presumably laid by strange hens – were added to c/4 in 1983 and 1984. In 1984, however, all the chicks hatched from a full clutch of five eggs. In 1957 Grosskopf recorded a nest containing six and two others with seven eggs, but noted that the extra eggs had appeared after the 'legitimate pair' had been sitting for between one and two weeks.

If a clutch is robbed or destroyed some hens lay replacement clutches, the first egg of which is laid about six days later. Patrick found that replacements were completed between 11–17.5 days after clutch loss. Hens often lay one and probably sometimes two repeat clutches. Hens also lay replacement clutches after losing very young chicks. In 1984 at least eighteen hens laid repeat clutches 11.5–19.5 days after losing their broods.

Table 4 gives details of clutch-size in different locations.

INCUBATION

Experiences differ about the start of incubation. We have found that many redshanks sit intermittently on the second egg, occasionally steadily at night, and sometimes by day between the third and fourth eggs. H. Noll (1924) suggests that the birds waited 1–2 days before starting to incubate a complete clutch. Walpole-Bond (1938), on the contrary, considered that incubation often started on the first egg. Grosskopf (1959) found that casual brooding frequently began on the second egg and that there was some brooding by day at the three-eggs stage and regular brooding at night, but steady incubation was usually delayed until the clutch was complete.

Cocks and hens both incubate the full clutch by day. Grosskopf found that there was a daily average of half-a-dozen exchanges, with the cock usually sitting at night. The hen changed with the cock early in the morning; and then at about noon the cock starts to sit again and was relieved during the afternoon and evening. H. Sielmann (1943) recorded an even greater number of exchanges with sessions of only 2–3 hours.

The returning bird calls and yodels from a dyke, post, gate or tussock before flying and then walking to the nest; but we have not watched any set ritual or special cries. However, it is always exciting to watch the redshanks change over. The outgoing bird usually flies right away to its feeding ground.

Redshanks are usually light sitters. Arthur Whitaker recorded behaviour at 29 nests in different parts of Britain. At 23 of these the sitting bird rose at 150–250 m ahead of the searcher, five rose at less than 5 m, and one bird allowed itself to be lifted from the nest.

One pair on Dorback Moor, which was frequently disturbed, incubated for 25 days before the eggs hatched. On the Ribble, Patrick measured 31 incubation periods in 1983 which ranged from 23–31 days (mean for May, 26.85 days; for June/July, 25.5 days). In 1984, 87 periods ranged from 23.25–29.5 days (mean for May, 25.7; for June, 25.15; for July, 25.35 days). In 1984 two of Patrick's redshanks sat for 63 and 64 days respectively. From the latter a single chick hatched out after 26 days, but one adult sat on the remaining three eggs for a further 38 days before deserting them.

Grosskopf (1959) measured the incubation periods of 73 clutches which ranged from 21–29 days (mean 23.8 ± 1.4 days). On Kirr Island, 41 periods ranged from 22–36 days, with 27 clutches hatching out after 24–26 days. Nine clutches had incubation periods of 27–36 days, probably partly due to disturbance (Stiefel and Scheufler 1984).

HATCHING

The eggs are generally chipped for over 60 hours, occasionally up to 96 hours. On the Ribble marshes, which are intensively worked during the season, the mean for 99 nests was 89 hours, with extremes of 31–153 hours (P. S. Thompson).

	Marsh nests		*Field/enclosure nests*
	1983	*%*	
Hatched	78	39.39	5
Deserted due to trapping	19	9.59	
Deserted	4	2.02	
Flooded	71	35.86	
Predated	9	4.54	1
Addled nest failed	7	3.53	
Not completed	8	4.04	
Crushed	2	1.01	2
Unknown	–	–	1
	198		9
	1984	*%*	
Hatched	166	84.26	2
Deserted due to trapping	13	6.6	
Deserted	2	1.01	
Flooded	6	3.05	
Predated	1	0.51	1
Addled	1	0.51	
Not completed	8	4.06	
Crushed	–	–	4
	197		7
	1985	*%*	
Hatched	106	64.24	5
Flooded	26	15.76	
Deserted due to trapping	14	8.48	
Deserted	6	3.64	
Predated	1	0.61	3
Crushed	2	1.21	
Nest collapsed	5	3.03	4
Not completed	5	3.03	
	165		12

Fig. 6   Redshank. Comparison of hatching success on Ribble marshes 1983–85.

Chicks usually hatch fairly synchronously but they are sometimes brooded in the nest for up to 24 hours, particularly if hatched in the evening. In 1983, Patrick found that 22 broods stayed in the nest from 4 hours 45 minutes to 23 hours 35 minutes (mean 10 hours 57 minutes). In 1984, 53 broods stayed there from 3 hours 25 minutes to 22 hours 5 minutes (mean 10 hours 13 minutes). They thus tend to stay longer in the scoop than do young greenshanks. On 19 June 1983, a very hot day, one redshank on the Ribble marsh kept her newly-hatched chicks in the nest all day. Patrick suggests that extremes of heat or cold are probably equally harmful to the small young. The eggs appear to have remarkable vitality. Patrick twice replaced eggs which consecutive high tides had washed out of the nest for at least 10 hours. The redshanks then resumed brooding and successfully hatched them.

Sitting birds lift and carry away hatched eggshells which they drop in flight or occasionally in a pool. On the Ribble, shell fragments were found 20–100 m from nests. Some redshanks are, however, more lax than others in shell disposal. We have sometimes found large fragments and considerable debris in the scoop after the chicks have left. Patrick considers that birds whose clutches hatch during the night, or are in deep vegetation, may be less careful about eggshell removal.

Between 1952–59, on the Sylt Reserve, a random selection of redshanks produced 2.84–3.21 chicks per nest (*in* Glutz 1977). At Wangerooge, between 1955–58, 1,047 eggs from 271 nests produced 810 chicks (77.3%), an average of 2.99 chicks per nest; 87 eggs (8.3%) were lost, 15 (1.4%) when they contained small young; 135 (13%) were robbed, swamped in floods or destroyed in other ways.

Figure 6 shows an interesting comparison of hatching success on the Ribble marshes between 1983 and 1985.

In 1983 an average of 1.15 chicks hatched from 190 nests of known clutch size. In nests in which at least one egg hatched, 70% of the eggs laid hatched. In 1984, when there was minimal flooding, there was an average of 2.86 chicks from 186 nests of known clutch-size. Again, in nests in which at least one egg hatched, 86% of the eggs produced chicks.

YOUNG

The chicks have black crowns with black round their ears. Throat, breast and belly are cream to cream-buff coloured and the sides of neck and breast are tinged with yellow-brown. Their legs are pinky grey with soles flesh coloured. Bills are black to navy blue and irides dark blue.

Table 5 records weight of newly-hatched chicks. Grosskopf (1958) found that chicks weighed 14–16 gm at birth; at 20 days 54–60 gm; at 30 days 66–73 gm; and a flying youngster weighed 90 gm. On the Ribble, Patrick recorded that 417 newly-hatched chicks weighed 12–19.5 gm (mean 15.6 gm). One chick weighed 96 gm when 25.5 days old; one, which fluttered when 27 days old, weighed 87 gm; and another fluttering chick weighed 112 gm.

At first cock and hen accompany and periodically brood the chicks during the hours of daylight and regularly at night. On the Ribble marsh, however, probably because the chicks so often resort to deep ditches, Patrick never saw adults brooding chicks after they had left the nest.

Newly-hatched chicks are often led to wet ground with good cover, at distances varying from 150 m to over 2 km. These journeys tend to be longer in dry seasons. G. T. Rope watched redshanks carrying their chicks over formidable obstacles. Hale recorded a pair and brood moving 2 km in 24 hours. In this trek the chicks had to negotiate four drystone walls, two roads, two tall thick hedges, and a wide ditch with

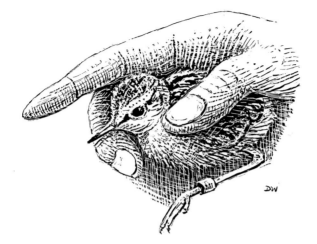

a rush-covered fence on the far side. The parents transported their chicks one at a time, holding them between their legs as they crossed over the wire.

Patrick met with a possible crèche. He first caught a single chick in a channel beside which both adults were in attendance. A further search revealed two more chicks in the same channel. All three chicks were of different ages and no other adults were present.

Waders almost always lose a high proportion of chicks between hatching and fledging. P. Gloe (*in* Glutz 1977), for example, estimated that 75 young redshanks flew from 30 clutches of eggs. Grosskopf (1960) reckoned that out of 286 eggs from 72 nests 86% hatched, but only about 50% of the chicks ultimately flew. On the Ribble, Patrick also found that chick losses were very high during the first couple of days; only twice were two well-grown chicks found with an adult. Perhaps the broods moved too fast for the weakest to keep up with their siblings.

Measurements of free-flying periods vary greatly. R. W. Robson recorded chicks flying weakly at 23 days and P. A. Rayfield noted one fluttering on its 26th day and flying fairly easily on the 28th. Grosskopf (1956–63) found the chicks started to fly between 27 and 35 days. Patrick recorded one chick fluttering strongly at 27 days; another fledged between 26.5–27 days. In captivity young redshanks first flew in 25 days (O. Heinroth 1927–28), and at 28 days (von Frisch 1959). At a later stage in the fledging process one parent – usually the hen – often deserts mate and brood.

DISTRACTION BEHAVIOUR

Redshanks have not apparently developed the elaborate batteries of distraction displays shown by so many other waders. However, when nesting in groups, they join with neighbours in combined scolding of intruders, sometimes dropping down close to a dog, or once near an otter (G. Warburg 1952). At other times a few birds make switch-back displays over the marsh and stand on tussocks, *chipping* and bobbing repeatedly.

VOICE

The noisy yelping cries of redshanks belong as much to the lowland marshes and saltings as do the mournful songs of lapwings to farmlands and the evening chorus of golden plovers to northern moors. They have a large range of cries, some of which are so subtle that they can only be properly studied from tape recordings.

(1)   Like golden plovers, they have two different forms of song.

(a)   A single sweet note *too-too*, which the cock usually gives continuously in his advertisement switch-back flight to call up a mate. These notes are also given in pairs during sex chases on the ground (Hale *in* Cramp and Simmons 1983).

(b)   The yodel, which we render *taweeo-taweeo*, is often uttered before and after the cock alights, particularly after an advertisement flight. Both sexes use it during fights and sexual incidents, with great insistence and first gathering speed before, and then 'running down' after, copulation, and before and after nest relief, possibly as an emotional releaser.

(2)   The alert cry is a long drawn out single whistling *too-oo-oo* given on the ground and in another variation in high alarm.

(3)   When alarmed, the contact call is *too-hoo-hoo*, a most familiar sound to anyone who has watched waders on the marshes.

(4)   The cock gives forms of *tyoo* or *tuu* to call up its mate, rendering the calls usually in pairs during ground chases.

(5)   The copulation rattle of the cock, *ee-ee-ee*, is rendered in quickly rising speed as the cock flutters onto the back of a hen. The hen gives a double note *too-too* (N. J. Collar in Cramp and Simmons 1983), and her copulation cries are high-pitched squeaking *tyee-tyee-tyees*.

(6)   While scrape making the cock utters 'quiet insistent calls of two to four syllables' in rising emphasis, the pitch rising on each syllable preceded by mechanical clicks *k-tu-tyu ... k-tu-tyu*. These important cries are audible at about 30 m (Hale and Ashcroft *in* Cramp and Simmons 1983).

(7)   Scolding notes, the insistent sharp *chip-chips*, rather thinner than those of green-shanks, are given on the ground, from stumps, fences or other perches, and continuously while the bird is flying. This is the stock note given by a bird anxious for its nest or while leading young. These cries are common to both sexes.

(8)   A series of *teu* anxiety cries is often associated with the *chip* calls and rendered in flight or from a perch.

(9)   The all-clear to chicks is a clucking *chup-chup-chup*; and the all-clear response call of a sitting bird is *chee-chee-chee* (Hale *in* Cramp and Simmons 1983).

(10)   To call up chicks the parents give low *too-tootoo* cries which are inaudible beyond 50 m (Hale *in* Cramp and Simmons 1983). These cries are not unlike the cock's call to the hen to join him at the scrape.

(11)   The brooding call of both sexes is a brief bubbling *turup-p-chup* (Hale *in* Cramp and Simmons 1983).

(12)   Conversational calls of adults to chicks include supressed *chip* and mate calls.

(13)   Feeding calls, *teoo-oo tee-oo* and high-pitched conversational *peee-peees* are also given when feeding and at the roost (Hale *in* Cramp and Simmons 1983).

(14)   Fighting calls, used by birds during scuffles, are high pitched *kiiuus*.

(15)   Cries of anxious young sound like thin high pitched *bsi-bsi-bsi*.

In 1985, Patrick tape-recorded many of the special calls used by parents and their chicks before and after the hatch. A comparison between the vocabularly of redshank and greenshank, with tape recordings and further sonagrams, would be most rewarding.

PREDATORS

Redshanks have many enemies. I sometimes found eggs, which carrion crows had sucked, lying on the Sussex marshes. Other likely predators there were kestrels and magpies, which nested in isolated clumps of trees, and sparrowhawks and foxes from nearby woods. Grazing cattle occasionally trampled on the nests of the marshland birds. Marsh and Montagu's harriers were other predators on the Norfolk Broads. In salt marshes in Easter Ross, herring, common and lesser black-backed gulls, hooded crows and jackdaws are all egg and chick robbers.

Bill Hale lists man, fox, stoat, weasel, lesser black-backed, common and black-headed gulls, carrion crow, magpie and little owl as possible predators in his early study areas in Lancashire. Patrick has found that crows, black-headed gulls and rats occasionally rob nests or destroy chicks. In 1983 a redshank, found dead less than 2 m from its nest, had probably been destroyed by a fox. However, he emphasises that very high tides which flood the marshes are far more dangerous to the redshanks than any predator.

D. A. Ratcliffe (1980) recorded that peregrines frquently took redshanks in the Scottish Highlands, southern Scotland, northern England and north Wales. E. L. Roberts (1947) watched a peregrine quarter a marsh, hovering like a kestrel, before dropping down to pick up a young redshank. On 7 April 1984 a ringed redshank was found on the Ribble marsh, probably freshly killed by a peregrine. Kestrels are known to attack injured redshanks and to take their chicks. In north Cornwall B. H. Ryves (1947) watched a sparrowhawk catch a redshank which was bathing and feeding.

Abroad, O. Uttendorfer (1952) found the remains of redshanks in sparrowhawk, buzzard and peregrine pellets. Grosskopf (1959) watched a sparrowhawk flying with a redshank in its talons; and he found bits and pieces of others which peregrines had killed and torn to pieces. Kestrels, dogs, cats and rats were also robbers. Grosskopf found that redshanks react to otters and to polecat mounts as if they were known enemies. On Kirr Island ravens, hooded crows and gulls as well as fox, pine marten, mink, hedgehogs and rats predated the redshank groups; cattle also trampled on nests (Stiefel and Scheufler 1984).

FOOD

J. D. Goss-Custard (1979) has specialised on the food and feeding behaviour of the redshank. On the Wash, in summer, it feeds mainly on crabs *Carcinus maenas* and shrimps *Crangon* spp. In spring they eat crabs, ragworms *Nereis diversicolor* and the small crustacean *Corophium volutator*; and in winter, when crabs and shrimps are not available, the diet changes to the small mollusc *Hydrobia ulvae*.

On the Ythan estuary feeding redshanks move at a speed of roughly 12 m per minute, finding their food by sight and taking it by means of quick pecks with their bill tips. Goss-Custard (1969) found an intriguing temperature effect on the redshanks' diet. At mud temperatures above 4°C *Corophium* was the main prey, below that the shrimps became less active, and redshanks turned to *Macoma* and *Nereis*. At night, when visual foraging is near-impossible, birds feed by touch and take mainly the molluscs *Hydrobia* and *Macoma*.

In April, insects are preferred, even by birds living on salt marshes. This food has a greater content of energy than that dervied from marine invertebrates (Hale *in* Cramp and Simmons 1983).

Glutz (1977) records a diet principally of animal matter with an insignificant amount of vegetable food in the form of leaves, grass, buds and seeds.

Inland they take mainly earwigs (Dermaptera), mayflies (Ephemeroptera), dragonflies (Odonata), larvae of *Agrion*, water-bugs (Heteroptera including *Gerris, Notonecta, Corixa*), beetles (Coleoptera, *e.g. Dytiscus, Silpha, Phosphuga, Aphodius, Agriotes, Chrysomela, Haliplus*), ants (Hymenoptera), flies (Diptera) including larvae of tipulids and Trichoptera. They also feed on land and freshwater molluscs (*e.g. Planorbis*), earthworms

Lumbricus and woodlice (Isopoda).

Redshanks periodically take a few small fishes measuring from 2.5–4.0 cm in length. Frogs and tadpoles are also occasionally recorded.

Eight stomachs of redshanks, collected in central Sweden contained beetles *Haliplus confinis* (up to 58 in one stomach), and the remains of adult *Haliplus*, Carabidae, Elateridae, *Corixa*, larvae of Trichoptera and Brachycenra and some gastropods (A. Norlin 1965).

On the sea coast and estuaries redshanks favour mudflats and pools between high and low tide. Philip Burton (1974) found that they also fed in fresh or brackish dykes and rough grassland on the Essex mudflats. On the Kent and Sussex marshes rough pasture was a favoured feeding habitat.

Redshanks feed at night as well as by day. On the Ribble, M. E. Greenhalgh (1975) discovered that they took only half the amount of food at night and that they preyed more on *Hydrobia*, possibly because *Corophia* were more difficult to find in their burrows in the dark.

R. W. J. Smith found that redshanks occasionally alight on open water to feed on hatches of emerging insects. In April they tend to seek pasture and salt marshes where a smaller quantity of beetles and Diptera provides greater energy. Moving over the mudflats they catch small animals with quick pecks and jabs, and at other times by mowing movements and by shallow probes in the mud. Like many other waders, redshanks sometimes wash their food before swallowing it.

A comparison of the food of redshank and greenshank, on a common breeding ground, would probably lead to exciting discoveries. The redshanks possibly seek smaller prey, but tiny *Plateumaris* leaf beetles show up in the pellets of both species.

DISTRIBUTION AND NUMBERS

In the early 19th century large schemes of drainage greatly reduced the redshanks' breeding haunts in Britain; by 1842 they were almost restricted to counties bordering the North Sea. Thenceforward, they spread west and south-west in England, in Wales, and in southern Scotland, until about 1940 when a series of hard winters probably checked their advance. In Ireland, in historic times, redshanks have always appeared to be rather scarce and local, with few pairs nesting on coastal marshes, and the main breeding groups centred around the lakes of Connacht in Eire and Lough Neagh in the Six Counties. Intensive agriculture and reclamation of wetlands in Britain have led to the loss of many small inland habitats; but large numbers still breed, particularly on the salt marshes of north and north-west England and in the machairs of the Outer Hebrides.

The Breeding Atlas records confirmed breeding in 1,265, probable in 333, and possible in a further 327 10 km squares. This led to an estimated of 38,000–48,000 breeding pairs for Britain and Ireland (Sharrock 1976).

Hale and his students have estimated that in recent years about 400 pairs breed annually in their study area on the Ribble marshes. Drainage has greatly reduced redshank numbers in many inland haunts, particularly in southern England. Redshanks are scarce in Devon, absent from Cornwall, and from Pembroke in Wales.

In April–July 1983 a survey by the Wader Study group and the Nature Conservancy Council estimated that 1,974 pairs bred on 131 km^2 of South Uist, Benbecula and North Uist. This compares with a total of 2,014 pairs on the entire damp grasslands of England and Wales in 1982 (G. H. Green 1984).

J. Kålås and I. Byrkjedal (1981) estimated that there is a total breeding strength of 29,000 pairs in Norway – 13,000 in the north and 16,000 in the south of the country.

In Sweden, S. Ulfstrand and G. Högstedt (1976) reckon about 20,000 breeding pairs. In recent years redshanks have increased on the Finnish mainland, where numbers now probably considerably exceed Merikallio's figure of 2,000 pairs calculated in 1958. They have greatly increased in Iceland, but are still scarce in the Faroes.

During this century drainage and tilling have led to a decrease in Denmark, where I. Clausager (*in* Cramp and Simmons 1983) indicates a breeding strength of between 2,000–4,000 pairs.

R. M. Teixeira (1979) considered that 20,000 pairs nested in the Netherlands in 1978–79, but there has been a considerable drop in numbers since then. They are probably decreasng in Belgium, where L. Lippens and H. Wille (1972) estimate that there were less than 200 breeding pairs. The same two ornithologists also suggest a total of only five pairs for Luxemburg. R. Mahéo (1983) calculates that 490–760 pairs breed in France, mainly on the west coast. The strength of the West German population lies between 18,000–19,000 pairs; but, as in Britain, inland groups tend to fluctuate or decrease. Changes in habitats are again the likely cause. Fewer redshanks now breed inland in East German habitats. G. Klafs and J. Stübs (1977) estimated that between 470–480 pairs were nesting in Mecklenberg in the early 1970s.

Redshanks are scarce in Poland and decreasing in lower Silesia, but have increased around the Mazurian Lakes (L. Tomialojc 1976). They are also decreasing in Czechoslovakia where Glutz (1977) estimated that there are only 50–100 pairs. The main breeding groups in Austria are concentrated around the Neusiedler See where there are about 150 breeding pairs; but only 9–15 pairs in other Austrian habitats. Redshanks are scarce in Hungary. N. Spagnesi reports a breeding strength of only 1,000 pairs in Italy. They are also decreasing in Greece. Alfredo Noval estimated that 3,000–4,000 pairs nest in Spain. Redshanks are common in Turkey and up to 250 pairs nest in Tunisia. They are numerous in many parts of the Soviet Union, where groups of about 6,000 pairs nest in Estonia SSR.

In their many different haunts, at home and abroad, on marsh, saltings and heath, redshanks belong to most exciting bird communities. No wonder that so many keen wader watchers have been dedicated to their study.

RINGED PLOVER

A burly little wader with a large squarish head, the ringed plover is constantly on the move, making short flights, running in fits and starts, and bending forward to pick up food. It has a conspicuous broad black pectoral band, a white breast and forehead, and distinctive white bars on its wings; back and crown are light brown, underparts white, tail brown with white tips and sides and a black subterminal band. It has an orange bill with a black tip and its legs are usually orange in adults and dull yellow in juveniles; the wing bars show up well in flight. Slightly larger than little ringed plovers, they lack the yellow orbital ring and the flesh-pink legs. Ringed plovers call almost continuously, soft musical *klooees* which often alert you to the running bird.

Mainly birds of the sea shore and marine islands, ringed plovers nest on shingle banks, marram grass in dunes and sandhills, on stony ridges, and bare farmlands close to sea walls. Smaller groups nest inland on river shingle up to about 350 m ASL on the Scottish mainland. They nest freely in the machair of the Outer Hebrides and on sandy and flinty warrens in East Anglia. On the Continent, Glutz (1975) records them nesting in fields of rape, potatoes and cereals, in gravel pits and moorland, and beside fish farms and in lignite excavations. Some pairs nest in colonies of sandwich, arctic and common terns, probably gaining warning and protection from their neighbours' vigilance and aggression. In East Greenland, ringed plovers choose stony ground on the coast and beside rivers as well as inland hills.

There are two races of ringed plovers; the nominate, *hiaticula*, which nests in northwest Europe from south Scandinavia, south to France, west to Ireland, and in Iceland, Spitsbergen, Greenland, and the east coast of Ellesmere and Baffin Islands in North America. The smaller and darker race, *tundrae*, is confined to coasts and tundras in Lapland and USSR.

In my youth I watched ringed plovers breeding on the coasts of Sussex, Kent, Norfolk and Co. Down, and on the breckland of East Anglia which they shared with stone curlews. But most of my later work was carried out along rivers and beside lochs in Spey Valley. Recently I have spent many happy days watching their behaviour on the Shin marshes in Sutherland.

On the shingle beside the Dorback burn and around Loch Morlich the ringed plovers usually returned singly, but occasionally in pairs. Soon after arrival the cocks established territories from which they chased away intruders by means of quick 'hunched runs', bending forward horizontally to the ground and suddenly spreading their tails just

TEMMINCK'S STINT approaching nest and eggs in a northern marsh. Olavi Hildén discovered that these stints have evolved a remarkable breeding system. (Photo: A. Y. Kondratyev).

WOOD SANDPIPER at an unusual nest site, in a tree. Usually, this wader nests on the ground. (Photo: J. B. & S. Bottomley).

WOODCOCK, well camouflaged, at the foot of a conifer. We are slowly learning the secrets of a most mysterious bird. (Photo: D. A. Ratcliffe).

DOTTEREL cock, a gem of a bird, about to brood on an English fell. In 1986, breeding numbers were exceptionally high in Britain. (Photo: D. A. Ratcliffe).

before reaching their rivals. The black and white frontal and tail patterns are used in different postures to express varied emotional intensities. From time to time the cock, and later the hen, lands with wings uplifted or he raises them immediately after alighting. Attacking birds raise their wings as they drive away trespassers. Like the little ringed plover, the cock often flies in circles and figures-of-eight. His wings are now held stiffly and beaten through a small arc and the bird tilts from side to side, all the time giving its song, a repeated *teeleea-teeleea*. In these song dances a cock often ranges outside his territory and is sometimes joined by others, all then participating in these exciting flights. This song dance is a dispersion mechanism and one performed before and after pair bonding, but it does not prevent the intrusion of neighbours and strangers.

Besides attacking intruders on the ground, cocks and hens fly at rivals and predators. On 6 June 1984, for example, I watched a cock, whose hen had just laid her first egg, fly about 50 m and then momentarily raise his wings before turning away a flying common gull. On the Continent these pugnacious little birds often attack little ringed plovers and Kentish plovers; and are particularly aggressive during the egg laying and hatching phases, when the black-and-white frontal patterns of pied wagtails seem to excite them. George Edwards, Eric Hosking and Stuart Smith (1947) also watched ringed plovers attacking wheatears and mistle thrushes; and Ken Simmons watched one directing a 'hunched crouch display' at shelducks.

TERRITORY

These little plovers are strong territorialists. In some places they apparently never stray outside the boundaries of defended living space throughout the breeding season (H. Laven 1940). Others maintain separate feeding territories in which the off-duty birds spend much time during incubation. In inland Scottish haunts, however, we have found well-dispersed pairs holding nesting territories and also often feeding on unoccupied neutral ground up to 300 m from the nest. Sometimes, as on 4 June 1936, I have watched a cock displaying sexually to an off-duty hen which fed on his territory for about 45 minutes. The incident ended when the hen made a series of quick runs before exchanging with her own mate which was sitting on a nest about 300 m away. In the groups that we have watched, pairs apparently do not establish fixed 'brood territories', but both cocks and hens drive away any others which approach their chicks.

The size of a territory, and its use for feeding, varies greatly. In a north-east Greenland group, for example, M. W. Pienkowski (1984) found that the pairs were widely dispersed, with an average of 30 ha for each defended territory; but an off-duty bird often fed on neutral ground well away from the nest, sometimes at a distance of 3 km. The groups he studied in Northumberland, on the other hand, had different patterns; with small condensed territories of 0.3 ha to 10+ ha on which the birds found most of their food during incubation. Ringed plovers thus adapt their territorial patterns to meet local needs.

PAIRING AND COURTSHIP

Ringed plovers have evolved elaborate courtship and sexual attitudes and postures. Before coupling, the cock runs towards the hen with his tail depressed and body horizontal. The hen then moves in front, with her tail fanned and erected and breast lowered and shows her cloaca; she may now call softly. The cock then moves behind her and both temporarily stay put. Later the sexual rhythms of the two birds are synchronised during the nest dance. At first the cock dips down on his breast, as if about to sit

on eggs. He then raises his closed wing tips almost vertically and fans his tail and scratches with his feet (J. K. Stanford 1927). Sometimes, when the cock jumps onto her back and makes cloacal contact, the hen abruptly jerks forward and topples him. He then snatches at the feathers in her crown, neck or mantle, which he continues to hold when he has dismounted. This possibly prolongs cloacal contact (Laven 1940). Afterwards the pair feed or 'false feed' nearby. In a later phase the hen also works in the scoop and the cock performs the actions of nest relief; she stands up and he creeps under her slightly expanded tail into the hollow. When the hen repeats this ploy, she does not stand so long over her mate and does not straighten her legs as much as he does; both utter soft *meet-meet* calls (Laven 1940). This attractive behaviour is not unlike that of a pair of nest dancing dotterel.

Copulation is not confined to nest dancing. Sometimes a cock makes a characteristic swerving and tilting butterfly song dance before landing and slowly approaching the

hen in a stiff upright posture, with the black upper neck ring upright and prominent. He then marks time with grotesquely high steps; but in the earlier phases of sexual passion the hen sometimes moves and flies away before he takes her.

DISPERSION AND BREEDING DENSITY

Dispersion varies greatly in different districts. The Dorback groups consisted of

3–5 pairs, spread over roughly 1,600 m of river shingle, with nests placed 300–500 m apart. At Loch Morlich up to four pairs had nests on shingle close to the loch; these were often dispersed less than 300 m apart, partly through lack of suitable nesting habitats. The Loch Shin haunts in Sutherland consist of stony beaches and inlets, each with a couple of pairs, and nests are about 250 m apart; but much unoccupied neutral ground intervenes between the groups.

In the Netherlands, J. Walters (1983) recorded many nests separated by about 100 m. K. Greve (1969) estimated a breeding density of 0.3 pairs/60 ha on the North Sea island of Neuwerk in 1937–39. There were 10–16 pairs/10 km² on a narrow tongue of land on Kurskaja Kosa (Laven 1940). R. Berndt (1970) recorded 42 pairs in 78 km, with a maximum density of 1.5 pairs/km along 4 km of coast, between Olpenitz and Schönhagen on the east coast of Schleswig-Holstein. There was also a local concentration of 9–15 pairs/15 ha, with a minimum distance of 5 m between two nests, on the East Friesian coastland (J. Seitz *in* Glutz 1975). C. Ferry (1955) met with strong local groups near Lytiry in Britanny, with pairs dispersed about 60–70 m apart on 2 km length of sea coast.

There are similar differences in the density and dispersion of *tundrae* groups. S. Uspenski (1965) was familiar with a population on the banks of the Jugor Peninsula with nests sited about 50 m apart. Glutz (1975) records 5 pairs/km² on the north east bank of the White Sea.

NEST, EGG AND CLUTCH

A ringed plover's nest is a shallow scrape, usually scratched out of sand, gravel, or short vegetation. The eggs are often open to the sky but are occasionally placed among growing plants. Less usual nest sites include rough stony roads or tracks and the sawdust of old mills; in flint-strewn warrens in East Anglia nests often have rabbits' dung and splinters of flint in the lining. Scoops are occasionally lined with a substantial mass of material. H. Lynes recorded one containing 2,000 small stones which weighed 198 gm. Lining material is usually carried in from around the nest or from a short distance away. Walters (*in* Glutz 1975) gives 10.3 × 10.8 cm as the average diameter of 34 nests in the Netherlands.

Eggs have been recorded in southern England in early March; but the peak laying season there usually starts at the end of April. We have found that in the Scottish Highlands it is fully 10 days later. Omitting known replacements, Whitaker's dates for 31 clutches ranged from 25 April–12 July (mean 15 May).

The peak in central Europe is in the first half of May; in southern Finland, at 62°N about mid May and between 65°–66°N in early June; in south Norway it is late May and on the coast of central Norway from May to early June; in Iceland from the end of April to the end of May; and in Greenland and Spitsbergen seldom before mid June (Glutz 1975). The first eggs in seven nests at Mestrevig, north-east Greenland, were adjudged to have been laid between 22 June–1 July (Pienkowski 1984).

The latest hatch recorded in the Netherlands took place on 22 August 1916; and in Suffolk, Stanford (1927) watched a young ringed plover which was still unable to fly on 10 October.

On the afternoon of 6 June 1984, the hen, which was about to lay her first egg, visited the nest several times within the hour; and before laying she half stood over the nest, bobbing her head nervously all the time. Just before a ringed plover lays, both birds sometimes take part in a nest dance, with the hen entering the scoop under the tail of her mate.

The eggs are rather squat and usually have a greyish white or very light buff ground colour; scarcer varieties range from blue-grey to reddish yellow. Normal eggs are spotted with almost black-brown and dark grey. In Norfolk, in 1936 and 1937, Whitaker met with an unusual type which had several large nearly black blotches but was otherwise unmarked. Spotless white and greyish eggs are also on record.

One hundred British eggs averaged 35.76 × 25.95 mm (Jourdain 1940); and 194 Netherlands eggs averaged 34.86 × 25.39 mm (Walters *in* Glutz 1975). Eighty-five eggs from southern Norway were slightly smaller with a mean of 34.3 × 25.1 mm.

Walters weighed 104 freshly-laid eggs which varied from 9.8–13.6 gm (mean 11.5 gm). The weight of 34 hens, breeding in the Netherlands, ranged from 55.4–74.5 gm (mean 64.8 gm). A normal clutch of four eggs is thus approximately 70.0% of the hen's body weight (Table 2). M. Schönwetter (1952) weighed 200 blown eggshells which averaged 0.65 gm.

A clutch normally consists of four, occasionally three, and exceptionally of five eggs. In his analysis of 301 British clutches, Prater (1974) noted that 2% contained 2, 36% 3, 60% 4, and 1% 5 eggs (mean 3.79). Whitaker, who found nests as far apart as Yell in Shetland and the Isles of Scilly in Cornwall, recorded 10/3, 38/4 (mean 3.77). At Lindisfarne, Northumberland, Pienkowski (1984) recorded 1/2, 13/3, 72/4, 1/5 (mean 3.84) (Table 4).

Prater (1974) recorded the intervals between 196 eggs. The mean between first and second averaged 1.74 days; between second and third 1.66; and between third and fourth 1.99 days. At Lindisfarne, intervals between 17 eggs ranged from 1–3 days, with an average of *c* 1.5 days (Pienkowski 1984).

A clutch is usually completed in six, but occasionally in 4–7 days.

INCUBATION

The cock intermittently broods an incomplete clutch while the hen is feeding-up before egg laying. He also broods incomplete clutches for short spells during heavy storms of rain or hail, and at night. Steady incubation starts between the penultimate and final egg and both birds incubate. The ringed plovers tend to sit for longer spells in bad weather, particularly in heavy rainstorms.

At five nests in Norfolk, P. J. Oliver (1983) recorded nine brooding sessions by cocks averaging 19 minutes, and seven by hens averaging 55 minutes. The eggs were uncovered 10% of the time. Pienkowski (1984) found that incubation duties were fairly evenly shared by the two partners. In Greenland brooding spells ranged from 58–209 minutes for cocks and 51–178 minutes for hens; and in Northumberland cocks sat for 31–112 minutes and hens for 24–174 minutes. O. Koehler and A. Zagarus (1937) recorded that nest relief was irregular, with brooding stints ranging from 9 minutes to 6 hours 35 minutes. N. A. Rubinshtein recorded that *tundrae* sat for spells varying from 5 minutes to 5 hours 20 minutes.

Exchanges are of varied forms. We have watched a cock leave the eggs and fly or run away just before the hen arrives. At other nests the hen stood up, fanning her tail under which the cock slipped onto the eggs. Exceptionally the incoming bird has to peck, push or jostle its mate from the eggs. From time to time the nest is left unattended.

Incubation periods have varied from 21–28 days (mean 23–24 days). Prater (1974) timed 90 periods in Britain; 8% lasted 21 days; 11% 22 days; 23% 23 days; 18% 24 days; 19% 25 days; 10% 26 days; 10% 27 days; and 1% 28 days (mean 24.0 days). One incubation period in the Dorback group lasted 25–26 days. Pienkowski (1984) timed one incubation period at 25–26 days in Greenland; nine at Lindisfarne ranged from 23–35 days (mean 24.8 days). The abnormal period 35 days referred to the fourth replacement clutch of a Northumberland hen. The cock took no part in brooding and this led to a protracted and asynchronous hatch and to the early death of the brood.

Either bird rolls back an egg that has been dislodged from the scoop or placed outside it experimentally, just as do lapwings, oystercatchers, greenshanks and probably most other waders.

HATCHING

Ringed plovers' eggs are incubated for 19–24 days before the first chip appears; two days later the chicks are heard squeaking in the eggs. I watched the hatch in Spey Valley during a sleet storm when the cock and hen frequently exchanged on the eggs; and I could hear the hen conversing with the emerging chicks by means of continuous soft cries (Nethersole-Thompson 1951). The intervals between the hatching of the first and last chick in a clutch varies from 5–25 (max 44) hours (Laven 1940). In Greenland and Northumberland, Pienkowski (1984b) found that there was often a hatching spread of about half-a-day.

In *tundrae* Rubinshtein (1968) also recorded four chipping periods of 2.5–4.0 days before the chicks emerged. There were intervals of 14–18 hours between the first and last chicks in a clutch.

The sitting ringed plover usually carries away large fragments of eggshell soon after the chick has emerged. Occasionally, however, the wind blows them away. Only tiny pieces of shell remain in the nest after the parents have herded away their chicks. So minute are these fragments that the sitting birds have probably deliberately broken them up.

In west European haunts ringed plovers tend to have a modest hatching success. Between 1965–71 only 13% of the eggs laid in East Anglian study groups produced chicks. Other British haunts had an average hatching success of 40%, with 46% in the Outer Hebrides (Prater 1974). In Northumberland hatching success ranged from 1.4% to 43% (Pienkowski 1984). Laven (1940) found that only 35.9% of 284 eggs hatched in his study grounds. Over a period of six years, H. Bub (1962) recorded that 54.1% of 85 eggs hatched and Walters (*in* Glutz 1975) noted that 56% of 173 eggs produced chicks near Amsterdam. At Hiddensee, East Germany, only 17.9% of 28 eggs hatched out. In two studies in the Arctic, a far higher proportion of eggs hatched out; 78% in north-east Greenland and 85% on Baffin Island (Pienkowski 1984).

The proportion of chicks surviving from hatching to fledging also varies considerably. Pienkowski recorded 40–60% in Northumberland; and in three broods in north-east Greenland, initially with 12 chicks, six young (50%) flew.

YOUNG

Chicks have white foreheads, greyish buff crowns, and upper parts speckled with cinnamon-buff and black-brown. 'A narrow black line from the base of the bill through the eye continues as a black band on the nape above the white hind neck' (Cramp and Simmons 1983). They have black bills, purplish brown feet with olive yellow soles, and dark brown irides.

These lovely little plovers are capable of leaving the nest soon after they are dry, but in stormy weather the parents periodically continue to brood them in and outside the scoop. In three Greenland families the older chicks left the scrape before their younger siblings, thus causing the brood to divide into two or three groups. Both cock and hen fairly equally brood the chicks. In parts of Northumberland the parents and broods tended to stay in their territories; but, in Greenland, where ringed plovers are single brooded, territories were abandoned after hatching (Pienkowski 1984b).

Young ringed plovers fly in about 20–24 days, when weighing about 55–60 gm, and become independent soon afterwards. At least 59% of the young fledged in Northumberland survived to about 1-year old; but minimum survival from 1–2 years was only 57%. Most of these survivors returned to their breeding grounds and attempted to breed in their second calendar year (Pienkowski 1984b).

Double brooding

Ringed plovers are double brooded in southern England, France, Netherlands and West Germany; but at Oldeeog, on the Baltic, H. Rittinghaus (1975) never recorded a genuine second brood in 28 years experience. In Germany, Bub (1962) recorded intervals between two broods of 40, 46 and 60 days. O. Koehler and A. Zagarus (1937) reported that a particular pair produced a brood and three replacement clutches; and Laven (1940) met with a hen which laid five clutches in the same season, without producing a single chick.

In Greenland ringed plovers were single brooded and made only one attempt at breeding; but in Northumberland some hens produced five (mean 2.6) clutches in the year. The intervals between the first replacement and the loss of a clutch varies from 5–20 days. Intervals tend to be longer when the bird is replacing hard-set eggs (Pienkowski 1984). *Tundrae* is usually single-brooded, seldom replacing a lost clutch (V. V. Bianki 1967).

DISTRACTION BEHAVIOUR

Ringed plovers have many forms of distraction behaviour and displays.

(1)   Fast running, occasionally allowing one wing to droop, is usually employed in low intensity situations.

(2)   Both wings are outstretched and the tail fully spread but depressed.

(3)   Tail depressed and fanned, wings slightly open, to show off the white rump and flanks (K. Williamson 1947).

(4)   Tail lifted to display the vent, flanks and undertail coverts (Williamson 1947).

(5)   'Exhausted bird display', lying with head forward, spread tail and open wings.

(6)   Near wing raised regularly as if the bird is lying on its side.

(7)   Fast running with fanned tail, white outer tail feathers and wings held half open, with little or no flicking; or almost fully extended, and flicking then most pronounced (Williamson 1947).

(8)   'False scrape making' and 'false brooding', when the bird appears to be making scoops or sometimes settles down and arranges imaginary eggs.

In addition to these more formal displays, ringed plovers act as 'busy birds' and frequently 'false feed'. Distraction flights, with partly spread depressed tails, are not elaborate and not continued for long distances.

VOICE

Ringed plovers have a considerable range of rather soft cries. Laven (1940) and Walters (*in* Cramp and Simmons 1983) have analysed their vocabulary.

(1)   Liquid *poo-lee-poo-lees* indicate contact or slight alarm, often heard before seeing the bird running over the shingle.

(2)   A lower-pitched but more emphatic series of *kweeks* indicates a state of greater

alarm or emotional intensity. These cries are given singly or sometimes in sequence.

(3) Threat calls, emphatic *deel-leea deel-leea kee-lee*, are 'used mainly during horizontal crouch displays or occasionally given during threat flights at intruders or interspersed among flight song calls' (Walters 1983).

(4) A cock's flight song is a rhythmic *deela-deela* of '24–30 units per 10 seconds' (Walters 1983).

(5) The pair's contact cry is a soft *pjoop-tjoop*.

(6) Nest dancing starts with rhythmical *pju-pju-pjus* and then merges into a series of sharper *pi-pi-pi-pi-pi-pis* (Walters 1983).

(7) A loud croaking call is used when the bird is standing still during a lure display.

(8) I have heard the sitting bird give soft *kee-kee* cries to chicks squeaking in the eggs.

(9) Parents call up the chicks with soft *pu-pus*, perhaps like the *kees* described in (8).

PREDATORS

Carrion crows, sometimes rooks in England, hooded crows, and often common gulls in Scotland, are all egg robbers. Merlins are known to prey on ringed plovers on migration and are present in some inland breeding grounds. Peregrines at least occasionally take ringed plovers. In his list for 1974–75, Derek Ratcliffe (1980) recorded the remains of three in the southern Uplands; there was one in Lakeland in 1961–62 and also one in Snowdonia between 1950–57. Sparrowhawks, goshawks, harriers, as well as foxes, dogs and stoats are other likely enemies of the ringed plover in their European breeding haunts.

In Greenland, Pienkowski (1984) noted that arctic fox, stoat, ermine, gyr falcon, long-tailed skua, glaucous gull and raven were all on the ground but were not proven predators. In Northumberland he recorded that black-headed gulls sometimes took swimming chicks; carrion crows were other possible predators, but were not seen to attack the young ringed plovers. Short-eared owls, foxes and brown rats were known to be active in these habitats. Most predation apparently took place at night.

FOOD

Ringed plovers feed in typical plover fashion, making short runs, frequent stops and pecks. From time to time they also use foot pattering movements to activate small items of prey. The Spey Valley and Shin river and loch groups often appear to feed largely on small Diptera, beetles and their larvae; but no precise study has yet been attempted here.

The Northumberland breeding birds feed mainly on polychaete worms *Notamastus latericeus* and small crustacea. The chicks took sandhoppers *Talitrus saltator* from their fifth day, along with small flies, particularly *Coelopa*. They also fed on intertidal invertebrates – thin red worms (*Arenicola*), and occasionally snails *Hydrobia*. Later, adults and chicks took many small Diptera, Nematocera – midges, gnats and mosquitoes – and often spiders (Araneae) and probably large Lepidoptera larvae. In Greenland the adults and chicks fed mainly on small Diptera and their larvae.

Outwith their breeding grounds, various Diptera, beetles (Coleoptera), polychaete worms *Nereis*, periwinkles *Littorina* and amphipods *Corophium* are all recorded in Western Europe. Food on coastal habitats includes molluscs *Macoma* and *Hydrobia*, *Talitrus* and opossum shrimps (Mysidacea) and small oligochaetes (Dementiev and Gladkov 1951). The chicks appear to be entirely self-feeding, but tend to take smaller items of the same food as their parents.

DISTRIBUTION AND NUMBERS

The British Isles and Ireland form the south-westerly fringes of the ringed plover's breeding range. Here they nest from Shetland in the north to the Isles of Scilly in the south-west. Ninety per cent of the ringed plover population in England and Wales breeds on the sea coast, but they are now nesting in increasing numbers on river and lake shingle, particularly in northern England and in Scotland. They are, however, scarce in Devon and Cornwall in England, Pembroke in Wales, and Cork in the Republic of Ireland. In the early years of the century about 400 pairs nested in the Suffolk and Norfolk brecklands, but extensive afforestation and changes in farming methods have reduced these exciting groups to a few pairs. The Outer Hebrides are the head-quarters of ringed plovers in Britain, with particularly high density groups nesting in the machair of North and South Uist. There are also high numbers in Shetland, Orkney and the coastlands of Norfolk (J. T. R. Sharrock 1976).

The Breeding Atlas confirmed ringed plovers as breeders in 916, probable in 1,952, and possible in 1,961 10 km squares. Numbers fluctuate from year to year and drop markedly after severe winters such as that of 1962–63. In a census carried out in 1973–74, Prater (1976) estimated that 1,878 pairs were breeding in England, 186 in Wales, 75 on the Isle of Man, 93 in the Six Counties of Northern Ireland, and possibly 3,565 in Scotland, a total of about 5,800 pairs. Further research in 1983–84 suggests, however, that the Scottish and particularly the Outer Isles population has been considerably underestimated. As many as 6,000 pairs probably breed in Scotland and the Islands (Thom 1986). C. Hutchinson (1979) reckoned that there were over 2,000 pairs in the Republic of Ireland.

There are many healthy populations in Europe. J. Kålås and I. Byrkjedal (1981) estimated that 300–600 pairs were nesting in Spitsbergen in 1979. Iceland harbours fair numbers but there is no precise estimate of breeding strength. Ken Williamson (1970) reported ringed plovers breeding widely in the Faroes; and D. Bloch (1983) recorded six pairs on two islands there. S. Ulfstrand and G. Högstedt (1976) suggest a total breeding population of *c* 20,000 pairs for Sweden while Kålås and Byrkjedal (1981) estimate that about 12,500 pairs breed in Norway. There has been no updated census in Finland since E. Merikallio (1958) suggested a breeding population of 5,700 pairs. Olavi Hildén, however, considers that numbers have dropped considerably on the coastlands.

J.-Y. Monnat (1980) estimated that 50–60 pairs nested in Britanny in 1972; and R. M. Teixeira (1979) records that 400–600 pairs were breeding in the Netherlands and that numbers are increasing. There have been many fluctuations in West Germany, but more pairs now nest than in the 1930s, with 975–1,120 breeding pairs in Schleswig-Holstein and 150–300 pairs in lower Saxony in 1980. Since 1940 numbers have dropped in East Germany; but in 1972–73 120 pairs bred along the Baltic coastlands. At least 260–285 pairs nested in Poland in 1973 (Glutz 1975); and in 1966 S. Onno estimated that about 500 pairs bred in Estonia SSR.

In Sutherland we live in ringed plover country. This is not perhaps its land of plenty like the machair of the Uists, but there are enough pairs to enjoy. We love to watch their exciting displays and thrilling butterfly flights and to listen to these soft liquid calls which bring back so many happy memories. We look forward to many more days with these pugnacious little waders. Always the hope of discovery makes the heart beat faster!

8:   The forest marsh

The huge forest marshes of northern Europe and the muskegs of Canada have always excited the Wader Watchers. They read the notes and diaries of the pioneers – Wolley in Scandinavia and Finland, and Rowan and Randall in the greater yellowlegs country in Canada – and identify with them as they splash hopefully through the swamps and mires.

In Britain our few forest bogs are shrinking and disappearing as machines move in to scarify, drain and plant. As a young man, I used to watch and hunt for hobbies in the gentle valley bogs of Surrey heaths and the New Forest. I often watched that beautiful little falcon swerving and clipping after gorgeous dragonflies, momentarily dropping a claw and scarcely pausing as it flashed low over a reedy pond. Here, in bogs containing scattered clumps of pines and a few isolated tarns, single pairs of curlews and occasionally common snipe were the only waders.

When I went north I found that the forest bogs in the old Caledonian Forests were entirely different. I first worked in the cluster of deer forests – Abernethy, Glenmore, Rothiemurchus, Inshriach and Glenfeshie – which lay east of the Spey in the shadow of the Cairngorms. Here there were dips, patches and pockets of authentic forest bog. How I loved those wet morasses which had many broken trees, trunks, and branches often half-submerged in moist peat or brown slime. There were islands of tall pines and in the bog the trees were small and stunted, resembling saplings, which never grew high; many were mere 'Christmas trees'. On these bogs and the surrounding hillocks the vegetation was deer sedge, tufted cotton sedge, cross-leaved heath and ling, and in some places there was much sphagnum moss.

For me, the forest bogs held an almost magical fascination. I would lie up beside the trunk of a fallen tree or among dead grey branches to watch and listen for homing greenshanks. On still days you might hear the cock's song dance high up above the forest or perhaps watch the pair fly in to select their nest site. Later, in May, I waited for the change-over at the nest. The only other wader regularly breeding in these bogs was the common curlew; but common sandpipers nested on the edges and Temminck's stints occasionally laid their eggs close to a forest loch. In the 1930s the song dance and sharp calls of green sandpipers were almost familiar sounds; and in later years wood sandpipers nested in one of the forest bogs.

Outwith Spey Valley, there are still some small patches of squashy forest bog, but most are mere dips and pockets. In north Inverness, magnificent Glen Strathfarrar has patches of bog in the pinewoods where greenshanks nest and over which wood sandpipers have sung. Golden eagles have eyries in the pines and merlins nest on the flanks of rounded hills. In the Black Isle, in Easter Ross, there is perhaps the most remarkable forest bog in all Britain. Derek Ratcliffe considers that, with its old pines, mires and large ponds, it is more like a Scandinavian forest bog than any other that still survives in Britain. Here curlews and redshanks breed and wood sandpipers have been recorded. On its shoulders crested tits and capercaillies nest. The surrounding morainic ridges are covered by Scots pines and carpeted by bilberry, crowberry and ling.

Sutherland has few relics of the old Caledonian pines, but there are some woodland bogs in the more mature plantations. There is one wooded marsh where greenshanks, common sandpiper and snipe nest. Around a small loch are hill shoulders covered by a tangle of blown, felled and rotting pines submerged in rank heather. Scottish pine crossbills often nest in the trees and siskins sing in the plantations. Hen harriers hunt, sky dance, and nest in perimeter plantations as do short-eared owls in good vole years. Sparrowhawks, kestrels, buzzards and hooded crows have nests in the surrounding woods. In another pinewood, where ospreys have nested and goshawks sky-danced, there are small tarns and ponds surrounded by trees which look ideal for green sandpipers and where greenshanks sing above the braes outside.

Exciting as these forest bogs are, they are minute and almost insignificant compared with the huge marshes of northern Europe and the muskegs of Canada; and the numbers and variety of waders is similarly restricted. In a small way, the Spey Valley bogs resemble the vast morasses and wooded fells of the Langfjordal of Finnmark, Norway; that formidable, undulating country is a wonderful haunt of sub-arctic waders. On the drier ridges, crowberry, whortleberry and bearberry grow profusely as do several mosses and lichens, particularly reindeer moss. All over the great bog are thick tangles of dwarf birch and strongly-scented azalea-like *Ledum palustre*. Here, in different niches, Hugh Blair found dusky redshanks, greenshanks, wood sandpipers and bar-tailed godwits. In the flooded birchwoods smews also nested.

Throughout northern Europe, even in the great wastes and expanses of forest marsh beside the River Pasvik on the Norwegian-Soviet frontiers, reclamation has destroyed many marvellous wader habitats in the last half century.

In his Diary for 1928, Norman Gilroy described the Pasvik marshes near Svanvik in Finnmark, Norway, where he and E. S. Steward had almost incredibly exciting experiences. On the great plateaux were 'various browns and greys dotted with innumerable lakes shining like a mirror of silvery gold in the perfect summer'. It was a country of bogs and hillocks with pine-clad spurs, chains of pools and lakes, and tall dead trees standing stark against the horizon. On 25 May, their first day out, the hills and lakes of this wonderful country were still ice-bound. But the waders had already returned, were in pairs, and almost ready to start nesting. The greenshank was possibly the most abundant wader; 'every pool had its one, two or three pairs, and larger sheets of water an amazing number'. On this first field day Gilroy also met with dusky redshanks. What an exciting story of nest hunting and observations unfolded during the next five weeks!

All over the open marsh and the drier tundra-like ridges whimbrels sang their silvery trilling songs and later noisily defended their broods; Gilroy and Steward found 13 nests. The greenshanks made their scoops in wet clearings in the marsh, laying their eggs beside fragments of dead wood or beside pine saplings. Some dusky redshanks shared niches with the greenshanks, their nests surrounded by a litter of dead branches and twigs; others chose bare burnt hillsides overlooking the bog. Six nests fell to the hunters. In that year there were good numbers of the normally scarce and attractive bar-tailed godwits. Six nests were found on the slopes and flats of peatlands containing many pools. Wood sandpipers sang high in the air or from the tops of tall pines. Two pairs laid on dry grey pool-studded ground surrounded by the pine forest. On open ground in the marsh, colourful ruffs fought and displayed, with the reeves laying their eggs on wet ground not far away. Broad-billed sandpipers were few; two pairs nested in the middle of an exceptionally wet and shaky morass, with their eggs lying in small tussocks which rose just above the brown slime of the bog. Only one rare northern wader defeated the two hunters; the jack snipe was recognised too late.

In that year, waders were one of many attractions. Gorgeous waxwings hawked butter-flies on ridges studded with scattered trees, with two nests in clumps of bearded lichen *Usnea barbata*, well out on the lateral branches of tall pines. Gilroy managed to reach both nests and their eggs! Pine grosbeaks and bramblings also nested in thin and straggly forest while Lapland bunting and bluethroat were on the open marsh. Towards the end of the expedition arctic warblers were already singing. Great grey shrikes mobbed merlins; one nest was close to a colony of fieldfares. Ospreys fished the lakes, goshawks glided low through the trees, and male hen harriers tilted and hunted over the marshes. Gilroy found two pairs of merlins, which laid their clutches of red-brown eggs in old hooded crows' nests. Rough-legged buzzards soared and circled over the fells. Smew and bean geese were in other parts of the bog.

Now, over 50 years later, how difficult to determine whether 1928 was an outstanding nesting year in the Pasvik marshes or whether Gilroy and Steward were exceptional nest finders. But by the 1930s Steward and John McNeile found that wader numbers had fallen quite dramatically.

Ivan and Mary Hills tell us that the great swamps where Gilroy had hunted in 1928 have disappeared and that there is now only a sprinkling of bar-tailed godwits, dusky redshanks and greenshanks. A few broad-billed sandpipers favour the wetter and more shaky bogs slimy with brown ooze; and wood sandpipers still nest, some choosing wet birchwoods.

The wild forest marshes of the Pasvik and those in many other parts of northern Europe, have been tamed. Even in the Estonian wooded bogs, where John McNeile saw over 30 green sandpipers' nests between 1935–58, drainage ditches aim at re-claiming the marsh. Happily, however, Ingvar Byrkjedal reports that there are rich and pristine marshes west of the Pasvik where naturalists can still enjoy the wonders that enchanted the pioneers.

What a challenge the forest marshes offer to the young ornithologist! Everywhere man is continuously draining these marshes to which the exciting waders belong. It is for the present generation to ensure that they have sufficient living space to survive.

TEMMINCK'S STINT

The Temminck's stint is a tiny, brownish grey-mantled wader with a white throat, breast, and outer tail feathers. The colours of its short legs vary considerably; some are greenish yellow or greenish brown; the bird I watched in Spey Valley in 1956 had greenish legs. These little waders are so small that at first glance one might be watching a common sandpiper chick. Temminck's stints tend to tower when flushed from the ground and they fly quickly and erratically.

It was quite unexpected to find Temminck's stints nesting in Britain. On 13 June 1934, while working in Spey Valley, two northcountry birdmen, George Edwards and Bernard Crapnell, flushed a small wader from a rather deep unlined nest in flotsam about 2 m from a small loch. The ground was so soft that each egg was embedded in a small hollow. With their olive green ground colour and dark and purple-brown markings they were not unlike those of one type of dunlin's eggs, although much smaller. Two days later, during a violent rainstorm, the Temminck's stint deserted its clutch. Edwards and Crapnell collected the eggs and submitted them to Dr Percy Lowe at the Bird Room of the British Museum, who confirmed that they were those of a Temminck's stint.

In 1935, George Edwards again saw a pair of Temminck's stints in the same district but found no nest. In 1936, however, he found a nest in the 1934 locality and filmed the sitting bird from a hide. Later Ralph Chislett, of Rotherham, photographed the stint which subsequently deserted its eggs.

The next breeding record was still more surprising. On 1 July 1951, in Yorkshire, A. Lee and S. Jackson watched a small wader fluttering over the ground about 130 m from the waterline. After searching, they found four tiny greenish brown eggs blotched with dark brown in an almost unlined scrape. Lee and Jackson give an detailed account of the distraction display of the Temminck's stint, which finally settled on its nest almost beside them. The birds were again unlucky. On 12 July the discoverers found that a rat or weasel had mauled and killed the sitting bird.

While greenshank hunting I always looked out for Temminck's stints. But it was late May 1956 before I heard sharp tittering cries that were unknown to me. I eventually saw a tiny wader singing from the top of a small stunted pine not far from the edge of a loch. Several times it rose with fast-beating wings in an almost moth-like flight and hovered abouve the loch shore; and when it landed it ran with wings raised almost vertically over its back. 1956 was a vintage year; I was also watching a pair of ospreys at their eyrie only 250 m from a greenshank's nest in a forest clearing.

On 29 May I watched one of the stints making scrapes while its mate was running, head down and tail cocked, a few metres away. Eventually, on 16 June, I found the nest about 200 m from earlier scratchings. The brooding bird flicked over the ground a few metres ahead, showing its white outer tail feathers. Some minutes later it returned, skimming low over the ground, and finally ran the last few metres to its nest and four eggs on which it froze. Next day the scrape was empty, with no shell fragments in the cup or around the nest.

Temminck's stints were reported in every year between 1969–74 from river marshes in Easter Ross. On 16 July 1971, Christopher Headlam found two small chicks with an agitated parent, and on 22 July he ringed them. On 13 June 1986, Bill Sinclair tape-recorded a pair courting and copulating on this marsh. On 16 July, Bill and Patrick were back on the ground where they located an adult with a single chick which Patrick caught. Bill recorded its high-pitched cries while the parent flew around giving alarm calls. On leaving the site they saw the single parent running with two chicks.

The formidable team of David Clugston, John Mullins and N. J. Cowlard discovered a new haunt in Caithness on 20 June 1978. They flushed a Temminck's stint, which was associating with a flock of dunlin, beside a fair-sized loch. The stint ran alone to the edge of the pool and then took off, calling and trilling. In the ensuing search Cowlard saw a trip of three and possibly five – the hunt was on! In the next two days they watched Temminck's stints courting and copulating on the edge of the loch and song dancing in the air; but the hen had not started to lay when they had to leave early on 22 June.

In the late 1970s, Douglas Weir discovered a breeding haunt in wild country in Inverness-shire, where Temminck's stints bred in every year between 1978–84. On 30 June 1984, G. Dickson and Charlie Young watched a parent with a single chick. In 1979, Bill Sinclair tape-recorded the thrilling song dances of three cocks. It is extraordinary how quickly the haunt of a rare bird becomes known. By 1979 men working nearby asked a searcher if he was looking for 'yon wee birdie from Russia'!

John Mitchell, a very keen wader watcher, photographed a nest with four eggs close to Loch Lomond in Dunbartonshire in 1980. The Temminck's stints' nesting habitat comprised a gently sloping ridge of wind-blown sand 'colonised by low growing plants such as Creeping Yellow Cress (*Rorippa sylvestris*), Corn Spurry (*Spergularia arvensis*), Silverweed *Potentilla anserina*), Marsh Cudweed (*Gnaphalium uliginosum*), Common Knotgrass (*Polygonum aviculare*), Water Pepper (*P. hydropiper*) and Sheep's Sorrel (*Rumex acetosella*) amongst widely spaced tussocks of Soft Rush (*Juncus effusus*) and stunted Reed Canary Grass (*Phalaris arundinacea*)'. The nest, sited about 10 m from the edge of the loch, had an open cup made of dead grasses, partly hidden by overhanging leaves of a broad-leaved dock (*Rumex obtusifolius*) (John Mitchell 1983).

After reading about Temminck's stints records in the SOC Bird Report, our friend Charlie Young, along with Graeme Dickson, carried out some detective work, located a site, and went there in 1981. Charlie has kindly given us photographs of the stint and its beautiful eggs and a description of their hunt. Within an hour of their arrival they had spotted a Temminck's stint feeding on the river bank; it flew up on fast wing beats, trilling shrilly as it disappeared up river. Charlie then walked to a small island about 200 m from the loch where he heard an unidentified bird cry. Almost immediately the stint flew down to the water's edge a few feet ahead of him and started to feed and bathe, trilling softly. When Charlie moved away the stint gave a few short trills and then flew back to the island. As he again moved forward the bird walked off the island and back to the river bank where it fed and trilled. A few minutes later Charlie found the nest with four eggs, 3 m from the water's edge. It was a shallow scrape, well exposed, and lined with short stems of dry grass, on an island covered in flotsam and known to flood when the river is high.

In Scotland Temminck's stints favour habitat with short or sparsely-vegetated ground close to lochs or rivers where they also sometimes nest on islets. Nesting grounds in Spey Valley were on the fringe of the forest marsh, not far from the old pines. The Easter Ross river firth meadows are probably its most typical breeding haunts.

Their characteristic breeding grounds in Finland and Scandinavia are in meadows and ridges where horses and cattle formerly grazed. The absence of grazing, leading to higher vegetation and the growth of herbs and tall bushes, makes nesting grounds less attractive. In parts of their range they nest close to the sea, sharing breeding grounds with ringed plovers. They sometimes nest around towns, wooden houses, fishing huts, roadsides, the shunting or marshalling yards of railways, and even on bare patches in villages. Although they prefer flats or bare places containing short vegetation with larger numbers of insects, they like haunts with trees, fences, telephone poles and posts which serve as singing perches for the cocks. They are equally distributed in the birch zone and on the edges of the willow and lichen zone.

Temminck's stints usually return in small groups to their north European breeding grounds in late May; later the cocks break away to establish and defend territories. The Spey Valley cock I watched in 1956 made circling song flights with his wings whirring and his tail spread; time after time he trilled from small pines close to a loch.

Olavi Hildén, of the University of Helsinki, has made history with his classic study of the breeding system and population dynamics of Temminck's stints on the west coast of Finland. The ages at which 16 cocks first bred were six at 1 year, seven at 2 years, and three at 3 years. Seven hens nested in the area in which they were reared. All bred for the first time when one year old, with the exception of one bird which was 4 years old.

TERRITORY AND COURTSHIP

The cocks are strongly attached to their own territories, to which they return year after year. Each hen dominates a short line of shore from which she drives away other hens. There is, however, considerable crossing and re-crossing of air space; and the birds usually feed along the shore rather than in their nesting territories. This pattern helps the same individuals to re-mate. In five out of 13 examples the same two birds were paired in two consecutive years.

Territorial behaviour of the cocks probably determines population density in west Finland. If there are more birds capable of breeding than there are defended territories, surplus birds are forced to colonise marginal or inferior habitats, shift to other areas, or do without territories. Most of the birds settling for the first time fail to nest or to establish firm territories, thus producing few offspring. However, Hildén (1975) suggests that this floating surplus is always available to fill vacant territories in years of low numbers and to provide colonists for new breeding grounds.

In five out of 25 examples the mate of particular individuals was the same in two consecutive seasons. The tendency to re-mate is also probably assisted by the strong nest site tenacity of these birds. Cocks almost invariably established the same territories year after year, and half the hens returned to the same part of the area, thus increasing their chances of re-mating.

Temminck's stints nest in small groups or colonies in northern Europe, where up to four different cocks sometimes pursue the same hen in rapid twists, swerves and circles in which their wings beat fast and quiver. A territorial cock, like a cock dunlin, now tries to force a hen down into his living space. In his song dance he rapidly vibrates his wings and sometimes raises them into V above his back; and with his spread

tail he looks a little like a large moth. His trills remind one of the reels of grasshopper warblers.

Before pairing, a cock makes scrapes to which he later leads a hen. While scraping, he twists round with his tail held high or drooped. He then throws stalks over his shoulders while continuously calling, rather mechanical *put-put-puts*. As the hen approaches, the cock spreads his wings and she enters the scoop under his fanned tail, much as ringed plovers do in their nest-dancing displays. Clugston and his friends did not see the full scrape ritual in Caithness, but one bird brooded closely on the ground and a second nudged it away.

This ground display has grace and beauty. With tail half cocked and wings half open the cock runs purposefully towards the hen; and then he flicks onto her back, rapidly beating his tiny wings to balance himself. Afterwards the two birds fly away and sometimes alight on the same stone. The Caithness stints were in full passion. Between 06.45 and 09.10 on 21 June the cock successfully coupled three times; and in addition he again tried to mate the hen immediately after his first successful coupling. At 20.50 he again attempted to pair. After mating, cock Temminck's stints sometimes preen or feed; or they make for the water side, and their hens for stony patches nearby.

In 1975 Hildén published his sensational research on a colour-ringed population of Temminck's stints. He found that each cock selected, defended, and made scrapes in a territory to which he attempted to attract a hen. After the hen had laid her clutch of four eggs she left the cock and tried to find a second cock with which to pair on his territory. Here she produced a second clutch, laying the first egg of the new clutch 2–4 days after the last egg of her first. She then started steady incubation on this second clutch.

Meanwhile, the first cock delayed incubation while he continued his attempts to entice a second hen, often successfully pairing with one which had already laid her first clutch in another cock's territory. Thus, most cocks had two clutches by different hens in their territories. The second hen incubated her own clutch; and after a lapse, in which he attempted to copulate with still more hens, the cock settled down to incubate the first hen's eggs.

The first and second clutches of particular hens were spaced from 4–950 m apart (mean 247 m); out of 40 nests only 13 were less than 100 m apart.

About one-third of the hens shifted their breeding grounds from year to year, laying two clutches in different areas in the same season. Hens which yearly shift breeding grounds – described by Hildén as 'vagrant hens' – lay only one clutch in the same general area, while faithful hens lay two.

For a small wader, belonging to the boreal and tundra zones, a hen Temminck's stint has a remarkable ability to produce eggs in quick time. One of Hildén's colour-ringed hens laid three clutches (12 eggs) in sixteen days. One particular cock song danced and trilled over two different hens whenever they left their eggs to feed. Two hens laid three clutches in succession; one incubated the last clutch, leaving her first two clutches with different cocks.

Future research will determine whether this remarkable multiple-clutch pattern is common to other parts of Temminck's stints' range. Recently, in his fine study on Hardanger Vidda, Torgrim Breiehagen (1985) describes a similar strategy.

Polygamy

Hildén recorded simultaneous polygyny, polyandry and promiscuity. A cock courts and attempts to copulate with any hen which enters his territory. Some cocks were seen copulating, or trying to copulate, with two or three different hens on the same day or on successive days. A hen, staying near the boundary of the territories of two cocks, attracted both, which then competed for her.

Cocks are thus potentially polygynous. Several times a cock courted two hens simultaneously. On other occasions, the same hen was courted by two cocks simultaneously or on consecutive days.

The first pair-bond is broken immediately the hen completes her first clutch. A particular hen then sometimes associates with a new cock, on the same or following day, on a territory far removed from the original nest site. There are many variations. Cocks may mate with two hens, both of which may lay their first clutches in his territory. When this happens the cock sometimes starts by trying to incubate both clutches but soon deserts one of them. If, however, the clutch he is incubating is destroyed or taken, he may then start to sit on the other.

Two hens occasionally lay in the same nest. In 1968, for example, two hens paired simultaneously with the same cock and laid by turn in the same nest cup. This was the first clutch of one hen and the second clutch of the other, which consequently started to incubate the shared nest of seven eggs, preventing the first hen from laying her last egg in the joint scoop; she later deposited it in a new nest 38 m away.

DISPERSION AND BREEDING DENSITY

In some parts of northern Europe, Temminck's stints nest in loose colonies. In the most favoured habitats in the Gulf of Bothnia, Hildén recorded 25–42 displaying cocks/10 ha. Some small islands, of less than 1 ha, carried from 3–6 pairs. On the Jamal Peninsula, N. Danilov and V. K. Rjabizev (*in* Flint 1973) estimated that there were 2.0 pairs/km² in 1971 and 2.3 pairs/km² in 1972. In the West Taimyr, on the banks of the River Pjassina in 30 km of the upper half of the Agapa estuary, nests were spaced out at about 100–150 m. On the banks of Lake Purinski there was a pair to every 200–300 m, with a maximum density of 2–6 pairs/10 ha. In 1938 H. N. Southern and W. A. Lewis, in Swedish Lapland, estimated four territorial cocks displaying on an island of 0.2 ha in a river delta (Glutz 1977).

NEST, EGG AND CLUTCH

Nests are sometimes sheltered by large stones; placed beside fragments of dead wood or flotsam; or the eggs are laid in scoops in moss or heather in wet or gravelly ground. The chosen site is sometimes well vegetated and the sitting birds may add the nest lining during incubation. In northern Europe dry grass and occasionally leaves of dwarf birch or willow are constituents of the lining. Most British nests are very sparingly lined, although the one found by Charlie Young in 1981 contained quite a thick pad of grass, rather similar to that found in a skylark's nest.

V. D. Kokhanov (1973) measured the breadth of 44 nest cups which varied from 50–80 mm (mean 66 mm). The depth of 32 cups averaged 36 mm.

Temminck's stints have a late laying season. In Britain the earliest recorded clutch was completed about 4 June; all other clutches were laid in late June, with the Caithness birds not sitting on 21 June.

At Kokkola, Finland, laying starts between 25–30 May and the main laying season is in early June. The yearly laying season in upper Fenno-Scandia is slightly later. In the Karigasniemi district, in 1965–70, laying started between 1–5 June. The earliest hatching dates recorded there were 26 June 1970, 27 June 1967, and 30 June 1966. In Finnmark, Norway, laying begins from 7–12 June, with peaks between 13–20 June (59 clutches) and the last eggs are laid about 1–2 July (S. Haftorn 1971).

In USSR clutches were recorded between 11–20 June to mid July, with eggs starting to hatch on 1–10 July. On the Murman Coast on the White Sea laying starts from 5 June; on Kanin Peninsula about 10 June; on Timan Peninsula between 10–15 June; in west Taimyr between 15–25 June; and in the Anabar tundra and around Indigirka from about 25 June onwards (Gladkov 1951).

The laying period of each local group is usually concentrated in a period of about two weeks. Kokhanov (1973) gives an average of 14.4 days for a 5-year study at Kanda-lashka. When hens are laying two consecutive clutches there is an interval of 2–4 days (mean 3 days) between the laying of the last egg of the first clutch and the first egg of the second clutch. One hen laid three clutches (12 eggs) in 16 days (Hildén 1975).

When fresh, the diminutive pyriform or sub-pyriform eggs have greenish to yellowish or grey-green ground colour. They are usually heavily spotted with dark brown, often with clusters at their heavy ends, and as a rule are not as warmly marked as the eggs of little stints (Jourdain 1940). Hugh Blair found a clutch of four eggs, the ground colour of which was as olive green as a typical clutch of common curlew's eggs.

Eggs are laid at intervals of 23–40 hours (mean 30–31 hours). Hildén measured 706 eggs in his study area on the Gulf of Bothnia where the mean was 28.4 × 20.4 mm. Jourdain (1940) gives 28.0 × 20.4 mm as the average for 120 eggs, 65 of which were measured by Eugen Rey.

Kokhanov (*in* Flint 1973) weighed 36 fresh eggs at Kandalashka which ranged from 5.4–6.5 gm (mean 6.0 gm). The average body weight of a hen is 27.8 gm. A clutch of four eggs, averaging 6.0 gm per egg, is thus 86% of the hen's body weight. An exceptional hen, laying three clutches, therefore produces eggs weighing over two and a half times her own body weight (Table 2). The shell weight of an unspecified number of eggs averaged 0.28 gms (M. Schönwetter 1963).

A normal clutch consists of four eggs, five is exceptional, three occasional, and two probably abnormal (Table 4). Hildén recorded a clutch of seven eggs at Kokkola, as did J. B. and S. Bottomley in Swedish Lapland; in each instance two hens were responsible.

Genuine replacement clutches are seldom recorded. Of 13 nests, on which hens were brooding and which were destroyed by 25 June, only two were replaced. Both times the first egg of the repeat clutch was laid, at most, five days after the loss of the first. if a cock lost his clutch he depended for a replacement on finding a hen which had not yet laid her first clutch. Thirty-two nests, on which cocks were sitting, were destroyed by 25 June. Yet only one of these was later discovered with a fresh clutch.

INCUBATION

Temminck's stints sit for spells of 10–25 minutes, with periods of 5–10 minutes off the nest. This pattern, however, varies according to individuals and to the state of the weather. In cold or wet spells incubation rhythms are longer and the nests then sometimes become saturated and deserted. Incubation spells at night are also longer.

Hildén measured 16 incubation periods varying from 19–22 days (mean 20.8 days).

HATCHING

In Hildén's study area the annual hatching success varied considerably, ranging from 0.63 in 1970 to 2.37 in 1963, an average of 1.2 young per adult for the 10-year period.

Out of 106 nests there was at least one unhatched egg in 69 clutches, one in each of 25 nests, two in nine nests, and three in three nests. There was a proportion of 16.4% of unhatched eggs in nests incubated by hens (second clutches) and only 9.6% in those for which the cocks were responsible (first clutches).

The eggs are pipped for at least three days. The sitting bird lifts and flies away with large fragments of eggshell which it drops some distance from the nest.

YOUNG

The forehead and nape of the young Temminck's stint is pale yellow, crown and upper parts are intermixed with pale yellow to buff, and underparts pale white. The feet are flesh coloured to greyish pink and the base of the lower mandible is dark to greenish yellow or greyish yellow.

Within a few hours the chicks wander about 0.5 m from the nest and attempt to

catch insects. During their first few days the parent periodically broods them both by day and night. On their second day, Kokhanov (1973) found that chicks had moved about 150 m from the nest and that thereafter they made daily journeys of 100 m. The guarding parent hovers excitedly and gives noisy scolding cries to warn the chicks which then crouch on the ground.

On their fifteenth or sixteenth day chicks can fly or flutter a distance of up to 30–50 m and are capable of flying over 100 m when 17–18 days old.

At Kokkola the fledging success of the population varied considerably. In 1963 and 1964 65–70%, and in 1965 50–60%, of the young eventually flew. Between 1963–67 the fledging rate was *c* 0.9 per adult but in 1968–71 only 0.5. For the 10-year period an annual average of 0.7 young per adult fledged (Hildén 1978).

DISTRACTION BEHAVIOUR

Temminck's stints use rather simple distraction displays when flushed from eggs or small young. I particularly remember the Spey Valley bird fluttering with spread tail a few metres ahead of me; and a bird I watched in Sutherland in 1962 ran swiftly with fanned tail. Hugh Blair described them flying heavily over the scrub with legs trailing as if hard-hit or dragging themselves along the ground with outspread wings and tail, continuously giving anxious trills.

VOICE

(1)   The cock's song dance advertises his territory, thus helping to repel rivals and attract hens. He gives these flights in many situations of excitement and challenge. In the far north he looks like some exotic moth, turning, swerving and circling, and sometimes fluttering and hovering almost like a tiny kestrel. From time to time he spreads his tail and half-raises and beats his wings above his back. The song rises and falls several times, almost like the reel of a grasshopper warbler. When he goes to ground he may then run with half-cocked tail to a stone, or perch on a tree, bush, stump or pole. Sometimes several cocks display in the air together, all reeling over the same air space, as tape-recorded so beautifully by Bill Sinclair in 1979.

(2)   Tittering contact notes are said to be more subdued than those of the little stint; they have a mechanical buzzing sound.

(3)   Hildén describes a possibly slowed down variation of song *pip-pip-pip-pi-pi* which is give in anger.

(4)   When a cock is chasing a hen he sometimes gives a single excitement cry, described by Southern and Lewis as *cheer*.

(5)   Christopher Headlam described Temminck's stints in Easter Ross repeatedly uttering a single, clear, *tirr*.

(6)   The hen's sexual contact cry is a more tremulous *drrr* (Hildén).

(7)   Glutz (1977) describes the threat cry as a hissing *svee-svee-svee*.

(8)   The scrape call is a repetitive *put put*. However, I did not hear this in Spey Valley while watching one of the birds making a scratching.

(9)   Copulation cries are also hissing *svees* (Hildén).

(10)   Parents call up their broods with soft *pulu-pulu* cries.

(11)   The young use soft cries and keep in touch with their parents with soft trisyllabic *tidi-tidi-di* (Glutz 1977).

(12)   In distraction behaviour at the nest, Hugh Blair heard an anxious trilling which was 'somewhat different from the song proper'.

PREDATORS

Like all waders, Temminck's stints have many different predators. In Yorkshire a rat or weasel probably destroyed the eggs of the pair which bred there. Two clutches in Scotland were destroyed by flooding; and two others robbed by unknown predators. Hooded crows and foxes are present in most Scottish haunts.

Hildén suggests that hooded crow, common gull, weasel, minx, rat and hedgehog, are causes of nest losses in Finland as well as flooding. At Kokkola the common gulls learnt to quarter the ground like harriers. By these tactics they found and destroyed newly-hatched broods of redshank and ruff as well as those of Temminck's stints. Hen harrier, goshawk, sparrowhawk, kestrel, merlin, peregrine and fox are other likely predators in northern habitats.

FOOD

There is much to be discovered about the summer food of this fascinating little wader, which is sometimes capable of producing egg weights over two and a half times its body weight. In Hildén's study area the main laying period for first clutches coincided with 'the mass emergence of Chironomids'. At this time the low sea-level also produced large expanses of mud flats. In Scotland, Temminck's stints feed among stones and short grass close to loch, pool, river or firth. Charlie Young watched one feeding along the edge of a small island on which it was nesting.

These are predominantly insect feeders. Jourdain recorded beetles, particularly larvae of *Haliplus* and Staphynidae. Maud Havilland (1916) found only the remains of mosquito larvae in the birds she collected on the Yenesei. The remains of plants have been recorded in stomachs, but it is not clear whether these were taken accidentally or deliberately.

DISTRIBUTION AND NUMBERS

Temminck's stints breed westwards from the Lena River on the outskirts of the Arctic tundra. They nest in the tundra and dwarf shrub an forest tundra zone, also occasionally in adjacent parts of boreal Eurasia from west Norway to the Bering Strait in the east, and occasionally in the Chukchee Peninsula. In the Scandinavian fells they nest in Norway, south to Hardanger Vidda 60°20′ N and in Sweden to Harjedalen 62°30′ N. The northern part of their range includes most of Lapland and runs from 66° N southwards to Nordmore 62°50′ N, thence to the coast of the Arctic and Atlantic Oceans. In Finnish Lapland Temminck's stints breed in the north (Utsjoki, Inari and Enontekio), with a few pairs holding territories south to Kuusamo 66°10′ N, Kemijärvi 66°45′ N, and Rovaniemi 66°30′ N. They also breed along the rivers of Muonionjoki and Tornionjoki and on the northern coast of the Gulf of Bothnia, to approximately 63°30′ N (Glutz 1975).

In European SSR it nests on the Murman Coast and the islands of Kolguev and Waigatsch, northwards to Ljamtschina Bay and southwards to the White Sea up to the Arctic Circle.

Asiatic habitats extend to the northern fringes of the moss, lichen, and shrub tundra, continuing across the north of Jamal and Gydan Peninsulas and south through Taimyr, with casual records at 72° N in the Jenissej estuary to 74°30′ N on Chatanga Bay and thence to Anabar tundra northwards to Urjung-Chaja at 71°25′ N (Gladkov and Saletajev 1965); and in the Jana-Indigirka lowland bogs terminating on the Ljachowski Islands (E. Kozlova 1962). There are unconfirmed reports that the southern boundaries descend to the northern fringes of the forest tundra zone. They breed on the Ob up to between 64°–65° N, occasionally on the Tas between 64°–67° N, and in the Jenissej to 65°30′ N (H. Johansen 1960).

J. Kålås and I. Byrkjedal (1981) estimate a total population of 34, 000 pairs in Norway in 1979. S. Ulfstrand and G. Högstedt (1976) give a figure of 20,000 pairs for Sweden. Hildén considers that Temminck's stints are decreasing in Finland, due to changes in their habitat. The only figure available is 2,000 pairs, estimated by E. Merikallio in 1958.

The breeding records in Britain are therefore the furthest south and west so far recorded. K. H. Voous (1960) questions whether British records are casual, due to climatic change, or to re-occupation of former breeding grounds. Temminck's stints have nested in at least two widely separated districts of Inverness-shire, in Easter Ross and Dunbarton, and probably in Caithness and Sutherland. At most half-a-dozen pairs have nested in any one year. There has only been one English breeding record, that in Yorkshire in 1951.

When the first nest was reported in Spey Valley in 1934, I remember that Jourdain was puzzled and amazed that this little northern wader had come so far south to nest. Yet, after so many false starts, the charming Temminck's stint has become a very scarce but quite regular breeder in Scotland.

WOOD SANDPIPER

Within the very first hour after I had started to hunt a big flow in Sutherland, in 1968, I heard the sharp scolding cries of a bird that was new to me. Almost immediately I saw a pair of small waders – wood sandpipers – perched on the top of bog myrtle plants projecting above the flow. Soon they were flying all round me and occasionally giving rather flute-like songs. I now realised that they had a brood in the bog. These birds were exceptionally tame; at one time they fluttered and scolded within 20 m of where I was sitting. This was a grand start to our hunt for a new wader. A few days later Robert Moss and I momentarily glimpsed the chicks running in the flow, and the two birds – particularly the cock – scolded and mobbed us. We later found that there was another brood on the wing over that wonderful flow.

Next year we returned on 14 June. I sat under a peatbank overlooking the loch where the wood sandpipers fed, but at first all was silent. Then, at 20.15, I suddenly heard a wood sandpiper scolding; almost immediately it flew low over the flow and started a song dance. It rose with tremulous wing beats which took it upwards and then set its wings below the plane of its body and its impetus carried it a little higher. Along with the flight it gave its musical song and then glided slowly down with fanned tail. The song was a quite characteristic *leero-leero*, followed by a musical flute-like *toodle-toodle*. This time the wood sandpiper flew in wide circles, first over the flow and then far across the loch, giving a few scolding *chips* along with its songs. Again and again it returned and sang above me. Then, quite suddenly, it dived down with half-closed wings and pitched on a hump in the bog. By now the wind had dropped but the midges soon became almost unbearable; and when I moved the sandpiper had disappeared. I gave it 15 minutes and then searched the flow, but without success.

The next day Bruin and I made a good search without raising anything. We then lay up close to a dubhlochan which was just marginally higher than the part of the marsh into which the bird had disappeared on the previous evening. At 18.15 we picked up the pair and saw them drop down into a wet patch of grass heath about 200 m away. Soon the cock was singing overhead and then he flew back to the loch. We believed that there might have been an exchange so went in to search. At 18.35 a wood sandpiper rose almost between Bruin and myself, gave a few quiet *chip-chips*, and then flew over the bog. At our feet, in the short grass heath, was the much coveted nest, possibly the first with eggs ever to be found in Sutherland.

The three almost pea green eggs, spotted and speckled with dark sepia brown, lay in a small nest of grass in a mixture of grass heath with bog myrtle growing just behind it. The wood sandpiper hung overhead, alternately singing and *chipping*.

I now recalled reading about John Hancock's exciting hunt in Prestwick Carr in Northumberland in June 1853. 'About 3, our dogs, a retriever and a spaniel, raised the bird about 50 yards in advance of us which at once rose to a considerable height coursing about, rising and sinking somewhat in the manner of a snipe, and like it, while sweeping downwards with outstretched tremulous wings, produced a peculiar drumming note, but one much shriller than that of the snipe and almost amounting to a sort of musical whistle.... At first the watching dogs failed but at last the bird was marked to and raised from the nest with its four pretty eggs on the side of a dry hillock where grew some heath and grass in the midst of a wet swamp'.

Our find, so exciting to us, led to many happy hours watching the behaviour of these lovely waders. I particularly noticed that the orange to orange-yellow legs of the wood sandpipers projected appreciably behind the tail while flying. They had buff to whitish superciliaries, dark brown mantles with white spots, throats and upper breasts speckled with dark brown, and white rumps. Their scolding cries were quite as persistent but much less sharp than those of greenshanks and redshanks.

The wood sandpiper has been a lucky bird for the family. In June 1981, Patrick, with his friend Colin Galbraith, flew to Iceland for a birdwatching holiday. Heavily laden, they hitch-hiked from Reykjavik to Lake Myvatn in the north where they camped for five days. On 26 June a pair of wood sandpipers was located acting as if it had young, and they later heard one chick. On the 27th a thorough search revealed that the birds had moved some 150 m from their pervious position. After watching for some time two chicks were seen following one of the adults. One chick, about two days old, was caught and examined. This was the first proven record of wood sandpipers breeding in Iceland.

Around Lake Myvatn, where the wood sandpipers nested, there were several small lochs separated by areas of marshy ground. The vegetation consisted of grasses and sedge with underlying carpets of mosses. Neighbours of the wood sandpipers were redshank, dunlin, golden plover and red-necked phalarope.

The German ornithologist, Heinrich Kirchner (1963), along with his family, has intensively studied pairs of wood sandpipers on the upland peat bogs of Schleswig-Holstein, where they nested on at least thirty different bogs.

In Fenno-Scandia and USSR wood sandpipers nest in the coniferous zone; and further north on hilly tundra in the spruce, willow and dwarf birch country. They also breed in vast bogs and openings of mosses in the forest steppes (Cramp and Simmons 1983).

Norman Gilroy found wood sandpipers nesting in the great forest bogs of the then undrained Pasvik marshes, along with challenging rarities like dusky redshank, bar-tailed godwit, broad-billed sandpiper, waxwing and great grey shrike. Each had its own special niche in that exciting country.

Wood sandpipers have chosen some grand country in Scotland. In the Insh Marshes in Spey Valley, where it now nests regularly, spotted crakes sometimes whiplash in the bogland and grasshopper warblers reel in the evening. In the surrounding pine forest there are crested tits in the old pines; and ospreys fish in the loch and have nested on dead trees not far away. Capercaillies and blackcocks have leks in adjacent clearings. Some of the few wood sandpipers in Ross nest close to the edges of quite large lochs. However, G. M. Ireson (*in litt*) tells us about a rather different Ross haunt where he found a nest in 1984. This was boggy runelled ground with long outcrops of rock about 50 m apart and fully 600 m from the feeding loch.

In north Sutherland the wood sandpipers have quite different habitats and neighbours. Common sandpipers creak shrilly while their chicks hide in rough vegetation beside a big loch; and not far away are piping parties of oystercatchers. As you stumble over the rough ground, reed buntings jingle in the rushes and whinchats tick excitedly close to a clump of old birches. A little further on the music of waders is all around you. A pair of redshanks occasionally yodel or song dance over the loch, dunlins purr, golden plovers wail mournfully, and curlews bubble, all blending their songs and calls into a wonderful chorus. Snipe bleat over the peat bogs; and in the evening an incoming greenshank *chips* excitedly before changing over with its mate on a vast grey flow. Greylag geese sometimes nest in the deep undergrowth close to the loch; later they swim with their goslings well out on the water. If you are lucky, you may see a golden eagle high above the craggy tops, a peregrine soaring over a distant hill, or a short-eared owl flapping and tilting over the flow.

ARRIVAL, PAIRING AND COURTSHIP

We have never had the good fortune to watch wood sandpipers actually arrive on their breeding grounds. A pair arrives simultaneously; possibly like some greenshanks they have met or mated up in particular places outside their breeding grounds.

In Sutherland we found that unmated cocks sang over future territories and living space. If unsuccessful in their search they moved on to other areas.

The conspicuous song dance, which both sexes perform, but hens less frequently than cocks, starts with a clipping flight low over the bog before the bird reaches a height of about 20–100 m; and then it performs the classic switchback flight, fluttering upwards and then gliding forwards on stiff decurved wings, legs dropped, and tail

spread. On descent the bird sings before repeating these movements again and again. The song dance is important as a means of advertising to and for a mate, and probably indicates possession of territories to other cocks. J. A. Duthie (1983) described an excited courtship flight in which the birds started with fast clipping beats and then the cock chased the hen in wide circles and sometimes in figures-of-eight; periodically they stopped, landed, copulated, and then resumed their sex chase.

In both Sutherland and Spey Valley cocks circle over special parts of the bog and then fly away to other places where they repeat their song dances up to 800 m or more from their main nesting territories. Occasionally they fly very high, possibly up to 300 m or more. Wood sandpipers on the Insh Marshes displayed most frequently between 06.00–07.00 and between 11.00 and 12.00, but they sang little when there was no surplus population. In Sutherland, however, we found that the birds sang persistently in the evening after 18.00. Unmated cocks covered a lot of ground, singing periodically without performing full song dances. If unsuccessful in their search for living-space they moved on to other places.

Kirchner (1963) watched mated wood sandpipers take part in a ground display when they trilled and both raised their wings on high while running together. He also watched copulation in which the cock flew with quivering wings and dangling legs onto the back of the hen; she leaned forward with fanned tail before the cock fluttered off her back. In the act of mating the cock gave special quick trilling cries and afterwards the two birds flew away to a marsh. Duthie, however, has watched some entirely silent couplings.

DISPERSION AND BREEDING DENSITY

In Scotland there are seldom enough breeding pairs to make a precise study of spacing behaviour and density. The cocks are usually able to fly and display unchallenged over what is essentially neutral ground, as well as over their own territories. But on the Insh marshes, in some years, and in Sutherland and Ross, the wood sandpipers tend to form rather loose nesting groups. In 1968 there were two breeding pairs in the same Sutherland moss; and in 1984, Ireson's nest with eggs, a pair with small young, and an additional single bird were all in the same flow in Ross.

Gilroy recorded a high density of nesting wood sandpipers on the Pasvik marshes in 1928, with two or three pairs based on the same small tarns late in May. In Mecklenberg, north Germany, Forester Hintz Sr reported 7–9 breeding pairs in a marshy area of 24 ha; on 25 May 1858 he was given 26 fresh or incubated eggs from these habitats.

In Schleswig-Holstein, Kirchner (1963) found isolated pairs nesting in bogs of less than 2 ha; larger marshes had a density of 0.3–0.5 breeding pairs/10 ha. E. T. Pedersen (1959) estimated a breeding density of 0.25–1.0 breeding pairs/10 ha in Denmark. On the high forest marshes of Finland, density was less than 0.1 breeding pairs/10 ha (M. M. Sammalisto 1955). In wet marshes, south of the Jugor Peninsula, S. M. Uspenski (1965) gives a figure of 0.1–0.4 breeding pairs/ha (up to 1.1 breeding pairs/ha locally). For 1970–72, V. E. Flint (1973) records a breeding density of 0.4–2.6 (mean 1.6) breeding pairs/km^2; and on the forest marshes up to 24.1 breeding pairs/km^2.

Nest finding

It would require much experience before planning effective methods of nest finding. After his remarkable success with many difficult waders in Finnmark, Gilroy (MS) wrote: 'there is no doubt that the nest of wood sandpiper is extraordinarily difficult to find and I can think of no satisfactory method by which its discovery might be facilitated'. However, his Diary suggests that the two wood sandpipers' nests found were located while searching for other waders.

As wood sandpipers periodically leave their nest to feed or to carry out nest relief, it pays to watch the feeding places and then follow the out-going bird into the marsh. The relieving bird often perches first on a tree or plant before going to the nest. The song dance, particularly when accompanied by a short burst of *chipping*, is an excellent lead and is often given by a cock 'dancing' above his sitting mate. Searching of a big flow or marsh can only be tiring, frustrating, and doubtfully productive.

Lennart Raner has found many nests by waiting for and watching nest relief, a method he has also most successfully used in his hunts for nests of greenshanks and green sandpipers. Ireson also watched the wood sandpipers in Ross change over from a great distance away at 18.13 hours on 13 June 1984, and the following morning at 06.14 he found the nest, probably by the next exchange – a fine feat of nest finding.

NEST, EGG AND CLUTCH

Wood sandpipers make a small scoop which they line with stalks from surrounding plants like cotton sedge, cowberry, moss, heather etc. One measured by Kirchner was 8–10 cm broad and 4–4.5 cm deep. A Sutherland nest was well screened with deers hair grass and lined with blades of this plant, *Molinia*, some sprigs of heather, and a few bog myrtle leaves, possibly from a plant growing almost beside the scoop. Duthie and Leavett (1983) recorded a hen laying in the same scoop in two successive years.

Gilroy described two nests found on 18 June 1928 on the Pasvik Marshes. The first was a small deep hollow, well lined with fine grasses and short stalks of different plants; the eggs were open to the sky. This was a much better constructed nest, in every respect, than that of a dunlin or common sandpiper. The second nest was beautifully concealed in short heather, lined with withered grasses, and the eggs completely screened; it was placed on a tiny island in squashy ground in a growth of dwarf sallow. The cup was shallow but well built of fine grasses and not unlike a large skylark's nest.

In north Fenno-Scandia and USSR, particularly in years when the bogs are flooded, wood sandpipers sometimes nest in old nests of tree-nesting birds like song thrush, redwing, fieldfare, great grey shrike, magpie and turtle dove; they have even nested in an old waxwing's nest.

We estimated that one Sutherland hen completed her clutch in early May and the second in the last week of May 1968. The hen we watched in 1969 laid out in the second week of June. The brood of small chicks found in the Sutherland haunt on 11 June 1982 was probably from a clutch completed about 16–17 May. In 1984, one of the Ross pairs had unpipped eggs on 14 June; but the very agitated behaviour of a second pair that day suggested that they had small chicks nearby. A rough approximation for that clutch would be 17–18 May.

On 25 May 1928, Gilroy wrote that three pairs of wood sandpipers had not started to sit. He later found two clutches which had been completed between 14–16 June and a chick from a clutch on which the hen had begun to sit about 1 June.

In Schleswig-Holstein the earliest hen started to lay about 29–30 April and the latest on 27 May; eight clutches were completed about 15 May (Kirchner 1963). Hens lay their first eggs from about 10 May onwards in the south, and in the last week of May in the north of Finland. In south Varanger, Norway, incubation starts at the end of May but is usually delayed until early June; Hugh Blair recorded deeply incubated eggs on 10 July. Wood sandpipers on the White Sea usually lay between 22 May–15 June. On the Lower Ob the laying season lies between 1–20 June and in the south of the Jamal Peninsula between 8–28 June (Glutz 1977). The chicks which Patrick found in Iceland on 27 June must have hatched from eggs laid about 4–5 June.

The eggs are usually pointed ovate but occasionally pyriform in shape. They are thin shelled and slightly glossy, a little larger than those of the green sandpiper. Ground colour varies from olive brown and olive buff to warm buff. When fresh, some eggs are of a vivid pea green ground colour. Some are slightly speckled and blotched with sienna brown and others richly marked and particularly capped with reddish and purplish brown and with grey and lilac undermarkings. Erythristic eggs are on record.

214 Swedish eggs averaged 37.95 × 26.80 mm (P. Rosenius 1937). H. Kirchner (1962) measured 22 eggs from his Schleswig-Holstein study area which were slightly smaller, 37.65 × 26.40 mm. Ten eggs from this area varied from 11.0–15.5 gm (mean 14.07 gm) (Table 3).

A clutch of four eggs weighs roughly 86.6–100% of the hen's body weight (Table 2).

Table 4 gives clutch size. No fives or double clutches of wood sandpipers' eggs appear to have been recorded. Eggs are frequently laid daily, occasionally at longer intervals; the clutch is completed in 4–5 days and occasionally six. One hen in the Insh Marshes had laid three eggs in a nest three days after she and her mate arrived on the breeding ground (Duthie 1983). No one appears to have studied the egg-laying behaviour of wood sandpipers.

INCUBATION

Wood sandpipers briefly brood incomplete clutches but do not start steady incubation until the last egg has been laid. Both cock and hen sit. In Sutherland we watched exchanges in which the sitting bird left the nest, flew to the feeding loch and returned with its partner which then took over incubation. In the afternoon and evening the cock took the greater share of incubation, occasionally leaving the nest to feed at long intervals, and staying away for 15–20 minutes. In 1984 Ireson (*in litt*) watched a Ross pair exchanging at 18.13 on 13 June and 06.14 on 14 June.

Kirchner watched no special ceremonies during nest relief. He recorded one exchange at 15.45, when the eggs had been brooded for eight days. Calling noisily, the incoming bird flew into the territory and pitched on a dwarf pine about 50 m from the nest.

The brooding bird then ran silently from the eggs and its partner flew down into the bog, covering the last 2 m on foot. He also watched exchanges between 13.15 and 14.00 on 12 June and at 16.10 on 16 June. Kirchner estimated that the incubation period lasted 22–24 days; Elizabeth Kozlova's estimate was slightly less at 22–23 days.

HATCHING

Eggs are chipped for 3–4 days before they hatch. At two nests Kirchner found that the cock alone hatched the eggs and led away the chicks. There is sometimes an interval of at least 10 hours between the hatching of the first and last chick in a clutch.

The sitting bird lifts and flies away with large fragments of eggshell, dropping them in the bog a short distance away. However, they are occasionally lax about eggshell disposal, leaving large fragments of shell in the nest after the chicks have left. Smaller bits of shell usually stay in the scoop.

YOUNG

Gilroy described wood sandpiper chicks as 'beautiful little creatures marked with silvery grey and brown'. Patrick noted in his diary that the young were 'like very small greenshank chicks'. Head, breast and belly are dusky brown and crown and nape blackish brown. The legs are bluish to olive grey, bills grey and irides dark brown. Four chicks, weighed by Kirchner, ranged from 8.0–9.7 gms (Table 5).

In Sutherland, in 1968–69, the parents led their broods to lagoons of the loch and to the edge of a very wet flow which was roughly 300 m from the 1969 nest site. In 1968 both sexes were with the brood for at least a week, with the cock brooding and the hen noisily guarding them. At the 1969 nest the cock alone appeared to be in charge, the hen disappearing soon after the hatch.

Parents in Schleswig-Holstein often called on trees, fences or wire, giving excited calls and bobbing their heads up and down. In Sutherland, where there were no trees in the nesting territory, the parent perched on the tallest bog myrtle plants; and in Iceland Patrick recorded that both the old birds stood on lumps of volcanic lava while calling to the chicks.

The only estimate of a free-flying period is that of 30 days recorded by Heinroth (1931).

DISTRACTION BEHAVIOUR

We have not seen a wood sandpiper carry out an elaborate distraction display. When flushed, sometimes nearly at our feet, the sitting bird flew low almost touching the bog, *chipping* loudly and then rising and periodically singing to call up its mate from the loch. The birds were never as aggressive as are many greenshanks in similar situations. Kirchner, however, watched a bird holding out its wings and stumbling over the marsh; and Blair describes a parent wood sandpiper running over the ground with raised wings. In Iceland, when Patrick and Colin Galbraith were looking for the chicks, the cock sang very high in air.

VOICE

(1)   The full song *toodle-toodle-toodle-leero-leero-leero-toodle-toodle-toodle* is given in full switchback song dance; a shortened version is restricted to *leero-leero* when the bird is flying from flow to flow. Both cock and hen sing, but the cock's song is more

sustained and continuous than that of the hen. Either sex may sing briefly after nest relief or the cock may sing during his displays on the ground. The *toodle-toodle* phrase reminds us, and has recalled to other naturalists, a phrase in the song of the woodlark.

(2)   The stock alarm or contact cry when flushed, and also while on passage, is usually a sharp succession of *chiff-chiff-chiffs*. The bird occasionally gives these notes singly but usually in sequence; they are less resonant and musical than the equivalent cries of greenshanks and redshanks.

(3)   'A shrill liquid *chew-ew-chew-ew*, with the second syllable lower than the first, is distinct from and more musical than (2), although one may grade into the other' (Cramp and Simmons 1983). I heard the Sutherland birds use this cry when anxious near the nest or brood, and described it in my notes as a plaintive disyllabic *chic-choo*.

(4)   *Chip-chip-chip* is used in many different emotional situations on the breeding ground. These cries are less forceful and penetrating than those of greenshanks but are sufficiently loud and metallic to earn the wood sandpiper the nickname of 'The Tinsmith'.

(5)   The cock's copulation cries are described as *gip-gip-gip-bibi-bibi-bi-bi*, ending in a rattle which corresponds to the remarkable copulation cries of a cock redshank (Kirchner 1963).

(6)   Wood sandpipers use a quiet conversational *djup-djup* and a short *trill* when they are feeding or meeting one another in the bog. Parents use a variation of these cries to contact the chicks.

(7)   Situations of great anger mixed with fear lead to shrill screams *chrri-krschii*, which has its equivalent in the greenshank's vocabulary.

(8)   Exchanges at the nest are prefaced by the incoming bird using a sequence of *gip-bip* cries, which are not nearly so characteristic as the special *chipping* cries used by nest-relieving greenshanks.

(9)   The chicks have shrill piping cries.

Wood sandpipers apparently have a less distinctive battery of cries than redshanks or greenshanks; but a fuller analysis of sound recordings would doubtless reveal many additional signals.

PREDATORS

In Sutherland wood sandpipers are at some risk from hooded crows, hen harriers, short-eared owls, common and black-headed gulls, as well as foxes and sheep dogs. Possible predators in Spey Valley include hooded crow, hen harrier, sparrowhawk, buzzard and fox.

Their enemies in Schleswig-Holstein were few, but hooded crows and foxes were present on the breeding ground. There are more hazards in the forest marshes and peat bogs of northern Europe where potential predators include hen harrier, goshawk, merlin, hooded crow, Siberian jay and fox, but predation is not reported to be high.

FOOD

Wood sandpipers run, wade and probe for food on the more sheltered parts of wet, muddy banks of creeks and lagoons (K. H. Voous 1960). Very occasionally they capture insects in flight or by means of little jumps. Terrestrial and freshwater insects predominate in their diet in which plant matter is accidental or insignificant.

They feed on the larvae of Diptera and Trichoptera, particularly on beetles and water bugs. Earthworms *Lumbricus*, small freshwater molluscs, and occasionally frogs and small fishes are also taken. Hymenoptera, Lepidoptera and Libellan dragonflies are other items in their diet (Glutz 1977).

On the bogs of Schleswig-Holstein, H. Bucholz (1961–2) analysed some of their pellets, most of which were 5–10 mm long. These contained Dytiscids (most commonly *Rhantus* and *Agabus bipustulatus*, occasionally *Hydroporus*, *Coelambus impressopunctatus* and *Bidessus geminus*). Wood sandpipers also fed on Hydrophilids (particularly *Hydrobius fuscipes* and *Philydrus*), and occasionally took dor beetles Geotrupes (up to 22 mm). Two pellets held small weevils *Phyllobius*, one a single Carabid beetle *Pterostichus*, and one a bumble bee, probably *Bombus lucorun*. Small emperor moths *Saturnia pavonia* were also identified. Beetles, however, were probably their main food. In one pellet Hesse (1920) found nothing except a larva of *Stratiomys* and the Heteropteran *Plea*; others contained only beetles like *Haliplus*, *Hydroporus*, *Dytiscus*, *Berosus*, *Dryops* and *Helichus*.

In Estonia SSR, E. Kumari (1958) analysed the stomach contents of 27 breeding birds. All contained the remains of beetles, including 74 leaf beetles *Plateumaris*, a species which is also important in the diet of lapwing, golden plover, common curlew and greenshank. He also identified 44 Chironomid larvae, 25 Trichopteran larvae, the larvae of 22 Libellan dragonflies and one adult insect, 8 Heteropteran, 3 Hymenopteran (including two ants), 1 *Decticus verrucivorus* and a single Lepidopteran larva, together with 18,600 eggs of unidentified insects.

Outside the breeding season amphipod crustaceans *Gammaridae*, shorecrabs *Carcinas maenas*, molluscs *Planorbis*, and in Sénégal snails *Bulimus* are recorded (Glutz 1977).

DISTRIBUTION AND NUMBERS

The wood sandpiper has a Transpalearctic breeding range, mainly in the boreal but spilling into the temperate and tundra climatic zones. Its breeding limits range between the July isotherms of 50° and 73° F, thus showing a more northerly distribution than green sandpipers (Voous 1962).

Northern fringes of its range stretch to the north and north-west coasts of Norway up to the Murman Sea. It nests at 68° N on the Kanin Peninsula. Further east it breeds at the mouth of the River Pechora and nests at 68°30′ N on Jugor Peninsula, 68°10′ N on Jamal Peninsula, 69° N at Jenissej, 71° N in the north Siberian lowland bogs, 70°40′ N on the River Lena, 70°30′ N in the Indigirka River and 69° N on the River Kolyma. The most easterly known breeding habitats are located at the mouth of the Anadyr, Kamtschatka, and the Commander Island and Schumschu and Paramuschir in the N. Kurile Islands. Since 1894, wood sandpipers have been reported breeding sparingly in the Aleutians and probably in the Pribilov Islands. Southern boundaries run along the middle course of the Amur, S. Transbaikalia, Tannu-Ola, and the Altai Mountains, then through north Kasachstan and along the Ilek estuary on the middle course of the River Ural. They nest through Saratov and Rjasan in north-west Ukraine and in central Europe in the north-west of the German Federal Republic (Glutz 1977).

Changes in habitat have reduced the West German population (in Schleswig-Holstein and Hamburg) from about 50 pairs in 1968 to 40–45 pairs in 1973. It is doubtful if wood sandpipers now breed regularly in lower Saxony; and from 1900 onwards they have probably only occasionally and irregularly nested in East Germany. They no longer breed in Poland and the Netherlands. In 1959 there were between 200–300 breeding pairs in Denmark but there are now only about 100 pairs (T. Dybbro 1976). This decline might be considered along with that of the golden plover which has shown a tendency to spread north; and simultaneously to be in decline or retreat in the south of its range, probably partly due to climatic and habitat changes.

E. Merikallio (1958) suggested that 180,000 pairs possible then bred in Finland, but we have no precise details. In Norway, J. Kålås and I. Byrkjedal (1981) estimated a total of 27,000 breeding pairs although they do not nest in the south-west of the country. S. Ulfstrand and G. Högstedt (1976) suggest a total of 250,000 breeding pairs for Sweden; since 1960 they have nested regularly on Öland and Gotland. H. Veromann (1980) gives a total of 700 breeding pairs for Estonia; they are scarce in Latvia and Lithuania.

Wood sandpipers were suspected of breeding in Iceland in 1959 and in later years (A. Gardarsson 1956). Between 1959 and the first confirmed breeding in 1981 they had been repeatedly seen during the summer months, suggesting that nesting had occurred – possibly even regularly. Since 1981, breeding has been recorded in the same district in subsequent years (C. A. Galbraith and P. S. Thompson 1982).

There has been no substantiated record of breeding in England since John Hancock's discovery at Prestwick Carr in Northumberland in 1853, and possible breeding there in 1857.

Wood sandpipers have nested in Scotland at least since 1959, the same year that they were also first suspected of nesting in Iceland (I. Downhill and G. Dallas, 1959). Nests or broods have been recorded in Caithness, Sutherland, Ross, east and west Inverness and breeding has been strongly suspected in Aberdeen, Perth, north Argyll and the Outer Hebrides. In 1978 they probably reached their peak with seven sites occupied and between 4–10 pairs breeding. The previous peak year was 1972 when 5–8 pairs nested. In 1982 a pair hatched chicks in a Sutherland flow; and in 1984 two, and possibly three pairs bred on one flow in Ross and at least one pair in another (G. Ireson and C. Young, *pers comm*).

The attractive wood sandpiper, a most welcome addition to the breeding birds of Scotland, now joins greenshank, dotterel and whimbrel as one of the great prizes for wader watchers and photographers who go north in the spring.

GREEN SANDPIPER

Almost every wader watcher has a bogey – a bird which has fascinated and compelled, but finally defeated every effort to find its nest. The green sandpiper has been, and still is, mine!

In 1933, while waiting on a hillock overlooking a greenshank tarn in Spey Valley, I vividly remember watching a small to middle-sized wader, which looked like a greenshank although its darker mantle, vivid white tail and rump patch contrasted even more sharply in black and white. This wader, which I later identified as a green sandpiper, had sharp cries and a most dramatic song dance. It rose abruptly and acutely; and when high above the forest carried out a flight in which it zoomed and dived far more steeply than a greenshank.

That winter Jourdain sent me a copy of A. C. Bent's *Life Histories of North American Shorebirds* which contained his own concise account of the bird's behaviour in the forest marshes of northern Europe. I now read avidly about the two remarkable German foresters, Weise and Hintz, and another equally able self-taught naturalist, H. W. Wheelwright, who had separately discovered that the green sandpiper laid its eggs in the old nests of small forest birds and in the dreys of squirrels. The whole story was one of the romances of wader watching.

To my surprise, I found that green sandpipers, usually unmated cocks, also displayed over the forest marshes of Spey Valley in almost every year; occasionally, too, there were pairs. I watched singing males in 1933–34, 1936–41 and 1952. There were pairs in 1935, 1942 and 1948. Mr and Mrs Frank Clafton found a parent with a chick in a forest bog in 1959. In 1960 we watched a pair; one of the birds flew high up into another forest, but although a second bird was present no nest or young were found. In 1979 and 1980 John Kirby saw and tape-recorded a cock singing over another forest in Spey Valley.

The pioneering green sandpipers chose attractive haunts in Spey Valley. Their habitats contained a few small tarns and pools, many squashy dubs, streams and rills surrounded by scattered pines and alders overlooked by old Caledonian pinewoods. In 1960 the birds often fed in drainage ditches in a block of felled forest. In another part of this attractive marsh greenshanks nested, a pair of ospreys sometimes built an eyrie on a rickety old pine, and golden eagles formerly had an eyrie on the steep pine-studded hillside above. Scottish pine crossbills and crested tits were other regular nesters.

We have only once watched green sandpipers in the breeding season in Sutherland. In late June 1968 Robert Moss and I saw a pair together close to a loch on quite possible nesting ground.

In Germany Weise and Hintz worked in wooded marshes containing sluggish streams. Typical habitats in Denmark contain spruce thickets with wet marshy ground below, along with small ponds and ditches. Here the nests of song thrushes are often extremely well hidden; although usually built on trees near the edge of the forest, they are sometimes placed 10 m above ground. West of Tartu, in Estonia, John McNeile found the green sandpipers nesting in large tracts of swampy spruce, birch and popular. 'Much of the country was more or less primeval forest, a morass with dead and rotting branches lying half-submerged between the treacherous hummocks and moss-covered trees'. Swarms of mosquitoes and abundant ticks made the life of the hunter unpleasant and most exhausting.

Lennart Raner, who has an almost unique experience of nesting green sandpipers in southern Sweden, has recorded cocks arriving about 1 April. For the first two days they sing above their old territories. After the hen arrives the pair search for suitable nests, flying from tree to tree, *wipping* softly. For about two weeks the pair seems only to feed and sing, possibly a part of the mating phase. In the last week of April the green sandpipers again start nest site prospecting, with the cock perching on tree tops while the hen visits and scrapes in several different nests; sometimes the hen removes the strong roof of a squirrel's drey. When she has made her final choice she breaks down the rim, particularly if a song thrush's nest is too deep; Raner has found small flecks of down and moss in these.

In Denmark, Bill Hobson and his companions found that the best time to locate the nesting site was in mid April when the birds were making their mating flights and examining suitable old nests and squirrels' dreys. The hunters always tried to find all suitable old song thrushes' nests, carefully marking their position and destroying any difficult ones. All thrushes' nests in good positions and at low height were robbed and new thrushes' nests enclosed with wire netting. They soon learnt, however, that the green sandpipers preferred very old nests, those indeed which were almost dropping to pieces.

COURTSHIP AND TERRITORY

I never watched the full epigamic display on the ground. But in 1937 both David Lack and I, independently, saw unmated green sandpipers direct courtship displays at greenshanks. The greenshanks never reacted although the green sandpipers followed them when they flew away, singing and song dancing behind them. Each time that I saw a cock green sandpiper sexually approach a greenshank it drooped its wings but did not raise and beat them. Lennart Raner tells us, however, that this is abnormal behaviour; in full sexual displays cocks raise and beat their wings as the run towards the hens. In 1942 a hen greenshank in Spey Valley repelled a green sandpiper's attempt to copulate by shaking the bird off its back and pecking it violently, drawing out a bunch of feathers.

On Dovre Fjell, Norway, John Buxton watched two green sandpipers chasing over a marsh. When one pitched the other stood immediately behind, raising its wings and spreading its tail. This bird fluttered up and dropped just ahead of the other, which then repeated this behaviour. The tail of the bird in flight was fanned out and the grounded bird spread its tail and opened its wings. Leap-frogging continued for several

minutes before the two birds flew away.

We have watched two different forms of aerial pursuit flight. One closely resembled that of a greenshank, with the pursued bird twisting and swerving quite low over the ground and the pursuer carrying out a modified song dance just behind. The other reminded me of nuptial flights of a pair of greenshanks. The two birds rose high, turning and swerving in tight circles before flashing downwards over a ridge.

In Västergotland, Sweden, Lew Oring (1968) found that green sandpipers sometimes established and defended two quite separate and distinct territories, one for feeding and the other for nesting, separated by large blocks of quite unsuitable forest. With no competitors to restrain them, unmated cocks in Spey Valley established several display centres, with extremes up to 10 km apart. In each of these, with their complexes of pools and tarns, they periodically sang and displayed high in air.

DISPERSION AND BREEDING DENSITY

There is little on record about breeding density and spacing of green sandpipers. In south Sweden, where he carried out his research, Oring (1968) estimated that there were 20–25 breeding pairs in 50 km^2. The minumum distance between two nests was 400 m.

NEST, EGG AND CLUTCH

In Estonia and south Sweden old and disused, and occasionally new nests of song thrushes are favoured; jays' nests and squirrels' dreys are also on record. The nests of redwings, fieldfares, mistle thrushes and blackbirds have also been chosen by the green sandpipers. In Germany, in the 19th century, nests of red-backed shrike, wood pigeon and hooded crow were recorded.

One hen more than half filled a song thrush's nest with small pieces of lichen, the colour of which harmonised so well that even at short range, the eggs were extremely difficult to see (McNeile MS). The eggs are laid in nests from 0.25 m, exceptionally 27 m, above ground in deciduous trees (alder, birch or poplar) or in confiers (pine or spruce).

In early seasons, in central Europe, green sandpipers sometimes start to lay from the middle to end of April; but fresh eggs have been recorded as late as 18 June. In Scandinavia the earliest hens lay their first eggs in the last week of April but mostly not until May. Hens in the north of the their range delay laying until early June. The earliest record for Norway is of four-day old chicks on 9 May 1920; this clutch must have been completed about mid April.

There were some differences in the annual laying season in Estonia, where McNeile and his local assistants found 28 nests between 1935–38. In the earliest year – 1937 – eight clutches were completed between 28 April–9 May (mean 5 May). However, in 1936 the earliest completed clutch was about 1 May and the latest on 25 May; in 1938 the earliest was on 1 May and the latest on 31 May. This gives an average clutch date of 10 May for both years.

Green sandpipers' eggs are pointed ovate, sometimes sub-pyriform, and are slightly glossed. Their ground colour is often greenish but seldom as bright pea green as are some wood sandpipers' eggs. Their colours range from olive to buff and pale ochraceous and are flecked and spotted with purple and brown with lilac or ash grey undermarkings.

P. Rosenius (1937) gives a mean of 39.75 × 28,45 mm for 197 Swedish eggs. Danish eggs appear to be slightly smaller; T. Jessen (1931) measured 68 which averaged 38.70 × 28.40 mm.

The estimated weight of a fresh egg is 15.5 gm (M. Schönwetter 1963) (Table 3). Four eggs from Schleswig-Holstein, incubated at most 2–3 days, each weighed between 15.08–16.25 gm (mean 15.56 gm) (H. Kirchner 1972). A clutch of four eggs weighs roughly 73% of the hen's body weight (Table 2). Rosenius (1973) weighed 197 eggshells which ranged from 0.69–1.01 gm (mean 0.84 gm); and 125 eggshells weighed by Schönwetter (1963) averaged 0.85 gm.

A normal clutch consists of four, and occasionally of three eggs (Table 4). Jourdain (1940) mentions a clutch of seven eggs which two different hens had laid in the same nest. In Estonia, McNeile (MS) recorded 3/3, 21/4 (3.87) in first clutches and 4/4 (4.0) in replacement clutches. Three replacement clutches were produced in 9, 15 and 17 days (mean 13.7 days). Raner tells us that a hen takes 4–6 days to lay her clutch of four eggs, the intervals depending on the food available in particular years.

INCUBATION

Steady incubation appears to start when the clutch is complete. The cock is extremely quiet while the hen is sitting, feeding beside one of the many small pools. After incubation has started he often feeds up to half a mile from the nest, but never apparently as far away as do some greenshanks.

Raner and Hobson both found that early in incubation the cock and hen often changed over 3–4 times daily. The cock arrived, called quietly, and the hen left the nest silently; perhaps when about 100 m away she uttered a few fluke-like calls. By then the cock, which had pitched on a tree top, slipped quietly off the nest, usually out of sight of the watcher. Later in incubation the exchanges took place twice daily, one particularly about 18.00 hours. Otto Steinfatt and H. Kirchner had similar experiences in Schleswig-Holstein where the pairs they studied changed over at the nest twice daily. Kirchner watched the homing bird pitch on a tree top while the sitting bird flew off. Sometimes, however, the incubating bird quit the nest immediately it heard it mate's warning cries in the distance.

T. Jessen (1931) estimated that incubation lasted from 20–23 days from the laying of the first egg in the clutch to the hatch of the last. Raner, however, has found that the chicks jump down from the nest 20–21 days after the start of incubation.

Towards hatching, a brooding green sandpiper sometimes drops to the ground and gives a distraction display. It would be fascinating to observe whether it quits the nest using a special distraction flight with spread tail and quickly beating wings.

H. W. Wheelwright (1864) and W. Grossmann (1918) found large fragments of eggshell in nests after the young had left.

YOUNG

Hintz watched newly-hatched chicks drop unhurt to the ground where they hid themselves; once they almost immediately started to swim across a pool. Raner has watched and photographed parents calling from the ground to encourage chicks to jump out of the nest.

The bill of the chick is blue-black, irides dark brown, feet bluish grey with bluish nails; toes and ankles are dusky. The nape is blackish brown with greyish white down; eye stripes and cheeks are greyish white and the upper breast consists of white down with sooty black bases.

At first both parents guard and lead the chicks. J. Rohde (*in* Glutz 1977) recorded adults and chicks moving at least 300 m on their first day. Steinfatt (1940) found that the family had moved 500 m from the nesting tree by the time the chicks were only a week old. At a later stage, Grote (1939) watched the parents flying round the head of an intruder. After about 10 days the hen usually leaves the brood in charge of the cock, thus resembling greenshank and many other waders. Fledging period is about 28 days (Cramp and Simmons 1983).

VOICE

Lew Oring (1968) tape-recorded and later made sonagrams of the songs and calls of green sandpipers in southern Sweden. A full summary and analysis is given in Cramp and Simmons (1983).

He identified two different kinds of song, given from the time the birds on their breeding grounds until the chicks are free-flying. The greatest intensity of song is recorded between the arrival of the hens and the laying of their first eggs. As with greenshanks, lesser peaks are given during egg laying and hatching. The first type of song is delivered on the ground, from a perch, or in the air; and a more subdued version is given when the pair are together at the nest, in flight, taking off, or putting down. The second type is part of the song dance in switchbacks over mating and feeding territories, especially in the early morning and evening; it is also sometimes delivered by a cock song dancing over a hen.

(1)   We have described the song heard in Spey Valley as *tit-tit-tit toorhee-toorhee-toorhee-tit-tit*, in various different sequences.

(2)   Mate call, a chattering *tit-it* continued with musical *tooee-tooees*, is given on the ground or from a perch, from the arrival of the hen to the start of incubation and again during the hatch.

(3)   Contact call is described as *di-di-di* (Glutz 1977).

(4)   Scolding *chip* cries which, to us, sound like *tit-tit-tit*, are used when the chicks are in danger, above feeding or nesting territories, before departing to or from the nest, and in the course of aerial pursuits (Oring 1968).

(5)   The alarm-flee call, a 'loud shrill sharply ascending' single or short series of cries given from a perch when adult or brood are in danger. These cries are sometimes given from the nest before incubation has started, or when an intruding pair attempts to challenge the tenant for a feeding or nesting territory (Kirchner 1972).

(6)   A musical *too-eet too-eet too-eet*, is often given when the bird is flushed.

(7)   Chick cries include various persistent and subdued sounds used in contact, mild distress, and great distress (Oring 1968).

PREDATORS

The literature tells us little about the predators of green sandpipers in their nesting haunts. In southern Sweden, however, jays are particularly deadly; in 1983 and 1984 Raner found four nests all of which they later robbed. Hobson also found eggshells which jays had sucked; nests in open sites on the edges of woods were particularly at risk. Hooded crows and red squirrels are other likely nest predators; and foxes would take any chicks they might find. On migration peregrines are often present. Where they are nesting in the same habitats, goshawks and sparrowhawks could be dangerous enemies of this small wader.

FOOD

Green sandpipers feed in shallow ditches or muddy streams and beside small lochs and tarns, but in Spey Valley they appeared to avoid the edges of large lochs.

In summer they feed largely on insects and their larvae. Coleoptera, Trichoptera, Diptera and the larvae of Culcidae are taken on the surface of muddy ground and in shallow water. They sometimes take fish fry up to 4–5 cm long. A. Norlin (1969), in Sweden, recorded larvae of *Haliplus* and *Corixa*, and adult Dytiscids, Hydrophilids and *Haliplus*. In the Ukraine, stomach contents contained 34 Diptera (15 *Eristalis*, 2 Culcids and 9 Tipulid larvae), 1 Elaterid, 1 Psychid and 1 Chironomid larva, 8 beetles (4 Curculionids, 2 Hydrophilids, 2 *Bembidion assimile*), 5 Hymenoptera, 5 scorpions and waterbugs (Nepidae and Naucoridae), 5 dragonfly larvae, 1 Noctuid moth, 6 unidentified insects and 1 spider (O. B. Kistyakivski 1957). At Saratov, USSR, the remains of many green plants were identified in birds collected in mid summer; spring food included aquatic beetles and dragonfly larvae. Ernest Blezard found amphipods and some larvae cases of caddis flies in a cock killed in Cumberland in March.

Philip Burton (1971) examined the stomach contents of five migrant green sandpipers from Afghanistan. There were amphipods in four and fragments of plants in two; single stomachs held water beetles *Haliphus fulvus*, unidentified Hydrophilids, Ostracod crustaceans and gastropod snails.

DISTRIBUTION AND NUMBERS

The green sandpiper has an almost Transpalearctic distribution, covering the boreal conifer forest zone and the mountains; it also sporadically breeds in the north temperate zone. Breeding limits lie between the July isotherms 59°F and 66°F (K. H. Voous 1962).

In North America the green sandpiper is replaced by the solitary sandpiper *Tringa solitaria*, which also lays its eggs in old nests in rather similar habitats. These two species, therefore, are probably different forms of an originally Holarctic species.

The regular breeding area starts in Denmark, where it colonised in the 1950s. Thence it passes through south-east and central Norway up to the line Mandal – West Dovre

Fjell – Surnadal – Grane/Nordland. It then runs eastwards to the lower Kolyma and the cost of the Sea of Ochotsk, up to the Santar Islands and the lower Amur.

Northern limits of the bird's distribution go to 65°30′ N in Norway, where nesting took place in Finnmark at 69° N in 1960–62. It nests up to 68° N in Swedish and Finnish Lapland and so along the White Sea up to the Arctic Circle. From here it runs to the northern taiga zone of the upper Pechora 66°30′ N, Ob 64°–65° N, Jenissej 66°30′ N, Lena 70° N and east Siberia up to 69° N on the Kolyma. The southern boundaries are not well known, but are along the northern fringes of the steppe zone.

In central Europe it breeds in north USSR, south to North Germany and the Baltic states. Numbers have probably declined in Poland and the Ukraine through changes in habitat. It has possibly occasionally bred in the Netherlands and sometimes in Switzerland, Tyrol, Italy, Carinthia, Jugoslavia, Transylvania and the Black Sea coast in Crimea and Caucasia. In Asia it breeds north to Tobolsk and south to N. Persia, Transcaspia, Turkestan, Semipalatinsk, Altai, and N. W. Mongolia.

The only records of green sandpipers breeding in Britain are those for Levens Park, Westmorland, in 1917 and Spey Valley, Inverness-shire, in 1959; in neither case was the nest found but young were seen with excited adults.

After their colonising of Denmark in the 1950s, breeding numbers rose to about 40 pairs in the mid 1970s (T. Dybbro 1976). J. Kålås and I. Byrkjedal (1981) estimate that about 13,000 pairs breed in Norway, all except 10 pairs in the south. Sweden carries a large population, which S. Ulfstrand and G. Högstedt (1976) estimate at 60,000 pairs. Large numbers also breed in Finland, but there is no later estimate than the 22,000 pairs suggested by Merikallio in 1958. Estonia, SSR, carries about 700 pairs. Green sandpipers are also breeding in good numbers in Latvia but are scarce in Lithuania.

In many ways the green sandpiper, with its thrilling song dance, is one of the most exciting waders in Europe. It will always test the skill and patience of the most dedicated wader watcher as he splashes through forest mires, tormented by a thousand biting insects, but ever hopeful of spotting that head and beak projecting over the edge of an old thrush's nest.

9: The Woodcock

Just after dawn on a cold March morning many years ago, I was walking through a glen in Co. Antrim; higher up the stream dippers were nesting on a bank. In the grey half-light a dark bird flew overhead giving deep frog-like croaks followed by a sequence of sharp cries almost like those of a pied wagtail. A few minutes later the bird appeared again, apparently travelling on the same route. This was my introduction to the mysterious woodcock – a strange bird, usually just a voice moving above the trees or flying swiftly overhead on its famous roding circuits; or you briefly see a brown-backed wader with its long bill held downwards.

Watching the bird feed in a ditch or marsh, or in the undergrowth of the forest, the shortness of its grey-pink legs surprises you. But you seldom see the woodcock before it sees you; and then it rises and deftly swerves through the trees. Sometimes, however, if you stand beside a woodcock brooding her eggs, you see the rich red-brown mantle with its pale greyish patches and the black bars going from side to side on its crown and neck. She may now shut her brown eyes, which would otherwise shine in the sun, and occasionally she lies on her eggs as if she was dead. Arthur Whitaker described one sitting on a nest in green grass, a foot high in a hay field bordering a plantation. 'Even when the grass above her was parted she lay on the nest with eyes tightly closed. We stroked her and almost had to lift her off'.

Woodcocks favour many different kinds of woodland and forest country. In the midlands and southern England they often choose large woods of oak, birch and hazel, with trees of different sizes, but particularly those containing large open rides or paths along which the roding cocks fly. I sometimes had the good luck to listen to woodcocks flying above the trees while enjoying the pungent scent of wood smoke from a keeper's cottage in a clearing. In places like these, Whitaker found nests in birch scrub overgrown with bushes and brambles.

John Walpole-Bond writes about the woodcock's usual preference for large woods in Sussex; 'occasionally smaller coverts are patronised even in spinneys, shaws and shrubberies'. A few pairs nest on rough heaths around and within the open spaces of the woodland. Spots rich in oak, birch and hazel sometimes contain nests close to or actually at the feet of trees.

Holly and laurel bushes often feature in woodcock haunts. Monica Shorten (1974) believes that the shining leaves of these shrubs prevent loss of heat through radiation as well as 'sheltering the birds from the coldness of grey skies'. Woodcock often collect in boggy patches in rides or clearings, along the edges of small streams, or in ditches in the policies of large mansions. These enable them to feed without having to make perilous flights away from their nesting grounds.

I had watching stances in several different kinds of woodland in Spey Valley. The hen woodcocks nested in wet and often soggy birch scrub over which the cocks frequently flew and extended their flights over large expanses of open moor. I soon learnt that their flight paths were irregular and of differing lengths. In a large pine wood near Loch Garten, where the old trees were well-spaced, I used to sit up on the heath edge after the crossbills had gone to roost. There I remember occasional glimpses into the courtship and display of this remarkable wader. I never had enough time to make a connected history, but what I did see was always fascinating to watch and inevitably puzzling to interpret.

The woodcocks favoured edges of clearings where they had no wader neighbours; but curlew, golden plover, snipe and oystercatcher always nested and red grouse held territories on the adjacent moor. Hooded crows had well-concealed nests high up in the pines; and the cocks' roding circuits were always within a sparrowhawk's hunting range.

In Rothiemurchus Forest, woodcocks made roding flights over pines, birches and expanses of moorland. Here they nested in open but soggy birch scrub as well as on dry heath close to paths. In the drier pinewoods crested tits bored holes in old stumps and Scottish pine crossbills often sat on their nests in tall pines or on smaller trees scattered through the bog. The old pines and hillside birches around Loch-an-Eilean and Loch Gamhna were other favourite roding grounds.

Some habitats in north-east Scotland are different. In 1970 John Tester and Adam Watson (1973) studied the spacing and territorialism of woodcock to the south of the Dee in Kincardine. Nine home-ranges included Norway spruce, sitka spruce and Douglas fir; and in three other haunts the woodland was broken by mixed strips of hydroelectric lines, rides, paths, planted and felled trees, as well as by large tracts of pasture and ploughed land.

After watching the cock roding over several small plantations of young pines and birches, near a north Sutherland shooting lodge in 1914, Walpole-Bond and a friend found the nest 'beside a small sapling fir growing in a tiny clearing in a spinney'; woodcocks dislike woods with closed canopies and no openings. Sometimes, however, they display over open country. In July, W. R. P. Bourne (1972) watched woodcocks roding over large bogs and moors on Colonsay in the Inner Hebrides.

RODING

Soon after sunset, or shortly before dawn, woodcocks make roding flights which cover irregular beats over woodland and open country for periods lasting for fifteen to forty-five minutes. The cock flies in rough circuits from a few metres or up to over 30 m above the tree tops. In his roding flight he flies quite swiftly; and then suddenly hesitates and half-flutters while giving frog-like croaks followed by sharp *tiziks*. Individual cocks have quite distinguishable voice patterns. For example, a cock may give two, three, or four croaks, perhaps two separated croaks, followed by a quick double croak. On 3 February, Graham des Forges (*pers. comm.*) recorded six roding flights in 11 minutes; but he did not hear the croaks as well as the *chizik* calls until 6 February.

A particular cock's flight path sometimes takes him right away over a distant ridge, when he disappears into another cock's home range. I have often watched a cock chasing a trespasser suddenly change direction after first hearing the pattern of the roding bird's calls. He then put on speed and chased his rival while giving quick excited *sip-sip-sip* cries. Towards the end of a chase pursuer and pursued sometimes flew beside one another without aggression before parting and going on their different routes.

During roding I have also seen what appeared to be sex-chases, the roding bird twisting after the other in a typical wader sexual pursuit pattern and giving high-pitched squeaking *pip-pip-pips*. Occasionally, when I was able to watch the chase for a long distance, the two birds certainly did not re-start roding circuits. On 19 March 1946 I saw two cocks chasing a third bird, possibly a hen. The pursued bird dipped almost to the ground as it swerved through the trees. On 13 June 1978, Dr K. J. Brewster saw a woodcock join a croaking male, and two loops later a third woodcock joined them. Two birds were 'peeanting'; the observer assumed that this was a kind of nuptial display. Graham des Forges, who has done such splendid work on woodcock in Sussex, has sometimes seen two, three, and four woodcocks flying together or after one another during roding. Dozens, or even hundreds, of times he has watched two woodcocks together, but believes that these were usually cocks and that hens were seldom involved.

For 33 days, between 11 April–29 June 1970, Tester and Watson (1973) studied roding flights in nine home ranges from about half-an-hour before sundown until it was too dark to see the birds. They assumed that each woodcock nightly covered the same ground and were able to predict accurately when two or more birds would meet. The rough roding circuits were possibly traditional and 'aligned with topographical and other features of the habitat, so that new recruits came from a population of birds that already knew the routes'. When a roding bird was killed, in June, by collision with an electric wire, another bird, following the same flight path, replaced it within two days. All the roding circuits were of an irregular oval or circular shape, with an average coverage of 6.00–12.75 ha. However, one cock, to the east of Banchory, had a more isolated flight-range which covered 19.5 ha.

Graham Hirons (1980) found that, in Derbyshire, roding grounds overlapped and were not completely exclusive. Two cocks sometimes followed approximately similar flight paths. On the same evening one flew over less than a minute after the other. The roding cocks periodically alighted and stood in openings of the woods. Marked cocks often fed in the same part of a wood, sometimes less than 30 m apart and without overt aggression. Radio-tagged cocks had flight circuits covering from 43–112 ha. In Ireland five roding cocks flew in together and landed in a field in a tight group where upon they jumped up in bunches, probably in aggression before dispersing and flying away (H. J. Wilson 1983).

There is still much to be discovered about the functions of roding flights. In Sweden, Professor V. Marcström (1974) shot all woodcocks using croaking calls which passed over a particular spot several days in succession; only two out of 400 of these birds proved to be hens. Using similar methods, M. Hulten (1970) recorded that only 11 hens (6.5%) were shot from birds making roding flights; these particular birds had been silent.

(1)   Roding flights appear to mark out the sexual home ranges of dominant cocks, thus enabling them to meet and copulate with hens, which some observers believe call them down (C. M. Pay (1937); Y. Hagen (1950); D. Müller-Using (1960); and others).

(2)   There is possibly a different pattern in high populations, with rivals frequently intruding on the master cock's home-range. Hirons (1980) showed, by radio-tagging cocks in a study area in Derbyshire, that roding periodically ceased for intervals of from one to at least 11 days. 'In every instance the marked cock was found to be accompanying a second bird and then both flew off together if flushed .... On two occasions nests were subsequently found in the same area after the cock had begun roding again'. It is likely, however, that while the master cock is consorting with a particular hen for a few days, less dominant intruders are able to mate with other hens within the roding circuit.

(3)   Tester and Watson (1973) suggest that roding enables cocks to assess numbers and dominance and possibly assists the groups to replace any casualities without delay.

SEXUAL BEHAVIOUR

The similar plumage of cock and hen makes interpretation of their sexual behaviour extremely difficult; there is still much confusion about the usual patterns of pairing. O. von Zedlitz (1927) in Sweden, H. Bettmann (1961) in Germany, and P. Géroudet (1952) in Switzerland, suggest that woodcocks are promiscuous, the hens calling down different cocks on different evenings. On the other hand, Otto Steinfatt (1938) concluded that woodock were monogamous but that after a brief period of pairing and sexual activity, the cock lost interest in the hen while she was sitting on the eggs.

Formal polyandry, with two or more cocks firmly mated to the same hen, is an unlikely pattern as cocks do not take part in incubation and in rearing of the young. Polygyny or promiscuity is more probable. If there are surplus hens in the home-range of the dominant cock, other males may fertilise them for first, second or replacement clutches while he is courting, guarding and coupling with a particular hen.

My own observations suggest, however, that the cock and hen stay together at least for a short period; I have found three nests within 50 m of where I previously flushed two woodcocks squatting close together. On 20 April 1937, Arthur Whitaker also flushed two woodcocks side by side from a suitable nest site in the middle of a patch of dog mercury. On 1 May he found a hen sitting on three fresh eggs, less than 30 m from where he had flushed the pair. In 1976, 1977 and 1978, des Forges (*pers. comm.*) flushed two woodcocks 'very close together and found nests within 100 m or so'. On 28 February 1977 he flushed a pair within a metre of each other; 'and between the two was an egg'. It was cold to touch and there was no nest. In April 1940, however, I watched two cocks with fanned, erected tails and drooping wings encircling and later aerially chasing what I took to be a single hen. On another evening I flushed a group of about ten woodcock participating in a display which I could not accurately interpret.

There is still little knowledge about the association of the cock and hen after the eggs are laid. In April 1940, while watching a nest on which the hen was sitting on four fresh eggs, I saw the roding cock – which had already passed over several times – suddenly drop down to the nest and display to the sitting hen. Almost immediately she rose and flew off, followed by the cock. I also saw a roding cock suddenly dip and flutter, with his legs dangling, over a small clump of pines and birches from which a second woodcock rose which he then chased in a twisting flight. Two days later I searched the clump and flushed a hen from four slightly incubated eggs. At four nests watched during the early morning and late evening, the roding cock appeared to have no influences on the hen's feeding spells.

A few observers have had similar experiences. W. Pulchalski (1938) watched a cock fly down to a hen which was sitting on an incomplete clutch, and then copulate with her. On successive evenings David Stubbert and a friend saw a cock drop down to a nest, in a clump of trees close to a house, and fly away with the hen. On several nights Macomb Chance climbed to the top of a tall tree and watched a hen fly out while a cock was roding overhead; the cock had already passed over several times without incident. The hen eventually returned on roughly the same line and the nest was found on the following morning. Walpole-Bond (1938), in St Leonard's Forest, Sussex, saw a second woodcock suddenly dart up to the roding cock and then return almost immediately. 'Next day a nest was there found, and the presumption is that the bird which had arisen the preceding evening was the sitting female, but, of course, the evidence was by no means conclusive'. One of des Forges's correspondents recorded similar behaviour.

There is no connected history of the sexual behaviour of the woodcock. I once saw a pair fluttering a couple of metres or so above ground but they saw me and flew away before I could interpret their behaviour. I have also watched a pair courting during the afternoon; the cock raised his tail and swayed from side to side, apparently showing off his chestnut-coloured flanks, while he pursued the hen which ran forward with raised tail and loosely-drooped wings. J. Martinel and G. Chantrel (1977) watched almost complete courtship sequences. One bird stood with vertical tail and the other with tail horizontal and head slightly raised. One turned 180° to face away; the other stretched its neck, head and bill up to 45°. There was mock feeding, fluttering, jumps with half-open wings, and mutual bill tapping followed by two quick couplings.

By means of radio-tagging, Hirons discovered that the cock stays close to the hen during courtship and egg laying; this short pair-bond endures from 3–4 days and exceptionally up to 11 days. More than one cock may briefly stay with the hen on the ground, but she may also change partners during the courtship period. After the hen has completed her clutch (once after her third egg) the cock resumes his roding flights. One cock may fertilise as many as four different hens (Hirons). Pulchalski (1938) and Haller (1944) describe the cock standing upright and violently flapping his wings while copulating with the hen which had previously squatted near the nest and now gave cackling cries.

Y. Hagen (1950) suggests that the white tips of the tail feathers reflect light and possibly have an important signalling function during displays which are carried out in the half-light of early morning and late evening.

AMERICAN WOODCOCK *Philohela minor*

The American woodcock makes display flights in wide circles and ellipses, each lasting about one minute. After chasing away rivals the cock glides back to his stance in zig-zags. These flights prompt a hen to fly up, and when she alights the cock ceases to give 'peeanting' cries; then uttering his *tuko* calls, he advances stiffly towards her and raises his wings just before coupling.

In Massachusetts, American woodcock are polygynous and probably promiscuous. In the same spring 23 different cocks were captured on different singing stances from 400 m to 5.6 km apart. On one night a cock was trapped 4.2 km from his usual territory, but on the next he was displaying from his own stance. This behaviour probably leads to a cock mating with several hens on different sites. A cock American woodcock thus resembles master great snipe or master ruffs which periodically desert their own stances to visit leks as far as 10 km away from their own.

'Floating males', which have no settled territories, probably display over greater expanses of ground than do cocks with firm stances. W. G. Sheldon (1971) found that the distance between nesting and feeding areas of 55 singing sites ranged from 15–400 m. The cocks usually flew from their daytime haunts to their singing stances without displaying over the intervening ground. Sitting hens apparently go only short distances to feed.

Intriguing research lies ahead for the student who makes a comparative study of these two quite different woodcock species.

DISPERSION AND BREEDING DENSITY

I have found two nests within 100 m in the same wood, but have no precise measurements in a known population. In Derbyshire, Hirons found four nests within a radius of 170 m; two were only 75 m apart, and a replacement clutch was laid 300 m from the original nest site. S. H. Smith (1913) recorded three nests in a wood of 0.8 km²; and S. R. Douglas (1917) knew of a 62 ha wood in which 50 nests were found in a single season.

We do not know how the hens disperse, apparently without territorial fighting. From our own experience of waders, however, we believe that the hens probably have a considerable knowledge of the presence and movements of their neighbours.

Near Potsdam, West Germany, D. Flössner (*in* Glutz 1977) reckoned there were 10 breeding hens in 2,800 ha (0.36 hen/km²). In Småland, Sweden, there were often 3–4, and in one year six nests, on an island of 10 ha, suggesting a breeding density of 0.35 hen/10 ha. At Vogelsberg, Hesse, in 1964, there were high numbers in a tract of wet conifers mixed with birches, where probably 6–8 breeding 'pairs' nested in 10–12 ha (0.62 hen/km²) (Glutz 1977).

NEST, EGG AND CLUTCH

I have watched a woodcock, accompanied by a second bird, which I assumed was a cock, preparing a nest cup on the edge of an old pinewood. Early on 6 April 1920, a second bird was not present when Whitaker put up a woodcock from a fresh scoop on the floor below young birch trees. However, this bird was possibly about to lay. I once saw a woodcock go into a clump of trees at about 1500 hours and within an hour flushed her from a nest with two eggs, one of which was warmer than the other. I have twice flushed woodcocks in the evening from incomplete clutches of two and three eggs respectively, which suggests that some presumed hens brood incomplete clutches at night.

Woodcocks scrape out shallow hollows which are often lined with dead leaves and dry grass and are occasionally quite bulky. A Yorkshire nest was lined loosely but fairly thickly with 'dry grass, fir needles and ash seed pods ... which appeared to have been either scraped or collected from the adjoining ground which was bare shale and freely scattered with both fir needles and ash pods' (Whitaker diaries).

A nest is often placed beside a tree or sapling or under a dead branch or bramble on the edge of a wood, or at the side of a ride, or in an opening or clearing. Eggs, however, are occasionally laid in quite long heather, in rushy bogs, or in bracken on hillsides, fully 400 m from the nearest wood (Nethersole-Thompson and Watson 1974). In wet habitats the eggs are sometimes laid in sedge or in grassy humps. Horst (1938) gives average nest measurements as 3.5–4.5 cm in depth and 12–15 cm in diameter.

R. Morgan and M. Shorten (1974) give mid March to mid April as the peak laying period. Early dates include 2 March 1975 in Hampshire and 5 March 1956 in Surrey. Whitaker found that seven clutches were completed between 28 March–23 June (mean 15 April). My own average data for 26 clutches from Spey Valley was 11 April.

On the Continent, laying starts from mid March onwards. In Luxemburg, Hulten (1970) found that over half the hens were brooding in the second half of March and that the earliest chicks were recorded on 24 April. In lower Saxony, 32 clutches were completed between 1 April–30 June, with seven between 1–14 April; the last unfledged chicks were found at the end of July. The main laying season in Denmark ranges between 24 March–22 April; very late clutches have been recorded in September and even in early October. The earliest eggs were laid between 1 May–20 June in Finland, with a peak between 11–20 May. In western Siberia the main laying season is in late May (Glutz 1977).

Woodcocks eggs are usually ovate to blunt-ovate in shape. Their ground colour varies from greyish white to light buff brown, sometimes reddish brown, and they are blotched and spotted with red-brown on a glossy surface. Two eggs found in Hockley

Woods in Yorkshire were of an almost erythristic type; they were long and heavily blotched with chestnut caps. A. L. Thomson (1907) recorded a clutch of pure white eggs from Glenbervie, Kincardine; these are now in the Aberdeen University Collection. H. E. Dresser also knew of a pure white clutch. Hugh Blair tells us that he examined a single egg showing faint smudges of violet on a warm cream ground and a complete clutch all of which were veiled with lime. These scarce varieties are extremely beautiful.

One hundred British eggs had a mean of 44.2 × 33.5 mm (Jourdain 1940). This differed little from a larger series of 217 eggs from Sweden which averaged 44.2 × 33.8 mm (P. Rosenius 1973). A short series from central Europe, 43.9 × 33.2 mm (44), was slightly smaller (W. Haller). G. Nemetschek (1974) found a small egg measuring 38.9 × 32.7 mm. Marcström (1975) records 23–26 gm as the weight of a fresh egg in Sweden. Assuming the average body weight of a breeding hen as 320 gm, a clutch of four is only about 31.0% of hen's body weight, very light eggs for the bird's size (Table 2). One hundred and ninety-four eggshells ranged from 1.15–1.6 gm (mean 1.4 gm) (Glutz 1977).

At one of my nests the third and fourth eggs were laid on alternate days at intervals of *c* 48 hours. Pay (1937) recorded that eggs in Sweden were occasionally laid at intervals of 3–4 days. I. Clausager (1970) noted that a four-egg clutch in Denmark is often completed in five days, with an interval of two days between the third and fourth eggs. Morgan and Shorten (1974) record that some hens lay their eggs daily, at approximate intervals of 24 hours, but that others occasionally lay on alternate days.

The normal clutch consists of four eggs; genuine clutches of three or five are rare or occasional, and six is exceptional and probably due to two hens laying in the same scoop (Table 4). Three hundred and thirty British clutches averaged 3.84 eggs (W. B. Alexander 1945–47). Edgar Chance's collection contained notes of 1/3, 20/4, 1/5 (mean 4.0); and my own records are of 3/3, 25/4 (mean 3.89).

W. M. Congreve (1924) recorded a replacement clutch 7–9 m from where the first clutch had been taken. Chance recorded an apparent replacement clutch completed in 20 days; but it is not certain whether the same hen was responsible. Hirons (1980) discovered that a radio-tagged hen, which had lost her brood, re-laid 12 days later.

O. von Zedlitz (1927) concluded that some hens were regularly double brooded in southern Sweden. Hens are certainly able to produce two clutches in the same year, but not necessarily to the same cock. In a Suffolk wood, however, where only one 'pair' was known, Eric Hosking saw a brood in June and a nest with three eggs in July. W. B. Alexander (1945–47) noted six examples of two successive clutches in the same scoop; and two instances of cocks and hens displaying and mating after the hen had reared a brood. However, the birds were unmarked and the shape and colour patterns of the eggs were not recorded. Sequential breeding, as reported in the golden plover (Parr 1979) is also possible. Full proof of double brooding, therefore, must await the results of telemetry and a 'marked' population.

INCUBATION

To the best of our knowledge, the hen alone sits. Steady incubation starts after she has completed the clutch; some hens, however, brood incomplete clutches at night. The hen sits very closely, but des Forges (1975) noticed that one changed position about every hour, usually by 90°. 'Sometimes only 10 minutes elapses and, now and then, having changed position and settled down, the bird immediately changed again'. Before changing position the hen made head movements; each time she shuffled and poked her bill downwards as she did when returning to the nest from feeding. Sometimes her eyes were at least half closed and occasionally fully closed. Preening of tail, back and breast feathers was frequently recorded and 'if disturbed, the hen raised her neck and fully opened her eyes'.

At four nests, which I watched during incubation, the hens left for 25–40 minutes, and occasionally longer, in the early morning and late evening. On returning, they often crashed down noisily close to their nests. Haller (1932), on the other hand, noticed that the hen put down 1.5–30 m from the nest and approached it while 'false preening', later going through the motions of turning the eggs.

Des Forges in Sussex has learnt much about incubation. Between 5–24 March 1975, assisted by W. H. Lambert, he watched a sitting woodcock for a total period of 24 hours of daylight. This hen left her nest on average four times daily for periods of 14–40 minutes (mean 27.4 minutes), at intervals of 2 hours 35 minutes. On the two days before hatching, however, she left only twice. Before leaving, she turned her head quickly from side to side at intervals of a few seconds. At first she did not fully raise her head, but before she rose from the eggs she did so two or three times. While feeding, she never went more than 30 m; four times she only moved 0.5–4 m and then flew off in the direction of her feeding ground.

Between 10–25 April 1976 des Forges (1977) made further observations at a second nest, placing a thermistor under the eggs and connecting it to a chart-recording machine. This hen left the nest 5–7 times during periods of 24 hours; the average absence was 29 minutes (range 12–46 minutes in 81 instances). She always left the nest shortly before sunrise, the average of 13 departure times being 45 minutes before sunrise (range 39–52 minutes). He recorded an average of 14 minutes before sunset for 15 departure times (range 38 minutes before, to 15 minutes after sunset). She did not quit her nest during the night.

The cryptic mantle of a sitting woodcock blends so well with its environment among the leaves and short vegetation that she is extremely difficult to spot. When flushed, she usually flies straight off her eggs and, in our experience, never attempts to give distraction displays. At a nest which I watched in 1935, however, the hen ran off her eggs when she was disturbed; she was extremely noisy while returning, rustling through leaves in the undergrowth.

Some hens appear to be most hardy. In 1966, in Moray, D. R. Rose met with a hen which sat through snowfalls of up to 50 cm, apparently never quitting the nest for a week (Shorten 1974).

I have only measured one incubation period; hatching took place 24 days after I had found the complete clutch. In Sweden, Pay (1937) recorded a period of 23 days; Glutz (1977), 20–23 days in Switzerland; and Steinfatt (1938), 22 days in East Prussia. Morgan and Shorten (1974) give 21–24 days (mean 22.3 days) for the incubation periods of seven clutches detailed in BTO records.

HATCHING

At one nest I felt a bump or roughness on the shells approximately 60 hours before the chicks hatched; and at another there was an interval of approximately 36 hours between bump and hatch. At Steinfatt's nest in East Prussia, however, the last chick hatched 31 hours after the first egg was pipped.

While the chicks are still in the egg the hen uses special throaty cries to communicate with them. These are later used to control the chicks when they are hatched.

Most hens leave all the large fragments of eggshell in the nest or drop them on the edge. Small pieces are usually left in the scoop or are poked under the lining. Occasionally, however, a hen lifts and flies away with a large shell fragment, one of which I found about 75 m from a nest. Watching from a hide, Eric Hosking saw the hen fly off with large portions which she apparently dropped in flight and then returned to the nest.

Steinfatt had a most exciting experience. When the newly-hatched chicks would not follow her, the hen lifted the eggshells on to the edge of the scoop and then brooded the chicks. Later she lifted one of the chicks at the end of her bill and carried it about 1.5 m; she then dealt with the other chicks in the same way. After brooding her family in this position for 45 minutes she again picked them up in her bill and transported them a further 2–3 m; but she did not attempt to fly over a small fence which the observer had erected. Finally, she returned and replaced the eggshells in the scoop.

Graham des Forges did not see the hen touch the hatched eggshells at any of his nests. In one clutch two out of three eggs split along the long axis; but in another, 'three eggs opened in the more usual way and one along the long axis'. Eggs splitting lengthwise are also recorded in the American woodcock but we have insufficient records to assess the proportion in the European species.

In the British Isles, between 1945–71, Morgan and Shorten (1974) recorded that 288 out of 453 eggs (63.6%) hatched. Predators destroyed 68 (15%); 61 eggs (13.4%) were deserted; and 26 eggs (5.7%) were infertile. The remaining 10 eggs (2.2%) were lost in severe weather or through other hazards. Nest loss was high in Denmark where Clausager (1974) reported that no chicks hatched in 40% of 86 nests.

YOUNG

Woodcock chicks have a brown buff stripe over the eye and nape; the crown, and middle of the nape are reddish brown and underparts pale russet brown with white patches. Mantle and sides of the head have irregular bands and patches of buff and russet; legs and feet are pinkish flesh and irides dark brown. Newly-hatched chicks weigh 16–20 gm (Table 5). The average weight of four 2-days old chicks was 19.6 gm and that of seven 3-days old chicks 21.5 gm. By their seventh day three chicks averaged 71.7 gm (Glutz 1977).

Within a few hours the hen usually moves the brood away from the nest; but des Forges (1975) found hen and brood only 30 m away from it on the following morning. F. Varga (1976) watched a hen help the chicks to find food by turning over leaves; and Willie Workman (1954) once saw an adult – presumably a hen – feeding a chick bill to bill. However, H. J. Wilson (*in* Cramp and Simmons 1983), who studied the movements of 14 broods, never saw either of these actions. Woodcocks are indeed remarkably individual birds.

The brood is later herded to rides and clearings and sometimes to the edges of paths or even of public roads. The family does not appear to wander as widely as do many other waders, but before dispersing one ranged over 5–6 ha in the space of $2\frac{1}{2}$ weeks (Hirons 1980b).

The hen alone normally guards and rears the brood. But, in west Inverness, Whitaker recorded a second woodcock joining a very demonstrative hen with a brood. 'The cock appeared, and both dropped down together on a bit of open ground about 30 m from us. They stood fairly closely, each bird flapping its wings rapidly and rising high on its legs, looking like birds held in traps by the feet. While giving these displays they made a soft whistling noise'. If these two birds were members of a pair distracting over a brood this was quite abnormal behaviour. Is it not possible, however, that the hen and brood had pitched close to the chicks of another hen which then also started distraction?

O. von Zedlitz (1927) records that chicks could flutter 10 m when 10 days old and fly 75 m at 19 days. Lennart Raner, who has watched young woodcock flying at 15–18 days, suggests that this short period may be an adaptation to compensate for the shortness of the chick's legs; and consequently their inability to run far and fast like the long-legged greenshank, purple sandpiper and many other wader chicks. The hen continues to accompany the young long after they can fly. Hirons followed a family which only separated after $5\frac{1}{2}$ weeks. Pay (1937) also watched family groups in which parents and young were of equal size.

Broods of more than four chicks are exceptional. In Cumber Park, Notts, however, Whitaker found a brood of five young 'crouched together and touching one another'; the parent was absent. Two chicks then flew a few metres and dropped down in the bracken and the other three ran away with wings raised above their backs. In the Woodcock Inquiry, Alexander (1945–47) records 2 broods with 1 chick, 5 with 2, 15 with 3, 36 with 4, and 1 with 5. Morgan and Shorten (1974) analysed the number of chicks in 59 broods; 2 consisted of 1, 5 of 2, 15 of 3, 36 of 4, and 1 of 5 chicks.

I have never watched a woodcock attempt to carry its chicks, but I have twice been temporarily deceived by distraction displays. Each time the bird flapped heavily low over the ground with drooped tail and dangling legs. At Windermere, Whitaker and W. K. Moss described a woodcock rising heavily and flying very slowly for about 80 m before dropping in the middle of a rut where it stood rapidly flapping its wings like a bird caught in a trap. When Whitaker ran towards it, the bird rose and appeared to be 'carrying something large and heavy between its thighs'. It flew about a metre, again dropped and beat its wings, and then flew away into the wood leaving nothing behind. Meanwhile, Moss had found the brood of four chicks where the bird had originally risen. V. P. W. Lowe (1972) gives a detailed description of a distraction flight in which the woodcock held its tail vertically between its legs and spread it like a curved fan. There were four chicks on the ground but the bird never carried any away, although it appeared to do so. During the performance the woodcock screeched like a jay to warn the chicks.

These accounts describe a performance which, we feel sure, has sometimes deceived observers. However, a number of reliable watches have recorded woodcocks carrying their young between their thighs or between bill and breast. Our friend, David Duncan, NCC Warden for Sutherland, has had the good fortune to watch two woodcock using different methods to carry their young. The first time was in May 1972, in a birch wood on the north side of Loch Rannoch, Perth, when he was accompanied by Sandy Nicholson. 'As we walked through the wood a woodcock flew up and landed some 18 m away. The three chicks she had been covering scattered cheeping loudly. She then flew back, picked up one of the chicks by using her bill to grasp the feathers at the back of the neck, and then flew off carrying it some 22–27 m. Sandy turned and casually remarked to me, "Look there's a woodcock carrying its young", as though it were a regular occurence; which to him, being originally from Speyside, it may well have been. The bird returned but, with the remaining two chicks now hidden in cover, we did not see her attempt to lift any more. The second occasion was in May 1981, in the Mound Alderwoods NNR, Sutherland, an area which usually holds good numbers of breeding woodcock. I saw the bird rise from below a willow bush and fly off leaving her two chicks. I stood absolutely still and within 20 seconds saw her return and pick up a chick by holding it tucked between her bill and breast. She carried it some 18 m, dropped it, and then came back to carry off the second chick in a similar manner'.

Previously, Steinfatt (1938) was one of the few observers to have recorded seeing a woodcock lift a chick at the end of its bill.

VOICE

Woodcocks appear to have a smaller vocabulary than many other waders.

(1)   The roding song of the cock, restricted to the breeding season, consists of 2–4 croaks followed by a series of sharp *tziks* which are rather like the usual calls of pied wagtails. Early in the season the roding song appears to be restricted to the *tziks*; croaks start a few days later. In the roding flight the cock croaks in a special 'hesitant attitude' with open beak and head inclined downwards. A cock may give two separate croaks followed by two joined together; these are normally restricted to roding flight. However, C. Ingram (1967) recorded a woodcock croaking on a perch while a second woodcock sat on the top of a hedge. Other observers have occasionally heard woodcocks croaking on the ground.

When a cock is chasing a hen or another cock, the *tzik* cries often merge into high-pitched twittering *sip-sip-sips*. I have also heard fighting cocks give excited squeaking cries in their pursuits.

Pulchalski (1938), Haller (1945), Bettmann (1975), and others, have heard hens giving softer versions of the cocks' cries to entice the cock down to the ground; but Steinfatt was unsure whether these calls actually did attract them. I did not hear the hen call when the cock dropped down from his roding flight; he displayed and then flew off again. Steinfatt, however, heard the hen give cackling cries during copulation.

(2)   Hens use special cries to the chicks before and after they hatch and while they are in or outside the nest. I have heard a series of soft subdued calls and also rippling cries at this stage.

Philip Hollom (*in* Cramp 1983) heard a hen give a rapid hollow *godop* while returning to a nest in which the chicks were calling in the eggs. At a later stage she gave a throaty *whohh* and a quick series of trisyllabic *whududuhs*. Hollom also noticed that chicks became silent when the hen gave a series of rapid pattering sounds; and Steinfatt recorded several different cries which a hen used to lead or summon her brood.

(3)   The cries of the chicks in and out of the eggs are shrill and high. Steinfatt renders them as *psieh*.

(4)   A harsh *scaap*, resembling that of the common snipe, is sometimes used in winter when a bird is flushed from a field at night or while flying from cover to its feeding grounds (Hirons 1983).

(5)   Hens sometimes use loud chattering cries during their distraction displays.

Lowe (1972) described a hen screeching almost like a jay; and Whitaker watched two woodcocks stand on tiptoe, flapping their wings and giving whistling sounds.

Glutz (1977) and Cramp and Simmons (1983) have analysed what is known about the woodcock's voice. The vocabulary of the American woodcock appears to differ greatly, but we still await a series of sonagrams before attempting to make comparisons.

PREDATORS

Man, the hunter, is by far the most formidable predator, H. Kalchreuter (1982) describes the methods of hunting and shooting woodcocks used in different parts of Europe.

There are also many natural enemies. In different habitats, goshawk, sparrowhawk, peregrine, golden eagle, buzzard and tawny owls are all known to take woodcocks or their young. I also saw a hobby carry in a well-grown woodcock chick, but this was probably exceptional. M. Seago (1967) watched a kestrel strike a woodcock down. S. Sulkava (1968) found that woodcock, lapwing and ruff amounted to 18.6% of the gross weight of peregrines' prey in Finland. Jays have been recorded as egg predators; and in Spey Valley I have found woodcocks' eggs in pools containing the shells of the many eggs taken by hooded crows. Carrion crows in England are equally likely predators.

Foxes occasionally rob nests; I have found one which a fox had taken and the woodcock's feathers scattered around. Pine marten, stoat and weasel are other enemies. Des Forges watched a stoat emerge near the nest just after the hen woodcock had alighted nearby. However, the stoat moved away and the woodcock quickly returned to its eggs.

The woodcock is a shy bird which seems to desert its eggs more readily than most other waders. Particularly while laying, or early in incubation, hens sometimes abandon nests from which they have been disturbed.

FOOD

Woodcocks probe for worms in soft moist places, using the exceptionally sensitive tips of their bills to locate them. Philip Burton (1974) found that woodcocks had 'a highly refined method of probing'. At each step it placed its weight on the forward foot and inserted its bill to about one-third of its length. Woodcocks also turn over leaves in woods and are said to investigate cow dung in woodland pastures (Kalchreuter 1982). I have sometimes flushed them from puddles or ditches beside paths and estate roads in the policies of mansion houses.

Steinfatt (1938) lists the items of food identified, between the end of March and early April, in 13 woodcock in East Prussia. There were 43 dipteran larvae in six stomachs; 30 carabid and elaterid beetles in nine and 7 unidentified larvae in four; four stomachs held 5 earthworms, two had 3 millipedes Diplopoda, and two held snake flies *Raphidia*; there was also one snail, one spider and one woodbug. Two stomachs only contained plant remains and spruce needles and there were at least seven small stones or grains of sand.

In des Forges's study the hen never went further from the nest than about 30 m. 'The bird usually probed at an angle, not pushing its beak vertically, and after 3 or 4 probes the bill was fully withdrawn and the bird could be seen swallowing something'. It fed for about 10 minutes in a small area of about 4 m², where it occasionally impaled an oak leaf on the end of its beak and then brushed it off with its foot. At nests which I have watched in the early morning and evening, however, the hens flew right away apparently to known feeding grounds.

Glutz (1977) describes the small vegetable element in the diet, consisting of seeds of Ranunculacea, Euphorbiaceae, Cyperaceae, Leguminosae and Gramineae. H. Grote (1941) noted that woodcocks in USSR ate roots and small seeds when they were the only available food in early spring. Other authorities have recorded fruits of *Vaccinium, Rubus, Sambucus* and *Sorbus*.

A detailed and connected account of the woodcock's diet in different seasons, however, still remains a great research challenge. Shorten (1974), Glutz (1977), Kalchreuter (1982), Cramp and Simmons (1983) have summarised our present knowledge.

DISTRIBUTION AND NUMBERS

Woodcocks probably spread and increased in Britain and Ireland during the 19th century. Shooting woodcock in the breeding season had stopped and woods and coverts were then controlled for pheasants. But we suspect that there are other equally fundamental factors which are not yet fully understood.

In *The Breeding Atlas*, woodcocks were recorded as confirmed breeders in 1,098, probable in 769, and possible in a further 323 10-km squares in Britain and Ireland. In most counts, however, numbers are given as 'pairs' when roding cocks were probably the basis of the approximation. Estimates of numbers are extremely vague. J. T. R. Sharrock (1976) suggests a breeding population of between 18,000–46,000 'pairs' in the British Isles.

L. J. Yeatman (1976) estimated a population of under 10,000 'pairs' in France and L. Lippens (1983) about 1,000–1,200 'pairs' in Belgium. H. Kalchreuter (1982) suggests that there are about 320 'pairs' in Luxemburg; and M. Teixeira (1979) considers that woodcocks have increased in the Netherlands, with possibly 2,000–3,000 'pairs' now breeding. Woodcocks are doing well in the north and north-west of Germany and holding their own in the south. In East Germany they appear to have increased in the north, although there has been a slight decline in some parts. They have decreased in Poland, Czechoslovakia, Austria and Italy, but there are no precise estimates of numbers. Small groups nest in northern Spain. J. Kålås and I. Byrkjedal (1981) estimated that 34,500 'pairs' bred in Norway in 1979; and S. Ulfstrand and G. Högstedt (1976) suggest that there are 75,000 'pairs' in Sweden. There may be 16,000 'pairs' in Finland.

Many of us have now learnt a little about the life of the mysterious woodcock, but the sum total of our knowledge is still very small. However, with the aid of telemetry and dedicated watchers, many more problems may soon be solved.

10: The Dotterel

By any standard the dotterel, a bird with a reversed courtship and sexual differences, is an unusual and colourful wader. The slightly larger and more brightly coloured hen takes the initiative in courtship, leaving her smaller mate to incubate and hatch the eggs and largely to rear the family.

Face on, the dotterel is a most beautiful bird. Its broad white eye-stripes meet in a V on the neck; the crown is blackish brown and the short bill black. A great white pectoral band separates grey throat and neck from a magnificent chestnut red upper breast, and there is a huge jet black inky blotch on the lower belly. Its yellow legs almost twinkle as it runs quickly over the grey moss of our high tops. But, when the bird squats or turns away, it abruptly vanishes, so well does it harmonise with the surroundings.

From the early 19th century the story of the dotterel has had a special place in British ornithology. Most of the early enthusiasts concentrated in the Lakeland district of England. But, on 16 June 1873, J. Harvie-Brown and H. W. Feilden, with the help of a local gamekeeper, found the first authenticated Scottish nest, on a west Drumochter hill on the Perth-Inverness march. Since then, many ornithologists have fallen under the spell of the lovely dotterel in Scotland and England. Some have been famous nest hunters and egg collectors; others have studied its pattern of reversed courtship; many have been photographers; but all have come to love a fascinating wader.

In 1933 I started to watch dotterels in the Grampians and Cairngorms. *The Dotterel* (1973) told the story of the long struggle with the 'Moss Fool', and of camping for hundreds of nights on the roof of Scotland. But, as you grow older, the hills always grow steeper. Now I must be content to watch waders on the lower ground.

Bruin and Patrick, already students of the greenshank, soon wanted to hunt for dotterel. In 1976, travelling by train and on foot, and heavily laden with camping gear and provisions, they went to one of my old study areas. They had perfect weather

and, with beginners' luck, found two nests. Since then, all six members of the family have camped in the central Grampians in different years. It is nostalgic to see them toiling up to one of my old haunts. And how relieved we are to count their figures as they appear on the skyline on the appointed day for going home! Their field notes have helped to bring this dotterel story up to date.

Many other enthusiasts write to us and annually send their notes and observations. Abroad, particularly in Norway, Sweden, Finland and Austria, the present generation of wader watchers has brought the dotterel story far forward.

On the few warm and windless days, particularly in the Grampians, the dotterel is not a difficult quarry. Ahead of you, a small head appears over the skyline and then the lovely bird runs in fits and starts. You move backwards and, if all goes well, you end by seeing the dotterel make a sudden spurt, puff out its belly feathers, and shuffle down onto the nest. When you move forward, after marking the place, the little bird, tail fanned and wings beating, runs off a few metres ahead of you.

Yet, even in good weather, it is one thing to find a nest or two on the round tops of the Grampians, but quite another to make a real study of numbers, behaviour and populations. It is very easy to walk over a nest on which the cock sits so tightly that you may pass him time after time. Every acre of ground must be searched and searched again, and even then you will surely miss a few nests. In his diary for 16 June 1979, Patrick describes his method of dotterel hunting. 'I walked up and down in parallel strips, searching the plateau; this is a good method on flattish ground in fine weather. After hunting many, many strips I found a scrape and bent down to examine it. I raised my head as I rose and only then spotted a cock dotterel sitting no more than 2 m away from me! Had I not bent down to examine a scrape I might never have found this nest'. A few, always baffling birds, rise unseen 100 m or more ahead of the hunter and disappear over the brow and may then take an hour or more to return.

In normal 'dotterel weather' on the tops you walk fast, trying to keep warm in the grey mist which creeps thickly over all the folds of the ground; and you continually use your compass to keep direction. Often snow, sleet or heavy rain makes each trip a painful adventure. Any student of nesting dotterel must camp on the high ground to snatch every brief hour of clear weather. These may be few. On 14 June 1979, Patrick wrote: 'The weather in the night was very stormy and we awoke to a large pool of water. The new tent had leaked very badly'. On 19 June 1980, when Eamonn and Maimie camped with him on the plateau, his note for the day was equally brief. 'Rained all day. Mist and heavy wind prevailed. Tent had leaked during Wednesday night. Stayed in tent all day; no work done'. On 20 June: 'Weather much the same ... made a hot meal. Made an effort to go to the tops to weigh eggs'.

The dotterel is a bird of the high stony tops and grasslands in Scotland, seldom nesting below 800 m. In England the occasional pairs now nest between 750–880 m, though a few in this century have laid their eggs as low as 630 m. The English nesting habitats are described by Derek Ratcliffe as single stony tops, large summit plateaux and flat-topped spurs, where a few dunlin and golden plovers also nest. Skylarks and meadow pipits haunt the high grasslands and a few wheatears nest on block-littered ground. The occasional lapwing nests up to just over 800 m on limestone pasture.

In the central Cairngorms, where they nest on ridges and plateaux of stony ground, wheatears, meadow pipits, ptarmigan and sometimes snow buntings are neighbours. Across the Lairig Ghru the western hills are divided by Am Moine Mor; here the dotterel haunts are on gentler slopes, knobs and rounded hills to the west. In this famous 'Big Moss' dunlins purr and golden plovers wail and flap over bog and hill top.

West of Drumochter, in the central Grampians, the dotterel hills are much more stony than the bumps and ridges to the east; few golden plovers nest here. The family has also recorded snipe bleating and a greenshank, probably with a brood, at over 600 m on a western hill. There are also good groups of breeding goldies and dunlins in the peat bogs east of Drumochter.

Their Norwegian haunts are rich in interesting waders. On Hardanger Vidda, shore-larks, a few Lapland buntings, golden plovers, purple sandpipers, wheatears and ptarmigan all nest on dotterel grounds. Further north, on the fells north of Varanger Fjord, Hugh Blair recorded golden plovers, purple sandpipers, shore larks, Lapland buntings, long-tailed and arctic skuas, great black-backed gulls and arctic terns. He once found a Temminck's stint nesting on dotterel ground and watched little stints nest dancing on the same fell; turnstones also sometimes nest on these stony ridges.

In Norway, Sweden and Finland dotterels nest mainly on open high level fells and plateaux covered with mosses and lichens. In Finnmark, Norway, they nest as low as the 90–300 m contours; in south and central Norway seldom below 1,050 m. On

Hardanger Vidda and Dovre Fjell their principal breeding grounds are about 1,350 m. They nest from 540–1,290 m at 68° N in Swedish and Finnish Lapland. Further south they nest upward from the dwarf birch zone at about 840 m.

The dotterel's altitudinal range in USSR varies with latitude. They breed at very low altitudes in the northern tundra, but Elizabeth Kozlova found them nesting at 2,800 m, and higher, on the Changai Mountains in Mongolia. They also choose high plateaux in the Austrian Alps and the Italian Appenines where nests have been recorded between 1,820–2,270 m, with most of the Austrian nests between 2,000–2,150 m (E. Hable).

In the Netherlands, to the amazement of all, some of the dotterels visiting the newly re-claimed north-east polder stayed to breed. Here, from 1961–69, they nested on unexpected and seemingly unsuitable habitats in crops of flax, sugar beet, wheat, peas and potatoes, sometimes at 4 m below sea-level. In subsequent years no nests have been recorded, although sometimes up to 150 birds have been reported, some of which have been in display.

ARRIVAL, COURTSHIP AND DISPLAY

Dotterels do not return to their Scottish haunts in any set pattern. On 28 April 1984, while working on his redshank study, Patrick felt very homesick as he watched a trip of five fly quite low over the Ribble marshes; they were calling to one another and did not stop as they sped northwards. Small parties of hens arrive first, or sometimes singly; or there may be small trips of both sexes. Just occasionally a pair 'homes' together. The first birds often return fully three weeks before the earliest hen lays her first egg. On the Finnish fells hens sometimes arrive towards the end of May, well before the snow has melted; and yet some start laying within a week of arrival.

On Hardanger Vidda, Norway, the pattern is quite different. The dotterels pair up before they arrive on their breeding fells and start nest dancing almost immediately.

In the Cairngorms and Grampians the dotterels usually pair up on the broad ridges and whalebacks. You watch a hen raising her wings as she chases and tries to isolate a particular cock; or one may run out of the group for a few metres and squat or appear to brood on the ground. She may then stay in this position for several minutes; afterwards, if a cock does not make a move, she runs back to the trip. Sometimes

a hen runs with raised wings and *skirrs* angrily as she challenges another. Or two cocks run with quick steps, humped up almost into small balls, and then they too jump into the air or leap-frog over one another.

At last, when the pair is formed, the two birds start nest dancing, each independently making the movements of scrape-making in scores of different places without leaving the slightest mark on the ground or vegetation. In this phase we have often watched the two dotterels move anything from a few metres to 50 m or more apart. Their scraping movements are incomplete and uncoordinated. Gradually, however, this behaviour becomes more meaningful with the two birds leaning forward, rotating, and pressing down their lower breasts while appearing to scratch energetically with their feet. From

time to time one calls up the other and then they work together at the same scoop. During these lovely nest dances you frequently hear rippling cries. But the pair still seems unable to complete a scrape; the ground is still unmarked.

A day or so on, however, their behaviour subtly changes. No longer do the two birds flip almost like butterflies from patch to patch. For ten minutes or more they now sometimes work at the same scoop, scratching away with their feet and moving round the scrape. The hen bends forward, breast to ground and tail up. Then, with tail feathers fluttering in the wind, she bends down and appears to peck at the floor of the scoop. Periodically the cock replaces her in the scrape where he copies her actions and then sidles away. Meanwhile the hen, standing outside the nest, jerks blades of grass or small bits of moss over her shoulder, sideways or towards her mate. Leaning backwards, he now rather awkwardly works this material into the gradually enlarging scoop. At times the two beautiful birds pause, stand upright and face one another, and then both hold up their long graceful wings and partly spread their tails. Time after time they give those rippling cries and the cock sometimes sings his linnet-like song.

This is always an exciting phase, often full of unexpected action. The social drive is evidently still strong. Two newly formed pairs now fly restlessly from one stony flat to another, fighting or sparring when they are on the ground. These are usually, but not always, double fights, cock against cock and hen against hen, and they continue until one pair is dominant and finally settles on a territory. The subordinate pair then flies off and establishes its own living-space a few hundred metres, or occasionally up to 1.5 km, from where the fighting had taken place. Meanwhile the dominant pair nest dances and sometimes takes part in colourful displays.

Before the hen lays her first egg she sometimes squats between two stones or tussocks as if she was brooding eggs. You hear the sharp *ting* cries which the dotterels give to keep in touch with one another. In this period of mounting sexual excitement, the cock may approach the hen in stops and starts and gently bills her nape just before stepping onto her back. During coupling he sometimes raises his wings and holds them high. A hen may also tilt forward to an angle of about 45° and she runs ahead of the cock and then suddenly stops and inclines further forward, with her body and tail held at an angle of about 60°. Behind her the little cock runs in spasms until she stops; then he casually steps onto her back and takes her. I have seen the hen turn her neck and their beaks touch in a kind of kiss. Once, after the cock had stepped off her back, the hen shook herself and ran forward a few metres before flying. Both birds then put on speed, crossing and re-crossing their flight-paths rather like displaying ringed plovers, and giving soft tinkling cries as they flew down the hill.

The hen sometimes uses her dove-grey underwings to excite a courting cock. She may squat between two stones and rapidly flash them by half-raising and then abruptly shutting them, but this does not always lead to copulation. Cock dotterels are sometimes strongly sexed. One served his hen three times in less than five minutes, balancing himself with his wings held high above his back. He held his wings erect before stepping onto the hen, but he did not wave or beat them during copulation. At other times the cock merely steps onto the hen's back without any preliminary wing display.

Dotterels occasionally copulate after the cocks have started steady incubation. In the Cairngorms, birds which have lost their eggs sometimes continue to copulate when it is possibly too late in the season for the hen to replace a clutch. We have also occasionally watched cocks with broods copulating with apparently strange hens. H. Rittinghaus (1962) discovered that cocks with chicks sometimes associated with two other dotterels, tolerating one, but attacking the other.

Polygamy

Dotterels have abnormal sexual patterns. A Cairngorms hen occasionally runs with, and produces clutches for two different cocks. One of our hens, *Blackie*, laid her second clutch at an interval of roughly 11 days; and she then took spells of incubation at this second nest for at least the first ten days.

Polyandry has also been proved in Norway, Finland and Austria and is strongly suspected in Sweden and England. John Kålås told us that many hens on Hardanger Vidda were polyandrous, laying first clutches which the cocks incubated and hatched, and then produced second clutches for cocks that had lost their eggs. Twenty per cent of the hens in his study area took part in the incubation and hatching of these second clutches. As in Scotland, hens seeking mates late in the season make 'winnow-glide flights' calling in rapid sequences of *peep-peep-peep* as they fly high over the stony wastes. In Finnmark, Bill Hobson met with a hen which possibly had three mates; all three nests, containing eggs of the same type, were at different stages of incubation and quite close together. The only hen seen on the small hill gave advertising flights over all three nests. Erkki Pulliainen, who has intensively studied dotterels in Finland, discovered that a hen, which had put her first mate down on three eggs, laid the first egg of the second clutch 4.7 days later. She then assisted her second mate to incubate this clutch.

In May 1952, Hans Franke watched a different kind of triangle on the Seetal Alps in Austria. The hen was running with two cocks, one almost as bright as she, the other much drabber. Time after time the drab coloured cock attacked and drove away his beautiful rival. On 1 June the bright cock was close to the nest in which the hen

had already laid her first egg, but the drab master cock was still associating with the hen. At 05.00 on 3 June the dull bird was sitting on two eggs. Almost immediately afterwards, between 05.05 and 06.30, the hen laid her third egg in the scoop; a few minutes later she ran away. The drab cock then incubated the three eggs, from which two chicks hatched out on 26 June. However, on 8 July the hen reappeared with a court of two cocks, one much brighter than the other. Once again she mated with the drab bird and completed her second clutch on 15 July. The hen and the bright cock then left him sitting only 20 m from the first nest.

Hens outnumbered cocks in some Cairngorms groups in 1941, 1942 and 1968. In 1941, apparently unmated hens mobbed and chased cocks which had left their eggs in the course of incubation. On 5 June two nests were less than 100 m apart; a cock was brooding three eggs on one and a hen two eggs in the other. No cock was seen to approach the second nest at which the eggs were infertile.

On 15 June 1968, Sandy Tewnion came upon three dotterels, a cock and two hens, fighting and bickering. After the cock had temporarily disappeared, the two hens ran a few metres apart giving distraction calls. A third hen then joined them and started to run about as if trying to entice the cock from a nest. Tewnion now searched and found the cock sitting on a single egg. One of the hens then went to the nest; and when the two others approached she chased them away. However, one continued to run almost up to the nest and 'no matter how much the dominant hen chased her away she did not retreat further than about 50 m from the nest'; the third hen was content to stand about 50 m away. On 29 June the cock was sitting on four eggs, three clearly laid by one hen and the fourth by another. The dominant hen had possibly driven away her rival but not before she had laid an egg in her nest.

TERRITORY

Patterns of territory vary according to the habitat. Early fighting between newly formed pairs leads to dispersal, enabling cock and hen to court and adjust their sex rhythms. The hen can choose a nest site within the territory and produce her eggs; and a cock can mature his sex drive. Territorial defence during incubation deters late settlers. It also helps to conserve caches of food close to the nest, to be exploited by the sitting bird in exceptionally severe weather, and later by the newly-hatched chicks. During fledging, cocks attack other cock dotterel which approach their young too closely, thus conserving the food needed by the chicks. We have met with these patterns of territory in the Cairngorms and central Grampians, but in study areas on Hardanger Vidda dotterels did not consistently defend territories and had rather weak spacing mechanisms (Kålås, orally).

Dotterels appear to be weak in site tenacity. In our Cairngorms study we traced five hens only, all by means of peculiarly coloured or distinctly shaped eggs; one hen – *Blackie* – for five years, one for four years, two for at least three years, and one for two years. Evidence from Norway, Sweden and Finland also points to a weak ort-streue. Between 1978–81, Kålås colour-banded 25 cocks, eight hens and 81 chicks, of which only four cocks (16%) and one chick (1.2%) were again found on their birth fells in subsequent years. However, the chick ringed in 1977 was sitting on a nest on the same fell in 1978 and 1980 (J. Kålås MS).

DISPERSION AND BREEDING DENSITY

Even in years of high numbers, dotterels seldom nest at high density on all suitable ridges of the Cairngorms. In the central Cairngorms, in 1949 and 1961, there were about 5 breeding pairs/2.6 km². A few tend to nest in small groups or clumps. In 1941 and 1961 some nests were 270 m apart; but in 1936 three hens laid their eggs on the points of an equilateral triangle with sides c 225 m long. In west Cairngorms, in years of low numbers, two nests were often 1.6 km apart; and even when on the same whaleback 450 m separated them. The east Cairngorms groups appear to be more widely dispersed. However, in 1970, 12 pairs nested on a ridge about 4 km in length.

In some years dotterel nest at high density in the central Grampians. In 1976–80, while working in one of my old study areas of 3.5 km², the family found that breeding densities varied from 2.3–4.0 pairs/km² (Fig 7). The shortest recorded distance between nests was 100 m in 1978; that year two other nests were only 150 m and 350 m apart. All were located at altitudes between 870–1,000 m. Maximum densities were higher than those recorded in other parts of Scotland but lower than in northern Fenno-Scandia and north-west USSR (P. S. Thompson 1983).

Spacing on the English fells is similar to that in the Cairngorms and Grampians; but in 1911, J. F. Peters found two nests within 90 m. In the 1960s and 1970s, when the English population was so small, nests were sometimes closer than expected; in

	Nests found	additional broods seen	other males or pairs	total pairs	pairs km²
1976	2	0	6+	8+	2.3
1977	6	1	1	8	2.3
1978	8	3	2–3	13–14	4.0
1979	3	8	2–3	13–14	4.0
1980*	5	0	3–4	8–9	2.6

*Note: Possibly an underestimate because bad weather made observation difficult

Fig. 7   Estimated numbers of dotterel on central Grampians study area of 3.5 km²(P. S. Thompson).

1962 two hens laid their eggs roughly 225 m apart and in 1976 450 m separated two others (Ratcliffe *pers. comm.*).

In parts of Fenno-Scandia dotterels breed in good numbers. I. Byrkjedal and J. Kålås studied dotterel in a part of Hardanger Vidda where breeding density is very high. In 1983 they found 31 pairs and broods in an area of 6 km², a mean density of 5.1 breeding pairs/km² (Byrkjedal *in litt*). Hobson found three nests in Finnmark within 60 ha. The Finnish breeding density is also often high. In 1966 Olavi Hildén recorded six nests in 0.9 km², two of which were only 200 m apart. L. Saari (MS) also recorded a density of 4 pairs/km² in Forest-Lapland.

Eric Hable found an average population of 4–5 breeding pairs in the Kirbitzkögel Reserve, Austria – an average density of 0.18 breeding pairs/km², with a maximum of 0.32 breeding pairs/km². Here, in the last 20 years, the population has varied from 1–12 pairs; but two nests are occasionally sited within 100 m.

In USSR, S. Uspenski (1965) recorded 4–5 pairs/km² on lichen tundra on the Jugorski Peninsula and on the Island of Waigatsch. In 1959 there was a particularly high density of 8–10 breeding pairs/km² in the north of the peninsula. V. I. Kapitonov (1962) also reported 20 pairs breeding along 1.5 km of the River Lonka.

NEST, EGG AND CLUTCH

Dotterels make shallow scoops or scrapes in patches of woolly fringe moss *Rhacomitrium*, carpets or tussocks of deer sedge *S. caespitosus*, mat grass *N. stricta*, three-pointed rush *J. trifidus*, sheeps fescue *D. flexuosa*, and in other plants, among gravel and stones and on the tops of hummocks on unstable ground caused by solifluction. Scoops in peaty ground are sometimes quite deep. It is always exciting to look down at a dotterel sitting in a patch of pink moss campion *Silene acaulis*. Nests are lined with hill grasses, blaeberry *V. myrtillus* or crowberry *Empetrum nigrum* leaves, and bits of various mosses and lichens. A few droppings of mountain hares or ptarmigan and occasionally some small stones are found in the nests.

Warm sunny weather in the second and third weeks of May triggers off waves of hens to lay their first eggs; snowcover, late thaws, low temperatures or severe falls of snow in May delay them. In the Cairngorms warm weather activates insects and spiders and thus enables the hens to feed up before starting to lay. If a hen misses the early wave of laying she may not be able to form her first egg and laying is then delayed. There is, however, always a considerable lapse between the completion of the first and the last clutch on particular hill groups.

The laying season varies in different habitats in Scotland and England. Between 1940–70 (23 years of records), 27 May was the mean date for the first egg in the central Cairngorms, and 10 June for the first egg in the latest recorded clutch in 15 years. In the central Grampians the mean date for first eggs is earlier. Between 1898–1967, in 30 years, 22 May was the earliest, and 7 June the latest for 10 years of records. Just occasionally, as in 1980, most clutches appear to be laid extremely late despite a very warm May (Nethersole-Thompson family, unpublished).

In England the average laying season is remarkably similar to that in the central Grampians. Between 1908–70 23, May was the mean early date for 18 years of records.

Abroad dotterels tend to lay rather later. In the Seetal Alps and the Carpathians, however, some hens start laying in early May and quite regularly in mid and late May (Hable 1975). The earliest first egg was recorded in Finland on about 26 May, but in most years hens start laying in the first week in June. One Swedish hen laid her first egg about 31 May, but U. Houmann (*in litt*) considered that 12 June was the usual date for a full clutch. In Norway they have a variable laying season. On

Hardanger Vidda the earliest eggs are usually laid in late May and the latest clutches completed in mid June (Kålås, unpublished). At Nore Fjell in Buskerud a hen laid her first egg about 14 May and three hens on the Dovre Fjell laid in the last week in May. On the Varanger Fjord in Finnmark, Hobson recorded a hen laying her first egg about 31 May. However, in all these locations, the second week in June is a more usual date for the start of the laying season.

A hen dotterel sometimes performs a special ceremony to show the cock the scoop she has chosen for her first egg. She runs slowly to the scrape, stands in it, picks up moss and grass which she places on the rim, and then pecks in the floor. She may also do this before laying her second egg; and she and her mate may then change places on the scoop time after time. However, hens sometimes lay the first egg in the absence of the cock and without any special ritual.

I have seen different behaviour before the laying of a third egg. From noon on 12 June 1948, for almost an hour, a hen probed and pecked in a tussock of grass from which she lifted, shook, and then dropped a fox's dropping. Her mate, calling on a ridge above the nest and two eggs, suddenly started to run down the hill and then abruptly swerved towards the nest. The hen immediately followed; and when he squatted on the eggs she stood almost beside him. Then, calling softly, she pushed him off the scoop and brooded for almost an hour before standing up and sitting down again, as if she had laid an egg. A few minutes later she called to the cock, which came running up, and then she flew away in rather heavy flight. The cock now went to the nest, bent down to turn the eggs, and started to brood. Within a few minutes, I had confirmed that the third egg had been laid. At 10.45 on 13 June the cock was sitting; the hen was close to the nest, but she did not go to it during the next two hours.

Dotterels lay attractive ovate or pointed ovate eggs. Their ground colour varies from olive to olive green (which quickly fades), umber brown, clay or stone colour. Bryan Nelson, Michael Everett and Sandy Tewnion all recorded complete clutches of blue or greenish blue ground colour, and we have found single eggs like these. In 1971, Gordon Sutherland found a remarkable clutch of spotless blue eggs in the east Cairngorms; and in 1983 Evelyne Meek photographed a similar beautiful clutch in Finnmark. The markings, usually black, brownish black and red-brown, are in the forms of blotches, streaks and squiggles. Undermarkings range from light ash grey to violet.

Most eggs are laid in the middle of the day. An Austrian hen, which laid her third egg at 05.15, is responsible for the earliest record; and a Cairngorms hen, which laid her second egg at approximately 20.30, for the latest. In Scotland we have recorded 15 eggs laid at intervals of 24–30 hours, and seven others at longer intervals. Pulliainen in Finland and Kålås in Norway give 30.8 ± 2.1 hours as the average lapse between eggs.

One hundred eggs from Scotland and England had a mean of 41.1×28.9 mm (Jourdain 1940). The second hen in the polygynous trio which Tewnion found in 1968 laid the smallest recorded egg, 38×26 mm. The average for 53 Austrian eggs was 40.0×28.4 (E. Hable); and 15 eggs from Waigatsch Island, with a mean of 40.3×28.0, are also smaller than the British average (V. N. Karpovitch and V. D. Kokhanov). Hens on Hardanger Vidda laid progressively larger eggs in the first third of the egg-laying season and then progressively smaller eggs in the last third (Kålås MS).

Between 1977–80, in the central Grampians, the family weighed 47 eggs at all stages of incubation. Of these, 16 slightly incubated eggs averaged 16.2 gm (Table 3) and eight 'chipped' eggs had a mean of 12.2 gm. Hable (1975) weighed 45 apparently fresh dotterels' eggs in the Austrian Alps which ranged from 13–18 gm (mean 15.1 gm). In the Altai Mountains, USSR, three eggs, of undetermined incubation, weighed 15.9,

16.0 and 16.3 gm (mean 16.0 gm). Given a hen dotterel weight as roughly 116 gm (S. M. Uspenski 1962), a clutch weighing approximately 48 gm amounts to 41.2 per cent of the hen's body weight (Table 2).

Dotterels usually lay three, occasionally two, and exceptionally one or four eggs. In Scotland the average for 436 clutches is 2.91 eggs. Of these, 24 recorded in the central Grampians by the Nethersole-Thompson family between 1976–80, averaged 2.92 eggs. This does not differ significantly from the mean of 2.90 eggs recorded for 176 clutches in the central and west Grampians between 1898–1970.

In England a small sample of 58 clutches, recorded between 1784–1926, averaged 2.58 eggs. It is interesting that between 1900–1926, when the dotterel was decreasing in England, the average clutch of 26 hens was only 2.42, suggesting that the birds were possibly breeding from a less fertile strain or were occupying fringe or marginal habitats. Since 1956, however, when a few dotterel have started to re-colonise the English fells, clutches of three have been normal. Robert Moss, who tested the idea statistically, showed that in England dotterels produced more 'ones' and 'twos' than those in Scotland, at odds longer than 1000:1 (P < 0.001). The average clutch size is slightly larger (2.97) in Fenno-Scandia where clutches of four are apparently more frequent (Table 4).

In the Cairngorms only eight out of 34 robbed hens (23.2 per cent) laid replacement clutches. The first egg of a replacement clutch is sometimes laid on the fifth or sixth day after the loss of the first. We recorded replacement clutches in early and late nesting seasons but they are less likely if the eggs are robbed late in the season or are heavily incubated.

Hable (1975) recorded that hens breeding in the Austrian Alps regularly laid replacement clutches. Also in Austria, I. Präsent (1975) followed up a two-years old colour-marked hen which lost her first eggs in June and then laid two replacement clutches in July. On Hardanger Vidda replacement clutches are laid regularly (Kålås, orally).

INCUBATION

After the hen has laid her first egg the cock usually goes to the nest and broods briefly before flying away with her; but he occasionally continues to sit after she has left. In most pairs steady incubation does not start until a little after the second egg. Two cocks, however, delayed incubation until their hens had laid out. Another pair, with only one egg in the nest, changed places every few minutes. Weather and individuality sometimes greatly influence incubation rhythms. During and after a snowstorm, in June 1934, one Cairngorms cock sat without interruption for over 24 hours. Other cocks have sat for periods varying from 30 minutes to $3\frac{3}{4}$ hours or more and stayed off the nest for 2–27 minutes (Nethersole-Thompson 1973).

The Cambridge University Expedition of 1978 watched a dotterel's nest on Hardanger Vidda on which the cock evidently sat for much briefer incubation stints. The bird was off nest 9–12 minutes each hour during the day time, a total of 185 minutes per day.

In Scotland few hens appear to take any part in incubation. We have only proved that seven out of 138 hens incubated a full clutch. *Blackie*, the polyandrous hen of 1934, shared incubation at least until nearly mid way through the period of her second clutch. Other brooding hens are listed and described in *The Dotterel* (1973).

On 11 June 1950, Harold Auger, from a hide, watched a pair exchange at the nest on which the large brightly-coloured bird was first sitting. 'At 16.40 the sitter gave a short shrill call and sat very taut and erect'. A second dotterel, which now appeared, then ran towards the nest in short bursts, calling softly when it was about 2 m away. The sitting bird immediately ran off the nest and the relieving bird, which was smaller and much more dingy, settled down on the eggs. On 16 June the brightly-coloured bird was again sitting between 15.30 and 17.30, but there was no sign of its dingy partner. None of the eggs showed any sign of chipping.

The family found a pair birds standing beside a nest in the central Grampians on 20 June 1980, a very stormy day; the eggs were uncovered. Patrick suggests that after a long spell of brooding in rough weather the cock had left the nest to feed and that the hen was about to incubate.

In Sweden, Rittinghaus (1962) watched three nests at which cocks and hens changed over. Pulliainen (1970) also recorded hens at three nests in Finland in which cock and hen sat alternately towards the end of incubation. Another hen spent 10% of the incubation period on eggs during the first 15 days, but the cock then took over and sat until the chicks had hatched.

A polyandrous hen on Värriötunturi, Finland, behaved as unexpectedly as *Blackie*. While she was laying her first clutch she brooded for short stints. At her second nest she incubated for 53% and the cock for 47% of the period. At five other nests in Finland the cock alone was recorded on eggs. Hildén (*in litt*) also discovered that at least two hens in Utsjoki, Finland, helped to sit upon and hatch the eggs. Andrew Wilkie (*pers. comm.*) had a different experience on Hardanger Vidda. The eggs, which he and his colleagues from the Cambridge University Expedition watched for a total of 150 hours, were incubated solely by the cock.

Apart from the ritual behaviour during egg laying, or on these exceptional occasions of nest relief, hens are seldom seen close to nests during incubation. Occasionally, however, one or two hens, one probably the mate, will approach the nest; the sitting cock may then rise from the eggs and drive them away.

Almost immediately after the eggs are laid and the cocks are sitting and – sometimes before this – the hens form into small trips or parties. These little bands usually consist of 2–6 hens in Scotland, but are sometimes larger in Fenno-Scandia and the Netherlands. Later, hens, pairs which have lost their eggs, and occasionally off-duty cocks, join them. The hens now frequently spar and rather half-heartedly spread their tails and leapfrog over one another. Hen trips probably have a defensive function, as collective eyes are better able to forsee danger; and they possibly provide a rough hierarchy enabling unmated or robbed cocks to find new mates (Nethersole-Thompson 1973).

These 'grass widows' often feed close to streams and squashy places unsuitable as nesting habitats or chick feeding grounds. Just occasionally, however, they attach themselves to an off-duty cock and then follow him back to the nest.

On 15 June 1979, Patrick noted that a group of four hens fed rapidly and continuously bickered and squabbled. They covered a large tract of ridge and fell top where they fed almost anywhere, irrespective of the positions of their nests and sitting cocks. Between 13–15 June there had been a spell of cold and rough weather with showers of snow and sleet; but on the 16th the group was basking in the sun having apparently found little difficulty in maintaining themselves during the storm.

Many cocks sit remarkably closely, only leaving their eggs when the searcher is a few metres away. Some have allowed us to lift and replace them on eggs. Patrick had a wonderful experience on 15 June 1977, while present at a hatching clutch, when a cock brooded two chicks in his hand in preference to the pipped egg in the nest. Mrs E. Barth had a similar experience in Norway; but this time all three chicks had hatched and their shells lay a few centimetres from the scoop.

A nervous dotterel crouches stiffly on the nest, but when the chicks are piping in the eggs he sits in a more relaxed posture with head and neck upright. A brooding dotterel sometimes turns the eggs with his beak, rising and pushing his head down into the scoop; or he may shuffle the eggs with his lower breast and belly. Wilkie's

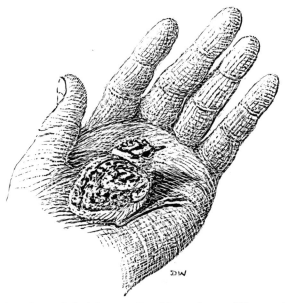

party noted that the cock had bursts of activity and rest. When active he held his head higher and periodically preened, frequently pecking at the ground and indulging in 'sideways building'. He would stand up and then sit down again, or open and close his bill, shake his head and give yawning movements.

Individual dotterels vary in their ability to cope with eggs which have been knocked or rolled out of the nest. We have seen a dotterel stand up and replace an egg using the underside of its bill. In 1941 I placed one egg 15 cm and another 7.5 cm on the upper side of a nest on a steep hillside. On his return the cock dotterel called and 'hiccuped' almost continuously, but by the end of five minutes he had failed to retrieve either egg.

The approximate incubation periods of 17 clutches in Britain and abroad ranged from 23.0–29.7 (mean 26.1 days) (Nethersole-Thompson 1973). Jon Kålås (MS) found that the mean period for six clutches on Hardanger Vidda was 24 ± 0.6 days. On the same fells, Wilkie and his colleagues estimated a period of 26 days for the nest they watched so intensively in 1978. Pulliainen (1970) found that the same cock hatched a clutch in 25–26 days and 27–28 days in successive years. Air temperature and the number and length of absences from the nest probably explain some differences.

HATCHING

In Scotland the eggs in nine nests were chipped for periods ranging from 25–112 hours (mean 62 hours). Hildén (*in litt*) found that the chipping period on a Finnish fell was about four days; but in Austria, Franke (1953) recorded one of roughly 25 hours. Wilkie (MS) measured a minimum chipping period of four days for the three eggs in the Hardanger Vidda nest – 104 hours for the first, 42 hours for the second and 66 hours for the third egg.

As soon as the first chick starts to call in the egg the sitting bird answers. Later it gives a rather deep call, *gruk*, resembling golden plover, curlew, greenshank, common sandpiper, woodcock and other waders which use special calls to communicate with and discipline their chicks, in and out of the eggs. When the egg is hatching, the dotterel usually manipulates the starred side upwards. In 1977 Patrick noticed that while the eggs were hatching the cock frequently tapped them with his bill.

At most nests all three eggs usually hatch out within a space of 12 hours; but two of our clutches had a hatching spread of 16 hours. The third egg in a clutch of three, therefore, usually has a slightly shorter incubation period than the first two eggs. On Hardanger Vidda the first chick probably hatched between 19.00–21.00 on 13 July and the third chick after midnight on the 14th; hatching was thus spread over a period of 28 hours (Wilkie MS). Kålås (MS) also recorded hatching intervals of 24.2 ± 5.5 hours between the hatching of the first and last chick.

In Finland Hildén (*in litt*) recorded all three chicks hatching on the same night; and Pulliainen (1971) gives a hatching spread of 5–19.5 hours, with 3–6 hours between the first and second chick and 2–13.5 hours between the second and third chicks.

After the egg has hatched the sitting bird usually pokes, lifts, or rolls the larger portion of shell out of the scoop; later he flies off, dropping it about 20 m away. But

one cock flew over 180 m before dropping a shell; another flew to a small stream about 40 m away, dropped the shell and then rinsed out his bill. On 15 June 1977, Patrick watched a cock lift and fly 40 m with an egg cap in its bill, land, and then drop it; he later flew away with a larger eggshell fragment. Small bits and pieces of eggshell are broken up, eaten, pushed under the nest lining, or completely ignored.

YOUNG

The attractive little chicks have tortoiseshell mantles, white chins, white napes mixed with dusky brown, and buff crowns. The superciliary, ear coverts and cheeks are white; a narrow blackish line extends from their lores through the eye and to the nape; and their irides are dark brown. When first hatched the chick's bill is lead grey but this soon becomes black. Legs are also leaden grey at first with patches of yellow on the joins and soles of the feet; claws are brown tipped with grey. The legs of 9-day old chicks have yellow calves but their shins are still leaden grey. At 16 days their legs are almost completely yellow with only grey streaks showing on the shins.

In the central Grampians five newly-hatched chicks ranged from 9.0–10.5 gm (mean 9.6 gm) (Nethersole-Thompson family, unpublished). In Austria 13 newly-hatched chicks ranged from 10.5–13.0 gm (mean 11.5 gm) (Hable *in* Glutz 1975).

Due to the dotterel's single parent incubation and young-rearing patterns, the earliest hatched chicks often stay in the nest up to 24 hours, or more, until the last chick has dried off and become strong enough to leave. At three nests in Finland, Pulliainen

(1970) found that the oldest chicks stayed in the scoop for 19.5–30 hours and the youngest between 10.7–14.2 hours. Older chicks, however, occasionally feed around the scoop.

At first the cock dotterel escorts his brood to feeding places within 50–150 m of the nest. On 17 June 1979, for example, Patrick recorded that a small chick had moved 125–175 m from where he had found it on the previous day; this chick had gained 3 gm within 24 hours. On 20 June he also located two small chicks which had moved 350–650 m from where they were ringed and weighed on the 17th; one chick had gained 3 gm and the other 5 gm.

In their first few days, and sometimes at least until the ninth day, the cock periodically broods his chicks by day as well as by night. He also warms them in this way during rain, sleet and snowstorms. Cocks and their families occasionally meet and intermingle, when the cocks skirmish until their families have separated. A cock usually, although not always, drives off his hen if she tries to accompany him and the young brood. In the central Grampians, cocks alone were tending the chicks in 16 out of 17 broods (P. S. Thompson 1983); but he often accepts her presence when the chicks are older and stronger, and he quite regularly does so when they are able to fly. Further examples of hens accompanying broods are given in *The Dotterel* (1973). When the chicks are older they often run very fast or crouch in tussocks. At this stage the cock flies off a long way ahead, making short circular flights and periodically dropping down, and then again rising and flying around calling excitedly.

In the Cairngorms three young dotterels, from different broods, flew strongly between their 26th and 30th days. This quite closely corresponds with Kålås's experience in Norway where chicks from two different broods flew at 24 and 26 days respectively.

Many chicks die in their first week. In a sample of 21 clutches, followed up in the central Cairngorms and Grampians, 56 out of 61 eggs (90.8%) hatched, but only 33 chicks (59%) had survived by the end of their first week. Four broods then had three chicks, six had two chicks, and nine had one chick. The young in the other two broods had disappeared (Nethersole-Thompson 1973).

Of twelve broods in the central Grampians, which the family located four days after hatching, three still had three chicks, five had two chicks and four only one chick – a survival rate of 63.8% (P. S. Thompson 1983). Figure 8 indicates the breeding success of dotterel groups on different Scottish hill systems in terms of the ratio between fledged young and adults. Dotterels appear to rear most young successfully on the Dalradian schistose of the east Grampians (1.0:1), less well on the Moine gneisses, schists and quartzite of the central Grampians (0.4:1), and poorly on the granite tops of the central Cairngorms (0.2:1). The influence of the different soils on the vegetation, and consequently on the insects, is likely to be an important factor in these differences.

In the Grampians and Cairngorms, between 1934–70, 427 adults produced 162 flying

	years	young reared	adults	young/old ratio
East Grampians	6	51	50	1.0:1
Central and west Grampians	3	22	56	0.4:1
East Cairngorms	5	17	60	0.3:1
Central Cairngorms	15	63	233	0.2:1
West Cairngorms	4	9	28	0.3:1
Cairngorms (all regions)		89	321	0.3:1

Fig. 8   Breeding success of dotterel in Scotland (Nethersole-Thompson 1973).

young, a rough ratio of 0.4:1. Hatching success in a small sample in the reclaimed polders of the Netherlands appears to be appreciably lower than in Scotland. In 1961–68, 10 nests with 29 eggs produced only 16 chicks, a hatching success rate of 55.1%.

DISTRACTION BEHAVIOUR

Dotterels use a remarkably varied battery of distraction displays to deflect and distract possible predators from nests or broods.

(1)   The sitting bird rises from its eggs and runs fast with spread tail and depressed wings, looking rather hump-backed. The white-tipped outer tail feathers are now most conspicuous and the bird almost always *chitters*. A few of the incubating hens have used low intensity forms of this display.

(2)   A dotterel runs with his wings drooped and beaten but with his tail closed.

(3)   Slow shuffles, in which the bird alternately beats and droops its wings but keeps its tail closed.

(4)   A run with drooped but beaten wings, but with tail partly opened and dragged along the ground.

(5)   The dotterel runs very fast, almost like a small mammal, with all feathers indrawn and usually crouching low to ground.

(6)   'Mock scrape making': the cock appears to scrape and half rotate while throwing bits of vegetation sideways or over his shoulder. We have watched this display given by a cock tending 9-day old chicks.

(7)   'Mock brooding' in which the bird sits in a tussock as if incubating and occasionally bends down as if to arrange imaginary eggs with his beak. This is probably caused when a very strong incubation drive is thwarted.

(8)   The bird flaps its wings high above its back. One cock flicked his wings upwards, continuously opening and shutting them.

(9)   'Explosion': a rare display directed at a human intruder. The bird explodes in your face as you bend down to look at the nest. One cock repeatedly did this, returning to the eggs and then running towards us, flapping his wings, but moving in an upright and erect posture.

On 10 June 1969, Derek Ratcliffe watched a Lakeland dotterel using this behaviour. 'When I put my hand out to touch the bird it suddenly erupted vertically off the eggs to about $\frac{3}{4}$ metre and pitched about $\frac{1}{2}$ metre to one side, screeching angrily at me with a *peer-peer-pee* call. It soon walked back to the three eggs and settled down again. After taking some photographs while lying beside the bird I again tried to touch it. This time it not only erupted, but flew at and touched my head before pitching beside the nest'.

(10) Few observers have had the opportunity of watching the way in which a dotterel deals with a large mammal other than man. On 14 June 1978, Bruin, Patrick and Richard watched a cock jump off an unfound nest about 2 m in front of a sheep.

'It rose about $\frac{1}{2}$ metre in the air and landed twice, flapping its wings while maintaining an upright posture with withdrawn head. This display lasted about 5 seconds. Then the cock carried out distraction displays about $1\frac{1}{2}$ metres in front of the sheep's front legs. It moved slowly ahead and drooped and beat its wings and fanned its tail. This continued for about half-a-minute during which the sheep ambled away about 15 m. The cock then walked back and sat down. It was only as a result of this behaviour that we found the nest and three eggs' (Bruin's diary).

(11) During distraction displays, or when running close to a nest, a dotterel frequently appears to 'false feed' giving downward pecks, sometimes without even touching the ground. This is probably displacement feeding or occasionally redirected attack.

(12) Distraction flights: slow, heavy wing flapping, tail partly expanded and depressed. In these the bird flies a few metres just above the ground.

VOICE

The cries of the dotterel must carry a long way in the wide open spaces of their windswept nesting and winter quarters. Their songs are less elaborate and beautiful than those of many other waders but, to the dotterel lover, they have their own nostalgic charm.

In winnow-glide display flights the hens give rhythmic sequences of *peeps* which act as songs and carry long distances. They thus resemble crossbills, which use sequences of social contact *chips* as a song. On the ground, and sometimes during nest dances, cock or hen many give a jumble of quite sweet linnet-like notes. Thomas Heysham, in 1834, was the first to record these rather subdued songs.

Bruin and Patrick have also watched a snipe-like up and down song dance in the central Grampians, given by a cock challenging trespassers close to a nest.

(1) *Social contact calls*

Groups maintain contact with one another with soft *kwips*; and cocks and hens also use soft far-carrying *peep peeps*. They also use other calls at the end of the breeding season when groups are forming and about to fly south.

(2) *Sex calls*

We have not heard distinctive copulation calls resembling those of greenshank, redshank, lapwing and oystercatcher. But during nest dances they use rippling or tittering *tee-hee tee-hees* which sometimes sound like twanging wires. Excited *ting* cries are also occasionally given on these occasions.

(3) *Alarm calls*

A slightly disturbed dotterel often flies away, giving soft long drawn tinkling cries which start with *wit-wit-wit wita-wita-wita-wees*. In situations of greater danger they use a trill which is softer and less shrill than that of an angry dunlin.

Possibly the most characteristic and evocative cry of a slightly alarmed dotterel is the squeaking sound which George Blackwood (1920) described as 'the regular creak of an unoiled wheelbarrow'. While giving this cry the dotterel often stands beside a stone on the skyline.

The sharp, explosive *ting*, a cry of greater urgency, is given during nest dances, on territory, at the nest, and sometimes in excited groups. This call is given in flight and on the ground.

(4) *Anger calls*

After being flushed from a nest, the brooding dotterel sometimes flies away uttering a harsh *skirr*. A female also *skirrs* when she flies over a nest on which her mate is sitting.

In sexual and territorial fighting dotterels sometimes *trill* loudly while holding up their wings.

(5) *Calls at nest*

There is a wide variety of calls at the nest. A cock exceptionally hisses when disturbed from its eggs and is about to threaten a human intruder. They also use soft whistling *wheeps*, a more explosive *toop toop*, a strident whistling *kwee*, an angry rattling *tirra*, a harsh *skirr*, and double *kwee-kwee-skirr*. A cock also gives soft *kees* while standing, bobbing, close to a nest. During distraction displays his chittering cries, given as the bird flaps and flounders at your feet, sound like *kweer-kweerik-kweerik*.

(6) *Calls to young*

A sitting dotterel uses several different calls and cries to the squeaking chicks as they slowly emerge from the eggs. On the central Grampians the family discovered that dotterels have harsh *gruk* cries with which they communicate and later discipline the chicks. This has the same function as the special calls used by golden plover, dunlin, curlew, redshank, greenshank and common sandpiper.

The cock uses a special call, *tree-lee tree-lee*, with which he recalls a scattered brood before nestling them. He also gives soft *kee-kees* to which the chicks answer with shriller *kree-krees*. When Rittinghaus (1962) held a chick in his hand a cock called *pu-puur*.

(7) *Chick calls*

In the hand, a chick of about a fortnight old gave a strident *kweea-kweea* while the cock chittered on the ground, terminating a burst of distraction cries with soft *kip-kips* (Nethersole-Thompson 1973).

A young dotterel uses the adult social contact call when it first starts to fly; it then also gives 'whirring' cries of anger.

PREDATORS

In all parts of its range the dotterel has predators and enemies. In the central Cairngorms and in the central and east Grampians peregrines occasionally kill and eat dotterels; we have found dotterel feathers in their 'kills'. Merlins seldom hunt the high tops, but they are likely predators. In the central Grampians kestrels sometimes fly away with chicks.

The tourist invasion has led to masses of litter on parts of the high ground, with mongrel crows now often working ridges where they were seldom seen before; we have found eggs sucked by crows. Thoughtless hill walkers also bring unleashed dogs to the tops; and we have seen foxes quartering the whalebacks.

Great skuas, great black-backed gulls and foxes were all recorded on the hill where the first Sutherland dotterel's nest was found in 1967. In May 1976, R. Mearns found the remains of dotterels in peregrines' kills in three different places in the southern Uplands. This was significant predation, even if the dotterels belonged to trips on the move.

The few Lakeland dotterels have many potential enemies. On 1 June 1972, Stuart Illis found bits of a dotterel in a peregrine's plucking. In 1920, J. F. Peters watched seven ravens, five buzzards and four peregrines in the air over dotterel habitats; and G. W. Temperley found three nests which ravens had apparently predated. Carrion crows, rooks, jackdaws and black-headed gulls also regularly work the Lakeland fell tops. Foxes, stoats and sheep dogs may also harry them; and in 1926 a fell sheep trod on a nest.

A list of predators in Fenno-Scandia is rather different. Yngvar Hagen (*in litt*) recorded the pluckings of dotterel in 10 merlin, three hen harrier and two snowy owl nests. Rough-legged buzzards are also known to take occasional dotterels and their chicks. In other parts of the far north, arctic fox, wolverine, raven and long-tailed skua are all likely predators. The Cambridge University Expedition to Hardanger Vidda in 1978 recorded 10 nests, six of which were apparently robbed. There, Kålås (MS) also reported that between 1979–81 22–67% of known nests were predated. Rough-legged buzzards, ravens, common gulls and foxes were all possible nest robbers. In Holland, where dotterels exploited living space in new polders in Flevoland, farmers have encouraged kestrels and owls as well as stoats and weasels.

Man has always been the most serious enemy of the dotterel. Down the ages they have shot, trapped and netted migrating dotterels in hundreds and thousands. In the 17th century, Nobles and Kings flew trained falcons at them on the heaths of Norfolk and Suffolk. In the late 18th century, Thomas Bewick recorded that dotterels for the table 'made only four pence', but that their feathers were to be purchased at 'six pence in the market'. In the mid 1850s indigent labourers turned a few coppers by shooting into the spring trips. This slaughter also maintained on the Scottish borders. Always, dotterels became tidbits on the rich man's table or dry flies for anglers.

In Sweden the Lapps captured thousands in hare traps. In 1884 alone, men with guns shot 10,000 on the Jylland heaths in Denmark; and in 1873 hundreds were on sale in the Valletta markets in Malta. Beside this massive slaughter, the predation of egg collectors in Scotland and England, and in fashionable egging districts abroad, were minimal (Nethersole-Thompson 1973).

What is the position to-day? In these years, when the climate of opinion is more kindly to wildlife, there is less slaughter of the fewer trips on their way to and from the high tops and fells. But gunmen still probably decimate the parties passing along the Mediterranean in winter en route to North Africa.

In Britain there are also far more people on the high tops. So far the central Grampians are still producing a fair crop of flying young. Egg collecting continues, but on a smaller scale than in the first quarter of this century; and there is little reason to believe that it has had a really serious impact on the dotterel groups breeding in Britain.

FOOD AND FEEDING

When they first arrive on the central Cairngorms the trips often feed in niches on moist ground and on the edges of snowpatches or snowfields. Parents and chicks later pick up Diptera, beetles and spiders on the ridges and flats, but 'grass widows' continue to hunt the squashy paces and find craneflies and larvae close to the melting snows. In the central Grampians the family often recorded small groups of hens feeding on the flats by day and then heard them flying to bogs below the tops at night.

Sitting birds often feed close to the nest; at other times they fly 200 m or more to a favourite feeding place, occasionally meeting their mates which may then accompany them back to the nest. At night I occasionally heard the tinkling cries of single birds or trips as they crossed the Lairig Ghru between the central and western Cairngorms, possibly on their way to tarns and peat bogs. In early mornings, on Hardanger Vidda, Hugh Blair also watched small parties of 4–8 dotterels, sometimes of both sexes, flying in to feed close to small pools.

Dotterels peck and snatch at insects and spiders which they easily pick up from stony ground. While feeding on craneflies they plunge their short beaks deep into black moss. In Sweden, Rittinghaus (1962) found that parents and young sought food in the root systems of alpine grasslands.

After the chicks have exhausted the nutrients in their yolk sacs they appear to feed greedily. E. Blezard recorded that a young chick had a very full stomach, including two craneflies *Nephrotoma* which they had swallowed complete with long wings and legs, four carabid beetles *Calathrus*, 1 scarabeid *Aphodius* and three weevils *Otiorrhynchus*. Two Norwegian breeding birds contained beetles, particularly *Bembidion*, larvae of click beetles *Elater*, weevils *Otiorrhynchus*, earthworms *Lumbricidae* and willow leaves *Salix* spp. Pulliainen (1970) found that dotterels on Värriötunturi, Finland, supplemented a mainly insect diet by taking flowers of chickweed wintergreen *Trientalis europaea* and bilberry *Vaccinium myrtillus* and berries of crowberry *Empetrum nigrum*. Adults and chicks use fragments of quartz or gravel to help them digest the wing cases of beetles.

On spring passage they visit bare or newly-ploughed land, favouring click beetles, chrysomelids and weevils. But on their return journey they seldom visit arable fields. Blezard recorded two carabid beetles *Pterostichus* and nutlets of *Polygonum persicaria* in a bird killed in the north of England in September. Spring and autumn migrants sometimes vary their insect diet by taking earthworms and snails *Planorbis*.

In their winter quarters in Israel, H. B. Tristram (1884) was the first to record that dotterels fed largely on small landsnails *Helix.*

DISTRIBUTION AND NUMBERS

Abroad, dotterels nest regularly in good numbers in Norway, Sweden and Finland. In Norway, where Byrkjedal and Kålås (1981) estimated a breeding population of 28,000 pairs in 1979, they nest on the great ridges of Dovre Fjell, Hardanger Vidda, Norefjell, and on fells around the Porsanger, Lax and Varanger fjords in Finnmark. About 7,500 pairs possibly nest on suitable Swedish fells from the frontiers of arctic Norway to Dalarna 60°30′ N. Dotterels also haunt great tablelands and isolated fells in Swedish Lapland. Possibly as many as 8,500 pairs breed in Finland, where they nest on high fells in Enontekiö down to Ounastunturi and Pallastunturi. They are particularly plentiful in Utsjoki and on Värriötunturi fjell and also nest in Inari district and as far south as Sallantunturi.

Their many breeding grounds in USSR mainly lie in the tundra zone from the Kola Peninsula to the Chukchee Peninsula, but they avoid wet tundra. The alpine zone in the Urals and the mountains of north-east Siberia also contain great breeding grounds, but no estimate of numbers has yet been accepted. A pair nested in the Caucusus in 1972.

From 1961–69 they bred in the re-claimed north-east polder in the Netherlands and they may still do so. A few pairs nest regularly in the Appenines in Italy and in the Austrian Alps. Single pairs nested in Switzerland in 1965, France in 1968 and Spitsbergen in 1974; a pair possibly laid eggs in Iceland in 1864. They previously nested in Czechoslovakia and Poland and on the borders of Hungary and Romania. In 1930 a pair attempted to nest in Alaska.

Dotterels ceased to nest regularly in England about 1927; but from the mid 1950s they have re-colonised some Lakeland fells and now appear to nest regularly in small numbers. An isolated pair probably nested in north Wales in 1968; and definitely bred there in 1969. In 1975 a pair nested in Ireland.

In Scotland small groups nest regularly in Ross, Inverness, Banff, Aberdeen, Angus and Perth. In the 1960s–1980s isolated pairs nested in Sutherland, Kirkcudbright, Selkirk/Peebles, and possibly Dumfries; in 1983 a pair nested in Argyll. The dotterels' main breeding grounds, however, are in the east, central and west Cairngorms and the east, central and west Grampians. In the Cairngorms over 50 pairs probably nest in some years. In the late 1970s the family recorded a higher average breeding population in their study area in the central Grampians than that estimated at any other time in this century. This increase coincides with the slightly cooling climate and a small increase and spread of breeding snow buntings in northern Scotland.

Between 1945–69, 60–80 pairs of dotterel probably nested in Britain in most years (Nethersole-Thomspon 1973); but from 1970 onwards numbers have possibly increased to 100–150 breeding pairs in favourable years.

The dotterel is part of an exacting environment. The watcher shivers at the memory of nights soaked in a small tent, with the wind beating and roaring. Yet every moment of nest-hunting is precious, for this is a bird of moods and many problems – a magic bird whose secrets only yield to its lovers.

11:   New or returning waders

Wader Watchers in Britain live in most exciting times. Conservation of nesting habitats at home and abroad, a slightly cooler climate, and more observers on the ground, have contributed to some of the discoveries about new or returning breeding waders.

BLACK-WINGED STILT

In 1945 three pairs of black-winged stilts chose the Nottingham Sewage Farm as a nesting ground. J. Staton, a keen local birdwatcher, found a nest and described the behaviour. Then, as now, news of a nesting rarity spread rapidly. Before the end of the season the indefatigable Arthur Whitaker had arrived on the ground, armed with permits from the Water Authority. Soon he and a friend were squelching their way through beds and pools escorted by the foreman. Before long they were thrilled to hear sharp *krek-kreks* 'evidently notes of anger and annoyance'. The stilts looked 'extraordinarily beautiful in flight, with their enormously long legs stretched out behind, reminiscent of the tail of a boy's kite'. In horizontal flight the stilts held their legs close together and straight out, but they often separated them widely when turning. On the ground they stood erect, leaning back on their heels and beating or fanning their wings. Soon Whitaker had marked down a stilt brooding a chick. 'It was greyish-brown of a very pale tone with two dark lines down its back and fine mottling on the rest of its upper surface; it was almost pure white underneath. Bill and legs were dark, the bill with a greenish-grey tinge'.

Whitaker later learnt that two pairs had nested in a radius of 8 m in the bed where he had found the chick. One nest, a slight scrape lined with a few dead stalks and grasses, was between roots of mayweed on a slight ridge of mud. Three pairs had laid clutches; one had been robbed by a boy, and a chick in another was probably squashed by cattle. In all, three young were believed to have fledged.

The courtship displays of black-winged stilts are outstanding. At first the birds stand silently side by side; later they learn to identify their partners by their calls before recognising them by sight. In a collective ground dance, in which 2–6 pairs take part, they stand in a rough circle, continuously rocking on their heels and periodically leap-frogging over one another and flapping their wings. These dances are given both by single birds and by pairs within the colony. The displays occasionally lead to copulation. When ready to pair the two stilts fly to shallow water close to the nest site and the hen signals readiness by bending slightly forward, with neck and head stretched out while uttering special cries. The cock then flies and runs towards her. Approaching from behind, swinging from side to side and standing in the water, he ducks his bill and splashes it up and down. The hen turns and she also splashes. At last the cock stands high on his long legs, balancing himself on the hen's back and holding up his stretched wings vertically. Mating usually lasts about 3–5 seconds before the cock slips to the ground with one wing beating and the other stretched over the hen's back. Then the two birds preen. The cock sometimes places his bill above the upper mandible of the hen and one after the other both briefly call. Afterwards the hen re-adjusts any displaced feathers or, like the cock, flies off to her feeding ground.

Four eggs are laid at intervals of 24–48 hours. The birds sit for short stints lasting from 25 minutes to 3 hours, but occasionally in fairly regular spells of 30–40 minutes.

The hen appears to take a slightly larger part in incubation and she apparently sits at night. At a nest, which George Yeates watched in the Camargue, the cock threw stalks and bits of vegetation over his shoulder while approaching the hen; and he knelt and prodded her with his bill before settling down on the eggs. The hen then walked away, likewise tossing bits and pieces over her shoulders. Incubation lasts 22–24 days and both parents brood the chicks. If disturbed, the chicks run into tall weeds, occasionally ducking down in shallow water. The young start to fly between their 29th and 33rd days and become independent of their parents 2–4 weeks later.

The next breeding record was in Cambridgeshire in 1983. This cosmopolitan and irruptive species occasionally nests far to the north or west of its regular breeding range; in 1894 it was recorded breeding in Saskatchewan, Canada. By 1967 there were 21 pairs in Belgium, six in the Netherlands, and one each in East Germany, Czechoslovakia and Austria.

AVOCET

Solitary pairs of avocets possibly still nested in Norfolk in 1824, at the mouth of the Trent in 1837, and in Kent in 1842 and possibly in 1843. But well before the mid 1850s the last of the old English stock had gone. Reclamation and drainage of marshes, shooting, collecting eggs for the table, and later – in that age of the Acquisitive Society – 'knocking off' the few survivors as trophies, all helped to exterminate this lovely wader.

In 1938 I was thrilled to hear that two pairs had nested almost side by side in Co. Wexford in Eire. A little later, between 1941–46, isolated pairs bred in Essex and possibly in Norfolk. But the real breakthrough came in 1947 when four or five pairs nested at Minsmere and an equal number bred on Havergate Island in Suffolk. G. Waterston and P. E. Brown (1963) described the dramatic story of the avocet's return and re-colonisation.

Restrictions imposed by the German occupying powers in Denmark and the Netherlands during the Second World War helped the avocets' revival. In 1983 Cramp and Simmons estimated a breeding population of over 10,000 pairs along the North Sea and Baltic.

Conservationists have achieved much in England by watching and guarding the Suffolk groups. These have continued to thrive, despite natural hazards and predators like rats, gulls and carrion crows. By 1982, 190 pairs produced over 150 fledged chicks, almost all in Suffolk and Norfolk.

The avocet is a grand addition to the British Breeding List. Its boldly patterned black and white plumage and rather slender upturned black bill, with which it feeds by skimming the surface of mud or shallow water, makes it unique.

Avocets have a battery of most beautiful sexual displays, in one of which both birds preen and simultaneously splash in the water. The hen then pauses, lowering her head and placing her bill and cheek on the surface. Still splashing, the cock advances, preening, before he positions himself just behind her. Then, between pauses, he moves from side to side before jumping onto the hen's back. He now often lowers his bill to touch hers and he vigorously beats his wings while the hen sways from side to side during the coupling. After the cock has finished he slips off the hen's back and then both birds lower their bills and quietly walk away.

As in all wader courtships there is a great range of actions and emotions, particularly if one or other bird is not ready sexually. In the nest dance which then follows, the two birds pivot, one after the other, and shuffle in a scoop, flinging bits of grasses or stalks over their shoulders. A little later they sometimes again perform the courtship sequence before copulating anew.

Avocets lay their eggs at intervals of 1–2 days, with a full clutch of four eggs often completed in five days. They start to sit after two or three eggs are in the scoop. Incubation periods have ranged from 20–28 days, with a mean of 23.4–24.7 days for 230 clutches (C. J. Cadbury *et al* 1977). An addled clutch was brooded for 73 days (P. J. Olney 1967).

The two birds share incubation, usually sitting for spells of less than one hour, but occasionally as long as four hours or more. Before nest relief they have a very pretty ceremony. The incoming bird lifts drops of water off its feet as it approaches its mate and chucks bits and pieces of nesting material sideways. Its partner meanwhile walks away, also flipping small objects over its shoulder.

Eggshell disposal mechanisms of avocets are intriguing. They sometimes lift large shell fragments with which they fly away; or they drop them in pools of water, perhaps first nibbling the shell at the water side. If a bird has dropped an eggshell in mid colony, another avocet sometimes lifts and flies away with it, probably to prevent a flying predator from marking the nest.

Eggs show chips for about three days before they hatch, and the chicks leave the scoop soon after they are dry. For the first week or ten days the parents intermittently brood their young; but they do not become independent or fly freely until about 35–42 days old.

An exceptionally beautiful wader bird, with unusual and most exciting behaviour, will the avocet yet grace more of the shores and islands of Britain and Ireland?

LITTLE RINGED PLOVER

In 1938, to the delight of local ornithologists, a pair of little ringed plovers quite unexpectedly nested beside the Tring Reservoir in Hertfordshire. In 1944 two pairs again nested at Tring and a third pair bred in Middlesex. Compared with the stouter ringed-plover the chief diagnostics of the smaller and slighter little ringed plover are the absence of white wing bars, conspicuous yellow orbital rings, yellowish flesh-coloured legs, and quite different calls.

Once again wartime restrictions on the Continent, and the grubbing up of stony ground, provided new habitats and raised numbers which overspilt into Britain. Like black redstarts, little ringed plovers established themselves on human artefacts – large gravel pits, rubbish pits, sewage farms and reservoirs. So quickly did little ringed plovers colonise these unaesthetic haunts in Britain that by 1957 70 pairs were recorded, of which at least 50 nested. By 1972, 467 pairs were breeding, with isolated pairs sometimes as far north as the Clyde Valley. Unlike ruff, black-tailed godwit and avocet, the little ringed plover was a new nesting wader rather than a recovered species.

In the early years, the finding of a little ringed plover's nest was a great challenge. Arthur Whitaker was soon trying to raise his life tally of British nesting birds. On 27 May 1947, after failing at Tring, he moved to Feltham, Middlesex. At the fourth gravel pit searched he heard, for the first time, the distinctive calls of a little ringed plover. Soon he discovered a bird near a narrow-gauged railway on which a locomotive and trucks passed to and fro with loads of washed gravel. Dozens of children and dogs were playing, sailing boats, and throwing sticks into a pool which was within the little ringed plovers' territory.

Always a sticker, Whitaker returned on 29 May when he located three birds, but the boys again disturbed the search. On 6 June he watched the cock's display flight, when the bird flew in rocking motion, occasionally running its calls into a trill. On the ground the cock stood upright in front of the hen, then crouched with partly fanned tail; but she ignored his display. From time to time a third bird flew in and fed quietly about a dozen metres from the pair. On 13 June Whitaker again failed to find the nest. However, on 7 July, Eric Parrinder took him to a partly constructed reservoir at Staines, Middlesex, where a little ringed plover was sitting on four eggs on flat gravel and mud on ground containing small pools. The nest was a tiny scoop, unlined apart from a few small pebbles.

Since those early years, British and Continental ornithologists have learnt much about the breeding behaviour of this pugnacious little wader. Cocks often arrive ahead of hens. Pairs are strictly territorial, mating, courting and partly feeding in living-space which they defend against ringed plovers and Kentish plovers as well as against their own kind. Cocks assert proprietorship by butterfly display flights, flying slowly backwards and forwards over their territories at a height of about 30 m, defending a greater expanse of air than surface space. These flights reach their peak before and during egg laying (K. E. L. Simmons 1956).

Some little ringed plovers re-pair annually, though many divorces are recorded from year to year, or occasionally in the same season after a pair has reared its first brood. The nest dance or scrape ceremony, first performed by the cock and later by the pair in turn, ends in the cock leading the hen from one favoured spot to another. Afterwards the cock runs towards her in horizontal posture and goose-steps up to her with his body held vertically. He then 'marks time', sometimes with toes raised so high that they touch his breast. The hen crouches and he mounts her, first standing and then continuing to 'mark time' on her back. When she tilts forward or turns her tail sideways both birds rapidly beat their wings. Then, when the hen shakes him off, he copulates as he dismounts. Little ringed plovers copulate well ahead of the first egg but not during incubation, though the full mating ceremony is still occasionally enacted. They have a rich assortment of other sexual, antagonistic and distraction displays.

In Holland, Belgium and West Germany the earliest hens are recorded laying in the first week of April, and in East Germany and England towards the end of April (Glutz 1975).

At Tring, in 1938, two eggs were laid at intervals of 29 and 38 hours respectively. J. Walters gives an average of 36 hours for the laying intervals of 132 clutches in north Holland. A clutch is normally four, occasionally three, and exceptionally five, with a mean of 3.87 for 1,006 clutches (Walters 1979).

Both sexes take approximately equal shares in incubation. There are regular exchanges, often accompanied by calling, but no set pattern. The incoming bird sometimes slips on to the eggs under the spread tail of its mate. Exchanges take place more frequently in the morning than in the afternoon or evening. Incubation lasts 22–28 days, with an average of 24.9 days in May (36); 25.8 days in June (42); and 24.0 days in July (12). Three clutches of five were incubated for 27, 29 and 29 days (Walters 1975). One hen laid 15 eggs in a season – a first clutch and three replacements. The first egg of a replacement clutch is laid 4–11 days after clutch loss. In England little ringed plovers are occasionally double-brooded, with the cock hatching out the first eggs and the hen pairing up and producing a second clutch for a new mate. In favourable seasons they also often rear two broods in the Netherlands and central and south Europe; but they are single brooded in Finland and Scandinavia.

Eggs are pipped for 2–4, exceptionally 6 days, and the chicks squeak in the eggs 3–4 days before they hatch. Small pieces of shell and addled eggs are left in the nest but the birds carry away and drop large fragments at anything from 20–250 m from the scoop.

Chicks leave the nest within a few hours of hatching. Both sexes guard and brood them in their first few days and during severe weather. They first fly on the 24th or 25th day and become independent of their parents 4–8 days later.

Just occasionally man provides as well as destroys habitats for waders. The gravel pits of southern England and midlands are not haunts of great beauty, but they have enabled an attractive little plover to colonise and thrive most successfully.

KENTISH PLOVER

Since the early 1930s the charming Kentish plover has nested only sporadically or irregularly in Britain. Pairs nested in Sussex in 1949–56, Suffolk in 1952, Lincolnshire in 1979, and in the Channel Islands in 1975.

The former main stronghold of the Kentish plover was in the great expanse of shingle near Dungeness in Kent where they had a sad history of harrassment and persecution. Gunners shot them for cabinet specimens and local hunters with trained dogs sought clutches of eggs. Later, conservationists tried to protect the birds and earned them a little respite; 44 pairs bred in 1906 and 30–40 pairs in 1908 (N. Ticehurst 1909). The bird is, however, a fringe species in Britain and its range was already possibly shrinking. On a fine day in May 1931, I found what must have been one of the last nests of the old stock on the shingle of Littlestone. The sitting bird was silent and in no hurry to return to its three eggs which were pointed downwards in the little scoop in the shingle.

On 14 May 1922, when small groups still thrived on beaches in the Channel Islands, Whitaker hunted the famous shell beach of Helm. It is easy to visualise the scene. Bare-headed, in his usual plusfours, and carrying the short walking stick with which he used to mark nests, Whitaker kept a sharp look-out as he slowly walked along the stretch of sand and shingle above high tide mark. In a search lasting only a few hours he found six nests, each with a full clutch of three eggs. The sitting plovers ran fast in a diagonal line between their nests and the water line. The first 'raced along, running low like a little grey shadow'. One nest was lined with straws and tiny shells collected from a distance; and one egg was laid or hooked inside an inverted limpet shell of about 3.5 cm in diameter. Two nests were roughly 300 m apart and one, further back from the beach, was in a shallow break in the sandhills. Whitaker noted that the Kentish plovers, lacking the black on the head, were less conspicuous than ringed plovers; they were remarkably silent throughout the day and he never heard a single call.

Kentish plovers often arrive on their breeding grounds in pairs. In Germany, Hans Rittinghaus (1975) found that the same two birds seldom nested together in more than one season, although once two birds paired for six years insuccession. G. Thielcke (1951) met with a cock mated to two hens which laid five eggs in a joint nest and another cock incubated the eggs of two hens which had nests 21 m apart.

In the Camargue groups in southern France, C. M. Lessels (1984) discovered that most birds annually changed mates even if their previous partners had returned; but pairs generally stayed together for replacement clutches. Two hens, however, changed mates and re-nested after hatching their first broods.

Cock and hen join in nest dancing ritual which helps to synchronise their sex rhythms; these displays appear to be restricted to the territory. In full nest dancing the cock steps out of the scoop, side on to the hen, with his near wing closed and his outer wing held out slightly and pointed obliquely upwards, and his fanned tail raised to about 30°. After the hen has left the scoop the cock approaches her from the rear and then pauses to 'mark time', but with less exaggerated steps than those used by ringed plovers and little ringed plovers. An unusual courtship then follows. The hen now briefly raises her folded tail to show her cloaca and the cock mounts, standing on her back flapping his wings and then 'marking time'. 'When the female tilts forward the male rapidly twists his tail under the hen's for cloacal contact, holding the female by the feathers of her neck or crown and often grasping her rump with his feet, and both fall backwards, still interlocked. Copulation presumably continues until the birds separate' (Walters 1983). A hen no longer copulates after laying her first egg, but a few are ready to do so after the clutch is complete.

In 'symbolic nest reliefs', which periodically take place, the hen usually enters the scoop in front of the cock, not under his tail. When she scrapes in the hollow, both call; and the cock periodically sidethrows but does not move away while doing so.

Rittinghaus (1961) found that 1–4 scrapes were made in the territory before the hen lays her first egg. A cock may scrape in the absence of a hen, particularly early in the season. Hens do not appear to make their own scrapes. Nest dancing revives towards the end of the breeding season.

The earliest eggs were recorded in the Netherlands on 4 April, in Belgium on 12 April, and on Oldeeog Island in the North Sea on 12 April. Rittinghaus, however, gives early May as the peak laying season on Oldeoog. In Kent, eggs were usually laid in early May and occasionally in late April.

Eggs are laid at intervals of 18–72 hours with a mean of c48 hours (Rittinghaus 1975). A clutch usually consists of three, and occasionally two eggs. Walters recorded only two clutches of four eggs in 389 clutches in the Netherlands; and P. W. Munn (1948) had one c/4 in 290 clutches in Mallorca. Lessels tells me that, in the Camargue, she found only one c/4 in approximately 700 nests recorded in 1980–82.

Steady incubation begins when the clutch is complete, but intermittent brooding

AVOCETS, elegant birds with fascinating sexual patterns, exchange at the nest. (Photo: J. F. Reynolds).

LITTLE RINGED PLOVERS in nest relief. These birds are now firmly established in Britain, often nesting in gravel pits and other artefacts. (Photo: M. Holiday).

KENTISH PLOVER about to sit at its nest in the sand dunes. This wader has fared badly in Britain during the last fifty years. (Photo: R. Vaughan).

RUFFS standing on a lek. On the larger leks a few Master birds have most of the couplings with the reeves. (Photo: Pekka Helo).

PURPLE SANDPIPER walking from nest and eggs. An attractive wader that has recently started to breed in the Scottish Highlands. (Photo: A. Christiansen).

BLACK-TAILED GODWIT scolding from a fence post. Pairs now breed regularly in small numbers in the East Anglian washes. (Photo: R. Vaughan).

TURNSTONE about to brood. This northern wader has probably nested in Scotland in recent years. (Photo: Eric Hosking).

sometimes takes place three days before the last egg is laid. The cock usually sits at night and the hen takes a greater share of incubation by day. Incubation lasts from 23–29 days, with an average of 26.3 days for 43 clutches in Germany (Rittinghaus) and 25.4 days for 22 clutches in the Netherlands (Walters). The occasional clutch of four, however, may take 1–3 days longer to hatch.

Kentish plovers are normally single brooded; but hens in haunts in Brittany and beside the North Sea have occasionally produced a second clutch for a new mate. Lost eggs or chicks are sometimes replaced; the first egg of a repeat clutch is laid 4–5 days after the loss of the first clutch. Lessels (1984) found that adults from six broods bred again in the same season after hatching their first young. Intervals from hatching of the first egg to estimated laying of the first egg in the second clutch ranged from 15–34 days.

The eggs are pipped for 5–48 hours (mean 12–15 hours). Large shell fragments are removed. The chicks, which stay in the nest for a few hours only, are at first tended and brooded by both parents. Later one or the other often leaves before fledging is complete. At Oldeoog, Rittinghaus recorded chicks flying on their 41st day. However, near Amsterdam, Walters found that free-flying took place earlier; two chicks flew after 27 days and a third at 31 days.

The Kentish plover has been a loser. By destroying its living space and hunting it to death we have lost an interesting fringe population; but in these more kindly years there is still hope for its future.

PURPLE SANDPIPER

Over a hundred years ago H. L. Saxby suspected that the purple sandpiper sometimes nested on Unst in Shetland. Since then, single birds have been seen on suitable fells in England and Scotland; but the first acceptable breeding record took place in the Cairngorms in 1978. In 1979 four young purple sandpipers flew from two broods in the same location. Then, in 1980, after a hunt lasting three days, John Mullins had the great joy of tracking down a nest with three eggs in short grass on a Cairngorms top where neighbours include snow bunting and dotterel. Mullins and N. J. Cowlard now watched the more brightly coloured bird give a distraction display on the ground and the duller bird – possibly the hen – fly in and start to sit on the nest and eggs. On 21 July 1980, Adam Watson watched a young purple sandpiper running very fast and for many metres in the company of a parent which called from the top of a rock.

In 1981 there were 4 broods with at least 2 chicks in each of 3 broods, and 1 chick in the fourth. 1982 was a less successful year, with only 1 chick flying and in 1983 one adult only was recorded (Dennis 1983). On 9 June 1984 purple sandpipers were again on their breeding habitats, but no eggs or young were located (G. Dickson *in litt*).

A smallish rather dumpy wader, with a large head and longish bill with yellow base, the purple sandpiper stands on short yellow legs. On its breeding ground the head and mantle are blackish brown and show a purplish sheen in good light. There are white bars on its secondaries, which show up in flight, and white streaks on the side of its neck.

We do not yet know whether the Scottish birds arrive in pairs; but in Spitsbergen, in 1976, our friend, Professor Sven-Axel Bengtson, found that they were in pairs soon after arriving, even while foraging in flocks. Purple sandpipers are territorial. They do not apparently use the territory for pair formation but do so for much of their sexual and nesting activity. In Spitsbergen and Norway nests are well separated. However, A. H. Joensen (1969) recorded 5–10 pairs/10 km^2 on Skúvoy in the Faroes; and Joensen and N. Preuss (1972) found 6–8 breeding pairs on 70 ha in north-west Greenland.

Cock purple sandpipers frequently raise one or both wings vertically while chasing hens on the ground, sometimes holding up a wing or wings for as long as 45 seconds. During sexual pursuit flights, usually low over the ground, cocks give moaning calls after their hens which they had previously been pursuing on the ground. On overtaking, he usually holds his wings in a V as he glides over and in front of her and often again starts his ground displays. A cock makes scrapes to which he attempts to entice a hen which may step into the hollow under his belly. Ground pursuits are usually the prelude to copulation when the cock hovers and then alights on the hen's back.

Eggs are laid at intervals of 24–28 hours and there is occasionally a lapse of 72 hours between the third and fourth egg. Early clutches were recorded in Faroes, Iceland and south-west Greenland on 14–15 May. A few were found in Finnmark, Norway, on the first week of June and in Spitsbergen on the second week of June.

Eighty two clutches in Spitsbergen contained 7/3, 75/4, with a mean of 3.91 eggs (H. L. Løvenskiold 1964).

Incubation starts when the clutch is complete. Both cock and hen sit but cocks take the greater share. C. Cane (1980) recorded both sexes sitting for stints of eight or more hours until the fourteenth day, when the hen no longer took any part. The incubation period lasts 21–22 days, with the chicks hatching over a period of 15 hours (Bengtson 1975). The hen disappears before the young are hatched, leaving her mate to rear them.

In these years, when northern birds are starting to colonise Scotland, there is no reason why purple sandpipers should not nest on other fells in Scotland, and even in England, as well as on those already settled in the Cairngorms.

RUFF

As late as 1871 ruffs and reeves regularly met at leks in Norfolk. Emma L. Turner photographed a reeve at a nest in the Norfolk Broads in 1907 and gave a graphic account of her experiences in the hide. Solitary reeves laid eggs in Suffolk in 1899, in Durham in 1903 and probably in 1901, and in Lancashire in 1910. In 1922 a nest was found in the Cley marshes. Attempts to re-introduce the bird to Norfolk, by means of eggs collected abroad, failed in 1939 and 1957. However, at least one distinguished naturalist believes that ruffs and reeves have never been absent from Britain as nesting birds.

The recent steady colonisation of the Ouse Washes from 1963 onwards has been a triumph for conservation. In 1964 there were 103 ruffs and in 1971 21 reeves in leks there. In the 1970s and 1980s reeves have also nested in Lancashire, where three out of four hatched chicks on a marsh in 1976 (Hale 1980). In 1980, John Massie photographed a reeve sitting on 4 eggs in north Sutherland, all of which hatched.

Males, with their gorgeous ruffs and head tufts of many colours, have a most complicated social and sexual system. In general terms ruffs are polygynous and some reeves polyandrous; and a proportion of both sexes are promiscuous in their sexual relationships.

Johanna Hogan-Warburg (1966) divides male ruffs into two main types – Independents and Satellites. Independents are further divided into (1) 'Independent Residents', those possessing residences (stances) in the lek on which they display and from which they drive away trespassers. (2) 'Independent Marginals', which do not possess residences, but stay on the fringes of the lek, usually only visiting it in the company of reeves and Satellite Males, when they are usually evicted by the nearest Independent Resident. By defeating an Independent Resident, however, a Marginal Male can raise himself to the full status of residence-holder.

Satellite Males – a lower social class – never establish residences, but exploit those of Independent Residents whose stances they usually try to visit when reeves are standing near them.

Hogan-Warburg found that Satellite Males had white ruffs and head tufts but Resident and Marginal Males possessed black, brown, yellow and red ruffs and head tufts.

A reeve shows her readiness to copulate by crouching in a particular residence. In a crowded lek she selects an individual ruff by turning towards him while still crouching. Some ruffs are thus chosen frequently while others are never selected. Ruff and reeve only copulate after she has crouched and has sometimes nibbled the feathers at the back of the ruff's head.

At a large lek two-thirds of the copulations were carried out by three of the nineteen resident males, six of which never succeeded in winning a reeve. Three Satellite Males each had one copulation (Hogan-Waburg 1966).

As with black grouse, copulations are more evenly distributed between the ruffs at small leks. Small isolated groups have certainly developed different behaviour from those studied in the larger leks on the Continent of Europe. In England, in 1983, five to six ruffs, with black and white ruffs and head tufts, displayed on different parts of the ground with no firm location for their lek.

One of our associates, who watches ruffs and reeves in England, emphasises the great shyness of the reeves. In 1984 he never saw a reeve leave her nest although on each visit the eggs were warm.

Several watchers have studied the breeding biology of the ruff in Europe. H. Mildenburger (1953) estimated that intervals between eggs in one German clutch were 25, 33 and 39 hours; but F. S. Andersen (1944) recorded a shorter interval of about 24 hours in Denmark. Incubation usually starts on the last egg of a clutch, occasionally a day earlier; periods range from 21 to 24 days.

Andersen (1944) recorded an average of 3.7 eggs for 18 clutches in Denmark. In one clutch the eggs were chipped for 3–4 days before they hatched. The first egg in two replacement clutches were laid 8 and 14 days respectively after the loss of the first clutches. The reeve rears the chicks, feeding them from her bill in the first few days. V. D. Kokhanov (1965) found that the young ruffs were 25–27 days old before they were able to fly.

From the pioneering work of Edmund Selous onwards, the fantastic displays and social castes of ruffs have offered delight and challenge to those fortunate enough to study them at their leks.

BLACK-TAILED GODWIT

The black-tailed godwit, a wader on which Julian Huxley carried out pioneer research on Texel in the Netherlands, nested regularly in Yorkshire and East Anglia until 1829, possibly in Norfolk until 1834, and as late as 1847 in the Cambridge fens; pairs also possibly nested in Norfolk in 1857 and in Lincolnshire in 1885. The decline and ultimate loss of the black-tailed godwit in the 19th century was probably due to drainage of the fens, heavy shooting for food, trophy hunting, and possibly the taking of eggs for the table; the influence of egg collectors is unlikely to have been significant.

After the old stock had disappeared occasional breeding pairs were suspected; but there is no proof of nesting in Britain until 1937 when eggs were laid in Lincolnshire but no chicks were reared. In the early 1940s pairs were again reported in the same part of Lincolnshire. Inevitably, Arthur Whitaker was on the move. On 5 May 1943 he visited Cowbit Wash, near Spalding in Lincolnshire, where he watched the undulating song dance of a cock black-tailed godwit performed about 60 m above the fen, the characteristic *kee-wick* calls synchronising with the display. On the next day he watched the pair, which had possibly lost their nest.

There is little to add until 1952 when a local ornithologist informed the RSPB that a pair was nesting in a fen close to his home in the Ouse Washes in Cambridge/Norfolk. Jeffrey Boswall was instructed to visit and report. I can well remember the 'cloak and dagger' atmosphere when he confirmed the good news. That year carrion crows probably destroyed the first clutch; but the pair re-nested in another field about 5 km away and were later seen with a brood of three freely-flying young. From this original pioneering the godwits thrived, with 11 pairs hatching young in 1961. Thenceforward, they have become firmly established in the Ouse Washes on the borders of Cambridge and Norfolk where over 60 pairs now breed in Reserves owned jointly by the Wildfowl Trust, Cambridge and Isle of Ely Naturalists Trust, and the Royal Society for the Protection of Birds. Single pairs also nest regularly in Unst in Shetland, occasionally in Orkney, Caithness, and south-east and south-west Scotland, and in scattered haunts in England.

In the breeding season this tall handsome long-legged and long-billed wader has a dark rump and a white tail with a broad terminal black band. Its head, neck and upper breast are bright chestnut red and its underparts are white. In flight it displays a broad white wing bar and its legs project well beyond its tail.

Some pairs are already formed before the birds arrive on their breeding grounds. Others reach former territories a little later and then sometimes re-pair with former mates. The cocks establish territories by means of special song dances, but boundaries are not rigid or well defined. After the pair is formed the two birds abandon those courtship territories, often wandering widely in search of suitable nesting habitat. They now mark out a new nesting territory by forming several scrapes which they defend against instruding pairs. When the hen has chosen a particular scoop, and laid her first egg, territorial defence is sometimes restricted to a radius not exceeding 50 m from the nest (Lind 1961).

When black-tailed godwits are breeding in good numbers they tend to nest semi-colonially, often laying their eggs close to lapwings whose aggression helps to ward off predators. F. Haverschmidt (1927 and 1963) recorded 67 nests on 20 ha and 20 nests on 3 ha in the Netherlands. In West Germany many birds maintain their old pairings and lay eggs within 150 m of old nest sites.

Black-tailed godwits have elaborate sexual displays, summaries of which are described in Glutz (1977). Unmated cocks fly song dances to attract hens. These flights contain several different elements including tumbling, zooming and rolling. While performing, the cocks are sometimes silent but often give long series of *grutto* cries before flashing down to their territories. During pair formation the cock invites the hen to follow him by briefly vibrating his wings, fanning his tail and upstretching his neck. Cocks chase hens for long distances, flying, like golden plovers, in series of inverted arcs. On the ground the cocks raise their necks, hold their wings almost vertically, and fan their tails. When the cock walks up to or retreats from the hen he sometimes twists his tail from side to side, displaying the upper surface to her. Later, before he copulates, he expands his tail as he walks after the hen and he occasionally pecks her if she pauses. When she finally stops, the cock beats his wings above his back and flutters onto her. Then, after copulating, he sometimes regains his balance and again takes

the hen. In small courting groups, particular cocks sometimes covet and cuckold their neighbours' mates (I. Byrkjedal *in litt*).

These fine waders have an elaborate scrape or nest dancing display in which the cock shows the white underside of his tail and belly to his mate. The hen also nest dances on her own and later shows the cock the scoop in which she has laid her first egg.

On the Ouse fens in East Anglia the earliest eggs are occasionally laid as early as 28 March, but most hens complete their clutches in the second half of April and early May. In the Netherlands, laying usually begins in the first week in April or a week later in drier habitats; and in central Europe the eggs are laid between the second half of April and mid May. Hens also start to lay in late April in south Sweden and in early May near Leningrad (Flint 1973). In Denmark the laying season lasts from 36–43 days. In four observations the latest egg was laid on 31 May (Lind 1961).

Lind gives 34.2 hours as the average interval between eggs in 17 clutches. If an egg is laid before 15.00 hours, the next is laid, on average, 28.6 hours later; but if laid after 15.00 the eggs are deposited at 37–45 hour in intervals (mean 39.2 hours).

Incubation usually begins on the penultimate or final egg, but in cold weather earlier eggs are sometimes brooded. Both sexes incubate for longish spells with the cock doing most in the evenings or at night; exchanges at the nest take place every 2–5 hours in the morning and late afternoon. There is no special nest-relief ritual, but one hen touched the cock's back with her bill. Sixteen Danish clutches had incubation periods varying from 22–24 days (Lind 1961). The first egg of a replacement clutch is laid 5–16 days, with an average of 7.2 days, after the loss of the original clutch. Replacements are laid 80–640 m from the lost clutches (van Balen 1959).

Eggs in the same clutch are bumped or chipped for various periods but the chicks are all hatched fairly synchronously. Both cock and hen tend and guard their broods which spend an average of about 16 hours in the nest. Afterwards the family may move up to 200 m in a few hours. Lind (1961) and Gunton (1941) recorded families moving 700 m in two days. Cock and hen brood their chicks for short spells of 15–20 minutes in rough weather and do so regularly at night. Both parents stay with their families until they start to fly, at some time between 25–35 days. A little later the chicks become independent and the families break up.

SPOTTED SANDPIPER

In 1975 a pair of spotted sandpipers, Nearctic waders, most unexpectedly nested on a stony beach in a sheltered tidal bay in Skye. The hen laid four eggs which were later deserted. This exciting discovery added a new species to the British Breeding List.

Those who have watched both spotted and common sandpipers in the breeding season distinguish *macularia* by its underparts which are liberally speckled by black-brown spots, greyer upperparts, pink or yellow-black tipped bills and pink to greyish brown legs. They have also narrower wing bars than *hypoleucos* and the usual alarm/contact cry *weet weet* is slightly more tinny.

Three ornithologists in the United States have discovered that some hen spotted sandpipers are polyandrous. One study was carried out by Helen Hays at Great Gull Island, New York (H. A. Hays 1972); and hundreds of miles away, and quite independently, Lew Oring and M. L. Knudson (1972) also proved polyandry at Little Pelican Island, Leech Lake, Minnesota.

In 1970–71, Hays discovered that 6 out of 11 hens were polyandrous. In 1970 two hens were monogamous; two mated with two, and one with three cocks successively.

In addition, one nest was destroyed and the hen did not lay a replacement clutch. The sixth hen mated with two cocks; but when her first mate lost his brood she again mated and laid eggs for him, 'her third clutch and his second'. Another nest hatched out at which no hen had been seen. 'In 1971, five females initiated 12 nests; each female nested with the following numbers of males: two females remained monogamous; two females each had two mates; one female mated successively with four males. In addition, one nest hatched, and I had seen no female near it. Again, one male lost his first brood and his female nested with him again – her third clutch, his second'.

Between 1975–77, seven hens were successively polyandrous in Minnesota, each mating with two or more cocks; one hen laid at least three clutches for the same cock.

The laying season starts in mid May in the USA but is delayed until early June in Arctic Canada and Alaska. Spotted sandpipers usually lay their eggs daily, occasionally at intervals of about 48 hours. A clutch consists of four, occasionally three, and exceptionally five eggs. J. R. Miller and J. T. Miller (1948) recorded 3/3, 33/4, and 1/5 (mean 3.9) in Michigan, USA. Incubation starts with, or slightly before, the completion of the clutch. In monogamous pairs both sexes incubate and polyandrous hens help their last mates to hatch out the final clutches. Some hens also assist their mates by sitting on first clutches until they have found new mates. Hays (1972) estimated an incubation period of 20–21 days; but one clutch hatched 26 days after the first cock had been flushed from four warm eggs.

In monogamous pairings both sexes help to rear the chicks. Polyandrous hens also assist in the rearing of chicks hatched from final clutches. The young fly at some time between 18–21 days and are independent soon afterwards.

A full comparison of the breeding behaviour of the spotted and common sandpipers is for the future. So far we have only been able to prove that one hen common sandpiper in Sutherland was polyandrous, laying clutches for two cocks in succession. In other common sandpiper groups does polyandry happen more frequently than we have hitherto suspected?

TURNSTONE

The turnstone has a tantalising history in Britain. H. L. Saxby (1874) possibly found a nest with three eggs on Unst; but a rascally Shetlander, who had been skulking behind a rock, took the eggs before Saxby had had time to confirm his find. Many years after I had read that exciting story I listened spellbound to Cecil Stoney describing how he had located what he felt sure was a nesting turnstone on a remote island off Co. Donegal. The behaviour of the bird was precisely the same as that described by Ralph Chislett at a nest in the Baltic. But a storm was brewing and Stoney had to leave the island in a hurry. He never ceased to regret missing the chance of a lifetime.

A fine, small to middling-sized wader, the turnstone has a rather square head of black and white pattern, a tortoiseshell mantle in summer, a brown-black pectoral band, and it stands on short orange legs. In flight it gives a bold piebald black and white appearance and its habit of turning up stones is its trademark.

Since Saxby's and Stoney's experience there has been other evidence of turnstones nesting in Britain. Professor W. G. Hale recently discovered a clutch of their eggs in an old Collection; these are said to have been taken on 30 April 1938 in the Outer Hebrides. In late June and early July 1974 a hen turnstone held a territory on Papa Westray on Orkney; and on 24 July, A. D. Ramsay watched a hen and juvenile on Westray. Three different territories in Orkney and Shetland were also occupied in 1975; and, in west Sutherland, on 9 August 1976 a turnstone gave excited alarm cries while close to a chick which unfortunately was not identified. Then, in 1978, a pair nest danced on North Ronaldsay, and there have been other promising records. At last the dreams of Saxby and Stoney seem set to come true.

One of the most arctic of all waders, the turnstone favours rocky or shingly coasts, often nesting close to the sea, but sometimes on slopes and terraces far inland at 100 m ASL. In Greenland they nest on stony flats sparingly covered with low growths of vegetation, and in the high arctic tundra they favour gravelly ridges and plateaux on wet hummocky ground, and habitats on flat low-lying islands.

The birds often arrive in pairs and sometimes stay mated or re-mate with old partners. On Victoria Island and Jenny Lind Island, David Parmelee and his companions (1967) found that some pairs nested in isolation; others were in small groups of 3–4 pairs, with much unoccupied ground in between. N. T. Rosenberg (1970) recorded small groups of 7–8 breeding pairs in 1–2 km² in Greenland; and on the Varanger Fjord in Finnmark, Hugh Blair located 20 breeding pairs along 3 km of beach, with some nests only a few metres apart. S. Vuolanto (1968) also discovered high density grounds in Finland, with 30 pairs nesting on an island of 22 ha and 10 pairs on a small island of only 0.5 ha.

Turnstones show remarkable territorial flexibility. On Fosheim Peninsula, Ellesmere Island, NWT, Parmelee and Macdonald (1960) found that pairs did not defend territories before or during egg laying. G. Bergman (1946) found that territorialism on the Finnish coast became stronger after the chicks had hatched, when the adults sometimes stayed in the territory after the young had moved away. Turnstones have no true territorial song dance; but on arrival cock or hen, or occasionally both together, circle silently up to 600 m from their territory. Cocks also sometimes fly with slow wing beats around their territory at heights of up to 50 m, and at other times settle on large rocks from which they call loudly for 3 minutes or more. These performances are usually brought about by the appearance of rivals and are less frequent in habitats where pairs are more widely dispersed. Small groups, sometimes composed of 2–4 cocks and one hen, fly rapidly over the tundra in jinking flight for up to 1.5 km from where they took off. This performance also takes place during incubation and is not unlike somewhat similar flights which we have watched in golden plovers. Are the cocks disputing for superiority or is the hen's mate attempting to guard her from hopeful rivals?

Some fighting on the ground is ritualised. D. Brearey (1983) describes the Tail-down Hunch in which the bird ruffles its body feathers, droops its wings, holds its head

DW.

down, slightly outstretches its downward arching neck and simultaneously depresses its tail. Bergman (1970) found that the turnstones were exceptionally aggressive when an intruder had invaded the centre of a territory. Then sometimes two or three cocks jointly evicted the intruder, afterwards returning to a common border where they sang and bobbed their heads, an indication of conflicting drives. When a territorial dispute continues without active fighting the birds sometimes give Tail-up displays, cocking their tails at acute angles, chattering loudly, then relaxing and turning away. The hens do little to assist their mates in defending the territory and expelling trespassers; but one will occasionally head-bob at a trespassing hen and then drive her away. In Finland, however, hens were much more aggressive than cocks during the hatching period.

In pre-copulatory manoeuvering a cock advances on a hen in the Tail-down Hunch; and when within 30 cm of her he raises his tail and she flexes her legs, lowering her breast until it touches the ground while holding her tail in horizontal position. In the early phases of courtship the cock guards his mate from other cocks, thus allowing her to feed more freely while she is building up before egg laying. Turnstones copulate both on and off territories. Immediately before mounting, the cock raises and stretches up his wings for a few seconds, sometimes repeating this several times in succession while within 2–3 m of his mate. He then flutters onto her back, violently beating his wings for up to half a minute, and occasionally pecks her neck; then he briefly twists his expanded tail under hers before fluttering off her back (Bergman 1946). Parmelee and Macdonald (1960) recorded no pre-copulatory activity. The hen merely crouched to invite the cock after he had chased her along the ground. A territory-holding cock, however, sometimes attempts to take a stranger hen which is trepassing in his territory.

Uttering special nest dancing calls, the cock walks quickly with his body tilted forward, while he looks for a suitable nest site. The hen co-operates, particularly when she is ready to lay her first egg, by approaching the cock and replacing him in the scoop. Usually, however, she forms her own scoop for the egg and while doing so gives her special nest dancing call.

Nests are usually sited in the open, on ridges, tussocks or hummocks, or in shallow cracks or clefts in the rocks. The eggs are occasionally under vegetation on the ground and quite invisible from above. S. Nordberg (1950) found that some turnstones, like redshanks, drew grasses together to form a canopy over the eggs. He analysed the position of 128 nests in Finland; 47 were in rocks or clefts with plants; 40 in clumps of vegetation; 23 in small clefts; 11 on rock vegetated shelves; and 7 in other positions.

Turnstones have different 'spot' laying seasons in different countries, ranging from 31 May in Denmark, 7 June in the Gulf of Bothnia, to 13 June in Finnmark, Norway. In southern Sweden laying begins around 28 May, on average six days earlier on the coast than inland. Bergman (1946) records the peak laying season as 10–15 June in Finland. On Ellesmere Island and in Greenland the average date is around 15 June; but eggs are occasionally laid in late May and early June in favourable seasons in NE Greenland.

Eggs are laid at intervals of one and occasionally two days, with a clutch usually completed in five days. The clutch is usually four, occasionally three, and exceptionally two or five eggs. On Ellesmere Island, Nettleship (1973) recorded 15 nests, 2/2, 3/3, 10/4 (average 3.53 eggs). Vuolanto (1968) analysed 24 clutches in Finland which contained 5/3, 19/4 (mean 3.79 eggs). In the Gulf of Bothnia a hen laid a replacement clutch of four eggs; but repeats are not recorded north of the Arctic Circle.

Cocks periodically brood incomplete clutches, but steady incubation usually starts after the third egg is laid. The hen does most of the day and the cock most of the night incubation. The two birds change over at intervals of 8–14 hours; but there is no special ritual at nest relief. At some nests the incoming bird flies directly to the eggs, more especialy when the nest is sited in tall vegetation. On Victoria Island NWT, Parmelee *et al* (1967) worked out an incubation period which lasted 21 days, 23 hours (± 11 hours) from the laying of the first to the hatching of the last egg of a clutch. Bergman (1946) estimated an incubation period of 22–23 days in Finland. On 19 nests in Spitsbergen, A. H. L. Paget-Wilkes (1922) found that the hen was usually sitting on fresh or partly-incubated eggs, with the cock standing on guard. After the eggs had chipped the cock incubated.

Nettleship (1973) found that on Ellesmere Island there was a difference of 1–2 days between the hatching of the first and last chick of a clutch. Eggs were chipped for 3–5 days before the chicks hatched. The sitting turnstone then flew away with the empty shell, dropping it 100 m or more from the nest. The chicks stay in the nest for about 24 hours, but they periodically leave the scoop and then return to their brooding parent.

As with many other waders, hens tend to abandon mates and broods before the chicks have fledged. Parmelee and MacDonald (1940) found that a chick could flutter about 19 days after hatching; and Bergman (1946) considers that the young turnstones were fully fledged in 26 days.

Like the oystercatcher, the turnstone sometimes behaves quite unexpectedly. A few habitatually rob and eat the eggs of terns and gulls and sometimes those of their own kind. It will be a grand addition to the British List if this execptionally attractive wader starts to breed regularly in these islands.

As the British Isles and Ireland are on the fringes of the breeding range of so many waders, we are likely to see many exciting changes over the next few years. The pectoral sandpiper, another Nearctic wader, gave its hooting song as it displayed over a flow on the Caithness-Sutherland march. This is one of those polygynous waders in which the cock displays and mates with two or more hens which exclusively incubate the eggs and rear the chicks. The eggs are laid daily. David Parmelee describes the intriguing ground display of the cock, 'his wings pressed in close, tail perfectly vertical, dewlap somewhat elevated but not puffed out, and with bill wide open and vibrating, he bubbled like a miniature turkey'. Shall we ever watch this fantastic display on the flows of the north-west Highlands or in other parts of northern Scotland?

12:   Pipe-dream waders

We have had a fair run with waders. Each problem solved has led to others equally exciting and usually more complex; but the work has brought us endless joy. We have only watched waders in the field in Britain and Ireland; but a few of those nesting in North America, in the great forest marshes of northern Europe, and in the high Arctic, have always intrigued us. These have been our pipe-dream waders.

In the muskegs or floating bogs of Alberta we particularly think of the greater yellow-legs, the Nearctic equivalent of our greenshank. Even now, only the barest outline of its breeding life is known. It is roughly the same size as the greenshank, has a slightly upturned bill, a dull grey mantle spangled with black and spotted with white, a white rump and yellow legs. Professor William Rowan, the pioneer who opened our eyes to this exciting wader, described the silence in their homeland when the birds were sitting; not a bird to be seen or heard. 'For every nest we have managed to find, by unremitting labour, footslogging it yard by yard, there must be another five or six that we have failed to find in spite of steady hunting, simply because the birds sit tight'. All greenshank hunters can sympathise with Rowan's later feelings of humiliation at finding family after family of greater yellowlegs scattered over habitats he had previously unsuccessfully hunted! Tom Randall and A. D. Henderson, fine self-taught wader watchers, enjoyed great success with this difficult wader. By constant watching, Henderson discovered the share of the sexes in night brooding. Randall was the first to describe the song dance, 'an undulating flight, continuous for perhaps 10–15 minutes, but there are frequent intervals when the yodelling ceases for perhaps 30 seconds'.

DUSKY REDSHANK

On this side of the Atlantic, John Wolley first wrote about the dusky redshank with

its black bill and legs and speckled sooty-coloured mantle. In 1946, Hugh Blair described how he had found nests and studied its behaviour in Finnmark; and Norman Gilroy and Edward Steward had four dusky clutches to report in that famous 'bag' collected in 1928. Gilroy vividly tells of tracking down the nest on 1 June. 'Suddenly overhead I heard the *tche-weeck*, three times in rapid succession, and a dusky redshank passed like an arrow. It was only moderately high but rose considerably on gaining some very tall trees ... here it flew round in a very wide circle twice then dropped like a bolt .... There was no water in the neighbourhood of the tall trees, and I could only conjecture that the bird had pitched on bare, dry ground. I determined, therefore, that I would return to the burnt hillside and search it out again, but this yielded nothing. I then tramped over to the tall trees, to find that they were on the crest of a grey ridge which sloped gently to a little pool with a soft margin of reeds and moss about 50 yards below .... The ground looked altogether good to me, but so desolate and lifeless that I felt despondent and a little lost. However, I started slowly down the slope towards the water and in a moment the dusky redshank sprang up, literally from under my feet'.

Dusky redshanks have an unusual breeding system. They do not have a reversed courtship but, to the best of present knowledge, the cock is entirely responsible for incubation and entirely or almost entirely responsible for the rearing of the young. This system lends itself to polyandry, provided that there is a surplus of cocks in breeding condition.

Numbers are insufficiently known, but J. Kålås and I. Byrkjedal (1981) estimated that 500 pairs nest in northern Norway; and S. Ulfstrand and G. Högstedt (1976) suggest a population of 20,000 breeding pairs in Sweden. In northern Europe nests are usually well-separated, 1 km or more apart; A. V. Krechmar (1966) recorded breeding pairs every 200–250 m on the west Taimyr Peninsula. Raner had two special study areas, each of about 2 km^2 in Swedish Lapland where, for 25 years, he annually spent

4–5 weeks. In one study area there were three pairs of greenshanks and four pairs of duskies and the other held two pairs of greenshanks and 3–4 pairs of duskies.

Dusky redshanks arrive in Swedish Lapland between 10–20 May. The cock arrives first and immediately starts to prospect for a nest site. A little later the hen joins him in a second bout of site hunting. In this phase the two birds are quite noisy, but they soon quieten down and then again become excited a few days before the hen lays her first egg. The original scoops are formed by the cock, but Raner watched a hen reject one used in a previous year and make her own scrape at the end of a dead branch about one metre long.

A cock establishes a territory from which he drives off other duskies and also occasion-ally greenshanks. He stays in his territory for 4–5 weeks longer than the hen; one held the same territory year after year.

Duskies usually nest on dry ridges of forest marshes, where they favour habitats containing many pools and lakes. John Little tells us that some nests are sited well inside thinly-grown pine, spruce and birch woods, sometimes as far as 700 m inside. They also favour recently burnt patches and their nests are often 100–500 m or more from feeding pools, lakes or marshes. Only three out of 66 nests were in wet marshes but seven were higher up on treeless fells (Raner, *pers. comm.*). Nests are usually 6–8 cm in diameter and are lined with dwarf birch leaves, pine bark, dead pine needles and fine dry grass (Glutz 1977). Raner has recorded that 95% of nests are sited beside dead sticks or branches or occasionally below small conifers or birches. In Finnmark, Norway, Steward recorded a greenshank laying her eggs in a scoop in which a dusky had nested three years earlier.

The cock dusky redshank has a dramatic sky dance in which the hen sometimes joins; but she apparently does not give this display on her own. The precise purpose of the sky dance is not yet known, but it probably has a sexual as well as a dispersion function. On 26 May 1928, Gilroy described the performance: 'the flight is rushing, rapid and even violent. There are descents of almost incredible swiftness and upwards sweeps of equal velocity, accompanied by a marvellous shaking, almost rattling motion of the wings. This is accompanied by song'.

While pursuing the hen in ground display the cock fans out his tail and flaps his wings, much in the same way as greenshanks and redshanks. He continues to flap while balancing himself on his mate's back. One cock had four different hens in six years; one of these, which laid particularly dark eggs, was his mate in the first and fifth years of his known breeding. A second cock had three different hens in eight years; a third had the same hen in his first, third and fourth years. Raner also met with a polyandrous hen which laid clutches for two different cocks, completing that for her second mate 13 days later; the two nests were 2 km apart. A different pattern is described by N. Danilov and V. K. Rjabizev (1973) in USSR, where one hen put down two cocks on nests about 50 m apart.

Lennart Raner tells us that the cock occasionally escorts the hen to the territory when she is about to lay her first egg. He then *wipps* and sky dances above her, but many times she arrives alone. In favourable springs they sometimes complete a clutch in 5–6 days, but usually there is a slightly longer interval between the third and fourth eggs than between the first and second. In dry springs the approximate intervals are 35–45 hours between each egg in the clutch. After completing her clutch the hen often feeds for a few hours beside a lake or in the nearest marsh and then quits the territory for good. If, however, the cock is flushed from eggs within 20 hours of clutch completion the hen sometimes arrives and joins him in demonstrating.

In a Finnish forest marsh in 1976 John Little found a dusky redshank sitting on four eggs one of which was of a pale and most unusual type. In 1983–85 Evelyn Meek discovered that the same hen, identified by her eggs, had laid in a particular nest scoop 500 m from Little's 1976 discovery. Both observers have no doubt about the identity of the hen which was thus at least 10 years old in 1985.

Dusky redshanks' eggs are beautiful, pyriform or sub-pyriform in shape and usually have some gloss. Their ground colour is olive yellow to olive green. Some are pea green and they are usually greener than those of greenshanks; a few are reddish brown. They are blotched, spotted and streaked with light to dark reddish brown, with blackish brown speckles usually concentrated at the heavy end; undermarkings are violet and ash coloured. Greyish white sparsely marked eggs are also on record.

A clutch is normally four, exceptionally three. Of the 66 nests Raner saw in the field, only two contained three eggs; all the rest held four. The mean clutch-size was thus 3.96 eggs.

Dusky redshanks are normally single-brooded; but apart from the occasional proven polyandrous hen, Olavi Hildén records replacement clutches.

A cock occasionally sits briefly on three eggs, but usually only starts steady incubation after the hen has completed the clutch. In Raner's wide experience the cock alone incubates, leaving the nest to feed for spells of about 20 minutes in the early morning and evening, with 2–3 supplementary meals in good weather. While returning to the nest, particularly from his regular morning and evening meals, the cock often gives distinctive triple calls.

Duskies usually sit tightly, only quitting their eggs when the hunter is almost beside the nest. A few are different, flushing at distances of 150–200 m. One cock regularly rose at about 150 m and flew straight over the marsh to meet Raner. Once a trip of six hens, all *wipping*, joined a cock just flushed from chipping eggs. Had one of these hens actually laid the eggs or was this unusual demonstration a reaction to the cock's scolding cries? Apart from this, Raner never met with a hen close to a sitting cock. But there is possibly some local or individual variation as Hugh Blair, John Little and others have occasionally met with a second dusky – presumably a hen – feeding quietly in a marsh close to cock and nest. At three nests the incubation period was approximately 23 days (Raner).

The eggs are chipped for 2–3 days before they hatch. From his hide, Ivan Hills found that the cock conversed with the unhatched chicks, using a special deep throaty call of the same kind as those used by greenshank, common sandpiper and curlew during the hatch.

Gilroy found eggshells in a scoop from which the young had hatched and left; but Ivan Hills watched a cock, on his way back to the nest, lift and fly away with a large shell fragment which was lying outside the scoop. After the chicks had gone this scoop was quite clear of shell. Raner once found a large portion of eggshell lying on the marsh about 25 m from a nest.

Within the first 24 hours the cock shepherds his brood to a suitable wet feeding marsh and thenceforward guards them as they move from one feeding place to another. Ornithologists have had different experiences about the part played by the hen in rearing the family. Raner has never met with the two parents guarding the chicks. On 18 June 1928 Gilroy noted that a cock, which was guarding his brood was joined by the hen; but on 20 June he wrote, 'most of the dusky redshanks now have young. I must have come across four males and I am puzzled to account for the fact that I did not see a hen at all'. In north Finland, on 12 June 1983, Evelyn Meek noted that a second dusky started to call only when the first was in a frenzy of excitement. One parent only was present with another brood. Possibly late-staying hens sometimes help to guard the chicks in the first few days, but their part in rearing the young is evidently negligible.

Lennart Raner, who is without doubt the King of the Dusky Redshanks, has pointed the way to a new generation of wader watchers in the far north.

BROAD-BILLED SANDPIPER

Gilroy and Steward met with two pairs of broad-billed sandpipers in the Pasvik marshes. Gilroy described them as small stumpy black-and-white waders which trilled rather like dunlins. While plunging through a fearsome quaking bog he heard 'a continuous sucking noise rather like that made by ducks with their bills in soft ooze'. A size smaller than the dunlin, the broad-billed sandpiper has a very dark mantle and a generally black-and-white appearance with a double eye-stripe, a rather long bill with heavy base and kinked tip. These little gems nest in some of the wettest bogs in Fenno-Scandia and the Soviet Union where only a few ornithologists have met their considerable challenge in the field. Already, however, Olavi Hildén, John Little, and others, have started to describe their behaviour in summer.

Broad-billed sandpipers usually establish small territories, but they sometimes nest semi-socially in groups or colonies of 2–10 pairs, with nests situated 40–100 m apart; but exceptionally two nests are separated by less than 10 m. The cocks sky dance but, although they are monogamous, their methods of pairing are not yet known. The cock makes several scrapes, in one of which the hen presumably lays her eggs. The tiny nests, lined with coarse grasses and occasionally with the leaves of sallow or other plants, are usually placed in mossy humps in the wettest bogs. The diameter and depth of five nests varied from 7.5 × 2.5 cm–10.5 × 5.0 cm (Little, *pers. comm.*).

The earliest full clutches at Kittila and Enontekiö in Finland were laid on 8–9 June. In south Norway laying starts in the first week of June, with a peak in the second half of the month. Little found 20 nests in Fenno-Scandia between 11 and 30 June; the latest date for a clutch of fresh eggs was 20 June.

Gilroy described a Pasvik clutch as 'marvellously beautiful, of a somewhat squat pear-shape, but of exceptional elegance: the pale brown colour was almost completely obscured by heavy chocolate markings of most wonderful richness'. Little found three eggs, which a predator later sucked, with a conspicuous yellow ground colour but hardly any brown markings. At least one hen laid her eggs daily.

Steady incubation sometimes starts on the third egg but not on the first two (Little *pers. comm.*). Both sexes incubate, sometimes sitting for long stints. Exchanges take place in the early morning and throughout the afternoon (Raner). Broadbills sit tight, only quitting their nests when the searcher is within 1–4 m of the nest. The behaviour of the flushed bird varies considerably. Gilroy reported the bird rising from eggs and 'mounting to a considerable height, flying round overhead, purring happily like a miniature dunlin'. Evelyn Meek tells us that two birds, off incomplete clutches, flapped about in the bog making piteous squealing noises.

Eighteen complete clutches, found in Fenno-Scandia, contained 2/3, 16/4 (mean 3.8) (Little *pers. comm.*). Two clutches hatched in 21.0 and 21.5 days respectively (Hildén 1983).

At first both cock and hen guard and rear the young, but the hen leaves her mate and brood before the chicks can fly. Clearly, there is plenty of research ahead for the keenest watchers!

JACK SNIPE

Generations of enthusiasts have delightedly read John Wolley's letter to William Hewitson in which he described the jack snipe's sky dance. One of the most exciting, and in some ways the most mysterious wader of the boreal marshes, the jack snipe is smallish, with a shorter bill than the common snipe, and can usually be identified by its different behaviour. When flushed, it flies slowly and more directly and without the characteristic zig-zags and harsh calls; and it usually drops down after a very short flight. The pale buff central stripe is also missing in its crown.

Many who have plodded slowly and dangerously through those water-logged boreal swamps and bogs, which the jack snipe often shares with broad-billed sandpipers and sometimes with red-necked phalaropes, have listened to and sometimes seen and heard the cantering flight; but few have analysed its pattern and sequences. S. G. and I. N. Nilsson (1978) describe how the jack snipe rises rapidly at an angle of about 45°, and when 50 m or more above ground flies straight, in semi-circles, or in circles. Then it abruptly stops beating its wings and makes a steep dive, sometimes rolling over with half-folded wings before zooming upwards; and all the time it gives those wonderful cantering calls. It may then interrupt its song dance by fluttering up and gliding down before proceeding in a series of repeated sweeps and curves.

Fewer watchers have seen jack snipe courting. Raner watched two or three cocks cantering over the same marsh but has never seen one seriously attack another. Several times he watched courtship on the ground. The cock pursued the hen and then copulated with her time after time. On three different occasions Raner has had the luck and

DUSKY REDSHANK calling in a forest marsh. Only the cock incubates the eggs and rears the chicks. (Photo: Hanna Hautala).

BROAD-BILLED SANDPIPER, a most elusive northern European wader, on eggs in a wet morass. (Photo: J. Luhta).

BAR-TAILED GODWIT. A fine portrait of this handsome wader of the Fenno-Scandian mosses. (Photo: P. O. Swanberg).

JACK SNIPE sitting at nest. The little wader with a display song which John Wolley described as like the sound of a horse cantering on a hard road. (Photo: P. O. Swanberg)

GREAT SNIPE cock on its lek. In USSR particular cocks have been found on leks 10 km apart. (Photo: P. O. Swanberg).

SANDERLING sitting on a nest in the high Arctic. A wader with two distinct breeding systems in different locations. (Photo: D. F. Parmelee).

KNOT, the blue riband wader that has tantalised and defeated so many great nest hunters. (Photo: D. F. Parmelee).

skill to watch hens fly up from their nests, giving loud harsh calls not unlike one of those of a mallard. Within 2–3 seconds she reaches the cock high in the air and then the pair takes part in a kind of nuptial flight dance, such as those greenshanks occasionally perform. A few minutes later the hen drops to her nest like a stone and the cock goes to a feeding place in the marsh. What a marvellous experience!

All 13 nests found by Raner contained four eggs. The hen alone incubates, feeding nearby 2–4 times hourly in good weather and staying off her eggs for 3–6 minutes. The hen alone also rears the chicks.

M. Schönwetter (1963) found that jack snipes' eggshells weighed from 0.56–0.74 (mean 0.67) gm, and were thus lighter than those of common snipe, 250 of which averaged 0.83 gm.

Ralph Chislett (1933) recorded a jack snipe which sat on a clutch of four eggs for at least 24 days before hatching; but it is uncertain whether disturbance extended the period. One of L. von Haartman's correspondents also measured an incubation period of not less than 21 days.

Raner found that jack snipe stayed in their breeding habitats until the snow drove them away. He considers them to be double-brooded, with first clutches laid between 1–12 June and second clutches between 20 July–1 August; he has found chicks in mid August. It is, possible, however, that young pairs are responsible, as in common snipe, for some of the latest clutches. But how little we know!

GREAT SNIPE

In the 1930s John McNeile found 30 nests of the great snipe in Estonia SSR. But the range of this intriguing bird is fast shrinking; it is now markedly scarcer in Norway, Sweden, Poland and Estonia; and it has become extinct as a breeding bird in East and West Germany, Denmark, Lithuania and possibly Finland. Drainage and changes in climate are two probable factors in its decline.

A rather bulky rounded wader, with a stout bill and much white on the sides of its tail, the great snipe rises slowly and usually flies straight, without the violent twists and swerves of a flushed common snipe. Unlike the ruff, and most other lek species, the great snipe is monomorphic, making it still more difficult to discover the roles of cocks and hens in their remarkable displays.

Leks are usually on flats on gentle slopes of marshes containing many mounds and grassy tussocks; at other times they are close to burnt patches of woodland or surrounded by large birchwoods and are sited from a little above sea-level to well over 1,000 m. Towards evening the cocks walk or sometimes fly into the lek. A master cock has his own stance; but, like ruffs he also sometimes displays in other leks. One cock was found in a second lek 10 km away from his own. Most displays take place in twilight (P. A. Lemnell 1978). In Jämtland, Sweden, birds usually arrived about 16.00 but did not start to display until 21.00, peaking between 23.00–02.00; afterwards activity tailed off. Lemnell watched the hens walk, or occasionally fly, into the lek in the company of one or more cocks; or they moved in slowly with bodies held low, feeding as they went.

In the late evening and small hours great snipe carry out most elaborate displays. Each cock ruffles his feathers, opening and pointing his bill obliquely upwards, and makes 'flutter jumps' to a height of about 2 m above ground. Complex sounds accompany the displays, including twittering, 'bibbing', and drumming or clicking sounds, which resemble a finger running over the teeth of a comb at increasing speed. At the end of the drumming the cock raises and spreads his tail to display his white tail feathers and he flaps his wings once or twice. When a hen has arrived in the lek excited cocks chase one another in their efforts to approach her. The hen squats to show readiness to mate and the territory-holding cock copulates if he is able to ward off his rival. This is a time of great excitement. Cocks on other territories sing and make 'flutter jumps' and determinedly attempt to approach the hen. Now the lek is in turmoil with the hen pursued up and down the territory. Apart from mating in the lek, cocks sometimes couple with hens outside it.

The part played by the cock in subsequent nesting behaviour is still in doubt, but his pattern appears to differ from that of the ruff. Before a hen has laid, John Little often put up pairs well away from the lek. This was also true at three nests where second birds – presumably cocks – were flushed nearby. After mating on the lek do particular pairs sometimes continue to associate? The Russian ornithologist, A. Alpheraky, described hens emerging from the undergrowth about midnight; and after the cocks had displayed to them until sunrise each hen flew off with a cock and returned again at night. On the other hand, Raner considers that the lekking pattern does not greatly differ from that of capercaillie and that the cock has no knowledge of where the eggs are laid.

Apart from its lek behaviour, little is known about the breeding biology of the great snipe. In Norway, S. Haftorn measured five and John Little two nest scoops which ranged from 9.5–13.0 cm in diameter and 3–6 cm in depth. Twelve Norwegian clutches (nine recorded by Haftorn, three by Little) contained 1/3, 11/4 (mean 3.91) eggs; and 9 Swedish clutches all contained 4 eggs (4.0) (Raner, *pers. comm.*). Great snipe lay lovely eggs with ground colouring of stone to brownish buff, richly blotched and smeared by purplish brown with many lilac undermarkings. They also occasionally lay eggs with a greenish ground colour and others are streaked with sepia or black.

Incubation is said to be 22–24 days but this requires further observation. R. Collett, T. Jessen and John Little all found that particular great snipe, like common snipe, left their eggshells in the nest after the chicks had hatched.

This magnificent and quite unusual wader is fighting a losing battle against man, but there is still time to save some of its haunts and to learn a few more of its secrets.

BAR-TAILED GODWIT

The bar-tailed godwit is another magnificent but little known wader. Gilroy described how he first met with one near Svanvik on the Pasvik. 'My attention was suddenly arrested by a strange new note, a penetrating, persistent and unvarying and rather fatuous *quacking* sound .... I presently found that it was being uttered by a fair-sized bird, with a grey striped back and beautiful dark chestnut breast, which was standing in a rather grey hummock'. Later he flushed the hen from a little pool – a grey bird, very like a whimbrel on the wing, with perhaps a slight pinkish tinge on the breast and, of course, a straight bill. Hens differ in their summer plumage; one watched by Ivan and Mary Hills had a primrose breast.

In northern Europe the bar-tailed godwit lives in immense tracts of lonely tundra-like country; 'wide grey ridges between squashy places and little pools'. Here it shares haunts, but not necessarily the same niches, with dusky redshanks, greenshanks, jack snipe, wood sandpipers and whimbrel. In some years the woods hold waxwings; and ospreys and hen harriers go about their hunting.

So far no one appears to have watched bar-tailed godwits throughout their breeding season. We do know that the cock has a wonderful sky dance which Gilroy described in his diary. 'This flight, which appears to be unaccompanied by any song and consists of a series of amazingly beautiful evolutions which reminds me at times of the flight of the hobby. Although the sweeps and forward movements vary a good deal in speed, they are rhythmically exact and are more often slow than otherwise. The head and neck are frequently outstretched, and sometimes, like a raven, the bird appears to turn nearly on its back'. It is not known whether this lovely flight has a mainly territorial or sexual purpose. Ivan Hills also watched a cock giving a superb high-flying dance, circling and singing over the marsh, once he broke rhythm to chase an osprey which was flying over to fish on the Pasvik.

Before the Pasvik marshes were drained, bar-tailed godwits sometimes nested in good numbers. Gilroy and Steward met with many nesting pairs and found six nests. There are now fewer of these lovely waders but Ivan and Mary Hills have found two pairs nesting in the same large marsh. Little is known about breeding density in other parts of its range. E. Kozlova (1962) recorded 15 nests in 15 km^2 in a haunt on the

White Sea; and V. E. Flint (1973) recorded 0.1 breeding pair/km² at Labytnanga and 2.6 pairs/km² at Chadyta in the south of the Jamal Peninsula in 1970.

No one appears to have recorded nest dancing or scoop preparation. The usually wide but shallow nests are often placed on bare dry ridges, carpeted with a little moss and scanty heather, or in crowberry or reindeer moss. Gilroy saw one 'under the heather fringe overhanging the edge of a large peat hole'. Nests are lined with dead grass, twigs and dead leaves of dwarf birch, and other plants.

In Finnish Lapland, Finnmark, Norway, and the White Sea, laying peaks in late May and early June, but is occasionally earlier in favourable years. Thirteen clutches in Finnmark contained 2/3, 11/4 (mean 3.84); and Raner has seen eight nests 4/3, 4/4 (mean 3.5) eggs. The eggs, usually broad pointed ovate to long ovate or occasionally pear-shaped, tend to be slightly more glossy than those of the black-tailed godwit. They are dull dark brown, sparsely marked with darker brown and grey. The eggs in one of Gilroy's clutches had light brown ground colour, sparsely spotted with darker brown and grey; one egg was paler and more heavily marked than the others.

Bar-tailed godwits sit tightly, only leaving their eggs at the feet of the hunter. Both cock and hen sit usually for long spells, sometimes at least for eight hours (Hills, *pers. comm.*). Exchanges are usually silent. At different nests Ivan and Mary Hills recorded nest relief at 08.54 (Cock for hen), at 12.40, and at 18.25. There are no recent observations on incubation periods, which Collett estimated at 20–21 days. But for the size of the bird this seems unusually short.

Gilroy and Steward found all six nests by systematically searching likely nesting habitat after the non-sitting bird had called excitedly and mobbed them. 'After three hours of ceaseless tramping up and down and along the ridges round the dry edges of the pools and wet places and through the tussocks again and again, I at last flushed the sitting hen godwit, and the second nest of this rare species was mine'. Gilroy believed that it was not feasible to find bar-tailed godwits' nests by watching. However, in the early 1980s, Ivan and Mary Hills have tracked down nests by watching exchanges; and they, and also John Little, have found nests by watching a pair or the sitting bird rise from a marsh to chase away a raven or hooded crow. After several morning watches the Hills also tracked a cock godwit from his feeding marsh to the nest, a distance of about 1,200 m. They used a compass to direct them on his line which passed over wooded ridges.

The Hills and Little noticed that bar-tailed godwits left empty eggshells in the nest, as do common curlew, common and great snipe.

Very little is known about the rearing of the young; but both parents are present when the chicks leave the nest; and they sometimes still stay with them when they have been herded many metres away. Lennart Raner had a different experience. He found an old red cock and an immature cock escorting a brood. The immature reddish bird had previously accompanied the nesting pair before the hen moved away from cock and brood. It was not uncommon for these reddish immature cocks to hold territories and to mob nest hunters (Raner *pers. comm.*).

Bird watchers who go north will gradually add to our knowledge of this grand wader. But, sadly, they will never know the glory of the Pasvik marshes where Gilroy and Steward hunted so successfully nearly 80 years ago.

SANDERLING

In June 1973 two sanderlings in breeding plumage – probably a pair – displayed on the stony ridge of a Sutherland hill. The sanderling is a plump and very active little wader, showing white sides on dark wings. In summer it has a chestnut brown head, neck and upper breast, and pale white underparts. Our friend David Parmelee, and his colleagues, made remarkable discoveries about its breeding pattern on expeditions to Bathurst Island NWT, in 1968, 1969 and 1970.

Sanderlings return to Bathurst in small flocks, some already paired. Unmated cocks use a beautiful song dance or advertisement flight to attract mates. Before starting, the cocks rise slowly or quite swiftly. 'In flight the forward part of the male's body is more or less parallel to the ground, the tail is level with the body, or downturned, and usually somewhat spread; and the head is drawn back, presenting at times a hunched appearance .... The wings held straight out from the body move up and down through a 45° arc, at such great speed that they literally vibrate, though the prominent white wings-bars are still clearly visible' (Parmelee 1970). These displays are given in bursts, followed by pauses on motionless wings and at heights of from 5–10 m, but they are occasionally carried out up to 20 m above the snowy wastes. A series of frog-like calls accompany the flights.

Hen sanderlings initiate copulation by displaying in special scoops which are not used for the eggs. Parmelee watched the preliminaries. 'With head low and tail almost vertical she squirmed a little and the male, which had been standing close by, ran and thrust his bill down beside her and several times removed bits of lining from the scrape. Then he stood on her back, stepped off, and deliberately eased her out of the scrape with his bill and forehead thrust beneath her belly. Both then ran off side by side, with bodies pressed together and rubbing vigorously. Having run some 10 feet the male lowered his head and pressed his bill forcibly against the breast of the female, immediately stopping her. She stood still and copulation followed'. Eggs were later laid in an entirely different set of scoops.

The nest site is chosen after different behaviour. Without uttering any calls, a hen 'settled in six depressions, each time fluffing out her feathers as though she were settling on eggs, and usually remained less than 6 minutes. She twirled, tossed bits of material out of the hollow, and at least once scratched out material with her foot'. While so doing, the cock tried to copulate but she rejected him. At 15.50 hours she settled down in the hollow in which she stayed for 5 minutes; finally the cock approached and prised her out with his bill. 'He then attempted a side to side rubbing run and even copulation, without success'. A few hours later the hen laid her first egg in this hollow (Parmelee 1970).

A sanderling normally lays 4, occasionally 3, and exceptionally 2 eggs in its clutch. Parmelee recorded 13/4, 1/2 on Bathurst; Manniche 11/4 in Greenland; Pienkowski and Green 9/4, 1/3 in north-east Greenland; and McNeile 9/4 in Spitsbergen (mean 3.93 eggs). The eggs are laid at intervals of 26–29 hours. They are pointed ovate or sub-pyriform in shape and have little gloss. Their ground colour is greenish olive to olive brown and occasionally rather vivid green, sparsely spotted with brown which is usually concentrated at the larger end. In north-east Greenland the Birds (1941) found a clutch in which two eggs were pale blue, 'the blotches pale mauve and at the apex were several black spots'.

In a sustained series of watches on Bathurst Island, David Parmelee's team kept a nest under observation for 14 days, 8 hours, 17 minutes. During the cool morning hours, 00–6.00, the cock sat for 95% of the time, leaving the nest in all 46 times for a total of 237 minutes, each spell lasting 1–27 minutes (mean 5.1 minutes). During the later morning 06.00–12.00 the cock was away from the nest 7–100% of the total time; in all, he left 116 times for a total of 1,719 minutes, each spell lasting 1–360 minutes (mean 10.1 minutes). There were some extreme observations. On 6 July the cock was off for 454 consecutive minutes, 05.46–13.20; on 7 July for 219 minutes, 05.33–09.12; on 8 July for 223 minutes, 08.21–12.04; and on 16 July for 333 minutes.

At this nest, and at others, only one sex was recorded during incubation. Incubation lasts from 24.2 days to over 31 days when there has been a delay in the start of steady brooding.

Parmelee came to suspect that hen sanderlings on Bathurst sometimes laid two clutches in quick succession, to the first of which she returns and incubates after laying a second which she leaves with the cock 5–6 days later. Although it was impossible to follow marked sanderlings away from the nest, the histological characters of two hens collected in 1970 showed that they had laid two clutches in little more than a week. Moreover, Parmelee and his team found no evidence that both sexes incubated at any one nest.

In north-east Greenland, on the other hand, M. W. Pienkowski and G. H. Green (1976) describe the sanderlings as having an orthodox monogamous system. A 24-hour watch, started at 00.40 on 14 July, showed that the cock sanderling incubated at a nest for 12 hours 10 minutes (00.40–03.19, 11.57–16.25 and 19.37–00.40); and the hen for 11 hours 38 minutes (03.22–11.55 and 16.30–19.35). At four other nests both sexes also shared incubation and both were in attendance on at least 13 family parties. Further research in different parts of the sanderlings' range will thus be of the greatest interest.

Some sanderlings' eggs take long to hatch. Parmelee (1970) recorded a lapse of 2.5–5 days between starring and hatching, although one egg hatched within 10.25–12.58 hours of the first 'star'. A parent was seen to fly off with the egg cap before the first chick had emerged; and it later lifted and flew away with the main portion.

On Bathurst Island only one adult, either cock or hen, was seen guarding or escorting the brood. The parent repeatedly left the chicks to feed for brief periods lasting 2–9 (mean 6.7) minutes. The roles of the parents appear to be more flexible in the Greenland haunts. Cocks and hens, separately or together, are recorded with the broods. When 17 days old a Bathurst chick flew a distance of about 50 m and by the end of the next week it was flying strongly.

This high arctic wader is unlikely to nest in Scotland; but in these years the impossible sometimes becomes almost commonplace.

KNOT

It would be a miracle if the knot, another high arctic bird, ever nested in Britain. This magic wader, smallish, stocky and short-billed, with a russet red head, chestnut and black mantle and red underparts in summer, has challenged and defeated many fine wader watchers on the great barrens of the high arctic.

In the early 1930s I sometimes looked at the huge flocks of knots gathered on British coastlands in winter; and in my dreams I pictured clutches of eggs, almost like those of roseate terns, clustered on some small arctic islands! But the sheer hugeness of the arctic is difficult to appreciate. Since those early daydreams we have been privileged to know some of those who have successfully hunted knots on their breeding grounds in the far north. Charles and Edward Bird, David Parmelee, Lennart Raner and Bill Hobson, all outstanding field ornithologists, have contributed much to the story of a most exciting wader which nests in both eastern and western hemispheres.

The story of nest hunting is a saga in its own right. Everyone who has hunted the knot on the stony barrens describes the difficulties of outwitting the quarry. The Bird Brothers in Greenland, Parmelee and Macdonald on Ellesmere Island, NWT, and V. E. Flint on Wrangel Island USSR, all found that a knot sat until almost trodden on, then briefly carried out distraction displays before flying away, and was seldom willing to return as long as the hunter was close by. Indeed, the Russian pioneer, A. Birula (1907), considered that there was no consistent method of nest finding.

'Attempts to trace them, which I repeatedly made, were never crowned with success, since the knot, especially at the beginning of nesting, once having been disturbed, does not go back to the nest for a long time. Only at the end of the incubation period does it not remain long away from the nest'.

Yet, in 1967 and 1968, Bill Hobson found that mated pairs in Greenland and Ellesmere Island were easily located by their nuptial flight displays and that: 'the best way to find nests is to locate the breeding pairs and then watch for either nest building, egg laying or change over'. On 19 June 1967 he also found a nest by dragging a long rope across the ground. On the 20th he watched nest relief; 'the cock rose and circled above a nearby lake uttering his wild and mournful song *curr-lew-eee* and, performing the song-flight display, dived straight down to the nest; without a sound the hen flew straight from the nest and disappeared over the hill'. An exchange also led to the discovery of a second nest at Thule. A lone knot circled over the stony wastes, 'performing the typical manoeuvres prior to change over; suddenly it swooped down behind a hill and out of sight and all was still. I knew that the change-over had occurred . . .. Suddenly 4–5 yards ahead of me the incubating bird flew up with a startled cry'.

Lennart Raner also tells us that in 1969 he found nests by watching nest relief, near Thule, Greenland. 'It was natural for me to watch for exchanges on likely breeding grounds as I always do so with green and wood sandpipers and with greenshanks'. The first time he saw a pair of knots change over he was over 400 m away, so he was not able to find the nest. 'The nest day I was a bit closer and watching it at almost the same time. I now saw the knots relieve one another at a distance of only 75 m. The sitting bird returned 5 minutes after I had flushed her and was very tame, almost ignoring me'.

The Bird brothers in the late 1930s and David Parmelee and Stu Macdonald in 1955 were the earliest students of the knots' breeding biology. Then, in 1966, David Nettleship gave the first rounded account of their nesting behaviour, from work carried out in study areas at Hazen Camp, Ellesmere Island.

The knots arrive on their breeding grounds in small flocks. The cocks immediately start to pursue one another at low heights over the ground, with the chasing bird gliding with wings held in a high V above his back and singing simultaneously. The beautiful song dance of the cock starts with a fast steep climb to 20–160 m, followed by (1) a diagonal forward glide, (2) a horizontal glide and (3) a quivering flight. The diagonal flight begins by the bird flying on outstretched wings held above the horizontal, usually calling *whip-poo-mee*; and the horizontal glide follows with wings in a horizontal position and the calls changing to disyllabic *poo-mees*. The quivering flight consists of rapid wing beats through a small arc which help the knot to regain the height lost in the original diagonal glide (Nettleship 1974).

Nettleship and Hobson watched ground displays and copulation. Once, when the nest already held one egg, the cock landed in front of the hen and gave wing-up displays, then moved behind and mounted her. During coupling, he vigorously flapped his wings and after the hen had shaken him off she walked over and settled down on the nest. On 12 June 1965, M. A. Colbo (*in* Nettleship (1966) watched slightly different behaviour. The cock twice unsuccessfully tried to mount the hen, pulling lightly at the feathers of her back and neck.

Nests are cup-shaped, scratched into the top or edge of *Dryas* and lined with dead leaves of *Dryas, Salix*, grasses and sometimes small twigs. Seven scoops averaged 11 cm in width and 4.4 cm deep. Hobson watched a knot, of unidentified sex, scrape making, but no one has recorded a full account of nest dancing.

On central Ellesmere Island in 1955, Parmelee and Macdonald estimated that the earliest clutches were complete about 13–14 June; and in 1968 Hobson recorded that three hens laid out between 21–23 June. In 1938 Charles Bird found one nest on Hochstetter Foreland, north-west Greenland, on 15 June; and hens laid out at Mygg-bukta by 21 June. On Wrangel Island laying appears to be earlier; Flint estimated that one clutch was complete on 7 June 1964 and another on 19 June 1965.

The slightly glossed eggs, ovate or sub-pyriform in shape, are not outstandingly beautiful. Ground colour ranges from pale green, particularly when fresh, to olive buff; and they are spotted, streaked and spiralled with dark olive brown and smoky grey. In a Wrangel Island clutch 'one of the eggs was covered with fine little spots splashed on in patches' (Flint *in* Hobson 1972). Parmelee found a clutch on Bathurst Island with eggs heavily blotched with dark purple.

A clutch is normally four and occasionally three, with several one-and two-egg clutches on record. Some hens probably lay smaller clutches or fail to breed in hard springs. Fifty clutches from Ellesmere Island, NWT, Greenland, Wrangel Island, USSR, Taimyr Peninsula, USSR, New Siberian Island, USSR, and Spitsbergen, contained 1/1, 3/2, 12/3, 34/4 (mean 3.58 eggs).

Hobson watched a hen lay her first egg at *c* 12.30 and the second almost exactly 24 hours later. D. R. Oliver (*in* Nettleship 1974) and Nettleship (1974) recorded intervals of slightly more than two days between the third and fourth eggs in clutches. A knot takes approximately six days to complete a clutch.

Both sexes incubate. The Bird brothers found that in north-east Greenland hens sat early and cocks in later stages of incubation. Parmelee and Macdonald (1966) never watched nest relief but found that both sexes had brood patches. Hobson (1972) suggests that the knots probably change duties 3–4 times in 24 hours. Nettleship recorded an incubation period of 21.5–22.4 days. The chipping period lasts 3–4 days and all eggs in a clutch usually hatch out within a period of 24 hours.

The chicks leave the scoop soon after hatching, and are accompanied by both parents. Chicks were found 225 m from the scoop 16 hours after they had hatched and had travelled 350 m by the next day. Parmelee and Macdonald confirmed that both sexes rear the young; 'but it was difficult to be sure which one was more attentive when the chicks were small'. One of the pair frequently exchanged with the other during the rearing of the brood. In Greenland, Charles Bird found that 'the female is chiefly concerned with looking after the young. At this time the males are flying about in flocks'.

Some of these pipe-dream waders may nest with us in the future. But, for the present, we cannot complain. We have lived with greenshanks in the vast flows of Sutherland, camped beside dotterel on the high Grampians, and listened to the throbbing wing-music of lapwings on farmlands around our homes. Who can ask for more?

All in all, the waders are doing well. We are heartened by the skill and dedication of wader watchers at home and abroad. We happily leave the birds and their haunts to them.

Selected bibliography

Alexander, W. B. 1945. The woodcock in the British Isles. *Ibis* 87: 512–50. (1946) *ibid* 88: 1–24, 159–79, 271–87, 427–44. (1947) *ibid* 79: 1–28.

Andersen, F. S. 1944. (Contributions on the breeding biology of the ruff). *Dansk. Orn. foren. Tiddskr.* 38: 28–30. (1948) *ibid* 42: 125–48; (1951) *ibid* 45: 145–73.

Angus, Stewart (ed) 1983. *Sutherland Birds.* Northern Times, Golspie.

Baerends, G. P. and Hogan-Warburg, A. J. 1982. The external morphology of the egg and its variability. The Herring Gull and its Egg, part II. (ed. by G. P. Baerends and R. A. Dent). *Behaviour* 82: 1–32.

Baker, J. K. and Morgan, R. A. 1983. (Notes on colour-ringed stone curlew). *in* Cramp and Simmons 1983.

Bakker, G. 1961. Morinelplevier broedt (met succes) in N.o. polder. *Het Vogeljaar* 9: 185–87.

van Balen, J. H. 1959. Over de Voortplanting van de grutto. *Ardea* 47: 76–86. (1961) (On the breeding behaviour of black-tailed godwit). *in* Bannerman, D. A. vol 10.

Bannerman, D. A. 1953–63. *The Birds of the British Isles* (vols 9–11). Edinburgh and London, Oliver and Boyd.

Banzhaf, W. 1933. Ein beitrag zur brutbiologie des triels. *J. Orn.* 81: 311–21.

Barnes, J. A. G. 1950. Repeated bigamy of oystercatcher. *Br. Birds* 43: 307–09.

Barnard, C. J. and Thompson, D. B. A. 1985. Prey size selection by lapwings in lapwing/gull associations. *Behav.* 77: 1–22.

Bates, S. S. 1984. (Fledging period of a lapwing). *Br. Birds* 41: 118.

Belopolski, L. O. *et al* 1970. (Contribution on annual variation in laying dates of whimbrel). *Trudy Kandalak gos. zapoved* 8: 3–84. and weight of dunlin chicks.

Bengtson, S.-A. 1968. Breeding behaviour of the grey phalarope in west Spitsbergen. *Var Fågelvärld* 27: 1–13. (1970) Breeding behaviour of the purple sandpipers in west Spitsbergen. *Orn. Scand.* 1: 17–25. (1975) (On the breeding biology of purple sandpiper). *Fauna* 28: 81–86.

Bengtson, S.-A. and Svensson, B. 1968. Feeding habits of *Calidris alpina* and *C. minuta* ... *Oikos* 19: 152–57.

Bent, A. C. 1927. Life Histories of North American Shore Birds ... Part 1. *U.S. Nat. Mus. Bull.* 142 Washington. (1929) *ibid,* part 2 *Bull.* 146.

Bergman, G. 1946. Der steinwalzer in seiner beziehung zur umwelt. *Acta zool. fenn.* 47: 1–151.

Berndt, R. 1970. (Breeding density of ringed plovers). *Corax* 3: 81–96.

Berry, R. L. and Johnston, J. L. 1980. *The Natural History of Shetland.* London, Collins.

Beser, H. J. 1975. (On the breeding biology of the lapwing). *in* Glutz 1975.

Bettmann, H. 1961. *Die Waldschnepfe.* F. C. Mayer Verlag Munich-Solln. 112 pp.

Bezzel, E. 1977. (Breeding density of common sandpiper). *in* Glutz 1977.

Bianki, V. V. 1967. (On the oystercatcher, turnstone and ringed plover) in *Trudy Kandalak gos. zapoved* 6.

Bird, C. G. and Bird, E. 1940. Some remarks on non-breeding in the Arctic, especially in north-east Greenland. *Ibis* 4: 671–78. (1941) The Birds of North-east Greenland. *Ibis* 5: 118–61.

Bird, G. 1933. (On the stone curlew). *Br. Birds* 27: 114–16.

Birula, A. B. 1907. Sketches of Bird Life on the Arctic Coast of Siberia. *Mem. Acad. Sci. St Petersburg* 8–18 (in Russian). (1928) (Observations on the knot). *Mem. Boston Soc., Nat. Hist.* 6: 267–73.

Blackwood, C. G. 1920. Notes on the breeding habits of the dotterel (*Eudromias morinellus*) in Scotland. *Scot. Nat.* 98: 185–94.

Blair, H. M. S. 1946. The dusky redshank in Norway. *Ool. Rec.* 20: 17–21 and 33–38. (1960 and 1961) Essays on Waders *in* Bannerman, D. A. vols 9 and 10.

Bloch, D. 1983. (Distribution of red-necked phalaropes and ringed plovers in Faroes). *in* Cramp and Simmons 1983.

Boon, J. 1961. (On a lapwing breeding in its first year). *in* Bannerman, D. A. 10: 269.

Booth, E. T. 1867–78. MS diaries. (1881–87) *Rough Notes....* in 15 parts. London, Porter and Dulau.

Bourne, W. R. P. 1972. Woodcock and thrushes breeding in open and snipe among trees. *Br. Birds* 65: 178.

Brandt, H. 1943. *Alaska Nature Trails.* Cleveland, Ohio.

Brearey, D. 1983. (On the behaviour of the turnstone). *in* Cramp and Simmons 1983.

Breiehagen, T. 1985. Breeding biology and mating system in an alpine population of Temminck's stints *C. temminckii.* Thesis, Zool. Mus., Bergen.

British Birds 1980. Rare breeding birds in the U.K. in 1978. 73: 18–19. (1982) Rare breeding birds in 1980. 75: 168–69. (1983) Rare breeding birds in 1981. 76: 14–15. (1983a) Rare breeding birds in the U.K. in 1982. 76: 82–3.

Brown, P. E. and Waterston, G. 1983. *The Return of the Osprey.* Collins, London.

Brown, R. H. 1926. (Breeding habits of the lapwing). *Br. Birds* 20: 62–68. (1938) (Breeding habits of dunlin). *Br. Birds* 31: 362–66. (1939) (Breeding habits of curlew). *Br. Birds* 33: 12–15. (1946) (Hatching periods of lapwing). *Br. Birds* 39.

Bucholz, H. 1961. (On food of wood sandpiper). *Mitt. faun. ArbGem. Schleswig-Holstein* 14: 51–53. (1962) *ibid* 15: 33.

Burton, P. J. K. 1971. (On food of green sandpiper). *Alauda* 39: 132–38. (1974) *Feeding and the Feeding Apparatus in Waders....* London, Brit. Mus (Nat. Hist).

Buxton, E. J. M. 1939. The breeding of the oystercatcher. *Br. Birds* 33: 184–93.

Byrkjedal, Ingvar 1974. The golden plover *Pluvialis apricaria* as a breeding bird in Co. Rogaland, SW Norway. *Sterna* 13: 1–14. (1978) Altitudinal differences in breeding schedules of golden plovers *P. apricaria* in south Norway. *Sterna* 17: 1–20. (1978) Variations and secondary intergradation in SW-Norwegian golden plovers *Pluvialis apricaria* populations. *Orn. Scand.* 9: 101–10.

Byrkjedal, I. and Kålås, J. A. 1983. Plover's page turns into Plover's parasite: a look at the dunlin/golden plover association. *Orn. Fenn.* 60: 10–15.

Cadbury, C. J. and Olney, P. J. S. 1977. The avocet population in England and its dynamics. *Br. Birds* 70.

Cadbury, C. J., Olney, P. J. S. and Richards, P. A. 1977. The breeding and feeding ecology of the avocet in Suffolk, England. MS.

Cane, C. 1980. (Contributions on the purple sandpiper). *in* Innes, J. (ed) 1980.

Casement, M. B. 1948. (Female snipe carrying newly-hatched chicks between its legs). *Br. Birds* 41: 352.

Cawkell, E. V. 1949. (On the calls of lapwings). *Br. Birds* 41: 93.

Chance, A. M. 1906–22. MS notes on greenshanks.

Chance, E. P. 1930. Delayed laying of lapwing. *Br. Birds* 24: 112. (1934) A communication on a trio of greenshanks. *Bull. Brit. Ool. Assoc.* September 1934. (various) Data files on waders *in* Brit. Mus. Nat. History.

Cheylan, G. 1951. (On the breeding dispersion of the stone curlew). *Alauda* 43: 23–54.

Chislett, R. 1923. The whimbrel in Shetland. *Br. Birds* 17: 150–54. (1927) Notes on the breeding of the jack snipe. *Br. Birds* 21: 2–6. (1928) Turnstones on a Baltic islet. *Br. Birds* 19: 2–9.

Christoleit, E. 1936. Zur balz des zwergstrandläufers. *Beitr. FortPflBiol. Vögel* 12: 177–87 and 259–51. (1932) Zur balz des waldwasserläufers. *Beitr. PortPflBiol. Vögel* 8: 185–87.

Clausager, I. 1974. (On the hatching success in woodcock). *Dan. Rev. Game Biol.* 8: 1–38. (1983) (On redshank numbers in Denmark). *in* Cramp and Simmons 1983.

Collar, N. J. 1983. (On the voice of the redshank). *in* Cramp and Simmons 1983.

Congreve, W. M. 1924. (On replacement clutch of woodcock). *Br. Birds* 18. (1932) Some notes on breeding greenshanks. *Kocsag* 5: 1–7.

Congreve, W. M. and Freme, S. P. 1930. (Breeding ratio in red-necked phalaropes). *Ibis* 6: 193–228.

Cook, M. 1976. (On the ecology of the lapwing). M.Sc. thesis, Univ. of Aberdeen.

Cowper, C. N. L. 1973. Breeding distribution of grey wagtails, dippers and common sandpipers on the Midlothian Esk. *Scot. Birds* 7: 302–06.

Crapnell, V. S. 1934. Temminck's stints nesting in Scotland. *Nat.* for 1934: 193–95.

Cramp, S. and Simmons, K. E. L. (eds) 1983. *The Birds of the Western Palearctic* (vol 3). Oxford Univ. Press.

Creutz, G. 1953. Beobachtungen am triel. *Beitr. Vogelkde* 3: 199–211.

Cuthbertson, E. I., Foggit, G. T. and Bell, M. A. 1952. A census of common sandpipers in the Sedbergh area, 1951. *Br. Birds* 45: 171–75.

Dabelsteen, Torben 1977. An analysis of the song-flight of the lapwing (*Vanellus vanellus*) with respect to causation, evolution and adaptations to signal function. *Behav.* 66: 136–78.

Danielson, M. 1946. (An incubation period of whimbrel). *in* Williamson, K. 1946.

Danilov, N. and Rjabizef, V. K. 1973. (On the density of Temminck's stints). *in* flint, V. E.

Dare, P. J. 1966. The breeding and wintering populations of the oystercatcher *Haematopus ostralegus* L. in the British Isles. *Fishery Invest.*, London (Ser II) 25: 1–69.

Dare, P. J. and Mercer, A. J. 1973. The foods of oystercatchers in Morecambe Bay, England. *Bird Study* 20: 173–84. (1974) The white collar of the oystercatchers. *Bird Study* 21: 180–4.

Dathe, H. 1953. *Der Flussregenpfeifer.* Leipzig. 1963. Zur brutbeteiligung des geschlechter beim flussregenpfeifer. *Orn. Mitt.* 15: 197–8.

Dathe, H. and Müller, H. J. 1932. Zur brutbiologie des flussregenpfeifers. *Beitr. FortPflBiol. Vögel* 8: 60–65.

Daukes, A. H. 1933. (On whimbrel nesting in Inverness-shire). *Br. Birds* 27: 76–8.

Dementiev, G. P. *et al* 1969. *Birds of the Soviet Union* (vol 3). Israel Program for Scientific Translations, Jerusalem.

Dennis, R. 1983. Purple sandpiper breeding in Scotland. *Br. Birds* 76: 563–66.

Dewar, J. M. 1915. The relation of the oystercatcher to its natural environment. *Zool* 4/19 1915: 281–91, 340–46, 376–83, 426–31 and 458–65.

Dircksen, R. 1932. Die biologie des austernfischers, der brandseeschwalbe und der küstenseeschwalbe.... *J. Orn.* 80: 427–521.

Douglas, S. R. 1917. (The breeding density of woodcocks). *Proc. zool. Soc. London* for 1917: 159–65.

Drinnan, R. E. 1957. The winter feeding of the oystercatchers on the edible cockle *Cardium edule. J. Anim. Ecol.* 26: 441–69. (1958) The winter feeding of the oystercatcher on the edible mussel *Mytilus edulis* in the Conway Estuary, North Wales. *Fishery Invest.*, London 221: 1–15.

Durango, S. 1943. Några iakttaglser av den mindre strandpiparen. *Fauna och Flora* 38: 145–54.

Duthie, J. A. and Leavett, R. 1983. (On the breeding behaviour of wood sandpipers). *in* Cramp and Simmons 1983.

Dybbro, T. 1970. The Kentish plover as a breeding bird in Denmark. *Dansk. Orn. foren. Tiddskr.* 64: 205–22. (1976) *De Danske Ynglefugles Udbredelse.* Copenhagen.

Dyrcz, A. *et al* 1972. (On the nest dispersion of great snipe in Poland). *Acta Orn.* 13: 343–422.

Dymond, J. M. 1983. (Red-necked phalarope: breeding density and voice in Shetland). *in* Cramp and Simmons 1983. 3: 635–38.

Edwards, G. R. 1934. Breeding of Temminck's stint in Scotland. *Br. Birds* 28: 97–99.

Edwards, G. R., Hosking, E. and Smith, S. 1947. Aggressive display of the ringed plover. *Br. Birds* 40: 12–19. (1948) Aggressive display of the oystercatcher. *Br. Birds* 41: 236–43.

Edwards, P. J. 1980. Plumage variation, territoriality and breeding displays of the golden plover *Pluvialis apricaria* in south-west Scotland. *Ibis* 124: 88–96.

Elliot, R. D. 1982. Nesting dispersion of lapwings in relation to predation and anti-predator defence. Unpublished thesis, Univ. of Aberdeen.

Engel, A. and Schmitt, P. 1975. Etude d'une population de courlis cendrés en Alsace. *Alauda* 42: 295–302.

England, M. D., Höhn, E. O., Pedler, E. G. and Tucker, B. W. 1944. The breeding of the little ringed plover in England in 1944. *Br. Birds* 38: 102–11.

Ens, B. and Zwarts L. 1980a and b. Contributions on social patterns and behaviour of curlews. *Watervogels* 5: 108–20 and 155–68.

Erckmann, W. J. 1983. The evolution of polyandry in shorebirds: an evaluation of hypothesis. *in Social Behaviour of Female Vertebrates* (ed S. K. Wasser). Academic Press, London.

Etheridge, B. 1982. Distribution of dunlin *Calidris alpina* nests on an area of South Uist machair. *Bird Study* 29: 239–243.

Everett, M. J. 1971. Breeding status of red-necked phalaropes in Britain and Ireland. *Br. Birds* 64: 293–302.

Fallet, M. 1962. (On the food of the lapwing). *Zool. Anz.* 168: 187–212.

Farren, W. 1908. The crouching habit of the stone curlew. *Br. Birds* 1: 301–08.

Ferdinand, L. 1966. Display of the great snipe. *Dansk. Orn. Foren. Tiddskr.* 60: 14–34.

Ferdinand, L. and Gensbol, B. 1966. Maintenance of territory in the great snipe on the display ground. *Dansk. Orn. Foren. Tiddskr.* 60: 35–43.

Ferry, C. 1955. (On the breeding density of ringed plovers in Britanny). *Alauda* 23: 81–93. (1956) Sur L'écologie de l'Oedicnème en Côte d'Or. *Oiseaux* 26: 61–5.

Flint, V. E. 1972. The breeding of the knot on Vrangelya (Wrangel) Island, Siberia. *Proc. Western Foundation Vert. Zool.* 2: 27–29. (1973) *Fauna i ekologiya kulikov.* Moscow.

Flössner, D. 1977. (On the breeding density of woodcock). *in* Glutz 1977.

des Forges, G. 1975. Behaviour of an incubating woodcock. *Br. Birds* 68: 421–28.

Franke, H. 1952. Unser mornellregenpfeifer. *Vogelkdl Nachr Österreich.* 1: 2–3. (1953) Zur biologie des Mornellregnepfiefers. *Photographie and Forschung* 5: 200–06.

Freitag, F. 1969. (On pair bonds in lapwings). *Luscinia* 40: 253–55.

von Frisch, O. 1956. Zur brutbiologie and jungendtwicklung des brachvogels. *Z. Tierpsychol* 13: 50–81. (1959a) (On age of first breeding in stone curlew). *Vogelwelt* 80: 97–101. (1959b) Kiebitzbruten in gefangenschaft mit aufzucht von rotschenkeln durch ein kiebitzpaar. *J. Orn.* 100: 307–12. (1964) *Der Grosse Brachvogel.* Wittenberg, Lutherstadt.

Fuchs, W. C. 1961. (On the lapwing). *in* Glutz 1975.

Fuller, R. 1981. The breeding habitats of waders on N. Uist. *Scot. Birds* 11: 142–52.

Galbraith, C. A. and Thompson, P. S. 1981. Flóastelkur *Tringa glareola* varpfugl á Islandi: *Nattur-fraedingutinn 51* 4: 164–68.

Gardarsson, A. 1956. (On the breeding status of wood sandpiper in Iceland). *Náttúrufraedingurinn* 26: 87–93.

Gerber, R. 1952. Der Triel, ein bewohner ärmsten ödlandes. *Urania* 15: 349–52.

Géroudet, P. 1942. *Les Echassiers.* Neuchatel and Paris. (1952) Nidification de la bécasse dans le pays de Genéve. *Nos Oiseaux* 21: 15–17.

Gillandt, L. 1972. Beobachtungen an einer brutpopulation des thorshühnchens in sommer 1970. Diploma thesis, Univ. of Hamburg.

Gilroy, N. 1923. *Field notes and observations on the greenshank.* Privately circulated brochure. (1928) *Birds of the Far North* (unpublished MS). (1923) Observations on the nesting of the dotterel. *Ool. Rec.* 3: 1–7.

Gladkov, N. A. and Saletajev, 1965. (Laying season of Temminck's stint in Russia). *Sborn. Trud. Zool. Mus. Mosk. Gos. Univ.* 9.

Glue, D. and Morgan, R. 1974. Breeding statistics and movements of the stone curlew. *Bird Study* 21: 21–28.

Glutz, U. von Blotzheim 1959. Verbreitung und haufigheit des kiebitz in der Schweiz.... *Orn. Beob.* 56: 178–205.

Glutz, U. von Blotzheim, Bauer, K. M. and Bezzel, E. 1975 and 1977. *Handbuch der Vögel Mitteleuropas* (vols 6 and 7). Wiesbaden, Akademische Verlagsgesellschaft.

Godman, F. and Godman, P. 1861. (On the breeding dispersion of great snipe). *Ibis* 3: 77–92.

Goethe, F. 1966. (Age of breeding oystercatchers). *Vogelwarte* 28.

Goethe, F. and Kramer, 1962. (On the maximum ages of oystercatcher). *Vogelwarte* 21.

Goss-Custard, J. D. 1969. The winter feeding ecology of the redshank *Tringa totanus*. *Ibis*. 111: 338–56. (1970) Factors affecting the diet and feeding rate of the redshank. *in* Watson, A. (1970a) pp 101–110. (1976) (On the food of the redshanks). *Ibis* 118: 257–63. (1977) *ibid J. Anim. Ecol.* 46: 867–74.

Goss-Custard, J. and Jones, R. E. 1976. The diets of redshank and curlew. *Bird Study* 23: 233–43.

Graul, W. 1973. Adaptive aspects of the mountain plover's social system. *Living Bird* 12: 69–94. (1974) Vocalizations of the mountain plover. *Wilson Bull.* 87: 6–31.

Green, G. H. (ed). 1984. A Survey of Waders Breeding on the West Coast of the Uists and Benbecula (Outer Hebrides). Wader Study Group and NCC.

Greenhalgh, M. E. 1969. (On breeding density of dunlin). *Naturalist* 43–7. (1975) (On food of the redshank). Unpublished Ph.D. thesis, Liverpool Polytechnic.

Greiner, H. 1977. (On the breeding biology of the curlew) *in* Glutz 1977.

Greve, K. 1958. Der sandregenpfeifer als brutvogel auf Neuwerk. *Vogelwelt* 79: 158–9. (1969) (Breeding density of ringed plovers). *Orn. Mitt.* 21: 169. (1970) (On the age of common sandpiper). *Orn. Mitt.* 22.

Grosskopf, G. 1958–9. Zur biologie des Rotschenkels (*Tringa totanus*). *J. Orn.* 99: 1–17; 100: 210–31. (1963) Weitere beitrage zur biologie des rotschenkels. *Vogelwelt* 84: 65–83. (1968a) Verbreitung und schutz des goldregenpfeifers im regierungsbezirk Hannover. *Ber. Int. Rat Vogelschutz Dtsch Sekt* 8: 45–48. (1968b) *Die Vögel der Insel Wangerooge*. Jever. (1970) Der einfluss von alter und partnerwahl auf des einsetzen des brutgeschafts beim rotschenkel. *J. Orn.* 111: 420–37.

Grote, H. 1931. Zur lebenweise und verbreitung von *Haematopus ostraegus longipes J. Orn.* 79: 346–9. (1939) (On the breeding behaviour of green sandpiper). *Beitr. FortPflBiol. Vögel* 15: 106–15. (1941) Ueber den Zug der Waldschnepfe (*Scolopax rusticola*) in Russland. *Vogelzug* 12: 73–80.

Gudmundsson, F. 1957. Icelandic birds. 15 The Whimbrel. *Natturfraedingurinn* 27: 113–25.

Gunton, W. S. 1941. (On breeding of black-tailed godwit). *Br. Birds* 35: 110–12.

von Haartman, L. 1973. (Breeding Biology of Birds). in Farner, D. S. (ed).

von Haartman, L. *et al* 1963. Pahjolan Linnut Värikuvin. Helsinki.

Hable, E. 1973. Der Mornellregenpfeifer in Kärnten. *Carinthia* 2 83: 603–08. (1975) (Observations on the dotterel). *in* Glutz 1975.

Haftorn, S. 1971. *Norges Fugler*. Oslo.

Hagen, Y. 1950. How a woodcock sitting on the ground attracts the attention of partners in mating flight. *Vår Fågelvarld* 9: 195–99.

Hale, W. G. 1973. The distribution of the redshank *Tringa totanus* in the winter range. *Zool J. Linn. Soc.* 53: 177–236. (1980) *Waders*. London, Collins. (1983) (Studies of redshank). *in* Cramp and Simmons 1983.

Hale, W. G. and Ashcroft, R. P. 1982. Pair formation and pair maintenance in the redshank *Totanus. Ibis* 124: 471–90. (1983) Studies of the courtship behaviour of the redshank *T. totanus. Ibis* 125: 3–23. *in* Cramp and Simmons 1983: 531–38.

Hall-Craggs, J. 1979. *in Greenshanks*. Berkhamsted, Poyser.

Haller, W. 1932. Ein beitrag zur brutbiologie der waldschnepfe. *Vögel der Heimat* 15: 37–39. (1942) Altes und neues aus den brutleben der waldschnepfe. *Vögel der Heimat* 15: 37–39.

Hantzsch, B. 1905. *Beitrag zur Kenntnis der Vogelwelt Islands*. Berlin.

Harris, M. P. 1967. The biology of oystercatchers on Skokholm Island, S. Wales. *Ibis* 109: 180–93. (1969) Effect of laying dates on chick production in oystercatchers and herring gulls. *Br. Birds* 62: 72–5. (1970) Territory limiting the size of the breeding population of the oystercatcher – a removal experiment. *J. Anim. Ecol.* 39: 707–13.

Hartley, C. H. and Fisher, J. 1936. (On breeding density of purple sandpipers in west Spitsbergen). *J. Anim. Ecol.* 5: 370–89.

Harvie-Brown, J. A. and Buckley, T. E. 1887. *A Vertebrate Fauna of Sutherland, Caithness and West Cromarty*. Edinburgh, Douglas. (1895) *A Vertebrate Fauna of the Moray Basin* (2 vols). Edinburgh, Douglas.

Haverschmidt, F. 1927. (On the behaviour of black-tailed godwits). *Ardea* 16: 45. (1943) De goudplevierenvangst in Nederland. *Ardea* 32: 35–74. (1963) *The Black-tailed Godwit*. Leiden, Brill.

Haviland, M. D. 1915. Notes on the breeding habits of the little stint. *Br. Birds* 8: 202–08. (1916)

Notes on the breeding habits of Temminck's stints. *Br. Birds* 10: 157–65. (1917) Notes on the breeding habits of the dotterel in the Yenesei. *Br. Birds* 11: 6–11.

Hays, H. 1972. Polyandry in the spotted sandpiper. *Living Bird* 11: 435–57.

Heim, J. 1962. (Laying season of the curlew). *in* Glutz 1962. (1974) (Incubation spells in lapwing). *Orn. Beob.* 283–8.

Heinroth, O. 1927–28. *Der Vögel Mitteleuropas* (1931–33) vols 3 and 4. Berlin.

Heldt, R. 1966. Zur brutbiologie des alpenstrandlaufers. *Corax* 1: 173–88.

Hellebrekers, W. P. J. 1950. *Measurements and Weights of Eggs and Birds on the Dutch List.* Leiden. (1964) (Six young lapwings hatching from a seven-egg clutch). *Limosa* 37.

Heppleston, P. B. 1968. An ecological study of the oystercatcher. Unpublished Ph.D. thesis, Univ. of Aberdeen. (1971) Nest-site selection by oystercatchers in the Netherlands and Scotland. *Netherlands J. Zool.* 208: 210–11. (1972) The comparative breeding ecology of oystercatchers in inland and coastal habitats. *J. Anim. Ecol.* 23–57. (1973) The distribution and taxonomy of oystercatchers. *Notornis.* vol 20, part 2: 102–112.

Hildén, O. 1965. Zur brutbiologie des Temminckstrandläufers *Calidris temminckii. Orn. Fenn.* 42: 1–5. (1966) Uber die Brutbeteiligung des Geschlechter beim Mornellregenpfeifer. *Orn. Fenn.* 4: 16–19. (1975) Breeding system of Temminck's stint *Calidris temminckii. Orn. Fenn.* 52: 117–146. (1978) Population dynamics in Temminck's stint *Calidris temminckii. Oikos* 30: 17–28. (1983) (On the breeding behaviour and breeding biology of the little stint). *in* Cramp and Simmons 1983: 306–09.

Hildén, O. and Vuolanto, S. 1972. Breeding of the red-necked phalarope *Phalaropus lobatus* in Finland. *Orn. Fenn.* 49: 57–75.

Hinde, R. A. 1956. Length in the pre-laying period in the lapwing *V. vanellus* in relation to its food resources. *Orn. Scan.* 5: 1–4.

Hirons, G. 1980b. (On behaviour of woodcock). *Game Conservancy Ann. Rev.* 11: 77–81. (1983) (On the voice of woodcock). *in* Cramp and Simmons 1983.

Hobson, W. 1972. The breeding biology of the knot.... *Proc. Western Foundation Vert. Zool.* Los Angeles. 2: 5–26.

Hoffmann, J. 1867 *Die Waldschnepfe....* Stuttgart.

Hogan-Warburg, A. J. 1966. Social behaviour of the ruff (*Philomachus pugnax*). *Ardea* 54: 109–229.

Högstedt, Goran 1974. Length of the pre-laying period in the lapwing *Vanellus vanellus* L. in relation to its food resources. *Orn. Scan.* 5: 1–4.

Höhn, E. O. 1965. *Die Wassertreter.* Wittenberg, Lutherstadt, Ziemsen. (1967) (arrival of red-necked phalaropes on breeding grounds). *Auk* 88: 220–44. (1968) Some observations on the breeding of northern phalaropes at Scammore Bay, Alaska. Auk 85: 316–17. (1971) Observations on the breeding behaviour of grey and red-necked phalaropes. *Ibis* 113: 335–48.

Holgersen, H. 1953. (On the maximum age of dunlin). *Bird Banding* 24.

Holland, P. K., Robson, J. E. and Yalden, D. W. 1982. The breeding biology of the common sandpiper *Actitis hypoleucos* in the Peak District. *Bird Study* 29: 99–110.

Hollom, P. 1983. (On voice of woodcock). *in* Cramp and Simmons 1983.

Holmes, R. T. 1966. Breeding ecology and annual cycle adaptations of the red-backed sandpiper *Calidris alpina* in northern Alaska. *Condor* 68: 3–46. (1966b) Feeding ecology of the red-backed sandpiper in arctic Alaska. *Zoology* 47: 32–45. (1970) Differences in population density, territoriality and food supply of dunlin on arctic and sub-arctic tundra. *in* Watson, A. (ed) 1970a 303–319. (1971) Density, habitat and the mating system of the western sandpiper *Calidris mauri. Oecologica* 7: 191–208. (1973) Social behaviour of breeding western sandpipers *Calidris mauri. Ibis* 115: 107–23.

Hosking, E. and Hale, W. G. 1983. *Eric Hosking's Waders.* London, Pelham.

Hosking, E. and Newberry, C. W. 1940. *Intimate Sketches of Bird Life.* London.

Hudec, K. and Cerný, W. 1977. (Contributions on the breeding biology of curlew). *Fauna CSSR Ptaci 3.* Prague.

Hulscher, J. B. 1971. (Oystercatcher populations in north-west Europe). De Scholekster en de Waddenzee. *Waddenbulletin* 6: 9–13.

Hulten, M. 1970. Zur henntnis der waldschnepfe. *Regulus* 10 (6): 187–200 (French summary).

Hussell, D. J. T. and Page, G. W. 1976. (On the breeding biology of the grey plover). *Wilson Bull.* 88: 632–63.

Hutchinson, C. D. 1979. *Ireland's Wetlands and their Birds.* Dublin.

Huxley, J. S. 1912. A first account of the courtship of the redshank (*Totanus calidris*). *Proc. Zool. Soc. London* 1912: 647–55. (1925a) The absence of courtship in the avocet. *Proc. Zool. Soc. London* 19: 88–94.

Huxley, J. S. and Montague, F. A. 1925. Studies on the courtship and sexual life of birds. 5 The Oystercatcher. *Ibis* for 1925: 868–897. (1926) Studies on the courtship and sexual life of birds. 6 The Black-tailed godwit. *Ibis* for 1926: 1–25.

Imboden, C. 1970. Zur ökologie einer randzonen-population des kiebitz in der Schweiz. *Orn. Beoob* 67: 41–58. (1971) Bestand, verbreitung und biotop des kiebitz in der Schweiz. *Orn. Beob.* 68: 37–53.
Ingram, C. (1967) Woodcock uttering roding call from perch. *Br. Birds* 60: 217–218.
Innes, J. (ed) 1980. Cambridge Norwegian Expedition 1978 Report.
Ivanova, N. S. 1966. (Breeding density of common sandpipers). *in* Glutz 1977.

Jackson, R. and Jackson, J. 1980. A study of lapwings' breeding population changes in the New Forest, Hampshire. *Bird Study* 27: 27–34.
Jenni, D. A. 1974. Evolution of polyandry in birds. *Amer. Zool.* 14: 129–44.
Jessen, T. 1931. Svalekliren som ny Dansk Ynglefugl. *Dansk. Fugle* 3: 104–07.
Joensen, A. H. 1966. *Fuglene på Faeroerne.* Copenhagen.
Joensen, A. H. and Preuss, N. 1972. (On the breeding of the purple sandpiper). *Medd. om. Gron.* 191: 1–58.
Johansen, H. 1960. (Distribution of breeding Temminck's stints). *J. Orn.* 101: 316–39.
Johns, J. E. 1969. Field studies of Wilson's phalarope. *Auk* 86: 660–70.
Jourdain, F. C. R. 1927 and 1929. Essays on waders *in* Bent, A. C. (1940) Sections on 'breeding', 'food', and 'distribution abroad' *in* H. F. Witherby *et al* (1938–41).

Kalchreuter, H. 1982. *The Woodcock.* Hoffmann, Germany. (English translation: Peter D. K. Hessel, Ottawa).
Keighley, J. and Buxton, E. J. M. 1948. The incubation period of the oystercatcher. *Br. Birds* 41: 261–6.
Keith, D. B. 1938. (Observations on the purple sandpiper in Northeastland). *Proc. Zool. Soc. London* 108: 185–94.
Kipp, M. 1977. (On the breeding biology of the curlew). *in* Glutz 1977.
Kirchner, H. 1963. *Der Bruchwasserläufer.* Neue Brehm-Bucherei, Wittenberg-Lutherstadt. (1972) Zur Brut des Waldwasserläufers in Schleswig-Holstein. *Orn. Mitt.* 24: 268–71.
Kålås, J. A. 1982. The mating system in the dotterel *Eudromias morinellus.* Ph.D. thesis, Univ. of Bergen, Norway.
Kålås, J. A. and Byrkjedal, I. 1981. The status of breeding waders *Charadrii* in Norway including Svalbard. *Proc. Second Nordic Congr. Ornithol.* 1979: 57–74. (1984) Breeding chronology and mating system of the Eurasian dotterel (*Charadrius morinellus*). *The Auk* 101: 838–847.
Kapitonov, V. I. 1962. *Ornitologiya* vol 4.
Kirchoff, K. 1971. Kiebitz, brutverbreitung, brutbiologie und zug in berichtsgebiet Hamburger. *Avifaun Beitr.* 9: 47–99.
Kirkman, F. B. 1910–13. *The British Bird Book.* London and Edinburgh, Jack. (1937) *Bird Behaviour.* London and Edinburgh, Jack.
Kistchinski, A. A. 1975. Breeding biology and behaviour of the grey phalarope. *P. fulicarius* in East Siberia. *Ibis* 117: 265–301.
Kistchinski, A. A. and Tchernov, Y. I. 1973. (food of red-necked phalarope *in* Flint 1973).
Kistyakivski, O. B. 1957. *Fauna Ukraini* 4. Kiev.
Klafs, G. and Stübs, J. 1977. *Die Vogelwelt Mecklenburgs.*
Klomp, H. 1970. The determination of clutch-size in birds: a review. *Ardea* 58: 1–124.
Klomp, H. and Speek, B. J. 1971. Survival of young lapwings in relation to their time of hatching. *Bird Study* 18: 229–30.
Koehler, O. and Zagarus, A. 1937. Beiträge zum bruterhalten des halsbandregenpfeifers. *Beitr. FortPflBiol. Vögel* 13: 1–9.
Kokhanov, V. D. 1965. (Fledging period of ruff). *Zool Zh.* 44: 784–7. (1973) (On the ecology of Temminck's stints in Kandalaschka Bay, White Sea). *in* Flint 1973.
Kokhanov, V. D. and Gaev, U. G. 1970. in *Scientific Works of the Kandalaschka State Reserve* 8 (in Russian).
Kozlova, E. 1961–6. *Fauna of the USSR: suborder Limicolae* (2 vols). Moscow and Leningrad, Academy of Sciences (in Russian).
Kraatz, S. and Wegner, W. 1969. Zwei erfolgreiche trielbruten im bezirk Frankfurt. *Falke* 16: 304–09.

Krechmar, A. V. 1966. (On the breeding of the dusky redshank). *Trudy zool. Inst. Akad. Nauk SSR* 39: 185–312.

Kumari, E. 1938. Das brutvorkommen des regenbrachsvogels in Estland. *J. Orn.* 86: 554–58. (1958) The food of waders in the peat bogs of Estonia. *Orn. Kogumik* 1: 195–215. (1977) *Der Regenbrachvogel.* Wittenberg, Lutherstadt.

Kumerloeve, H. 1950. Zur biologie amrumer austernfischer. *Columba* 2: 22 and 44–46. (1954) Vom austernfischer im nordwestdeutschen binnenland. *Kosmos* 50: 501–07.

Lack, D. 1938. Display of green sandpiper. *Br. Birds* 32: 86. (1954) *The Natural Regulation of Animal Numbers.* Oxford, Clarendon Press. (1966) *Population Studies of Birds.* Oxford, Clarendon. (1968) *Ecological Adaptations for Breeding in Birds.* London, Methuen.

Laven, B. 1941. Beobachtungen über balz und brut beim kiebitz. *J. Orn. Ergänzungsband* 3: 1–64.

Laven, H. 1938. Beiträge zur brutbiologie des halsbandregenpfeifers. *Beitr. FortPflBiol. Vögel* 88: 183–287. (1940) Beitrage zur Biologie des Sandregenpfeifers (*Charadrius hiaticula* L). *J. Orn.* 88: 183–281.

Lea, D. and Bourne, W. R. P. 1975. The birds of Orkney. *Br. Birds* 68: 261–83.

Leffler, S. R. 1966. (On the voice of the red-necked phalarope). *Wilson Bull.* 78: 124–5.

Leonovich, V. V. and Uspenski, S. M. 1965. (Breeding density of dunlin). *Trudy Inst. Biol. Akad. Nauk SSR. Yural Fil.* 1965: 38.

Lessels, C. M. 1984. The mating system of Kentish plovers C. *alexandrinus. Ibis* 126: 474–83.

Lind, H. 1961. Studies on the behaviour of the black-tailed godwit. *Medd Naturfredningrådets Reservatudvalg* 66. Copenhagen. (1956) Parental feeding in the oystercatcher. *Dansk. Orn. Foren. Tiddskr.* 59: 1–31.

Lemnell, P. A. 1978. (On the display of great snipe). *Orn. Scand.* 9: 146–63.

Lippens, L. and Wille, H. 1972. *Atlas des Oiseaux de Belgique et d'Europe Occidentale.* Tielt.

Lister, M. D. 1939. An account of the lapwing populations on a Surrey farm. *Br. Birds* 32: 260–71.

Løfaldi, L. 1981. On the breeding season biometrics of the common sandpiper. *Ringing and Migration* 3: 133–36. (1983) (Contributions on the voice of the whimbrel). *in* Cramp and Simmons 1983.

Lohscheller, H. 1972. (Unusual nest-site of lapwing). *Anthus* 9: 82–3.

Lowe, V. P. W. 1972. Distraction display of a woodcock with chicks. *Ibis* 114: 106–7.

Løvenskiold, H. L. 1947. *Håndbok over Norges Fugler* (3 vols). Oslo. (1964) *Avifauna Svalbardensis.* Oslo.

Lynes, H. 1910. (Lapwing distracting a stoat). *Br. Birds* 4: 157.

Maclean, S. F. 1974. Lemming bones as a source of calcium for arctic sandpipers (*Calidris* spp.). *Ibis* 116: 552–7.

Mahéo, R. 1983. (Redshank numbers in France). *in* Cramp and Simmons 1983.

Makatsch, W. 1966. (On breeding density of common sandpipers in N.E. Slovakia). *Zool. Abh. Mus. Tierkde. Dresden* 28.

Makkink, G. F. 1936. An attempt at an ethogram of the European avocet.... *Ardea* 21: 38–43. (1942) (Contributions to the knowledge of the behaviour of the oystercatcher). *Ardea* 31: 23–74.

Maltschewski, S. 1977. (On whimbrel numbers near Leningrad USSR) *in* Glutz 1977.

Marcström, V. and Sundgren, F. 1977. (Weight of newly-hatched woodcock). *Viltrevy* 10: 27–40.

Marler, P. 1984. Bird song: the acquisition of a learned motor skill. *Trends Neurosci* 4: 88–94.

Martinel, J. and Chantrel, G. 1977. (Contributions a l'étude de la bécasse S. *rusticola* en fôret domaniale de Compiegne (Oise). *Off. natn. Chasse, Sect. Bécasse,* Paris.

Mason, C. F. and Macdonald, C. M. 1976. Aspects of the breeding biology of the snipe. *Bird Study* 23: 33–8.

Merikallio, E. 1958. Finnish birds, their distributions and numbers. *Orn. Fenn.* 5: 1–181.

Mildenburger, H. 1953. (Egg intervals in reeve). *J. Orn.* 94: 128–43.

Miller, E. H. 1984. Communication in breeding shorebirds. *in Behaviour of Marine Animals* vol. 5, pp 169–241. J. Burger and B. L. Olla (eds.).

Miller, J. R. and Miller, J. T. 1948. Nesting of the spotted sandpiper at Detroit, Michigan. *Auk* 65: 558–67.

Mitchell, J. 1983. Nesting of the Temminck's stint in Dunbartonshire in 1979. *Loch Lomond Bird Report* No 11: 12–13.

Monnat, J.-Y. 1980. (Breeding of ringed plovers in France). *Ar. Vran.* 9: 1–8.

Morgan, R. 1983. (Observations on stone curlew). *in* Cramp and Simmons 1983.

Morgan, R. and Shorten, M. 1974. *The breeding of the Woodcock in Britain.* Game Conservancy.

Mousley, H. 1935. The birth of a snipe family. *Auk* 52: 408–11. (1937) Nesting habits of the spotted sandpiper. *Auk* 54: 445–51.

Müller, W. 1971. Zum brutvorkommen des kiebitz im Stadtkreis Oberhausen. *Charadrius* 7: 67–8. (1975) Brutbestandsaufnahme des flussuferläufers am unteren Hinterrhein. *Orn. Beob.* 72: 44–52.

Müller-Using, D. 1960. (On hen woodcock calling down roding cocks). in *Trans. 4th Cong. Int. Union Game Biol.* Arnhem.

Munn, P. W. 1948. (On the breeding biology of Kentish plover). *Ibis* 90: 595.

Murton, R. K. and Westwood, N. J. 1974. (Food influences on egg weights). *Br. Birds* 67: 41–69.

Nash, W. J. 1916. Snipe carrying young. *Irish Nat.* for 1916: 170.

Nemetschek, G. 1977. Beobachtungen zur flugbalz der waldschnepfe. *J. Orn.* 118: 68–86.

Nethersole-Thompson, C. and D. 1938–41. Contributions in H. F. Witherby *et al* (1942) Eggshell disposal by birds. *Br. Birds* 35: 162–69; 190–200; 23: 241–50. (1961) 'The breeding behaviour of the British golden plover' and 'Breeding behaviour of the dotterel' *in* Bannerman, D. A. 10: 206–14; 246–53.

Nethersole-Thompson, D. 1933. Some observations on the nesting of the stone curlew. *Ool. Rec.* 13: 82–90. (1938–41) Contributions to H. F. Witherby *et al* (1943) The nesting of the woodcock. *Field* 1943. (1951) *The Greenshank*, London, Collins. (1959) Notes on the breeding of Temminck's stint in Spey Valley *in* Bannerman, D. A. 9: 207–8. (1961a) Notes on the courtship displays of green sandpipers in Scotland. *ibid* 10: 66–7. (1961b) The breeding behaviour of the lapwing. *ibid* 10: 265–74. (1961c) The breeding behaviour and breeding biology of the oystercatcher. *ibid* 10: 310–18. (1963) On the behaviour of the stone curlew. *ibid* 11: 32–33. (1966) *The Snow Bunting*. Edinburgh and London, Oliver and Boyd. (1971) Highland Birds 3rd edition 1978. Inverness, HIDB and Collins. (1973) *The Dotterel*, London, Collins. (1975a) *Pine Crossbills*. Berkhamsted, Poyser. (1975b) Summer food and feeding habitats of the greenshank. *Br. Birds* 68: 243–5. (1976) Recent distribution, ecology and breeding of snow buntings in Scotland. *Scot. Birds* 9: 147–62.

Nethersole-Thompson, D. and Nethersole-Thompson, M. 1979. *Greenshanks*. Calton, Poyser.

Nethersole-Thompson, D. and Watson, A. 1974. *The Cairngorms*, London, Collins. (1981) *The Cairngorms* (second and enlarged edition). Perth, Melven Press. (in press) Bird Life in the Forest-zone at Glenmore in *The Glen More Forest Park*. N.E. Mountain Trust.

Nettleship, D. N. 1973. Breeding ecology of turnstones at Hazen Camp, Ellesmere Island, NWT. *Ibis* 115: 202–17. (1974) The breeding of the knot (*Calidris canutus*) at Hazen Camp, Ellesmere Island, NWT. *Polarforschung* 44: 8–26.

Nicholson, E. M. 1938–39. The Lapwing Inquiry. *Br. Birds* 32: 170–91; 207–29: 255–71.

Nilsson, S. G. and Nilsson, I. N. 1978. (On the cantering display of jack snipe). Vår Fågelvärld 37: 1–8.

Noll, H. 1924. *Sumpfvogelleben*. Vienna.

Noordwijk, A. J. van, Balen, J. H. van and Scharloo, W. 1980. Heritability of ecologically important traits in the great tit (*Parus major*). *Ardea* 68: 193–203. (1981) Genetic variation in the timing of reproduction in the great tit. *Oecologia* 49: 158–66.

Nordberg, S. 1950. (Contributions on the breeding biology of the turnstone). *Acta zool. fenn.* 63: 1–62.

Norlin, A. 1965. (On the food of redshank). in *Vogelwarte* 23: 97–101.

Norton, D. W. 1972. Incubation schedules of four species of *Calidrine* sandpipers at Barrow, Alaska. *Condor* 74: 164–76.

Norton-Griffiths, M. 1969. The organisation, control and development of parental feeding in the oystercatcher. *Behaviour* 34: 55–114.

Ogilvie, F. 1920. *Field Observations on British Birds*. London.

Oliver, P. J. 1977. Social behaviour of ringed plover. *Alauda* 45: 191–96. (1983) *in* Cramp and Simmons 1983.

Olney, P. J. 1967. Record breeding year of avocets. *Birds* 1: 138–39. (1970) Studies of avocet behaviour. *Br. Birds* 63: 206–09.

Onno, S. 1966. (Ornithological researches in Estonia). *in* Kumari, E. 10–20. (1968) *Bird Life in Matsalu Bay*. Talinn. *in* Kumari, E. (ed) 1967.

Oring, L. W. 1967. Egg-laying of a golden plover *Pluvialis apricaria. Ibis* 109: 434. (1968) Vocalizations of the green and solitary sandpipers. *Wilson Bull.* 80: 395–420.

Oring, L. W. and Knudson, M. L. 1972. Monogamy and polyandry in the spotted sandpiper. *Living Bird* 11: 59–73.

Owen, J. H. 1948. (Snipe raising level of the nest and nesting off the ground). *Br. Birds* 41: 352–53.

Parmelee, D. F. 1954. Possible moving of young by Wilson's snipe. *Jackpine Warbler* 32: 142. (1970) Breeding behaviour of the sanderling in the Canadian high arctic. *Living Bird* 9: 97–146.

Parmelee, D. F., Greiner, D. W. and Graul, W. D. 1968. Summer schedule and breeding biology of the white-rumped sandpipers in the Central Canadian Arctic. *Wilson Bull.* 80: 5–29.

Parmelee, D. F. and Macdonald, S. D. 1960. The Birds of west-central Ellesmere Island and adjacent areas. *Bull. Nat. Hist. Mus. Canada.* 169: 43–49.

Parmelee, D. F. and Payne, R. 1973. On multiple broods and the breeding strategy of arctic sanderlings. *Ibis* 115: 218–26.

Parmelee, D. F., Stephens, H. A. and Schmidt, R. H. 1967. The birds of south-eastern Victoria Island. . . . *Bull. Nat. Hist. Mus.* Canada, 222.

Parr, R. 1979. Sequential breeding by golden plovers. *Br. Birds* 72: 499–504. (1980) Population study of the golden plover *Pluvialis apricaria* using marked birds. *Orn. Scand.* 11: 179–89.

Parrinder, E. R. 1952. Little ringed plovers in Britain. *Bird Notes* 25: 49–56. (1964) Little ringed plovers in Britain during 1960–62. *Br. Birds* 57: 191–98.

Pay, C. M. 1937. *Die Waldschnepfe.* Munich, Mayer.

Pearson, H. J. 1904. *Three Summers among the Birds of Russian Lapland.* London.

Pedersen, E. T. 1959. (On the breeding density of wood sandpipers). *Dansk. Orn. foren Tiddskr.* 53: 53–83.

Penrose, F. G. 1912. Early nesting of the common snipe in Wiltshire. *Br. Birds* 5: 336.

Perry, R. 1945. *In the High Grampians.* London.

Pienkowski, M. W. 1983. Development of feeding and foraging behaviour in young ringed plovers *Charadrius hiaticula*, in Greenland and Britain. *Dansk. Orn. foren. Tiddskr.* 77: 133–147. (1984a) Breeding biology and population dynamics of ringed plovers *Charadrius hiaticula* in Britain and Greenland: nest-predation as a possible factor limiting distribution and timing of breeding. *J. Zool. London* 202: 83–114. (1984b) Behaviour of young ringed plovers. *Ibis* 126: 133–155.

Pienkowski, M. W. and Green, G. H. 1976. Breeding biology of sanderlings in north-east Greenland. *Br. Birds* 69: 165–77.

Pitelka, F. 1959. Numbers, breeding schedule and territoriality in pectoral sandpipers of northern Alaska. *Condor* 61: 233–64.

Pitelka, F., Holmes, R. T., and Maclean, S. F. 1974. Ecology and evolution of social organisation in arctic waders. *Amer. Zool.* 14: 185–204.

Phillips, D. R. 1983. (Contributions on the social pattern and behaviour of curlew). *in* Cramp and Simmons 1983.

Portielje, A. F. J. 1930. (Contribution on the displays of the ruff). *Proc. 7th Int. Conf.* Amsterdam 1930.

Präsent, I. 1977. (Observations on the dotterel in Austria). *in* Glutz 1975.

Prater, A. J. 1974. Breeding biology of the ringed plover. *Proc. IWRB Wader Symposium, Warsaw.* 1973: 15–22. (1974) Breeding biology of the ringed plover in Britain. *Bird Study* 23: 155–6.

Prater, A. J., Marchant, J. H. and Vuorinen, J. 1977. *Guide to the Identification and Ageing of Holaractic Waders.* B.T.O. Guide 17.

Prill, H. 1966. Über den kiebitzzug im mecklenburgischen binnenland. *Vogelschutz Vogelkde* 2: 65–72. (1968) Eine bestandsaufnahme des kiebitz. *Falke* 15: 200–02.

Pulchalski, W. 1938. (On the mating behaviour of two woodcocks). *in* Steinfatt, O. 1938.

Pulliainen, E. 1970. On the breeding biology of the dotterel *Charadrius morinellus*. *Orn. Fenn.* 47: 69–73. (1971) Breeding behaviour of the dotterel. *Rep. 24 Värriö Subarctic Research Station.*

Randall, T. E. 1960. (Polyandry in Wilson's phalarope). *in* Bannerman, D. A. vol 9. (1961) (The breeding biology of lesser yellowlegs and greater yellowlegs in Canada). *in* Bannerman, D. A. vol 10.

Raner, L. 1972. Polyandry in the red-necked phalarope (*Phalaropus lobatus*) and the dusky redshank (*Tringa erythropus*). *Fauna och Flora* 67: 135–38.

Ratcliffe, D. A. 1967a. Conservation and the collector: *in* 'The biotic effects of public pressures on the environment'. *Third Scientific Staff Symposium*, Monkswood Experimental Station 20–21 March. (1967b) Decrease in eggshell weight in certain birds of prey. *Nature*, London, 265: 208–10. (1970) Changes attributable to pesticides in egg-breakage frequency and eggshell thickness in some British birds. *J. appl. Ecol.* 67–115. (1976) Observations on the breeding of the golden plover in Great Britain. *Bird Study* 23: 63–116. (1977a) *Highland Flora.* Inverness, HIDB and Collins. (1977b) *A Nature Conservation Review* (vols 1 and 2). Cambridge, University Press. (1980) *The Peregrine Falcon.* Calton, Poyser.

Rayfield, P. A. 1944. (Fledging period of redshank). *Br. Birds* 37. (1961) (Fledging period of common sandpiper) *in* Bannerman, D. A. 10: 15.

Redfern, C. P. 1982. Lapwing nest-site and chick mortality in relation to habitat. *Bird Study* 29: 201–8. (1983) Aspects of the growth and development of lapwings *V. vanellus. Ibis* 125: 226.

Reynolds, J. 1948. (Large clutch of redshanks' eggs). *Br. Birds* 41: 191.

van Rhijn, J. G. 1973. Behavioural dimorphism in male ruffs. *Behav.* 47: 153–229.

Riddiford, N. 1975. Greenshank attacking fish. *Br. Birds* 68: 467.

Ridley, M. W. 1980. (On the breeding dispersion of grey phalaropes). *Ibis* 122: 210–26.

Rinkel, G. L. 1940. Waarnemingen over het gedrag van de kievit gedurende de broedtijd. *Ardea* 29: 108–47.

Rittinghaus, H. 1950. Über das verhalten eines vom sandregenpfeifer ausgebruteten und geführten seeregenpfeifers. *Vogelwarte* 15: 187–92. (1953) Adoptionsversuche mit sund-und seeregenpfeifern. *J. Orn.* 94: 144–59. (1956) Unterschungen am seeregenpfeifer auf der Insel Oldeoog. *J. Orn.* 97: 117–55. (1961) *Der Seeregenpfeifer.* Lutherstadt, Ziemsen. (1962) Untersuchungen zur biologie des Mornellregenpfeifers *Eudromias morinellus* in Schwedisch Lappland. *Z. Tierpsychologie* 19: 39–58. (1969) Ein beitrag zur ökologie und zum verhalten des goldregenfeifers zu beginn der brutzeit. *Vogelwarte* 25: 57–65. (1975) (On the breeding biology of ringed plovers) *in* Glutz 1975.

Roberts, E. L. 1947. (Predators of redshank). *Br. Birds* 40: 284.

Robertson, A. W. P. 1954. *Bird Pageant....* London, Batchworth.

Robien, P. 1929. (On the breeding density of redshanks). *Beitr. FortPflBiol. Vögel* 5: 24–6.

Rope, G. T. 1903. (Redshank carrying young). *Zool* 7: 275.

Roselaar, C. R. 1983. (Contributions on waders). in Cramp and Simmons 1983.

Rosenberg, E. 1930. Über die beteiligung der geschlechter des brachvogels an der aufzucht der jungen. *Beitr. FortPflBiol. Vögel* 6: 193–195.

Rosenberg, N. T. *et al* 1970. (On the breeding biology of the turnstone). *Medd. om. Gron.* 191: 1–87.

Rosenius, P. 1933. Eine begegnung mit der rostroten ufersschnepfe. *Beitr. FortPflBiol. Vögel* 9: 45–48.

Rowan, M. 1929. Notes on Alberta waders included on the British List. *Br. Birds* 23: 2–17. (1930) Notes on Alberta waders included on the British list, part 8. The nesting of the greater yellowshank. *Br. Birds* 24: 90–93. (1943) Yellowlegs. *Fauna* 5: 50–2.

Rubinshtein, N. A. 1970. (On the breeding biology of ringed plovers). *Trudy Kandalak. gos. zapoved* 8.

Rydzewski, W. 1974. (On the maximum age of golden plover and lapwing). *Ring* 80: 169–70.

Ryves, B. H. 1948. *Bird Life in Cornwall.* London, Collins.

Safriel, U. 1967. Population and food study of the oystercatcher. Unpublished D. Phil. thesis, Univ. of Oxford.

Salomonsen, F. 1935. *Zoology of the Faroes. Aves,* Copenhagen. (1950) *Gronlands Fugle.* Copenhagen.

Sammalisto, M. 1955. (On the breeding density in wood sandpipers). *Orn. Fenn.* 32.

Sauer, E. G. F. 1962. Ethology and ecology of the golden plovers on St Lawrence Island, Bering Sea. *Psychol. Forschung* 26: 399–470.

Sexby, H. L. 1874. *The Birds of Shetland....* Edinburgh.

Schamel, D. and Tracey, D. 1977. Polyandry, replacement clutches, and site-tenacity in the red-necked phalarope at Barrow, Alaska. *Bird Banding* 48: 314–24.

Schenk, J. 1930. (On the maximum ages of black-tailed godwits). *Aquila* 36–37 and *Orn. Mber* 38: 51.

Schiemann, H. 1972. (Distribution of red-necked phalaropes in Iceland). *Vogelwarte* 26: 329–36.

Schmidt, G. A. J. 1965. Beobachtungen über den wegzug des odinswassertreters.... *Beitr. Vogelkde* 21: 233–44.

Schnakenwinkel, G. 1970. Studien an der population des austernfischers auf Mellum. *Vogelwarte* 25: 336–55.

Schönwetter, M. 1960–66. *Handbuch der Oologie.* Berlin, Akademie Verlag.

Schubert, W. 1975. (On the breeding dispersion of lapwings). *in* Glutz 1975.

Scott, R. 1974. Two females stone curlews laying in one nest. *Br. Birds* 67: 165–66.

Seebohm, H. 1901. *Birds of Siberia*. London.

Sellar, P. J. 1983. (Voice of the redshank). *in* Cramp and Simmons 1983.

Selous, E. 1901. *Bird Watching*. London, Dent. 1906–07. Observations tending to throw light on the question of sexual selection in birds, including a day to day diary on the breeding habits of the ruff. *Zoologist* for 1906: 201–19, 285–94, 419–28; *ibid* for 1907: 60–5, 161–82, 367–81.

Sharrock, J. T. R. (ed) 1976. *The Atlas of Breeding Birds of Britain and Ireland*. Berkhamsted, Poyser.

Sheldon, W. G. 1971. *The Book of the American Woodcock*. Amherst, Univ. of Massachussets Press.

Shorten, M. 1974. The European Woodcock. . . . *Game Conservancy Rep*. 21: 1–93.

Sielmann, H. 1943. *Vögel Über Haff und Wiesen*. Konigsberg.

Simmons, K. E. L. 1951. Distraction displays in the Kentish plover. *Br. Birds* 44: 181–87. (1953) Some studies on the little ringed plover. *Avic. Mag*. 59: 191–207. (1955) The significance of voice in the behaviour of the little ringed and Kentish plovers. *Br. Birds* 48: 106–14. (1956) Territory in the little ringed plover. *Ibis*. 98: 390–97.

Simson, G. 1966. *A Bird Overhead*. London, Witherby.

Skeel, M. A. 1976. (On the breeding of Hudsonian curlew). M.Sc. thesis, Toronto University.

Sluiters, J. E. 1948. Notes on the breeding of the little ringed plover. *Limosa* 21: 83–5. (1954) Observations on the Kentish, ringed and little ringed plovers. *Limosa* 27: 71–86.

Smith, D. W. 1981. The status and distribution of waders breeding on wet lowland grasslands in England and Wales. *Bird Study* 20: 179–92.

Soikkeli, M. 1967. Breeding cycle and population dynamics in the dunlin (*Calidris alpina*). *Ann. Zool. Fenn*. 4: 158–98. (1970a) Mortality and reproductive rates in a Finnish population of dunlin *Calidris alpina*. *Orn. Fenn*. 49: 149–58. (1970b) Dispersion of dunlin *C. alpina* in relation to sites and breeding. *Orn. Fenn*. 47: 1–9. (1973) Population dynamics of dunlin in Finland. *IWRB Symposium, Warsaw* 1973: 61–62.

Sollie, J. F. 1961. Twee Broedgevallen van de Morinelplevier (*Charadrius morinellus*) in de Noordoostpolder. *Limosa* 34: 274–6.

Southern, H. N. and Lewis, W. A. S. 1938. The breeding behaviour of Temminck's stints. *Br. Birds* 31: 314–21.

Spangenberg, E. P. and Leonovich, V. V. 1962. (On the weight of oystercatchers' eggs). *Trudy. Kandalak gos. zapoved* 2.

Spencer, K. G. 1953. *The Lapwing in Britain*. London, Brown.

Spencer, R. 1961 and 1969. (Age of ringed birds). *Br. Birds* 49 and 62.

Spillner, W. 1971. Brutverhalten des grossen brachvogels. *Falke* 18: 122–29.

Stadie, R. 1933. (On the food of common snipe). *Ber. Ver. schles. Orn*. 18: 25–35.

Stanford, J. K. 1927. (Courtship displays of waders). *Br. Birds* 21: 75–80.

Staton, J. 1945. The breeding of black-winged stilts in Nottinghamshire in 1945. *Br. Birds* 38: 822–28.

Stein, F. 1958. Beitrag zur biologie des flussenregenpfeifers. *Beitr. Vogelkde* 5: 247–68. (1958–9) Zur biologie des flussregenpfeifers. *Beitr. Vogelkde* 6: 311–39.

Stein, G. 1926. Zur Brut biologie des flussuferläufers *Tringa hypoleucos*. *Orn. Mber*. 34: 163–9. (1928) Beitrag zur Brut biologie von *Tringa hypoleucos*. Orn. Mber 36: 129–35.

Steinfatt, O. 1938. Das brutleben der Waldschnepfe. *J. Orn*. 86: 379–424. (1940) (Observations on green sandpipers). in *Schr. phys.-ökon. Ges Königsberg* 71.

Steiniger, F. 1959. *Die Grossen Regenpfeifer*. Wittenberg, Lutherstadt.

Stemmler-Morath, C. 1951. Beobachtungen bei der aufzucht junger triele. *Zool Garten* 18: 47–53.

Stepanjan, L. S. 1957. Der flussuferläufer. *Falke* 4: 20–23.

Stiefel, A. and Scheufler, H. 1984. *Der Rotschenkel* Die Neue Brehm-Bucherei A. Ziemsen Verlag, Wittenberg Lutherstadt.

Sulkava, S. 1968. A study of the food of the peregrine in Finland. *Aquila* 6: 18–31.

Sutton, G. M. and Parmelee, D. F. 1955. The purple sandpiper in southern Baffin Island. *Condor* 57: 216–20.

Swennen, C. 1971. Het Voedsel van de groenpootruiter. *Limosa* 44: 71–83.

Tayles, K. V. 1981. (On the breeding of the curlew). *Magpie* 2.

Taylor, D. W. 1976. Greenshank eating large frog. *Br. Birds* 69: 409.

Teixeira, R. M. (ed) 1979. *Atlas van de Nederlands Broedvogels*. Deventer.

358   *Bibliography*

Tester, J. R. and Watson, A. 1973. Spacing and territoriality of woodcock *S. rusticola.... Ibis* 115: 135–8.

Thiede, W. 1960. Über den balzflug des rotschenkels. *J. Orn.* 101: 355–59.

Thiede, E. W. and Bruns, H. 1966. Die Verbreitung des rotschenkels in Niedersachsen. *Biol. Abh.* 31.

Thielcke, G. 1951. (On polygyny in Kentish plovers). *Vogelwelt* 72: 185–8.

Thom, V. 1986. *Birds in Scotland.* Calton, Poyser.

Thomas, J. F. 1939. Incubation periods and fledging periods of lapwing. *Br. Birds* 33: 85. (1942) Report on the Redshank Inquiry 1939–40. *Br. Birds* 36: 2–14, 22–34.

Thomson, A. L. (ed) (1964) *A New Dictionary of Birds.* London and New York, Nelson.

Thompson, D. B. A. 1984. Foraging economics in flocks of lapwings, golden plovers and gulls. Ph.D. thesis, Univ. of Nottingham.

Thompson, D. B. A. and Barnard, C. J. 1983. Anti-predator responses in mixed species flocks of lapwings, golden plovers, and gulls. *Anim. Behav.* 31: 585–593. (1984) Prey selection by plovers: optimal foraging in mixed-species groups. *Anim. Behav.* 32: 554–563. (1986) *Gulls and plovers.* London, Croom Helm.

Thompson, D. B. A. and Lendrem, D. W. 1985. Gulls and plovers: host vigilance, kleptoparasite success and a model of kleptoparasite detection. *Anim. Behav.* 33: (in press).

Thompson, D. B. A. and Thompson, M. L. P. 1985. Early warning and mixed species associations: the 'plover's page' revisted. *Ibis* 127: 559—62.

Thompsom, D. B. A., Thompson, P. S. and Nethersole-Thompson, D. 1986. Timing of breeding and breeding performance in a population of greenshanks. *J. Anim. Ecol.* 55: 181–99.

Thompson, P. S. 1983. Dotterel numbers and breeding in the Central Grampians. *Scot. Birds* 12: 190–191.

Ticehurst, N. F. 1909. *A History of the Birds of Kent.* London, Witherby.

Timmermann, G. 1938–49. *Die Vögel Islands.* Reykjavik.

Tinbergen, N. 1935. Field observations of east-Greenland birds. 1. The behaviour of the red-necked phalarope (*P. lobatus*) in spring. *Ardea* 24: 1–42. (1953) *The Herring Gull's World.* London, Collins. (1959) The behaviour of the red-necked phalarope on its breeding grounds. *in* Bannerman, D. A. vol 9.

Tinbergen, N. And Norton-Griffiths, M. 1964. Oystercatchers and mussels. *Br. Birds* 57: 64–70.

Tomialojć, L. 1976. *Birds of Poland.* Warsaw.

Townshend, D. 1980. (Contributions on food of curlew). Ph.D. thesis, Durham University.

Tremaine, M. M. 1974. (On hatching behaviour of whimbrel). *Wilson Bull.* 86: 77–8.

Tuck, L. M. 1972. *The Snipes.* Canadian Wildlife Service Monograph 5, Ottawa.

Tucker, B. W. 1940. Sections on 'display and posturing', 'habitat' and 'voice' *in* H. F. Witherby *et al* (1938–41).

Tully, H. 1948. (Share of cock lapwing in incubation). *Br. Birds* 41: 355–6.

Turner, E. L. 1920. (The ruff in *Broadland Birds*). London, *Country Life.*

Ulfstrand, S. and Högstedt, G. 1976. Hur många fåglar hachar, Sverige. *Anser* 15: 1–32.

Uspenski, S. M. 1956. *Pitch'i Bazary Novoy Zemli.* Moscow.

Uttendorfer, G. 1952. (Redshank as prey of raptors). *in* Glutz 1968.

Väisänen, R. 1977. (On the laying season of common snipe). *An. Zool. Fenn.* 14: 1–25.

Väisänen, R. *et al* 1972. Egg dimension variations in 5 wader species: the role of heredity. *Orn. Fenn.* 49: 25–44.

Varga, F. 1976. (On female woodcock helping chicks to find food). *Aquila* 83: 300–01.

Välikangas and Nordström, H. 1955. (On maximum age of turnstone). *Mem. Soc. Fauna Flora Fenn.* 31.

Vaughan, R. 1980. *Plovers.* Dalton, Lavenham, Suffolk.

Venables, L. S. V. and Venables, U. M. 1955. *Birds and Mammals in Shetland.* Edinburgh, Oliver & Boyd.

Veromann, H. 1980. (Breeding distribution of wood sandpipers). *in* Flint, V. E. 1980: 88–91.

Vogel, P. and C. H. 1972. Zur ökologie und verbreitung des triels im Elsass. *Orn. Beob.* 69: 153–68.

Voous, K. H. 1960. *Atlas of European Birds.* London, Nelson.

Vorontsov, E. M. and Khokhlova, N. 1963. (On the bird fauna of the Gorky Reservoir). *Trans. Ornith. 6, Moscow University.*

Vuolanto, S. 1968. (On the breeding biology of the turnstone at Norrskär, Gulf of Bothnia). *Orn. Fenn.* 45: 19–24 (in Finnish with English summary).

Wadewitz, O. 1952. Ein beitrag zur biologie des flussurerläufers. *Beitr. Vogelkde* 3: 1–20. (1955) Zur Brutbiologie des triels. *Beitr. Vogelkde* 4: 86–107. (1957) Weitere beobachtungsergebnisse am flussuferläufer. *Beitr. Volgelkde* 6: 2–10.
Walpole-Bond, J. A. 1914. *Field Studies of Some Rarer British Birds.* London. (1923) Concerning the greenshank. *Br. Birds* 16: 208–13. (1938) *A History of Sussex Birds* (3 vols). London, Witherby.
Walters, J. 1954. Der brutanteil der Geschlechter beim seeregenpfeifer. *Limosa* 27: 19–24. (1957) Über dem balzruf des flussregenpfeifers. *Ardea* 45: 62–72. (1962) Balzflug und ruf des seeregenpfeifers. *Vogelwelt* 83: 139–42. (1983) (Breeding biology and behaviour of ringed plover). *in* Cramp and Simmons 1983.
Warburg, G. 1952. (Distraction behaviour of redshank). *Br. Birds* 45: 37–38.
Warwick, T. and van Someren, V. D. 1936. The roding of the woodcock. *Scot. Nat.* 217: 165–72.
Waters, R. J. 1974. (On the food of common sandpipers). *Br. Birds* 67: 440.
Watson, A. (ed) 1970. Animal Populations in Relation to their Food Resources. *Br. Ecol. Soc. Symp.* 10: Oxford and Edinburgh, Blackwell. (1974) (Breeding density of golden plover) *in* Nethersole-Thompson and Watson 1974.
Watson, D. 1977. *The Hen Harrier.* Berkhamsted, Poyser.
Weaver, Peter, 1981. *The Birdwatcher's Dictionary.* Calton, Poyser.
Westwood, N. J. 1983. Breeding stone curlews at Weeting Heath, Norfolk. *Br. Birds* 76: 291–304.
Wheelwright, H. W. 1864. *An Old Bushman.* London. (1865) *Ten Years in Sweden.* London.
Wickens, J. C. 1948. (Share of cock lapwing in incubation). *Br. Birds* 41: 28–29.
Wiley, R. H. and Richards, D. G. 1982. Adaptations for acoustic communication in birds: sound transmission and signal detection. *in Acoustic Communication in Birds*, vol. I, pp 131–181. New York, Academic Press. D. E. Kroodsma and E. H. Miller (eds.).
Williamson, K. 1938. Suspected polygamy in the redshank. *Br. Birds* 32: 120–1. (1943) The behaviour pattern of the western oystercatcher in defence of nests and young. *Ibis* 85: 486–70. (1945) The relation between the duration of hatching and the incubation period. *Ibis* 87: 280–2. (1946) Field notes on the breeding biology of the whimbrel. *North-W. Nat.* 21: 167–84. (1947) The distraction display of the ringed plover. *Ibis* 89: 511–13. (1948) Field notes on the identification and distraction display in the golden plover. *Ibis* 90: 90–98. (1949) Nesting of the Faroe snipe. *Br. Birds* 42: 394–95. (1950) The distraction behaviour of the Faroe snipe. *Ibis* 92: 65–74. (1950a) Distraction behaviour of the oystercatcher. *Scot. Nat.* 62: 61–3. (1952) Regional variations in the distraction displays of the oystercatcher. *Ibis* 94: 85–96. (1960) Snipe at St Kilda. *Bird Notes* 29: 5–8. (1968) Bird communities in the Malham Tarn region of the Pennines. *Field Studies* 2: 651–68. (1970) *The Atlantic Islands.* London.
Wilson, G. W. 1976. Spotted sandpiper nesting in Scotland. *Br. Birds* 68: 288–92.
Wilson, H. J. 1983. (On unusual behaviour of roding woodcock). *in* Cramp and Simmons 1983.
Wilson, J. 1967. (On pair bonds in lapwings). *Br. Birds* 60: 217.
Wink, M. 1973. (Contribution on breeding density of whimbrel). *Vogelwelt* 94: 41–50.
Witherby, H. F., Jourdain, F. C. R., Ticehurst, N. F. and Tucker, B. W. 1940. *The Handbook of British Birds.* vol 4.
Wolley, J. 1905. *Ootheca Wolleyana.* London, Porter.
Workman, W. H. 1954. (On hen woodcock feeding chicks). *Irish Nat. Jour.* 11: 232.
Wynne-Edwards, V. C. 1957. The so-called northern golden plover. *Scot. Nat.* 69: 89–93. (1962) *Animal Dispersion in Relation to Social Behaviour.* Edinburgh and London, Oliver and Boyd.

Yalden, D. W. 1974. The status of golden plover (*Pluvialis apricaria*) and dunlin (*Calidris alpina*) in the Peak District. *The Naturalist* 81–91.
Yanushevitch, A. L. *et al* 1959. (Weight of newly-hatched common snipe). *Birds of Kirghizia* 1.
Yeates, G. K. 1947. *Bird Haunts in Northern Britain.* London, Faber and Faber.
Yeatman, L. J. 1976. *Atlas des Oiseaux nicheurs de France.* Paris.

von Zedlitz, O. 1925. Die Waldschnepfe.... *Beitr. FortPflBiol. Vögel* 1: 65–67. (1927) Contributions à l'étude biologique de la bécasse. *Rev. franc Orn.* 11: 74–81.
Zimmermann, H. 1951. Zur brutbiologie des seeregenpfeifers. *Orn. Mitt.* 3: 270–73.

Tables 1–5

TABLE 1: *Maximum recorded ages of waders*

---

	age	authority
Oystercatcher *Haematopus ostralegus*	36 years	F. Goethe (1966)
Black-winged stilt *Himantopus himantopus*	10 years 22 days (in captivity)	H. Wackernagel (1964)
Avocet *Recurvirostra avosetta*	24 years 6 months	W. Rydzewski (1978)
Stone curlew *Burhinus oedicnemus*	15 years 9 months (in wild) 15 years 11 months (in captivity)	*in* Glutz (1977)
Little ringed plover *Charadrius dubius*	11 years	J. Walters *in* Glutz (1975)
Ringed plover *Charadrius hiaticula*	> 10 years	G. Grosskopf (1968)
Kentish plover *C. alexandrinus*	13 years	H. Rittinghaus *in* Glutz (1975)
Dotterel *Eudromias morinellus*	5 years	D. Nethersole-Thompson (1973)
Golden plover *Pluvialis apricaria*	12 years 2 months	W. Rydzewski (1974)
Lapwing *Vanellus vanellus*	18 years 11 months	W. Rydzewski (1974)
Knot *Calidris canutus*	17 years	W. Rydzewski (1973)
Sanderling *Calidris alba*	11 years	R. Spencer (1972)
Little stint *Calidris minuta*	> 6–7 years	R. Spencer (1968)

	age	authority
Temminck's stint *Calidris temminckii*	11 years	O. Hildén (1978)
Purple sandpiper *Calidris maritima*	insufficient data	
Dunlin *Calidris alpina*	14.5 years	H. Holgersen (1953)
Broad-billed sandpiper *Limicola falcinellus*	no data	
Ruff *Philomachus pugnax*	8–9 years	*in* Glutz (1975)
Jack snipe *Lymnocryptes minimus*	5 years 3 months	*Ringing & Migration* for 1979
Snipe *Gallinago gallinago*	> 12 years	F. Goethe *in* Glutz (1975)
Great snipe *Gallinago media*	no data	
Woodcock *Scolopax rusticola*	12.5 years	W. B. Alexander (1945–47)
Black-tailed godwit *Limosa limosa*	17 years	J. Schenk (1930)
Bar-tailed godwit *Limosa lapponica*	17 years 11 months	W. Rydzewski (1974)
Whimbrel *Numenius phaeopus*	> 16 years in captivity	H. Wackernagel (1964)
Curlew *Numenius arquata*	oldest ringed bird, 31 years 6 months	*in* Glutz (1977)
Dusky redshank *Tringa erythropus*	6 years 1 month	*in* Glutz (1977)
	> 10 years	J. Little & E. Meek (*in litt*)
Redshank *Tringa totanus*	over 16 years	N. O. Preuss *in* Glutz (1977)
Greenshank *Tringa nebularia*	at least 13 years	D. Nethersole-Thompson (1951)
Green sandpiper *Tringa ochropus*	9 years 8 months	*in* Glutz (1977)
Wood sandpiper *Tringa glareola*	9 years 2 months	H. Johansen & O. H. Jørgensen *in* Glutz (1977)
Common sandpiper *Actitis hypoleucos*	> 9 years 3 months	K. Greve (1970)
Spotted sandpiper *Tringa macularia*	> 5 years 6 months	A. L. Spaans *in* Glutz (1977)
Turnstone *Arenaria interpres*	19 years 8 months	Välikangas & Nordström (1955)
Red-necked phalaropes *Phalaropus lobatus*	> 5 years	F. Gudmundsson *in* Glutz (1977)
Grey phalarope *Phalaropus fulicarius*	no data	

TABLE 2:   *Clutch weight as a percentage of female body weight*

	female body weight (g)	clutch	weight of clutch (g)	% of body weight	authority
Oystercatcher *Haematopus ostralegus*	616	3	140	23	A. J. Mercer (1968)
Black-winged stilt *Himantopus himantopus*	180	4	88	49	M. Schönwetter (1963)
Avocet *Recurvirostra avosetta*	325	4	129	40	Glutz (1977)
Stone curlew *Burhinus oedicnemus*	449	2	84	19	R. Morgan *in* Cramp & Simmons 1983
Little ringed plover *Charadrius dubius*	39	4	31	79	Glutz (1975)
Ringed plover *Charadrius hiaticula*	65	4	46	70	Glutz (1975)
Kentish plover *C. alexandrinus*	60	3	27	45	J. Walters *in* Glutz (1975)
Dotterel *Eudromias morinellus*	116	3	48	41	B., P. & R. Thompson
Golden plover *Pluvialis apricaria*	191	4	139	73	D. A. Ratcliffe (1973)
Lapwing *Vanellus vanellus*	217	4	100	46	D. A. Ratcliffe (1977)
Knot *Calidris canutus*	148	4	77	52	Glutz (1975)
Sanderling *Calidris alba*	55	4	44	80	M. Schönwetter (1967)
Little stint *Calidris minuta*	31	4	25	81	M. Schönwetter (1967)
Temminck's stint *Calidris temminckii*	28	4	24	86	Cramp & Simmons (1983)
Purple sandpiper *Calidris maritima*	80	4	53	66	Glutz (1975)
Dunlin *Calidris alpina*	55	4	40	75	Glutz (1975)
Broad-billed sandpiper *Limicola falcinellus*	39	4	36	91	V. E. Flint (1973)
Ruff *Philomachus pugnax*	118	4	88	75	Glutz (1975)
Jack snipe *Lymnocryptes minimus*	68	4	56	82	Glutz (1977)
Snipe *Gallinago gallinago*	112	4	68	61	L. Tuck (1972)
Great snipe *Gallinago media*	?	4	82	?	Glutz (1977)
Woodcock *Scolopax rusticola*	320	4	*c*100	31	Glutz (1977)
Black-tailed godwit *Limosa limosa*	315	4	162	51	Cramp & Simmons (1983)
Bar-tailed godwit *Limosa lapponica*	273	4	148	54	M. Schönwetter (1967)

	female body weight (g)	clutch	weight of clutch (g)	% of body weight	authority
Whimbrel *Numenius phaeopus*	398	4	200	50	Glutz (1977)
Curlew *Numenius arquata*	787	4	300	38	Glutz (1977)
Dusky redshank *Tringa erythropus*	157	4	98	62	Glutz (1977)
Redshank *Tringa totanus*	135	4	89	66	G. Grosskopf (1963)
Greenshank *Tringa nebularia*	200	4	145	73	Nethersole-Thompson family
Green sandpiper *Tringa ochropus*	85	4	62	73	M. Schönwetter (1957)
Wood sandpiper *Tringa glareola*	60	4	52–60	87–100	H. Kirchner (1963)
Common sandpiper *Actitis hypoleucos*	50	4	48	96	Nethersole-Thompson family
Spotted sandpiper *Actitis macularia*	51	4	35	69	L. Oring *in* Hildén (1975)
Turnstone *Arenaria interpres*	115	4	72	63	M. Schönwetter (1963)
Red-necked phalarope *Phalaropus lobatus*	35	4	25	70	M. Schönwetter (1967)
Grey phalarope *Phalaropus fulicarius*	61	4	31	51	L. Gillandt (1972)

Notes and Comments

Among waders laying light clutches in relation to the hen's body weight are oystercatcher (23%) and stone curlew (19%). Both species feed their chicks during long fledging periods.

Dotterel (41%) and Kentish plover (45%) lay light clutches of 3 eggs. Both are sometimes polyandrous and possibly have been forced through competition to live in harsh environments.

Compared to golden plover (73%), hen lapwings (46%) lay light eggs. Does this partly explain why lapwings are often able to produce up to four replacement clutches in the same season?

Hen woodcock (31%) lay light clutches but are entirely responsible for incubation and chick rearing. The light eggs and the short fledging period of the chicks tie in with this unusual pattern.

In at least some breeding groups of Temminck's stints each hen lays two clutches, one of which she incubates and hatches and then rears the chicks. Each clutch weighs 86% of her body weight. Little stints (81%) are likely to possess a similar system (Hildén).

Some hen spotted sandpipers produce three and exceptionally four, clutches for different cocks, each clutch weighing 69% of her body weight. Contrast this with the normally monogamous hen common sandpiper whose clutch weighs about 96% of body weight.

Hen grey phalaropes, which are possibly more prone to polyandry than other phalaropes, lay clutches weighing about 51% of body weight. The less frequently polyandrous red-necked phalarope lays a heavier clutch – 70% of body weight.

Hen dusky redshanks, which lay clutches weighing 62% of their body weight, take no part in incubation or in chick rearing. Their clutches are slightly lighter than those of the other *Tringa* species – redshank (66%), greenshank and green sandpiper (73%), and wood sandpiper (87–100%). Is this because the dusky redshank is struggling, breeding in a limited and exacting environment?

The high arctic knot, with clutches weighing about 52% of the hen's body weight, lays lighter eggs than the sanderling which in some parts of the arctic produces two heavier clutches (each 80% of body weight), one of which she incubates and the other leaves with the cock.

Hen curlews (38%) lay light eggs in relation to their body weight and their eggshells are thin and easily cracked. Is this because they have difficulty in finding enough calcium during the laying period?

TABLE 3:   *Weights of freshly-laid eggs*

	Location	Sample	Range (gm)	Mean (gm)	Authority
Oystercatcher	Germany	93	38.1–53.1	46.6	R. Dircksen (1932)
Haematopus ostralegus	White Sea, USSR	41	41.0–49.6	43.4	E. P. Spangenberg & V. V. Leonovich (1960)
Black-winged stilt *Himantopus himantopus*			calculated weight	21.8	M. Schönwetter (1963)
Avocet *Recurvirostra avosetta*	Netherlands	67	27.7–39.5	32.3	J. Waters *in* Glutz (1977)
Stone curlew *Burhinus oedicnemus*	S. England	29	36.7–48.2	42	R. A. Morgan *in* Cramp & Simmons (1983)
	Czechoslovakia (in captivity)	7	34.7–44.6	38.85	Glutz (1977)
		9	34.0–39.0	36.2	P. Mödlinger *in* Glutz (1977)
Little ringed plover *Charadrius dubius*	Europe	1,048		7.7	Glutz (1975)
Ringed plover *Charadrius hiaticula*	Netherlands	104	9.8–13.6	11.5	Glutz (1975)
Kentish plover *C. alexandrinus*	Europe	221	8.0–11.0	9.0	Glutz (1975)
Dotterel *Eudromias morinellus*	N. Scotland	16		16.2	P. S. Thompson MS
	Austria	45	13.0–18.0	15.0	E. Hable *in* Glutz (1975)
	Altai Mts, USSR	3	15.9–16.3	16.0	*in* Glutz (1975)
	Kanin Peninsula	2	18.2–20.6	19.4	*in* Glutz (1975)
Golden plover *Pluvialis apricaria*	Britain	102		35.0	D. A. Ratcliffe (1976)
	N. Scotland	36		31.0	Nethersole-Thompson family
	N. Russia	28		31.4	N. A. Rubinshtein (1970)
Lapwing *Vanellus vanellus*	E. Anglia, England (pasture)	54		26.26	R. Murton & M. J. Westwood (1974)
	(arable)	65		27.55	,,
	(breckland)	66		25.42	,,
	N.E. Scotland		20.0–31.0	26.4	M. Cook (1976)
	Belgium	56	22.48–28.03	25–27	R. Verheyen (1967)
	Holland	90	22.2–30.2	26.0	J. Walters MS
	Switzerland	158	21.0–30.0	24.7	J. Heim MS
Knot *Calidris canutus*			calculated weight	19.0	Glutz (1975)
Sanderling *Calidris alba*			,,	11.2	M. Schönwetter (1963)
Little stint *Calidris minuta*			,,	6.3	M. Schönwetter (1963)
Temminck's stint *Calidris temminckii*	USSR	36	5.4–6.5	6.0	V. Kokhanov (1973)
Purple sandpiper *Calidris maritima*			calculated weight	13.3	M. Schönwetter (1963)

	Location	Sample	Range (gm)	Mean (gm)	Authority
Dunlin *Calidris alpina*	Germany	16	9.0–11.0	10.6	R. Heldt (1966)
	N.W. Scotland	34	9.5–11.0	10.1	Nethersole-Thompson family
Broad-billed sandpiper *Limicola falcinellus*	USSR		8.4–9.7		V. E. Flint (1973)
Ruff *Philomachus pugnax*	Germany	17	21.07–23.69	21.98	Glutz (1975)
Jack snipe *Lymnocryptes minimus*			calculated weight	14.0	M. Schönwetter (1963)
Snipe *Gallinago gallinago*		16		17.2	G. Niethammer (1942)
			calculated weight	16.5	M. Schönwetter (1963)
Great snipe *Gallinago media*			,,	23.2	M. Schönwetter (1963)
Woodcock *Scolopax rusticola*	Sweden	?	23.0–26.0	?	V. Marcström (1975)
Black-tailed godwit *Limosa limosa*	USSR	10	39.15–45.25	41.86	O. B. Kistyakivski (1957)
	Germany	?	32.25–47.47	40.55	*in* G. Niethammer (1942)
Bar-tailed godwit *Limosa lapponica*			calculated weight	37.0	M. Schönwetter (1963)
Whimbrel *Numenius phaeopus*	Iceland		46.0–57.0		B. Hantzsch (1905)
	USSR	?	43.7–58.0	?	E. Kozlova (1961)
Curlew *Numenius arquata*	Germany	25	65.0–85.0	76.9	G. Niethammer (1942)
	E. Sutherland, Scotland	4	76.0–82.0	79.7	R. K. Thompson
	Belgium	20	62.74–83.05	75.0	R. Verheyen (1967)
Dusky redshank *Tringa erythropus*			calculated weight	25	M. Schönwetter (1963)
Redshank *Tringa totanus*	Germany	80	19.0–26.0	22.3	G. Grosskopf (1958)
Greenshank *Tringa nebularia*	Sutherland, Scotland	210	25.0–37.0	30.7	Nethersole-Thompson family
Green sandpiper *Tringa ochropus*			calculated weight	15.5	M. Schönwetter (1967)
Wood sandpiper *Tringa glareola*	Germany	10	11.0–15.5 calculated weight	14.07 13.5	H. Kirchner (1956) M. Schönwetter (1963)
Common sandpiper *Actitis hypoleucos*	N. Scotland	34	10.0–15.0	12.0	Nethersole-Thompson family
	Peak District, England	16		11.8	P. K. Holland *et al* (1982)
Spotted sandpiper *Actitis macularia*			calculated weight	9.0	M. Schönwetter (1963)
Turnstone *Arenaria interpres*			,,	18.0	M. Schönwetter (1967)
Red-necked phalarope *Phalaropus lobatus*			,,	6.0	M. Schönwetter (1967)
Grey phalarope *Phalaropus fulicarius*	Iceland	30	8.2–9.4	8.83	L. Gillandt (1972)

TABLE 4:   *Clutch size*

	Location	Sample	of 1	of 2	of 3	of 4	of 5	of 6	Mean	Authority
Oystercatcher *Haematopus ostralegus*	Skokholm, Wales (1939–65)	630	23	149	411	47	0	0	2.8	M. P. Harris (1967)
	Aberdeen-shire, Scotland (inland)	143	4	33	94	11	0	0	2.7	P. Heppleston (1972)
	Aberdeen-shire, Scotland (coast)	52	4	17	29	2	0	0	2.5	,,
	Dorback and Abernthy, Scotland	79	2	13	55	9	0	0	2.9	D. Nethersole-Thompson
	Argyll, Scotland (1921–29)	65	4	28	30	3	0	0	2.5	B. Campbell (1947)
	Norderoog, Germany	100	0	20	57	23	0	0	3.0	R. Dircksen (1932)
Black-winged stilt *Himantopus himantopus*	Belgium and Netherlands	23	0	0	3	19	1	0	3.9	L. Lippens *et al* (1966)
	Spain	47	5	3	3	35	1	0	3.8	A. P. Studer-Thiersch (1968)
Avocet *Recurvirostra avosetta*	Estonia, SSR	31	0	0	3	28	0	0	3.9	J. Kallas (1974)
Stone curlew *Burhinus oedicnemus*	Breckland, East Anglia	148	6	142	0	0	0	0	1.9	D. Nethersole-Thompson (37) D. Glue & R. Morgan (36) N. J. Westwood (38).
	Salisbury Plain, Wilts–Hants	10	0	10	0	0	0	0	2.0	A. Whitaker & others E. P. Chance MS
	Berkshire	14	0	14	0	0	0	0	2.0	,,
	Sussex	13	0	11	2	0	0	0	2.1	Various
	Kent	18	1	16	1	0	0	0	2.0	Various
	All England	203	7	193	3	0	0	0	1.98	

Species	Location									Source
Little ringed plover *Charadrius dubius*	N. Holland	1006						0	3.87	J. Walters *in* Glutz (1975)
Ringed plover *Charadrius hiaticula*	Britain	48	0	0	10	38	0	0	3.77	A. Whitaker MS
	Britain	301	0	9	108	181	3	0	3.79	A. Prater (1974)
	Lindisfarne, England	87	0	1	13	72	1	0	3.84	M. Pienkowski (1984)
Kentish Plover *C. alexandrinus*	Camargue, S. France	254	0	13	241	0	0	0	2.96	C. M. Lessels (1984)
Dotterel *Eudromias morinellus*	Scotland	436	2	35	398	1	0	0	2.91	D. Nethersole-Thompson & P. S. Thompson
	England	58	4	16	38	0	0	0	2.58	D. Nethersole-Thompson (1973)
	Fenno-Scandia	207	0	7	196	4	0	0	2.97	,,
Golden plover *Pluvialis apricaria*	Inverness and Sutherland, Scotland	126	0	2	15	108	1	0	3.85	Nethersole-Thompson family
	Britain	231	0	9	15	207	0	0	3.85	D. A. Ratcliffe (1977)
	Britain	23	0	3	5	15	0	0	3.52	A. Whitaker MS
	All Britain	380	0	14	35	330	1	0	3.83	
	Netherlands	23	0	3	5	15	0	0	3.78	F. Haverschmidt *in* Glutz (1975)
Lapwing *Vanellus vanellus*	Scotland	202	0	4	15	174	9	0	3.9	D. Nethersole-Thompson & P. S. Thompson
	Yorks-Derbys, England	125	1	3	20	100	1	0	3.8	A. Whitaker MS
Knot *Calidris canutus*	Switzerland	550	0	10	43	495	2	0	3.9	J. Heim *in* Glutz (1975)
	Greenland, Spitsbergen, Canada and USSR	50	1	3	12	34	0	0	3.58	Various
Sanderling *Calidris alba*	N. Canada	14	0	0	1	13	0	0	3.93	D. F. Parmelee (1970)
Little stint *Calidris minuta*	N. Norway	19	0	0	3	16	0	0	3.84	O. Hildén (1978)

	Location	Sample	of 1	of 2	of 3	of 4	of 5	of 6	Mean	Authority
Temminck's stint Calidris temminckii	USSR	56	2	5	49	0	0	0	3.98	V. Kokhanov (1973)
	Finland	182	0	2	21	158	1	0	3.87	O. Hildén (1978)
Purple sandpiper Calidris maritima	Spitsbergen	82	0	0	7	75	0	0	3.91	L. Løvenskiold (1964)
Dunlin Calidris alpina	S. Finland	203	0	4	20	179	0	0	3.9	M. Soikkeli (1964)
	W. Germany	295							*3.77	R. Heldt (1966)
Broad-billed sandpiper Limicola falcinellus	Finnmark, Norway	18	0	0	2	16	0	0	3.88	J. Little & N. Gilroy MS
Ruff Philomachus pugnax	Denmark	18	0	1	3	14	0	0	3,72	S. Andersen (1944)
Jack snipe Lymnocryptes minimus	Sweden	13	0	0	0	13	0	0	4.0	L. Raner MS
Snipe Gallinago gallinago	Britain	284	2	4	21	254	2	1	3.88	M. Macdonald & C. Mason (1976)
	Britain	68	0	1	11	56	0	0	3.84	A. Whitaker MS
	Sussex, England	25	0	1	2	22	0	0	3.87	D. Nethersole-Thompson
	St Kilda, Scotland	20	0	1	4	15	0	0	3,7	K. Williamson (1960)
	Switzerland	20	0	0	0	20	0	0	4.0	Glutz (1975)
	Finland	50							3.9	L. von Haartman MS
Capella g. delicata	Newfoundland, Canada	76	0	0	15	61	0	0	3.8	L. Tuck (1972)
Great snipe G. media	N. Norway	17	0	0	9	8	0	0	3.47	S. Haftorn & J. Little
	Sweden	9	0	0	0	9	0	0	4.0	L. Raner MS
	All	26	0	0	9	17	0	0	3.65	
Woodcock Scolopax rusticola	Britain	330							3.84	W. B. Alexander (1945–57)

Species	Location	n							mean	Source
Black-tailed godwit *Limosa limosa*	Netherlands	125	0	0	20	105	0	0	3.86	F. Haverschmidt (1963)
Bar-tailed godwit *Limosa lapponica*	N. Norway	13	0	0	2	11	0	0	3.84	Various
	Sweden	8	0	0	4	4	0	0	3.5	L. Raner MS
	All	20	0	0	5	15	0	0	3.75	
Whimbrel *Numenius phaeopus*	Finland	52	0	1	4	47	0	0	3.88	L. von Haartman (1963–64)
	Faroes	17	0	1	2	14	0	0	3.76	K. Williamson (1946)
	Finnmark, Norway	14	0	0	0	14	0	0	4.0	N. Gilroy & E. Steward MS
Curlew *Numenius arquata*	Scotland	35	0	0	5	30	0	0	3.85	Nethersole-Thompson family
	England	39	0	7	10	20	2	0	3.43	A. Whitaker MS
	Bavaria, Germany	127	0	5	18	104	0	0	3.85	H. Greiner (1977)
	Westphalia, Germany	24	0	2	5	17	0	0	3.63	M. Kipp *in* Glutz (1975)
	Switzerland	43	0	2	7	34	0	0	3.74	J. Heim *in* Glutz (1962)
	Estonia, SSR	38	0	0	5	33	0	0	3.86	S. Onno (1968)
	Finland	239	0	2	33	204	0	0	3.85	†L. von Haartman *et al* (1963–66)
Dusky redshank *Tringa erythropus*	Scandinavia	75	0	0	2	73	0	0	3.96	L. Raner, pers. comm (66) H.M.S. Blair (5); N. Gilroy & E. Steward (4)
Redshank *Tringa totanus*	Ribble marshes, England (1983–85)	533	22	5	26	476	3	1	3.82	P. S. Thompson (unpublished)
	Britain	53	0	1	7	44	1	0	3.53	A. Whitaker MS
	Spey Valley, Scotland	9	0	0	1	8	0	0	3.88	D. Nethersole-Thompson
	Wangerooge, Germany	381	0	0	21	356	2	1	3.70	G. Grosskopf (*in* Glutz 1977)
	Finland	1010	0	0	99	906	5	0	3.89	R. Väisänen (1969)

* clutches laid between 24 April – 10 May averaged 4.0 eggs and those laid between 1–13 June averaged 3.3 eggs

† von Haartman only knew of 2/5 in 593 known clutches

	Location	Sample	of 1	of 2	of 3	of 4	of 5	of 6	Mean	Authority
Greenshank *Tringa nebularia*	Sutherland	184	0	1	15	168	0	0	3.90	D. & M. Nethersole-Thompson (1979)
	Caithness	1	0	0	0	1	0	0	[4]	,,
	Ross and Western Isles	19	0	1	3	14	1	0	3.78	,,
	W. Inverness	21	0	0	0	21	0	0	4.0	,,
	Spey Valley, Inverness	130	0	0	7	122	1	0	3.95	,,
	Deeside, Aberdeenshire	10	0	0	1	9	0	0	3.90	,,
	Perth	4	0	0	0	4	0	0	4.0	,,
	Argyll	4	0	0	0	4	0	0	4.0	,,
	All Scotland	373	0	2	26	343	2	0	3.92	,,
	South Norway	1	0	0	0	1	0	0	4.0	,,
	Finnmark, Norway	46	2	0	0	44	0	0	3.86	,,
	Sweden	6	0	0	0	6	0	0	4.0	,,
	Finland	8	0	0	1	7	0	0	3.87	,,
	All Abroad	61	2	0	1	58	0	0		,,
Green sandpiper *Tringa ochropus*	Finland	24	0	0	3	21	0	0	3.87	J. H. McNeile MS
Wood sandpiper *Tringa glareola*	*insufficient data*									
Common sandpiper *Actitis hypoleucos*	Sutherland, Scotland	52	1	0	3	48	0	0	3.88	Nethersole-Thompson family
	Spey Valley, Scotland	27	0	0	4	23	0	0	3.85	D. Nethersole-Thompson
	Peak District, England	86	1	3	4	78	0	0	3.37	P. K. Holland *et al* (1982)

	Yorks-Derbys, England	19	0	1	18	0	0	3.94	A. Whitaker MS
	Roscommon, Eire	10	0	1	9	0	0	3.90	A. M. Chance MS et al
	Finland	98	0	4	94	0	0	3.94	L. von Haartman (1963–66)
Spotted sandpiper *Tringa macularia*	N. America	37	0	3	33	1	0	3.94	J. R. & J. T. Miller (1948)
Turnstone *Arenaria*	Finland	24	0	5	19	0	0	3.79	S. Vuolanto (1968)
interpres	N. Canada	15	2	3	10	0	0	3.53	D. N. Nettleship (1973)
	N. Europe and Greenland	484	0	39	442	3	0	3.9	R. Väisänen (1969)
Red-necked phalarope *Phalaropus lobatus*	Finland	71	0	1	70	0	0	3.9	O. Hildén & S. Vuolanto (1972)
Grey phalarope *Phalaropus fulicarius*	E. Siberia	83	4	7	72	0	0	3.82	A. A. Kistschinski (1975)

TABLE 5:   *Weights of newly-hatched wader chicks*

	Location	Sample	Range	Mean	Authority
Oystercatcher *Haematopus ostralegus*	Norderoog, Germany	12	29.8–34.8	31.9	R. Dircksen (1932)
	N. Holland	16	23.5–33.0	28.9	J. Walters MS
	Kandalashka, USSR	?	28–39	32	V. V. Bianki (1967)
Black-winged stilt *Himantopus himantopus*			not recorded		
Avocet *Recurvirostra avosetta*	Netherlands	14	18.2–24.0	21.3	J. Walters MS
Stone curlew *Burhinus oedicnemus*	East Anglia	14		29.7	R. A. Morgan *in* Cramp & Simmonds (1983)
Little ringed plover *Charadrius dubius*	Germany (South)	44	4.0–6.5	5.3	*in* Glutz (1975)
	Netherlands	462	4.2–6.2	5.3	J. Walters MS
Ringed plover *Charadrius hiaticula*	Lindisfarne, N. England			8.5	M. W. Pienkowski (1984)
	Scoresbyland, N.E. Greenland	27		8.5	M. W. Pienkowski (1984)
	Netherlands	84	7.0–9.6	8.0	J. Walters MS
	Norway	7	7.2–7.7	?	*in* Glutz (1975)
C.h. tundrae	E. Murman, USSR	13	6.8–8.3	7.1	N. A. Rubinshtein (1970)
Kentish plover *Charadrius alexandrinus*	Amsterdam, Netherlands	185		6.4	J. Walters MS
Dotterel *Eudromias morinellus*	Grampians, Scotland	5	9.0–10.5	9.6	Nethersole-Thompson family
	Austria	13	10.5–13.0	11.5	E. Hable *in* Glutz (1975)
Golden plover *Pluvialis apricaria*	Estonia, SSR	8	20.0–25.2	?	E. Kumari *in* Glutz (1975)
Lapwing *Vanellus vanellus*	Switzerland	171	14.0–21.0	17.1	J. Heim *in* Glutz (1975)
		60	13.0–19.0	16.9	W. Matter *in* Glutz (1975)
Knot *Calidris canutus*	Canadian Arctic	?	10.0–12.0	?	J. Fieldså *in* Glutz (1975)
Sanderling *Calidris alba*	Canadian Arctic	4	7.1–7.5	7.3	D. F. Parmelee (1970)
Little stint *Calidris minuta*	W. Taimyr Peninsula, USSR	1	4.8	4.8	*in* Glutz (1975)
Temminck's stint *Calidris temminckii*	Kandalashka Bay, USSR	12	4.0–4.6	4.3	V. D. Kokhanov (1973)
Purple sandpiper *Calidris maritima*			8.0–10.0		J. Fieldså *in* Glutz (1975)
Dunlin *Calidris alpina*	White Sea, USSR	2	7.8–8.7	8.2	L. O. Belopolski (1971)
	S.W. Finland	194		7.0	M. Soikkeli (1967)
	N.W. Sutherland, Scotland	8	5.5–7.5	7.0	Nethersole-Thompson family

	Location	Sample	Range	Mean	Authority
Broad-billed sandpiper *Limocala falcinellus*	N. Europe		6.0–8.5		J. Fieldså *in* Glutz (1975)
Ruff *Philomachus pugnax*	Germany	?	13.0–14.0	?	O. Heinroth (1928)
Jack snipe *Lymnocryptes minimus*	N. Europe	?	9.0–13.0	?	J. Fieldså *in* Glutz (1975)
Snipe *Gallinago gallinago*	Germany	?	10.0–11.0	?	O. Heinroth (1928)
	USSR	?	8.0–11.0	?	A. I. Yanushevitch *et al* (1959)
Great snipe *Gallinago media*	N. Europe	?	13.0–17.0	?	J. Fieldså *in* Glutz (1975)
Woodcock *Scolopax rusticol*	Germany	?	16.0–20.0	?	O. Heinroth (1927)
	Sweden	19	15.9–19.5	18.0	V. Marcström & F. Sundgren (1977)
Black-tailed godwit *Limosa limosa*	Germany	?	?	*c*32	O. Heinroth (1927)
Bar-tailed godwit *Limosa lapponica*			not recorded		
Whimbrel *Numenius phaeopus*	Estonia SSR	5	28.4–36.5	?	E. Kumari *in* Glutz (1975)
Curlew *Numenius arquata*	Bavaria, Germany	14	47.0–68.0	56.8	H. Greiner *in* Glutz (1977)
Dusky redshank *Totanus erythropus*			not recorded		
Redshank *Tringa totanus*	Wangerooge, Germany	?	14.0–16.0	?	G. Grosskopf (1958)
	Ribble, Lancashire, England	417	12.0–19.5	15.6	P. S. Thompson
Greenshank *Tringa nebularia*	N.W. Sutherland, Scotland	88	18.0–26.0	20.8	Nethersole-Thompson family
Green sandpiper *Tringa ochropus*	Germany	?4	?	10	H. Kirchner (1972)
Wood sandpiper *Tringa glareola*	Germany	4	8.0–9.7		H. Kirchner (1972)
Common sandpiper *Actitis hypoleucos*	N.W. Sutherland, Scotland	4	8.0–9.0	8.2	Nethersole-Thompson family
	Peak District, England	7		7.8	P. K. Holland *et al* (1982)
Spotted sandpiper *Actitis macularia*			not recorded		
Turnstone *Arenaria interpres*	Kandalashka Bay, USSR	60	9.0–14.0	12.2	V. V. Bianki (1967)
Red-necked phalarope *Phalaropus lobatus*	Finland	86	3.2–4.8	3.9	O. Hildén & S. Vuolanto (1972)
Grey phalarope *Phalaropus fulicarius*	USSR	3	5.0–5.5	?	V. I. Kapitonov (1962)

Sonagrams

Note on the interpretation of the sound spectrograms
by D. B. A. Thompson, Chief Scientist's Directorate, NCC, Peterborough
and P. S. Thompson, Liverpool Polytechnic

Waders are extremely vocal birds offering tremendous opportunities for those keen to understand avian communication. Anybody doubting this should read Miller's (1984) excellent review of communication in breeding shorebirds. He considers attributes underlying different kinds of information transfer, examines the acoustic components and functioning of displays, the role of communication in social behaviour and ecology, and, finally, discusses geographical and evolutionary patterns in displays. Such depth of coverage is possible because workers have managed to quantify displays and vocalisations with great accuracy.

The standard method of illustrating and analysing calls or song is the *sonagram* (sound spectrogram) providing a three-dimensional representation of sound (see Cramp and Simmons 1983). Periodic changes in the pressure of air produce bird sound waves differing over *time* in *amplitude* (height) and *frequency* (number of cycles per seconds, Hertz). Crudely, birds hear variations in these in terms of loudness and pitch respectively. In the sonagram, the horizontal scale shows time (seconds), the vertical axis shows frequency (kiloHertz), ie how high or low the sound is pitched, and the density of shading indicates relative loudness (*amplitude*). So long as the sonagraph, which produces sonagrams, is correctly calibrated, and the user does not read too much into the minutiae of frequency or amplitude variations, the sonagram gives a good reliable representation of the sound produced.

A sound varying only slightly in frequency (eg a whistle of constant pitch) appears as a pure *unmodulated frequency*, resembling a straight band. A whistle dropping in frequency is *frequency modulated*, and variations of this occur in many forms (see Catchpole 1979). If the sound covers a wide frequency in a short single burst it will resemble a click; if several such clicks are produced for slightly longer duration the noise is like a harsh buzz or rattle. Many sounds appear as upright blocks of alternate dark shading. These arise when the sound has a low *fundamental frequency* (first *harmonic*) with higher frequencies (harmonics) occurring as multiples of the fundamental. Although we hear the first harmonic, we do not hear the others individually. Instead, the tone of the sound is dependent on the distribution and relative strength of the other harmonics. Wide (300 Hz) or narrow (45 Hz) band-pass filters may be used to produce sonagrams. The wide filter is usually used because it spreads the frequency component to facilitate temporal measurements. Sometimes, however, we may wish to examine frequency characteristics with greater precision, and so use a narrow-band analysis. One obvious advantage of this, highlighted by Hall-Craggs (1979), is that the vocalisations of two duetting birds can be distinguished (poorer temporal resolution is a disadvantage). All vocalisations in this book were analysed using a linear frequency scale, ascending by 1 kHz increments, and most fell within the 2–8 kHz range of the spectrum. Because the scale is linear, harmonics appear as equi-distant.

Many ethologists find adaptations of song and calls to environmental dictates beguiling (eg Wiley and Richards 1982). Sounds travelling far are structurally simple, high in energy, and low in frequency with virtually no amplitude modulation. They are least susceptible to background interference such as wind. If they are to be locatable they are also stereotyped and highly repetitive. Anti-predator alarm calls are clearly audible but transmit minimal directional information by starting and finishing gradually and being produced within a high narrow frequency window difficult to detect by binaural predators. Calls designed to give directional information, however, tend to be short, cover a wide frequency range, start and finish abruptly, and may be modulated and repeated (Marler 1981, Catchpole 1979). The former may be given to warn incubating partners of impending danger, the latter to recall chicks into the nest. Songs are considerably more complex than calls and have many functions including female attraction and/or male repulsion. Experiments using song playbacks through loudspeakers in the field, and more recently using females implanted with sex hormones responding to different songs in the laboratory, are revealing a great deal about their function. Although most experimental work has been done on passerines we see no reason why attention shouldn't switch to captive waders.

REFERENCES

Catchpole, C. K. (1979) *Vocal Communication in Birds*. London, Arnold.
Hall-Craggs, J. (1979) in *Greenshanks*. Berkhamsted, Poyser.
Marler, P. (1984) Bird song: the acquisition of a learned motor skill. *Trends Neurosci* 4: 88–94.
Miller, E. H. (1984) Communication in breeding shorebirds. In *Behaviour of Marine Animals*. J. Burger & B. L. Olla (ed). Vol. 5, pp 169–241. London, Plenum Press.
Wiley, R. H. & Richards, D. G. (1982) Adaptations for acoustic communication in birds: sound transmission and signal detection. In *Acoustic Communication in Birds*. D. E. Kroodsma & E. H. Miller (ed). Vol. I, pp 131–181. New York, Academic Press.

I Song dances of four closely related *Tringa* species

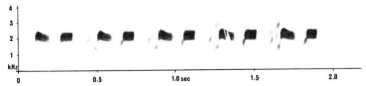

(a) Cock greenshank song dancing above nest: used in search of mates, in spacing and in some agonistic situations. Sutherland. (Authors and D. B. A. Thompson).

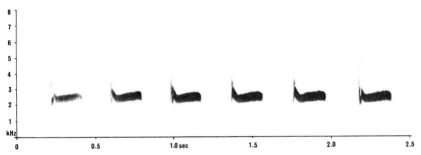

(b) Cock redshank in song dance *tü-tü*. Used largely in search for a mate. Scotland. (V. C. Lewis).

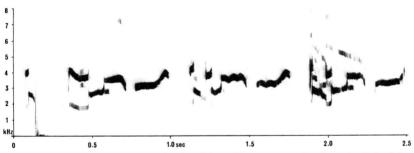

(c) Green sandpiper: given at great height while seeking a mate and at lower levels in defence of terrirory. Inverness-shire. (J. Kirby).

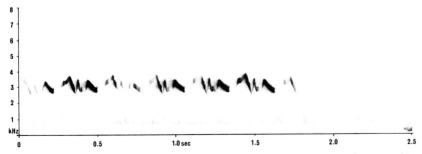

(d) Wood sandpiper: used mainly while seeking a mate and achieving spacing. Inverness-shire. (Bill Sinclair).

II Song dances of closely studied waders

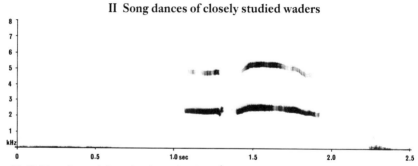

(a) Golden plover: delivered at lower height to assist in advertising territorial bounds. (Bill Sinclair).

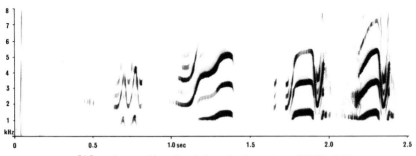

(b) Lapwing: used largely to help maintain territory. (Bill Sinclair).

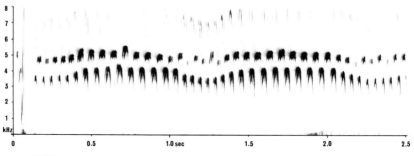

(c) Temminck's stint: used to attract mate and as part of sexual display. (Bill Sinclair).

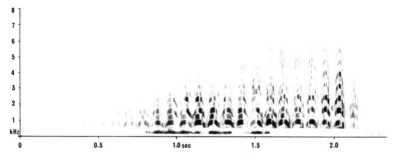

(d) Common snipe: 'bleating' or 'drumming' is an advertisement weapon used in territorial and sexual situations. When excited both sexes sometimes 'bleat'. (Bill Sinclair).

III Social contact calls of greenshank and greater yellowlegs

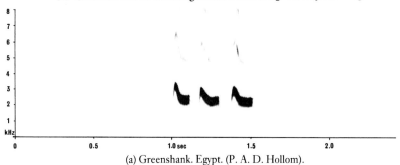

(a) Greenshank. Egypt. (P. A. D. Hollom).

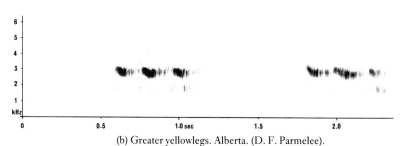

(b) Greater yellowlegs. Alberta. (D. F. Parmelee).

IV Nest relief and nest return calls of greenshank and redshank

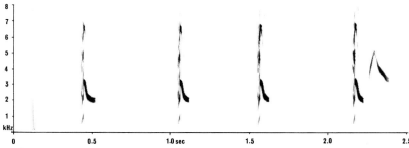

(a) Redshank approaching nest with slow, heavy *chip chips*. Chick calling as parent arrives. Compare with (b) below. Lancashire. (P. S. Thompson).

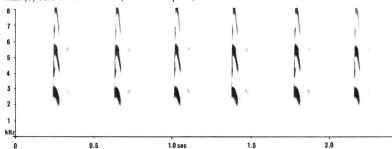

(b) Greenshanks use several different rhythms of chipping during nest relief and while returning to nest. This one is characteristic of a bird on way to its nest. Sutherland. (Authors and R. K. Thompson).

V Copulation calls of greenshank and redshank

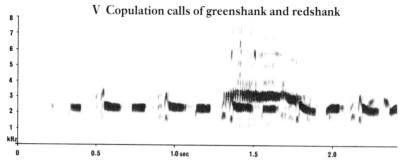

(a) Cock greenshank singing at climax of copulation, followed by scream of hen. Sutherland. (Bill Sinclair).

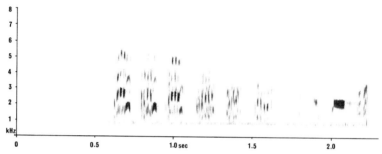

(b) Cock greenshank about to copulate with hen: grating cries followed by song. Sutherland. (Bill Sinclair).

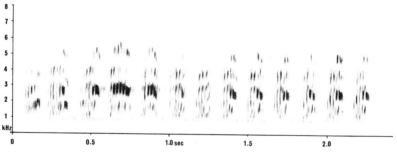

(c) Cock greenshank's copulation calls: 'gruffs' in two different rhythms. Sutherland. (Bill Sinclair).

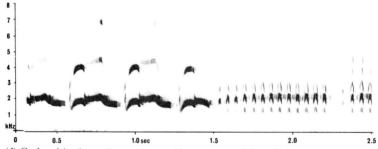

(d) Cock redshank copulation cries; rapid *taweeo* songs followed by excited rattle. Inverness-shire. (Bill Sinclair).

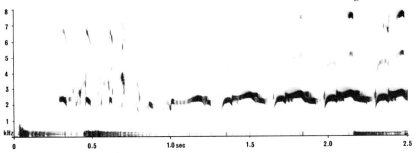

(e) Excerpts from redshank copulation calls showing part of climax. Inverness-shire. (Bill Sinclair).

VI Golden plover calls to chicks in nest

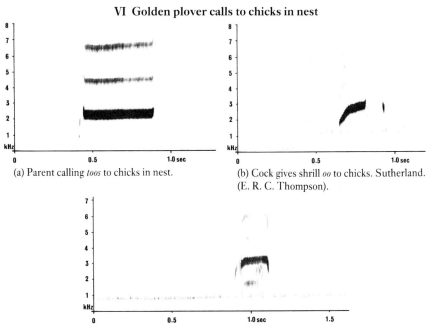

(a) Parent calling *toos* to chicks in nest.

(b) Cock gives shrill *oo* to chicks. Sutherland. (E. R. C. Thompson).

(c) Chick gives sharp *choc* with *whoo* above *choc*; in background, parent gives loud *whee* and *wheeuks*. Sutherland. (Bill Sinclair).

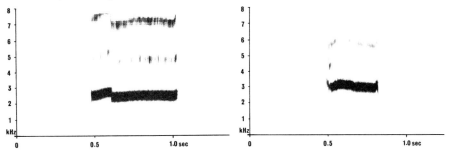

(d) Parent's mournful *too* given almost beside nest. Sutherland. (Bill Sinclair).

(e) Screaming cry of chick running away from nest. Sutherland. (E. R. C. Thompson).

VII Common sandpiper

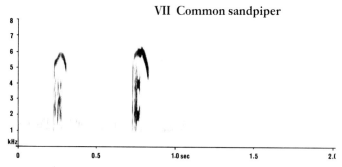

(a) Cock giving *kluk-kluk* to chicks in eggs. Sutherland. (Bill Sinclair).

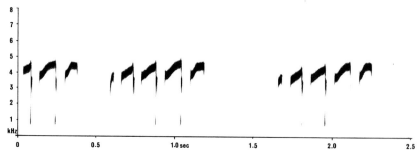

(b) Nest song of cock. Sutherland. (E. R. C. Thompson).

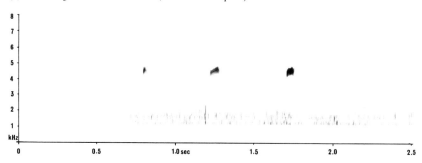

(c) Treble twitter of cock brooding hatching eggs and chicks. Sutherland. (E. R. C. Thompson).

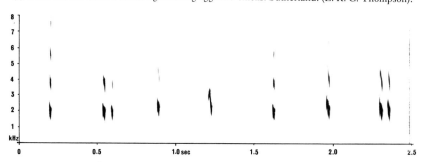

(d) Loud twittering of cock to chick in egg, sounding like a rod drawn along railings. Sutherland. (E. R. C. Thompson).

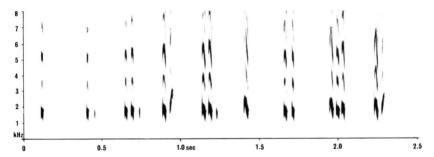

(e) Loud twitters of cock to chick in egg. Sutherland. (E. R. C. Thompson).

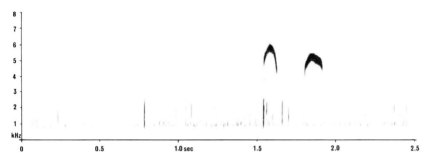

(f) Chicks tapping and squeaking in eggs. Sutherland. (E. R. C. Thompson).

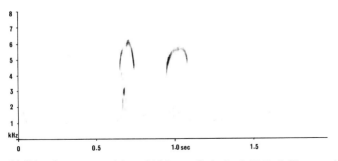

(g) Cries of common sandpiper chick in egg. Sutherland. (E. R. C. Thompson).

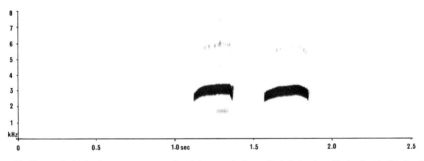

(h) Cries of chicks in nest, apparently giving rendering of adults' cries. Sutherland. (E. R. C. Thompson).

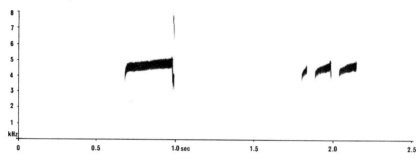

(i) Alarm cries of cock. Sutherland. (E. R. C. Thompson).

VIII Calls of parent and chick redshanks during and after hatch

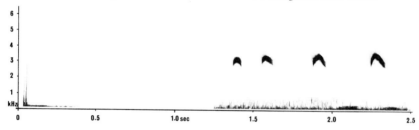

(a) Chicks calling *peep-peep-peep-pup* in absence of parent. Lancashire. (P. S. Thompson).

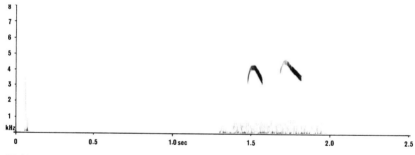

(b) Chicks calling – a lighter call. Lancashire. (P. S. Thompson).

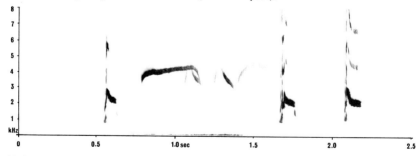

(c) Adult moving to nest usung explosive *kok-kok*. Chick gives different cries as parent approaches.
(P. S. Thompson).

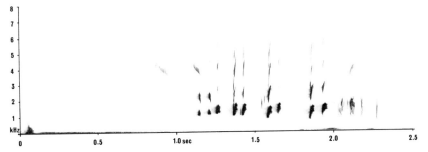

(d) Adult's ripping cries to chick – *whirra-whirra-whooh*. Lancashire. (P. S. Thompson).

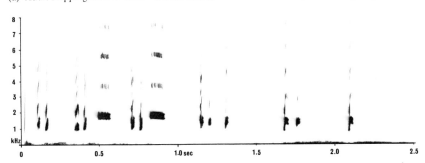

(e) Brooding calls: a series of *oo-rah-oo-roh-oo-roh-oo-ee-ooh*, quick bubbling calls. Lancashire. (P. S. Thompson).

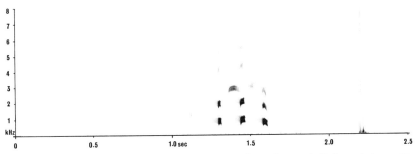

(f) Adults give loud *ook-ook-ooks* to chicks which are calling after eggshell disposal. Lancashire. (P. S. Thompson).

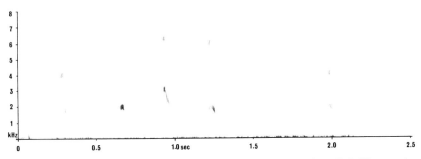

(g) Parent starts to communicate with chicks, *chip-chip-chee-chuh*. Lancashire. (P. S. Thompson).

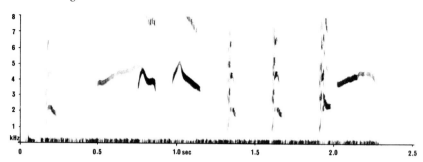

(h) Adult *chipping* and chick *peeping* in response. Lancashire. (P. S. Thompson).

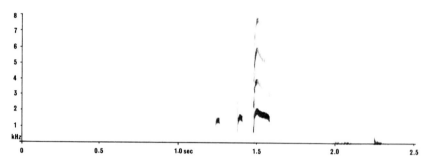

(i) Adult's explosive *pi-peh-peh* to discipline chicks – a tinny sound. Lancashire. (P. S. Thompson).

Index of birds

General index